2023/24

THE GUIDE TO
UK COMPANY GIVING

14th edition

Ian Pembridge
and Jessica Threlfall

dsc
directory of social change

Published by the Directory of Social Change (Registered Charity no. 800517 in England and Wales)

Office: Suite 103, 1 Old Hall Street, Liverpool L3 9HG

Tel: 020 4526 5995

Visit www.dsc.org.uk to find out more about our books, subscription funding website and training events. You can also sign up for e-newsletters so that you're always the first to hear about what's new.

The publisher welcomes suggestions and comments that will help to inform and improve future versions of this and all of our titles. Please give us your feedback by emailing publications@dsc.org.uk.

First published 1998
Second edition 1999
Third edition 2000
Fourth edition 2002
Fifth edition 2004
Sixth edition 2007
Seventh edition 2009
Eighth edition 2011
Ninth edition 2013
Tenth edition 2015
Eleventh edition 2017
Twelfth edition 2019
Thirteenth edition 2021
Fourteenth edition 2023

ISBN 978 1 78482 081 7

British Library Cataloguing in Publication Data
A catalogue record for this book is available from the British Library

Cover and text design by Kate Griffith
Typeset by Marlinzo Services, Frome
Printed and bound in the UK by Page Bros, Norwich

Contents

Foreword

We face an uncertain landscape as we move through 2023. But one thing is certain: bold, brave and purposeful giving by businesses can be transformational – and the impact of business on society has never mattered more.

During the COVID-19 pandemic, the private sector stepped up to play a wider role in the community and support the most vulnerable. Retailers worked alongside charities to relieve food poverty and funded sanitation programs in tandem with government, and high-profile brands donated time and resources, as well as funds. Confronted with the tragedy of war in Ukraine, the private and voluntary sector once again demonstrated that their joined forces could be a powerful driver of action; companies acted swiftly to raise significant amounts for those affected.

So many of the world's greatest challenges that responsible businesses want to help address – from food and energy security to migration, to collapsing wildlife populations and particularly the growing climate emergency – stem from the unsustainable pressures we are placing on our planet. We have the solutions, but the private sector's work with its charity partners will be integral if we are to provide a stable and secure future for the next generations.

Purposeful corporate giving not only helps charities deliver their crucial work but can also help businesses keep sustainability at the centre of their strategy, build consumer trust and employee pride, and drive positive social and environmental change. That's why *The Guide to UK Company Giving* is an invaluable and crucial work. This is a comprehensive resource that can help charities and businesses to navigate the corporate giving space, and work together for meaningful change.

Tanya Steele CBE, CEO, WWF-UK

About the Directory of Social Change

At the Directory of Social Change (DSC), we believe that the world is made better by people coming together to serve their communities and each other. For us, an independent voluntary sector is at the heart of that social change and we exist to support charities, voluntary organisations and community groups in the work they do. Our role is to:

▶ **Provide practical information** on a range of topics from fundraising to project management in both our printed publications and our e-books

▶ **Offer training** through public courses, events and in-house services

▶ **Research funders** and maintain a subscription database, *Funds Online*, with details on funding from grant-making charities, companies and government sources

▶ **Offer bespoke research** to voluntary sector organisations in order to evaluate projects, identify new opportunities and help make sense of existing data

▶ **Stimulate debate and campaign** on key issues that affect the voluntary sector, particularly to champion the concerns of smaller charities

We are a registered charity ourselves but we self-fund most of our work. We charge for services but cross-subsidise those which charities particularly need and cannot easily afford.

Visit our website **www.dsc.org.uk** to see how we can help you to help others and have a look at **www.fundsonline. org.uk** to see how DSC could improve your fundraising. Alternatively, call our friendly team at **020 4526 5995** to chat about your needs or drop us a line at **cs@dsc.org.uk**.

Introduction

Welcome to the 14th edition of *The Guide to UK Company Giving*, which continues to provide relevant, up-to-date commentary on the current state of corporate community giving in the UK.

This edition features 405 companies, which collectively gave around £452 million in community support in the UK, mostly in the 2020/21, 2021 or 2021/22 financial year. The guide also includes full details of 160 associated corporate charities, which together gave over £300 million to charitable causes. This figure was derived from the combined grant totals of the corporate charities listed and does not represent what was given by the companies themselves.

The corporate charities section on page 215 contains information on charities established by and closely associated with a company listed in the guide, which often act as a channel for corporate charitable giving. We hope that this section will be of additional use to our readers in their search for charitable funding given by companies.

Each of the 405 company records provides essential information for accessing funding and other resources. In compiling this guide, DSC researchers reviewed thousands of pages of annual reports, accounts and corporate social responsibility reports as well as companies' websites to provide the most comprehensive overview of the community-related activities of individual businesses. The records presented in this guide focus on companies' contributions to their local communities and wider society, which include cash donations (where figures were available) and all forms of in-kind support, from pro bono work to donations of equipment. Where relevant, we also describe commercially led community-related initiatives and other community-orientated contributions by companies.

The guide consists of individual company records and additional sections offering advice and information for fundraisers, voluntary organisations, community groups, companies and individuals.

Corporate social responsibility

Corporate social responsibility (CSR), also known as social or community investment, corporate citizenship or sustainable/responsible business, is a much-used term which covers a holistic attempt by businesses to act in an ethical manner and address the effects they have on communities, people and the environment.

Initially self-regulated, there are now several legal requirements to report on various activities that fall under the CSR banner, including reporting on a company's gender pay gap, responding to the risk of modern day slavery in the supply chain and ensuring that environmental damage is reduced or avoided. A CSR strategy should include the monitoring and review of a company's ethical policies and procedures, environmental policy, health and safety procedures, employee welfare and the effect the company's business has on its customers, suppliers, communities and stakeholders.

Many companies, depending on the nature of their business, quite naturally focus their CSR strategy on the impact they have on the environment and what measures they are taking to try to reduce their environmental impact. Environmental initiatives may include reducing carbon emissions, improving energy efficiency and reducing waste.

Workplace-based elements of CSR are focussed on improving the rights and well-being of staff. Initiatives may include improving equality, equity, diversity and inclusion in the workplace and improving workplace health and safety. These initiatives are especially important in multi-national companies where employment laws can vary from country to country.

The community aspect of a company's CSR strategy may include involving stakeholders in company decisions, ensuring local communities are part of the supply chain or engaging in charitable work.

There are numerous advantages companies can gain from having an effective CSR strategy, including:

- Developing a reputation as being a good corporate citizen, which in turn can have several advantages, including brand-building, business development and employee recruitment
- Gaining a deeper understanding of their customer base
- Benefitting from the advantages of staff development opportunities, where employees are involved in volunteering activities such as mentoring or pro bono work

This guide focuses on the community element of CSR, specifically the support companies provide to charities in the UK through community contributions, such as cash donations, in-kind donations and employee volunteering.

In recent years, charity partnerships have become a key vehicle for charitable involvement by companies. Working in partnership can be of mutual benefit to both the company and the charities it supports. Companies can bring core business skills, including financial or logistical expertise, and access to supply chains and high-level contacts; in turn, charities can provide professional skills and practitioner-level knowledge of what is needed on the ground and what approaches would be most effective.

The companies in this guide

Since reforms were made to the Companies Act 2006, companies have no longer had a legal obligation to declare charitable donations. In the wake of these changes, which took place in 2013, there has been a recognisable shift towards embedding CSR into company culture, by encouraging staff involvement, providing services pro bono or gifting products.

While DSC maintains that it is good practice for companies to declare charitable donations and applauds those companies that continue to do so, the shift away from cash donations towards corporate community contributions has presented an opportunity to draw attention to other, sometimes very innovative, ways in which companies contribute to communities. In this regard, the value of corporate contributions cannot always be directly translated into monetary terms.

For the benefit of our readers, we focus our research on companies' contributions to UK voluntary organisations. Where a company provides information of giving abroad, we include this in its record. However, this guide is written primarily for small and medium-sized charities working with beneficiaries in the UK, so we focus on aspects of giving that will be of most use to them.

Methodology
Companies

As it is no longer possible to use cash donations as the main criterion for inclusion in the guide, we have widened our criteria to include companies whose CSR activities benefit communities in the UK directly. Generally, this would include any of the following: charitable contributions (either cash or gifts in kind such as equipment, employee volunteering, mentoring or secondment of staff); community partnerships; or activities of an affiliated grant-making corporate charity.

We do not include companies whose CSR is geared mainly towards environmental sustainability, companies whose community support is given on a long-term basis to one or a limited group of named charities, or companies whose employees' fundraising or volunteering is the sole source of community contributions, as the recipients of funds such as these are nearly always predetermined.

DSC researchers examined the FTSE 350 (as of May 2022) in comparison to our extensive database, which holds historical information of corporate charitable giving in the UK. Any FTSE 350 companies not featured in our database were assessed to determine whether they fit our criteria for inclusion in the guide. To access each company's charitable giving, DSC's researchers reviewed companies' annual reports, CSR reports and websites; in some cases, we may also have had direct contact with the company.

Corporate charities

All the corporate charities included in the guide are linked to the companies in the main section of company entries. We have included only those that make grants to organisations. Some companies have corporate charities which do not make grants and instead deliver company-led activities directly or offer other forms of support. Where applicable, these are detailed in the main section, under the record of the relevant company.

To be deemed a corporate charity in line with DSC's criteria and to consequently have a place in this guide, a charity should have received a historical donation from a company or currently be receiving a substantial amount of income from a company through an annual donation from the company's profits.

Accreditation schemes and membership bodies

As with previous editions, during our research for this guide we recorded which companies were members of CSR bodies, specifically Business in the Community (BITC) and Business for Societal Impact (B4SI, formerly London Benchmarking Group). BITC is a membership organisation which works and campaigns with members to grow their responsible business practices. B4SI provides frameworks which its member companies can use to measure and manage their social impact. We include this information to demonstrate that there are dedicated organisations encouraging transparency and openness to assist voluntary sector and community organisations in their search for corporate support.

Within the guide there are 44 companies signed up to the B4SI, representing a 12% decrease since the previous edition. Our research found that 92 companies within our sample held BITC membership (compared with 118 in the previous edition).

The accreditation listing on page 293 shows the memberships and accreditations of the companies in the guide. As well as BITC and B4SI membership, the accreditations listing also includes the Armed Forces Covenant, Living Wage employers and Business Disability Forum members.

The corporate charities section

The corporate charities section focuses on grant-making charities which are associated with companies featured in this guide. The 160 charities listed within have some association, either historically or currently, with a company, and each record includes full details of the charity, its purposes and contact details. Information is provided on how much the charities donate, to which organisations and causes, and to which geographical areas.

As well as the traditional method of receiving donations directly from the yearly profits of a company, corporate charities can also receive income from other sources (for example, from employee/customer fundraising). Many corporate charities also receive in-kind support from the company, such as staff time and expertise, facilities and/or office space on the premises of the company.

Corporate charities can be an excellent vehicle for corporate giving. They:

- Provide a professional, structured and effective channel for charitable donations, with trustees acting in the best interest of the charity (and not the company)
- Often employ skilled, motivated staff
- Apply the Charities Statement of Recommended Practice (SORP), which provides openness and transparency which can be lacking in companies' reporting
- Are often a way for companies to focus their charitable giving while demonstrating long-term support for the voluntary sector

Through its corporate charity's activities, a company can contribute to the communities in which it operates, while also seeing an indirect benefit to its business. For example, a finance company that wishes to fund debt advice agencies can do so through its own corporate charity, provided this falls within the charity's objects.

Most corporate charities form part of a company's wider CSR programme and often focus on the same causes. Some are used as a vehicle to deliver other aspects of the company's CSR activities, such as the provision of matched funding for employee-led fundraising initiatives or support for a nominated Charity of the Year. There may be multiple corporate charities associated with one company, each delivering different aspects of the company's community involvement.

The ways in which corporate charities offer support may vary as much as their relationships with their companies. In this edition, there are corporate charities listed that give nationally and internationally as well as ones that give only in the areas in which the company or its parent company has a local presence. Some corporate charities focusing on local communities might also offer in-kind support, such as employee volunteering, to complement a financial grant. Application procedures can vary too; some corporate charities may favour charities or causes with which employees of the company are already involved or may allow customers to nominate charities for support, while others may welcome applications from any charity working in a particular area or for any cause. As when applying to any grant-maker, we advise readers to consider the eligibility criteria and exclusions of each funder carefully, and tailor approaches appropriately.

The corporate charities section of this guide is a valuable component of DSC's research into UK companies' charitable giving. Corporate giving is a traditional and straightforward source of charitable support but, nevertheless, is an important and worthwhile avenue for charities to consider when searching for funding. These grant-makers have the advantage of being familiar to fundraisers, who will understand the protocols and processes involved.

The top ten givers in the guide

Data on UK community contributions was available for 231 of the 405 companies featured in this guide. In total, UK community contributions from these 231 companies amounted to £452.1 million and included both cash donations and in-kind contributions (including donations of goods and employee time). Wherever possible, management costs have been excluded from this total as they do not provide a direct benefit to charities and there can be disparities in how they are calculated by companies.

The table below shows the ten largest corporate givers in this guide in terms of total UK contributions. The companies in the top ten account for £234.7 million (52%) of the £452.1 million total recorded for UK community contributions in this guide.

1	The Football Association Premier League Ltd	£59.0 million
2	Lloyds Banking Group	£46.0 million
3	Benefact Group plc	£28.4 million
4	Co-operative Group Ltd	£28.4 million
5	ScottishPower UK plc	£23.2 million
6	Vodafone Group plc	£14.9 million
7	Brit Ltd	£9.0 million
8	Goldman Sachs International	£8.9 million
9	Asda Stores Ltd	£8.5 million
10	London Luton Airport Ltd	£8.3 million

Ranking first in the table is The Football Association Premier League Ltd, which manages and sells the broadcasting rights to the Premier League. The company is a conglomeration of 20 Premier League clubs, each of which has a share of the company, with the Football Association acting as a special shareholder. Perhaps unsurprisingly, most of the company's charitable donations went to football-related charities, including large donations to the Football Foundation, and to support the charitable activities of the Professional Footballers' Association.

As with previous editions, the top ten givers table is dominated by financial institutions, which make up four of the top ten. These companies (Lloyds Banking Group,

Benefact Group plc, Brit Ltd and Goldman Sachs International) gave a combined total of £92.4 million. The second most common business type was retailers, with two in the top ten. These companies (Co-operative Group Ltd and Asda Stores Ltd) gave a combined total of £36.9 million.

Conclusion

In the past, we would normally have commented on whether the companies listed in this guide have given more or less than in the previous edition, providing a narrative on any change in the companies' funding landscape. However, in light of decreasing transparency in company reporting of cash donations, comparisons of financial contributions by corporates are not reliable. Furthermore, charitable cash donations are only one part of the multi-faceted approach companies now take to CSR. While cash donations declared can provide a categorical and measurable way to evaluate a company's input, they are not necessarily the best way to measure its impact.

Over the course of our research, we have seen the direct benefits of non-cash contributions, particularly of pro bono time and skills, gifts in kind, and unique and productive charity partnerships. In many ways, this sort of involvement demonstrates a commitment that the straightforward signing of a cheque does not. What is apparent is that many companies in this guide appear to be increasingly willing to facilitate and support their employees' community involvement – whether in the form of a volunteering policy, a payroll giving scheme or by matching funds or time. Furthermore, it is particularly encouraging that a high number of companies are willing to work in partnership with charities. The success of many of the charity partnerships we looked at in this guide is testament to the unique creativity and innovation that can be produced when two very different sectors come together to exchange their professional knowledge and values.

Good communication between charities and companies is mutually beneficial. It means that companies can find like-minded organisations to work with to fulfil their CSR objectives and that charities can access valuable support. Some very simple information published on a company's website can make a big difference. For example, it is helpful to potential applicants if companies provide clear information on the types of support they give to charities as well as contact details for the person that deals with charitable requests. It is equally helpful if companies state clearly that they do not support unsolicited requests from charities – this prevents charities using valuable time and resources on an ineligible application and avoids the company having to field queries from ineligible applicants.

As always, however, there remains a long way to go for companies in terms of transparency in their CSR reporting. Obtaining figures for a company's giving is dependent on its commitment to transparency. It is often difficult to ascertain how much is given, and in what manner, even for those companies that voluntarily release this information.

Over 140 companies are members of B4SI and use its model to break down and track their community giving. The B4SI model provides a comprehensive and consistent set of measures against which companies can determine their community contributions, including cash, employee volunteering time, in-kind donations and management costs. The model also captures the outputs and longer-term impact of the company's community investment projects. A wider adoption of this or similar methodologies in the future would help to develop a more accurate picture of community support from the business sector.

In recent years we have also seen an increase in the number of companies using Environmental, Social, Governance (ESG) to gauge their impact on society. ESG looks at a company's environmental impact, its relationships with stakeholders, such as employees and the communities in which the company operates, and its governance. There is a lot of overlap between ESG and CSR. However, while CSR is largely a self-regulating general framework, ESG is quantifiable assessment of a company's sustainability which is determined by measurable goals, performance metrics and reporting. The quantifiable nature of ESG means investors and ratings agencies can quickly see how sustainable a company is. Hopefully, the move to more data-based reporting will bring about an improvement in the quality of information being provided by companies on their charitable giving.

The aim of this guide is to provide the knowledge necessary to obtain corporate support through the provision of profile information on individual companies, identifying the kind of support available and how to access it effectively. We hope that this guide will continue to be an invaluable and comprehensive source of information for all of those with an interest in corporate giving in the UK.

Acknowledgements

We would like to thank all the companies that have helped to compile this guide, both those which we have contacted directly and those which have made their annual reports and accounts and/or their websites informative and accessible.

How to use this guide

Types of company

A company may be one of the following: a public limited company (designated plc), normally a company with shares quoted on the stock exchange; a privately owned company; or a subsidiary company. If it is a subsidiary, it may have retained its own identity for charitable donations and we would include a record in this guide. Other subsidiaries included are UK-based subsidiaries of an overseas company.

Where a company has been recently acquired, it may not yet have been decided whether the company will continue to manage its own charitable donations budget. Through acquisitions and mergers, companies may now be owned by a holding company, a conglomerate or a transnational company. You may have to do your own research to link local companies and plants with the head office that may have ultimate control over charitable donations. A company's annual report, usually available free online or upon request, will list subsidiary and associate (less than 50% owned) companies and report on the activity of the company during the year.

Interpreting charitable giving information

Where information was available – from an annual report and accounts, a CSR report or a website – we have included a figure for total UK community contributions. These contributions include cash donations as well as the value of employee time and skills and gifts in kind given in the UK. Where a separate figure for cash donations was available – albeit for the minority of companies in this guide – it has been specified.

A company's present level of donations does not necessarily indicate the level of future commitments. Sending an appeal to comparatively less generous companies may persuade them to increase their donations. Certainly, if they never receive appeals, there will be no outside pressure on them to change their policy; although, in general, if a company is only giving a little, your chances of success are reduced.

Normally, a co-ordinated corporate donor will budget a certain sum for its charitable contributions and stick to this amount. Some companies allocate their entire budget at an annual meeting; others spread contributions throughout the year. Some give to causes they wish to support until the budget is used up and then stop; others continue to give even after the budget is spent if an appeal takes their fancy. If companies reply to appeals, many will write and say that their budget is fully committed.

Information on a company's financial year end is important in that if readers submit appeals soon afterwards, the company may not have spent its charitable budget for the coming year. However, if a company allocates its budget evenly throughout the year and receives a flood of applications at the start of its new financial year, some causes that would have been supported later in the year may miss out. There is no fail-safe answer to this problem. Nevertheless, the chances of success are usually improved by sending an application earlier rather than later in the company's financial year.

Record layout

The layout used for the records in this guide is described in the breakdown of the fictional company record, Fictitious Productions plc, on page xiv. We hope that this example will help users in accessing the information they require on the various types of support that each company offers.

Caution – please note

We are told that companies continue to receive many unsolicited or inappropriate appeals for support. While many companies, arguably, bring this upon themselves due to a lack of clear guidelines for potential applicants, this should not be seen as an excuse to conduct blanket mailings. It is vitally important for success that readers thoroughly research prospective corporate supporters and only apply to those which are likely to consider an application or request.

Before approaching any company in this guide, its record should be read carefully. As we have stated previously, unless an applicant has some clear link with a company, or their project is clearly within the company's defined areas of support, success is unlikely.

We also recommend that you read the guidance on corporate fundraising provided by the Institute of Fundraising on its website. This gives a good overview of the issues involved in undertaking a relationship with a company and is available at: www.institute-of-fundraising. org.uk.

Fictional company record

Below is an example of a company record, showing the format we have used to present information obtained from the companies in this guide. (Before making an application, remember to always refer to the company's website for the latest information. You may also wish to ask the company or its corporate charity for details of its charitable giving policy or confirm the current contact details.)

Fictitious Productions plc

🔍 Social welfare, education, economic development

Company registration number: 111666

Correspondent: A. Grant, CSR Manager, 68 Nowhere Street, Anytown AN6 2LM (tel: 0151 000 0000; website: www.fictprod.co.uk)

Directors: Terence Story; Shelley Yarn; Luther Tale (female: 33%; male: 67%).

Nature of business: The company is involved in the production of fictitious information.

Financial information

Year end	31/12/2021
Turnover	£837,300,000
Pre-tax profit	£292,000,000

Total employees: 7,689

Main locations: Bristol (head office), Grimsby, Liverpool, Perth.

Community involvement

Much of the company's charitable giving is channelled through its corporate charity, the Fictitious Productions Foundation, which provides cash donations to a wide range of local and national charities. The company also provides in-kind donations to charities local to its offices in Bristol, Grimsby, Liverpool and Perth. The company also allows its employees to undertake secondments to local economic development initiatives and social enterprises.

In-kind support

The company donates surplus or used furniture and equipment to local causes.

Employee-led support

A charity is selected each year to benefit from employee fundraising, with the company making a contribution by way of matched funding.

Payroll giving

A scheme is operated by the company.

The following annotation boxes point to the relevant sections above:

- This section provides a summary of the charitable causes that the company is likely to support.

- Company registration numbers are taken from Companies House. In the case of a financial institution, such as a building society, FSA numbers are used.

- Some companies in the guide have dedicated staff to deal with appeals (in these cases, where available, we have included direct contact details). However, in other companies, appeals are dealt with by the company secretary, or public relations or marketing departments. The address refers to the most relevant address to send requests – whether this is the company's head office, the office where the CSR department is located or the company's corporate charity.

- The main area of the company's activity.

- These figures give an indication of the scale of the company's giving relative to its size (figures in brackets denote a loss). Some figures have been converted into GBP.

- This section provides information about the company's area of operation and the location of its offices.

- The 'Community involvement' section provides an overview of the company's community strategy and activities.

- Here, we provide a summary of any types of in-kind support offered by the company. Examples of in-kind support might include the distribution of used stock, free access to company facilities or pro bono work.

- The 'Employee-led support' section provides details of any charitable activities undertaken by company employees. Such activities may include donations made through payroll giving schemes, fundraising or volunteering.

Commercially led support

Sponsorship

The arts: Sponsorships typically range in value from £1,000 to £25,000. The company sponsors Southport Sinfonietta and has supported music festivals in Grimsby and Perth.

Here, we provide details of any of the company's charitable activities which have a commercial focus. Such activities may include sponsorship of local sports or cultural events, or the sale of 'charity products'.

Exclusions

No response is given to circular appeals. No grants are given for fundraising events, purely denominational religious appeals, local appeals not in areas of the company's presence, large national appeals, overseas projects, political activities or individuals. Non-commercial advertising is not supported. The company does not sponsor individuals or travel.

The 'Exclusions' section lists, where details were available, any causes or types of grant that the company will not consider funding.

Applications

Apply in writing to the correspondent. Applications are considered by a donations committee, which meets three times a year.

This section provides details of how and when to submit an application.

Corporate charity

Fictitious Productions Foundation (Charity Commission no. 123456) – see entry on page 243.

Here, we list the names and charity numbers of any of the company's associated corporate charities, details of which can be found in the corporate charities section of the book (pp. 223–298).

Community contributions

Cash donations UK	£420,000
Total contributions UK	£575,000

The company's community contributions totalled £575,000 in 2021. This amount included cash donations totalling £420,000.

Here, we provide a summary of the company's charitable contributions, including (where available) the value of its cash donations in the UK and overseas.

And finally . . .

If you have any comments about the guide, please get in touch with us through our Customer Services team via the following email address: cs@dsc.org.uk.

Companies in alphabetical order

3i Group plc

🔍 General charitable purposes

Company registration number: 1142830

Correspondent: Hanna Senakosava, Sustainability Manager, 16 Palace Street, London SW1E 5JD (email: sustainability@3i.com; website: www.3i.com)

Directors: Caroline Banszky; Simon Burrows; Stephen Daintith; Jasi Halai; James Hatchley; David Hutchinson; Lesley Knox; Coline McConville; Peter McKellar; Alexandra Schaapveld (female: 50%; male: 50%).

Nature of business: 3i is an investment company with three complementary businesses: private equity, infrastructure and debt management.

Financial information

Year end	31/03/2022
Pre-tax profit	£404,000,000

Main locations: The group's UK head office is based in London. It also has offices in Amsterdam, France, Germany, India, Luxembourg and North America.

Community involvement

The group focuses its charitable activities on disadvantaged people, young people, older people and education.

Partnerships

3i has charity partnerships with Community Links, Historic Royal Palaces, The Passage, Independent Age, Church Homeless Trust, Snowdon Trust, Re-engage, RBLI and the National Youth Orchestra.

Ukraine emergency donation

In March 2022, 3i donated £1 million split equally between UNICEF and the Médecins Sans Frontières Emergency Fund.

COVID-19 charitable fund

In May 2020, 3i established a £5 million COVID-19 charitable fund. Funding came from performance-based awards due to Private Equity and Infrastructure investment team members. The fund supported charities particularly affected by the pandemic, focusing on the most vulnerable communities in countries where 3i and its portfolio companies operate. Most of the funding was given in 2020/21 with any remaining funds being distributed in 2021/22. The fund supported around 100 charities across 14 regions.

Applications

Contact the correspondent for further information.

Community contributions

Total contributions UK	£1,700,000

The group's 'ordinary' charitable donations totalled £700,000 and included matched funding of £48,500. A further £1 million was donated to help people affected by the war in Ukraine. We were unable to determine how much of the £5 million COVID-19 funding was distributed in the financial year.

AbbVie Ltd

🔍 Community services and development, education and training, health

Company registration number: 8004972

Correspondent: The Grants Committee, AbbVie House, Vanwall Business Park, Vanwall Road, Maidenhead, Berkshire SL6 4UB (email: ukgrantsanddonations@abbvie.com; website: www.abbvie.co.uk/societal-impact/for-the-strength-of-our-communities/grants-and-donations.html)

Directors: Niall Maher; Alice Butler; Djamshid Ghavami; Todd Manning; Scott Reents (female: 20%; male: 80%).

Nature of business: AbbVie Ltd is a pharmaceutical company.

Financial information

Year end	31/12/2021
Turnover	£141,320,000
Pre-tax profit	£10,953,000

Main locations: The company's headquarters is in Maidenhead.

Community involvement

The company provides grants to primarily support health, science, learning and community-based projects undertaken by healthcare or charitable organisations.

Employee-led support

Patients at Heart is the company's employee volunteering scheme supporting health and social care charities around the UK.

Exclusions

According to the application form, the following will not be considered:

- Clinical research, including Investigator Initiated Studies
- Grants to individual healthcare professionals or commercial businesses
- Healthcare Professionals' individual training or development opportunities
- Travel grants to Healthcare Professionals to attend scientific conferences (NOTE – these need to be requested through your AbbVie Representative)
- Religious programmes
- Political party sponsorship
- Charity fundraising outside of the UK (eg: Climbing Mount Everest)
- Activities that occurred in the past.
- Applications exclusively linked to the use of AbbVie products
- Application forms completed with the input or influence of an AbbVie employee
- Funding of start-up or operating costs of entities (i.e., resources used by an organisation to exist such as payment of rent for the office space, staff salary, or cost of electricity)

Applications

Application forms and full details of the application process can be found on the company's website.

Community contributions

We were unable to determine a figure for the company's charitable contributions for the year.

Abellio Scotrail Ltd

Community services and development, education and training, the environment, health

Company registration number: SC450732

Correspondent: ScotRail in the Community, 5th Floor, Culzean Building, 36 Renfield Street, Glasgow G2 1LU (email: community@scotrail.co.uk; website: www.scotrail.co.uk/about-scotrail/scotrail-community)

Directors: Dominic Booth; Alexander Hynes; David Kaye; David Lister; Alexander White; Paul Wright (male: 100%).

Nature of business: Abellio ScotRail is a passenger railway service operator in Scotland.

Financial information

Year end	31/03/2021
Turnover	£931,300,000
Pre-tax profit	(£18,560,000)

Total employees: 5,211

Main locations: The company operates rail services across Scotland.

Community involvement

ScotRail's charitable support is focused on five main areas: health and well-being, education, sustainable cities and communities, the environment and the promotion of railways.

ScotRail Employee Charitable Giving Fund

The fund contributes towards employee fundraising efforts for the causes that matter to them by matching funds raised up to £250. Funding is available to charities supporting mental health, education, environmental causes and railway heritage. The fund is open to permanent Abellio ScotRail employees.

Partnerships

ScotRail's charity partner until 2022 was MND Scotland. Since 2017, together with Network Rail Scotland, ScotRail donated over £280,000 of support to the charity through staff fundraising, customer donations and gifts in kind. The company's staff nominate and vote for causes they wish to support.

Employee-led support

Employees are given one day of paid leave per year.

Applications

Contact the correspondent for more information.

Community contributions

Cash donations UK	£22,000

According to its 2020/21 annual report, during the year the company made charitable donations of £22,000.

abrdn plc

Community services and development, general charitable purposes, money and debt advice

Company registration number: SC286832

Correspondent: Sustainability Team, 1 George Street, Edinburgh, Aberdeenshire EH2 2LL (email: sustainability@abrdn.com; website: www.abrdn.com/corporate/corporate-sustainability/document-library)

Directors: Sir Douglas Flint; Stephen Bird; Stephanie Bruce; Jonathan Asquith; Catherine Bradley; John Devine; Hannah Grove; Brian McBride; Martin Pike; Cathleen Raffaeli; Cecilia Reyes; Jutta af Rosenborg (female: 50%; male: 50%).

Nature of business: abrdn plc is an investment company.

Financial information

Year end	31/12/2021
Turnover	£1,543,000,000
Pre-tax profit	£1,115,000,000

Total employees: 5,463

Main locations: The group has operations in 46 locations across Europe, the Americas, Asia, the Middle East and Australia.

Community involvement

The majority of the group's charitable activities are channelled through its corporate charities, the abrdn Charitable Foundation and the abrdn Financial Fairness Trust. It also has several partnerships with charitable organisations in the UK and abroad. According to the group's sustainability report, abrdn plc's charitable giving supported 95 charities globally.

Partnerships

The group began a partnership in 2021 with Hello World, a charity which aims to help bridge the digital divide and improve access to digital education and literacy worldwide. During the year, the partnership created 64 abrdn Hello Hubs across Uganda, providing access to digital educational resources for 80,000 people in disconnected communities.

In the UK, the group maintains an employability partnership with The Prince's Trust, mentoring young people and organising employability events with the charity.

Employee-led support

Staff are entitled to three days' paid volunteering leave each year. According to the group's 2021 sustainability report, staff volunteered around 2,600 hours during the year.

The group also provides matched funding up to £200 to employees engaging in various fundraising efforts. In 2021, employee-led fundraising, including matched funding, totalled £318,000, supporting 158 charitable causes.

Applications

Contact the correspondent for further information.

Corporate charity

abrdn Charitable Foundation (OSCR no. SC042597) – see entry on page 215; abrdn Financial Fairness Trust (OSCR no. SC040877) – see entry on page 215.

Community contributions

Total contributions UK	£858,000
Total contributions worldwide	£2,600,000

In the group's 2021 sustainability report, abrdn plc valued its total charitable contributions for the year at £2.6 million. The report also provides the following breakdowns of funds distributed by region and by area of focus.

Social welfare	37%
Health	25%
Education	21%
Economic development	9%
Environment	7%
Arts and culture	1%

UK	33%
Americas	11%
Asia-Pacific	11%
EMEA excluding UK	43%

Funding distributed in the UK totalled £858,000.

Accenture UK Ltd

Community enterprise and social entrepreneurship, education and training

Company registration number: 4757301

Correspondent: Corporate Citizenship Team, 30 Fenchurch Street, London EC3M 3BD (tel: 020 7844 4000; email: corporatecitizenship@accenture.com; website: www.accenture.com)

Directors: Daniel Burton; Simon Eaves; Ewan Mackay; Lisa Rose; Shaheen Sayed; Derek Simpson (female: 33%; male: 67%).

Nature of business: Accenture provides management consulting, technology and outsourcing services. Accenture (UK) Ltd is a wholly owned subsidiary of the Accenture group and the main trading entity for Accenture in the UK.

Financial information

Year end	31/08/2021
Turnover	£2,610,000
Pre-tax profit	£203,500

UK employees: 8,988

Total employees: 699,000

Main locations: Accenture has offices in Edinburgh, London, Manchester and Newcastle. The company has a global presence with offices in over 120 countries.

Community involvement

In the UK, the company's corporate citizenship programme, 'Skills to Succeed', focuses on environmental and social sustainability issues, with a particular emphasis on helping young people gain employability and entrepreneurial skills. The programme focuses on young people aged 18 to 24 who are not in education, employment or training and provides them with support to build skills and obtain work.

Partnerships

Accenture works with multiple partners to deliver the programme. The company has the following strategic partners:

- Doteveryone
- Good Things Foundation
- The Skills Builder Partnership
- Street League
- Tottenham Hotspur Foundation
- The Prince's Trust
- Movement to Work
- Worker Tech

Accenture has worked with the H&M Foundation and KTH Royal Institute of Technology to create the Global Change Award (GCA). The award identifies ideas that apply disruptive technology and new business models to change the way garments are designed, produced, shipped, bought, used and recycled.

Employee-led support

Employees are given three days' paid leave a year for volunteering.

Commercially led support

Accenture provides sponsorship to arts, sport and cultural organisations. Current sponsorship agreements include those with British Triathlon and the National Theatre.

Applications

Contact the correspondent for further information.

Community contributions

Cash donations UK	£2,360,000

In 2020/21, Accenture made charitable donations totalling £2.36 million.

Addleshaw Goddard LLP

Community services and development, education and training, social welfare

Company registration number: OC318149

Correspondent: Claire Cunningham, CSR Manager, Milton Gate, 60 Chiswell Street, London EC1Y 4AG (email: Claire.Cunningham@addleshawgoddard.com; website: www.addleshawgoddard.com)

Nature of business: Addleshaw Goddard is an international business law firm.

Financial information

Year end	30/04/2021
Turnover	£320,560,000
Pre-tax profit	£135,610,000

Total employees: 1,632

Main locations: In the UK the company has offices in Aberdeen, Edinburgh, Glasgow, Leeds, London and Manchester.

Community involvement

The company's CSR strategy is framed around its objective of 'unlocking young potential'. Young people and communities are supported through the company's three CSR pillars:

- Access to education
- Access to the legal profession
- Access to work

As well as company-wide programmes, there are local CSR leadership teams which oversee each office's efforts in the local community, such as pro bono work.

All of this is underpinned by a wider commitment and investment from the firm through The Addleshaw Goddard Charitable Trust (Charity Commission no. 286887), which was established in 2003 to support local charities and CSR-related projects.

Partnerships

The company has partnerships with charities that align with its objective. The four charities for 2020 to 2022 are Children's Heart Surgery Fund (Leeds), Coram (London), Manchester Centrepoint (Manchester) and The Rock Trust (Scotland). The charities are supported with employee fundraising, pro bono work and volunteering.

In-kind support

Employees are able to undertake pro bono legal work.

Employee-led support

Employees have the opportunity to volunteer, campaign and fundraise for charities that meet the company's main CSR objective.

Applications

Contact the correspondent for further information.

Corporate charity

The Addleshaw Goddard Charitable Trust (Charity Commission no. 286887) – see entry on page 216.

Community contributions

Cash donations UK	£76,800

We were unable to determine a figure for the company's charitable contributions. However, in 2020/21 the Addleshaw Goddard Charitable Trust received £76,800 from Addleshaw Goddard LLP.

Admiral Group plc

General charitable purposes

Company registration number: 3849958

Correspondent: The CSR Team, David Street, Cardiff CF10 2EH (tel: 0871 882 8282; website: www.admiralgroup.co.uk)

Directors: Geraint Jones; Jean Park; Justine Roberts; Andy Crossley; Mike Brierly; Karen Green; JP Rangaswami; Annette Court; Milena Focatiis; Evelyn Bourke; Bill Roberts (female: 45%; male: 55%).

Nature of business: The group sells and underwrites private car insurance in the UK.

Financial information

Year end	31/12/2021
Turnover	£3,510,000,000
Pre-tax profit	£769,000,000

UK employees: 8,000

Total employees: 11,000

Main locations: In the UK the group's principal offices are located in Cardiff, Newport and Swansea. It also has offices in Europe, Canada and Asia.

Community involvement

The group supports communities where it has a presence through charitable donations, matched funding and sponsorship. Most of its CSR is directed through the Admiral Community Chest and the Ministry of Giving.

Admiral Support Fund

The fund was established in 2020 to provide support to communities impacted by the COVID-19 pandemic. Through the fund, £2 million was donated to the ABI COVID-19 Support Fund, £1 million to UNICEF and £1.8 million to local UK organisations. The remaining £1.2 million was allocated to the group's overseas businesses to distribute to local causes.

Admiral Community Chest

The Community Chest provides funding for charities and local organisations with which employees and their families are involved. Employees' fundraising endeavours are matched by the group from the fund.

Recent beneficiaries of Community Chest funding include:

- 3rd Ammanford Brownies
- Abercynon Cricket Club
- Budokan Wales Karate
- Caerphilly and District Schools
- Cardiff Baseball Club
- Dolman Theatre
- Fenix Dance School
- Friends of Coed Gwilym Park
- Good Heart Animal Sanctuaries
- Llanishen Golf Club
- Saru Ju Jitsu
- Swansea Gymnastics
- Swim Wales
- West Wales Youth Darts

Employee-led support

The Admiral Group's Give A Day scheme was launched in 2021 and allows employees the opportunity to support local communities through volunteering. Each member of the group's UK operations is allowed two days' paid leave annually to volunteer and help a charity or organisation of their choice.

The Admiral Group also matches funds raised by employees for charities. Some of the charities that have benefitted from this include:

- Age Cymru
- Alzheimer's Society
- Diabetes UK Cymru
- Guide Dogs Cymru
- Red Cross Australia
- The Huggard Centre
- The Prince's Trust
- Cardiff Dogs Home, The Rescue Hotel
- Ty Hafan
- WWF-UK

Commercially led support

Admiral Group sponsors many different organisations and events in the South Wales area. The group's sponsorship portfolio includes Welsh Rugby Union, Chapter Arts Centre, Cardiff Schools Crossing Patrols, Pride Cymru and the Swansea Bay 10k.

Applications

Contact the correspondent for further information. Note: the group prefers to support organisations with which Admiral employees or their immediate family are involved.

Community contributions

We were unable to determine a figure for the group's charitable contributions for 2021. However, across 2020 and 2021, the group donated a total of £6 million through the Admiral Support Fund.

Adnams plc

Arts, culture and heritage, community services and development, education and training, the environment, health

Company registration number: 31114

Correspondent: Rebecca Abrahall, Adnams Community Trust Administrator, Sole Bay Brewery, Southwold, Suffolk IP18 6JW (tel: 01502 727200; email: charity@adnams.co.uk; website: https://adnams.co.uk)

Directors: Jonathan Adams; Dr Andy Wood; Jenny Hanlon; Dr Karen Hester; Nicky Dulieu; Bridget McIntyre; Steven Sharp; Guy Heald (female: 50%; male: 50%).

Nature of business: The principal activities of the company are: brewing and distilling, retailing and wholesaling alcohol, and pub and hotel ownership and management.

Financial information

Year end	31/12/2021
Turnover	£57,370,000
Pre-tax profit	£39,000

Total employees: 226

Main locations: The main office and brewery is located in Southwold, Suffolk.

Community involvement

The company's charitable giving is channelled through its corporate charity The Adnams Community Trust (Charity Commission no. 1000203).

Applications

See the company's corporate charity entry for further information.

Corporate charity

The Adnams Community Trust (Charity Commission no. 1000203) – see entry on page 217.

Community contributions

Cash donations UK	£12,000

Adnams gives 1% of its annual profits to charitable causes through The Adnams Community Trust. Donations to the trust in 2021 amounted to £12,000.

Aegon UK plc

Community services and development, education and training, general charitable purposes, health, money and debt advice, sports and recreation

Company registration number: 3679296

Correspondent: Charity Committee, Level 26, The Leadenhall Building, 122 Leadenhall Street, London EC3V 4AB (website: www.aegon.co.uk)

Directors: David Dalton-Brown; Michael Davies; Susanna Davies; Adrian Eastwood; James Ewing; Theresa Froehlich; Helen Heslop; Michael Holliday-Williams; Michael Merrick; Michael Rogers (female: 30%; male: 70%).

Nature of business: This company acts as a holding company for financial services businesses within the Aegon UK Group. Aegon UK is the brand name for Scottish Equitable plc and it is a subsidiary of Aegon N.V., a multinational life insurance, pension and asset management company headquartered in The Hague, the Netherlands.

Financial information

Year end	31/12/2021
Turnover	£279,100,000
Pre-tax profit	£327,600,000

UK employees: 2,000

Main locations: The company's head office is in London. It has additional offices in Edinburgh, Witham and Peterborough.

Community involvement

The group supports local communities through charitable donations, fundraising and volunteer work. The group supports two key themes:

- Financial security and education, which includes promoting financial literacy and later-life employment solutions
- Well-being and longevity, which includes promoting physical and mental health, disease prevention and support for liveable communities

In the UK, the company's charity committee organises a variety of fundraising activities undertaken in support of employee-nominated charities. The company also works in partnership with The City of Edinburgh Council to fund breakfast clubs in five Edinburgh primary schools, providing local schoolchildren with a free, healthy and nutritional start to their day.

Employee-led support

Employees are entitled to two days' paid leave each year to volunteer. Employees also take part in fundraising for local and national charities. The company donates £2 for every £1 raised by employees. Some of the company's UK charity partners include Children with Cancer UK, the RNLI, The Brain Tumour Charity and Brain House Hospice.

Applications

Contact the company for further information.

Community contributions

Cash donations UK	£148,200
Cash donations worldwide	£7,860,000
Total contributions worldwide	£8,110,000

According to the Aegon N.V. 2021 annual report and accounts, charitable contributions totalled £8.11 million. Cash donations totalled £7.86 million and the value of volunteering was costed at £250,900. This financial information has been converted from EUR to GBP using the exchange rate at the time of writing (August 2022).

According to Aegon UK's website, £148,200 was donated to charities in 2021, we have taken this as the figure for cash donations in the UK.

Aggregate Industries UK Ltd

Community services and development, education and training, the environment

Company registration number: 245717

Correspondent: Local Community Liaison Group, Bardon Hall, Copt Oak Road, Markfield, Leicestershire LE67 9PJ (tel: 01530 816600; email: sustainability@aggregate.com; website: www.aggregate.com/sustainability/people-and-communities)

Directors: John Bowater; Dragan Maksimovic; Phillip Norah (male: 100%).

Nature of business: Aggregate Industries and its subsidiaries are engaged in the exploitation of land and mineral reserves, principally for the supply of heavy building materials for construction activities.

Financial information

Year end	31/12/2021
Turnover	£1,301,830,000
Pre-tax profit	£82,270,000

UK employees: 3,700

Main locations: The company has sites throughout the UK, and in the Channel Islands, Norway and Northern Europe.

Community involvement

According to its sustainability strategy document, the company supports its 'neighbouring communities by donating staff time for volunteering activities, materials to help with local projects as well as monetary contributions'.

In-kind support

The company has previously donated materials and resources to support local projects.

Employee-led support

Employees can take 40 hours' paid volunteering leave each year.

Applications

Contact the correspondent for further information.

Community contributions

The company did not provide a figure for its charitable contributions in 2021.

Allen & Overy LLP

Education and training, human rights

Company registration number: OC306763

Correspondent: Kate Cavelle, One Bishops Square, London E1 6AD (tel: 020 3088 0000; email: kate.cavelle@allenovery.com; website: www.allenovery.com)

Directors: Wim Dejonghe; Gareth Price; Parya Badie; Tim Conduit; Sally Dewar; Shamita Etienne-Cummings; Roger Lui; Peter Myners; Kenneth Rivlin (female: 33%; male: 67%).

Nature of business: Allen & Overy is an international law firm.

Financial information

Year end	30/04/2021
Turnover	£177,000,000
Pre-tax profit	£822,000,000

UK employees: 2,000

Total employees: 5,600

Main locations: The company has offices around the world. In the UK it has offices in London and Belfast.

Community involvement

The company's CSR strategy is focused on two major themes: access to justice and access to education and employment. The company's corporate charity, The Allen & Overy Foundation (Charity Commission no. 1153738), is funded by contributions from all Allen & Overy partners around the world. Around 75% of funds are allocated to support local projects, with the remaining 25% being donated to international causes.

Access to justice

The company's programmes vary from community to community to reflect local cultures and priorities. It also advises charities and community groups on legal, strategic and business issues. The company undertakes pro bono work in the following areas:

- **Rule of Law** – Allen & Overy works with emerging economies to develop legal and justice systems.
- **Free legal advice** – free legal advice is provided to vulnerable people in a number of countries, either by providing in-person advice, end-to-end casework or organisational development assistance.
- **Human Rights Working Group** – pro bono support is provided to human rights charities and non-governmental organisations, such as Liberty, Amicus, INTERIGHTS and Fair Trials

International. This support ranges from representing marginalised communities in court and submitting interventions and amicus curiae briefs, to undertaking international comparative research projects to inform policy work.
- **Microfinance and Social Investment Group** – advice is provided to microfinance institutions and social enterprises in developing economies around the world.

Access to education and employment

The company forms long-term partnerships with schools local to its offices to advise them on issues around governance and financial sustainability, as well as to support pupils' academic achievement. In London, the local office's current partner is Raine's Foundation School, following a successful ten-year partnership with Bethnal Green Academy. In addition, the company runs the following programmes:

- **Education sector partnerships** – the company has several partnerships with schools worldwide and advises them on issues around governance and financial sustainability.
- **ReStart** – a skills development and mentoring programme for over-50s living in London who have been unemployed for between six months and a year. The programme supports people from any background or profession.
- **Smart Start** – a work experience scheme that gives year 12 students from underprivileged backgrounds the opportunity to work at Allen & Overy's offices for a week.

Charity partnerships

In 2018 the company began a partnership with Hope and Homes for Children, an international charity that works to protect vulnerable children by moving them out of institutions and into family-based care. Through the partnership, £1.83 million was raised through fundraising events by Allen & Overy offices. The charity also benefited from £507,000 worth of pro bono time and £6,000 worth of in-kind support in the form of training and use of company facilities.

Applications

Contact the correspondent for further information.

Corporate charity

The Allen & Overy Foundation (Charity Commission no. 1153738) – see entry on page 217.

Community contributions

Cash donations UK	£2,400,000

According to its 2020/21 annual report, the company donated £2.4 million to 'charitable funds' during the year, including £1.6 million to The Allen & Overy Foundation.

Allianz Insurance plc

Animal welfare, community enterprise and social entrepreneurship, education and training, general charitable purposes, health, mental health and well-being, sports and recreation

Company registration number: 84638

Correspondent: CSR Team, 57 Ladymead, Guildford, Surrey GU1 1DB (tel: 01483 568161; website: www.allianz.co.uk/about-allianz-insurance/social-responsibility.html)

Directors: Paul Evans; Colm Holmes; Simon McGinn; Teresa Robson-Capps; Christopher Townsend; José Rafael Vazquez; Fernley Dyson; Steve Treloar; Andrew Torrance; Christian Dinesen; Rosanne Murison; Denise Larnder (female: 25%; male: 75%).

Nature of business: Allianz is a financial services company. Its core businesses are insurance and asset management.

Financial information

Year end	31/12/2021
Turnover	£1,860,500,000
Pre-tax profit	£29,000,000

Main locations: Allianz has 26 offices throughout the UK.

Community involvement

Allianz provides financial and in-kind support to global and national charities as well as supporting causes that are local to the areas in which it operates. Support is given through various funds, partnerships and foundations.

Allianz Community Funds

The company has various funds that it contributes to, each of which has its own specific aims. Note: none of these funds are registered charities.

▶ **The Allianz Local Community Fund** – the fund aims to distribute money to charities local to its Guildford office. In 2021, the chosen charities were TALK Surrey, Surrey Care Trust and the Prison Advice and Care Trust (PACT).
▶ **The Allianz Sport Fund** – also launched in 2021, the Sport Fund gives financial support to grassroots sports clubs across the UK.

Partnerships

The company has a corporate partnership with a national charity which is voted for by its employees. The partnership lasts for three-years and the chosen charity will benefit from employee volunteering as well as employee fundraising, which Allianz will then match. In 2019, Allianz began its partnership with leading mental health charity Mind and its Scottish counterpart, SAMH, aiming to raise £1 million for the charities within the three years. The company reached this target in 2021 through employee fundraising and company contributions.

Allianz also works with a number of other charities in the UK that are aligned with its values. Examples of current partnerships include:

▶ **Help Musicians** – Allianz Musical Insurance has continued to financially support Help Musicians after forming an initial partnership during the COVID-19 pandemic
▶ **Saracens Sports Foundation** – the company is a principal partner of the foundation and sponsors its wheelchair rugby programme which works with disabled children in the London and Hertfordshire area to introduce them to the sport
▶ **British Paralympic Association**
▶ **Disasters Emergency Committee (DEC)** – in the event of a natural disaster that prompts an appeal by the DEC, Allianz will respond by offering an immediate one-off payroll giving facility through which employees can make a tax-efficient donation to the disaster appeal. This donation will be channelled through Care International, the company's chosen international emergency partner for employee donations in the UK.
▶ **SOS Children's Villages** – the company is partnered with SOS Children's Villages, which runs programmes for children from disadvantaged backgrounds and disaster-prone regions.

Allianz foundations

Allianz has established 13 foundations across the world that support charitable causes. The company's foundation in the UK is the Petplan Charitable Trust. The trust is associated with Petplan Ltd, a pet insurance company and subsidiary of Allianz. The trust receives the majority of its funding from policyholders, who can choose to donate when they take out or renew their insurance. It aims to promote the health and welfare of animals across the world. Funding is awarded to animal welfare charities and towards research for new treatments.

Employee-led support

Employees are encouraged to fundraise and volunteer for the company's charity partners as well as local organisations. The company also operates a payroll giving scheme through which employees can make a tax-efficient donation to a disaster appeal. Employees can take ten hours of paid leave annually to support a local charity or organisation

Commercially led support

Allianz sponsors Saracens Sports Foundation's wheelchair rugby programme.

Applications

Information about the latest funding rounds for the Allianz Sport Fund can be found on the company's website. To be considered for the Allianz Community Fund, applications can be made to the Community Foundation for Surrey. Details of how to apply can be found at www.cfsurrey.org.uk. For all other enquiries, contact the correspondent.

Corporate charity

Petplan Charitable Trust (Charity Commission no. 1032907) – see entry on page 267.

Community contributions

Cash donations UK	£430,000

In 2021 cash donations from Allianz Insurance totalled £430,000. This included £300,000 through the Allianz Musical Fund and £100,000 through the Allianz Sport Fund. The remaining £30,000 was donated to the Allianz Local Community Fund and distributed between charities local to the company's office in Guildford.

Alpkit Ltd

Education, the environment, health, sports and recreation

Company registration number: 5146091

Correspondent: Unit 12–14, Oak House, Engine Lane, Moorgreen Industrial Park, Newthorpe, Nottingham NG16 3QU (website: https://alpkit.com/pages/foundation)

Directors: Colin Fisher; David Hanney; Robert Savin; Nicholas Smith; Karen Stevens; Colin Stocker; Kenneth Stocker (female: 14%; male: 86%).

Nature of business: Outdoor clothing retailer.

UK employees: 81

Main locations: Alpkit has stores in Hathersage, Ambleside, Keswick and Gateshead.

Community involvement

The Alpkit Foundation (Charity Commission no. 1162585) makes grants of £50 to £500 for diversity and inclusion in the outdoors, education, conservation of the natural environment and health and well-being.

The Alpkit Foundation is a 1% For the Planet partner, meaning that any 1% For the Planet member can partner with the foundation to support various causes.

Commercially led support

Alpkit reports on its website that 1% of all sales goes to the Alpkit Foundation.

Applications

See the company's corporate charity entry for further information.

Corporate charity

Alpkit Foundation (Charity Commission no. 1162585) – see entry on page 218.

Community contributions

Cash donations UK	£137,000

Financial information on the company's charitable giving was not available. However, the foundation's website states that Alpkit donates 1% of sales and at least 10% of annual profits to support grassroots projects. In 2021 the foundation received donations of £137,000 which we have taken as the company's charitable contribution for the year.

Anglian Water

Community services and development, education and training, the environment, health, heritage, medical research

Company registration number: 2366656

Correspondent: The CSR Team, Lancaster House, Lancaster Way, Ermine Business Park, Huntingdon, Cambridgeshire PE29 6XU (tel: 0345 791 9155; website: www.anglianwater.co.uk)

Directors: John Hirst; Peter Simpson; Steven Buck; Natalia Ceeney; Dame Polly Courtice; Zarin Patel; Paul Whittaker; John Barry; Niall Mills; Duncan Symonds; Batiste Ogier (female: 27%; male: 73%).

Nature of business: Anglian Water supplies, collects and treats water.

Financial information

Year end	31/03/2021
Turnover	£1,276,000,000
Pre-tax profit	£119,000,000

UK employees: 5,000

Main locations: The company's headquarters is in Cambridgeshire. Its areas of operation cover east and south-east England.

Community involvement

Anglian Water contributes to the community in a number of ways.

Environment

One of the company's main aims is to protect and enhance the environment and wildlife in eastern and south-eastern England, the area in which it operates. It achieves this by:

- Partnering with environmental organisations such as the Wildlife Trust, Keep Britain Tidy and the British Trust for Ornithology.
- Working with local environmental charities and utilising their local expertise and skills.
- Providing funding for projects focusing on the protection of individual species. Currently, the company is supporting projects that are focused on ospreys, nightingales and pool frogs.
- Promoting the 'Keep it Clear' campaign, a behaviour change programme aiming to tackle the problem of pollution and flooding caused by avoidable sewer blockages. The company works alongside communities, local authorities, waste and recycling teams, environmental charities, schools and food premises. Anglian has also partnered with the Marine Conservation Society to support its 'Unflushables' campaign.
- Promoting the importance of surface water management, pollution prevention and coastline protection.
- Having a number of its sites managed by the Wildlife Trust.

Partnerships

Anglian Water formally recognises WaterAid as its nominated charity and therefore does not offer charitable donations or sponsorship to other charities and bodies.

Anglian Water provides support to the charity through donations, fundraising activities, a monthly WaterAid lottery and payroll giving. The company also sends out a fundraising leaflet to its customers along with their water bills, encouraging them to support the charity.

Education

The company operates an educational outreach programme in schools as well as in its purpose-built education centres. The interactive sessions aim to enhance the understanding of the water cycle and the company's role within it. Topics covered range from water efficiency and pollution to climate change and sustainability. At the time of writing (August 2022), school visits and trips to the education centres had been temporarily suspended – visit the website for updates.

Anglian Water Assistance Fund

The company has also established the Anglian Water Assistance Fund to support customers in financial hardship. Its website states: 'This fund might be able to help to cover the cost of bills when people are going through challenging times. We prioritise those who are most in need, but even if we aren't able to offer you this type of support there are lots of other ways we can help.'

Employee-led support

The company operates the Love to Help volunteering programme to enable its employees to volunteer for local causes. According to its website, the company pledges to match up to 30 hours of work time per year.

Through the programme, employees can:

- Volunteer with the RiverCare and BeachCare programme
- Volunteer to help at or organise regional or national WaterAid events
- Take part in voluntary activities in their local communities

Employees are also encouraged to take part in fundraising activities for the company's charity partner, WaterAid. In 2020/21, employees raised £334,700.

Applications

Anglian Water only supports WaterAid and does not give charitable donations or sponsorships to other charities.

Community contributions

Cash donations UK	£40,000

According to the company's 2020/21 annual report, it donated £40,000 to WaterAid.

Anglo American Crop Nutrients Ltd

The environment, social welfare, STEM

Company registration number: 4948435

Correspondent: CSR Team, 17 Charterhouse Street, London EC1N 6RA (tel: 01723 470010; email: cropnutrients.info@angloamerican.com; website: https://uk.angloamerican.com/our-community)

Directors: Anthony O'Neill; Stephen Pearce; Richard Price; Thomas McCulley; Jacqueline Flynn (female: 20%; male: 80%).

Nature of business: Anglo American is a mining company.

Financial information

Year end	31/12/2021
Pre-tax profit	£33,900,000

Total employees: 609

Main locations: The company has offices in Scarborough and London. Support is focused around North Yorkshire and Teesside.

Community involvement

Anglo American Crop Nutrients Ltd (formerly Anglo American Woodsmith Ltd) provides support through donations, fundraising, educational outreach programmes and through its corporate charity, the Woodsmith Foundation Ltd (Charity Commission no. 1163127). The company's parent company, Anglo American plc, also supports the Anglo American Foundation (Charity Commission no. 1111719), which makes grants for health, education and community development.

Charity partners

Each year the company supports three local charities chosen by its employees, through fundraising events and company donations. The chosen charities for 2021 were St Catherine's Hospice, Scarborough Mates and North Yorkshire Air Ambulance.

Education

Since 2012, the company has run an educational outreach programme aiming to increase the skills and aspirations of young people in the local area.

According to the website, the three main themes of the programme are:

- Supporting careers provision in schools and colleges
- Enriching the school curriculum with a particular focus on science, technology, engineering and maths (STEM)
- Specific projects targeted at disadvantaged students

The programme offers a range of activities including careers presentations and workshops, projects to improve STEM skills, work placements, site visits and initiatives specifically designed to help to improve the life chances of young people living in disadvantaged areas.

The company also funds a wide range of other education initiatives. In 2021, £85,000 was donated to borough councils in Scarborough and Redcar and Cleveland to support STEM careers provision.

Woodsmith Foundation Ltd

The company plans to contribute an annual royalty of 0.5% of revenue to its corporate charity, which funds community projects in the North York Moors National Park, Scarborough and Redcar.

Great Days

In 2019, the company launched 'Great Days', an initiative that measures daily performance against four key metrics: project milestones, environment, lost time from injuries and high potential events. For each day that is considered a 'great day', the company puts money into a dedicated charity pot, with the amount donated increasing as the run of great days gets longer. In 2021/22, the company donated £97,000 to its three charity partners.

Employee-led support

Employees are encouraged to get involved in a variety of community activities including educational outreach programmes, community events and environmental improvement schemes.

Commercially led support

Since 2011 the company has been the headline sponsor of Scarborough Engineering Week.

Applications

Contact the correspondent for further information.

Corporate charity

Anglo American Foundation (Charity Commission no. 1111719) – see entry on page 218; Woodsmith Foundation Ltd (Charity Commission no. 1163127) – see entry on page 287.

Community contributions

We were unable to determine the figure for total charitable contributions in 2021. However, according to the Anglo American website, the company donated £97,000 to charities through its Great Days initiative in 2021/22. It also provided £85,000 towards local councils for STEM careers provision. The accounts also note that 0.5% of the company's revenue is donated annually to its corporate charity, totalling £1 million in 2021.

Apax Partners LLP

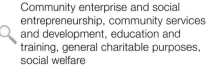

Community enterprise and social entrepreneurship, community services and development, education and training, general charitable purposes, social welfare

Company registration number: OC303117

Correspondent: Kate Albert, Manager of the Apax Foundation, 33 Jermyn Street, London SW1Y 6DN (tel: 020 7872 6300; website: www.apax.com)

Nature of business: Apax is a global private equity advisory firm.

Financial information

Year end	31/03/2021
Turnover	£248,316,000
Pre-tax profit	£231,049,000

Total employees: 242

Main locations: The firm's UK office is located in London. There are also seven offices worldwide, in Hong Kong, Mumbai, Munich, New York, Shanghai and Tel Aviv.

Community involvement

The firm channels its community involvement through its corporate charity, The Apax Foundation (Charity Commission no. 1112845), to which it donates a proportion of its profits. The foundation makes grants to charities working in the areas of social mobility and social entrepreneurship, in the locations in which Apax operates.

Employee-led support

Employee volunteering

Employees' fundraising efforts are matched through The Apax Foundation's matched funding scheme.

Employees can also volunteer through The Apax Foundation's community service programme, Apax Gives Back Days.

In 2020, the annual staff challenge raised around £20,000 to further develop a school in Uganda built after the Apax Challenge 2018.

Applications

See the firm's corporate charity's entry for further information.

Corporate charity

The Apax Foundation (Charity Commission no. 1112845) – see entry on page 219.

Community contributions

Cash donations UK	£3,427,000
Total contributions UK	£3,452,000

The company's 2020/21 accounts did not provide a figure for charitable contributions. The Apax Foundation's 2020 accounts state that it received a donation of more than £3.4 million from the company's profits and services from Apax employees worth £25,100. We have taken these figures to represent to company's giving.

Arla Foods Ltd

General charitable purposes, health

Company registration number: 2143253

Correspondent: Community Involvement Team, Arla House, 4 Savannah Way, Leeds Valley Park, Leeds, West Yorkshire, England LS10 1AB (tel: 0113 382 7000; website: www.arlafoods.co.uk/overview/arla-in-the-uk/community-involvement)

Directors: Afshin Amirahmadi; Peter Gioertz-Carlsen; Simon Ho; Pauline Hogg; Mogens Kaspersen; Anne-Frances Ball (female: 33%; male: 67%).

Nature of business: This company is a subsidiary of Arla Foods, which is a leading supplier of milk and dairy products in the UK market.

Financial information

Year end	31/12/2021
Turnover	£2,493,840,000
Pre-tax profit	£31,590,000

UK employees: 3,845

Total employees: 18,973

Main locations: The company's head office is in Leeds. It also has sites in Aylesbury, Hatfield, Denbighshire, Dumfries, Oswestry, Cheshire, Settle, Cornwall, Devon, Leicester, Wiltshire, Whitchurch and London.

Community involvement

Arla supports local charities through fundraising and donations. The company has a longstanding partnership with food redistributor FareShare and actively supports GroceryAid, a charity that supports the grocery industry. It also takes part in Mission Christmas, through which it donates gifts to Cash for Kids, a charity that supports disadvantaged children

In the UK, Arla is a corporate partner of Marie Curie Cancer Care and each site supports its local branch of the charity.

In-kind support

In the event that any Arla products cannot be sold, they are donated to food banks. The company has signed a partnership agreement with the European Federation of Food Banks (FEBA) to enable donations. According to its 2021 annual report, Arla Foods Ltd donated the equivalent of 1.5 million meals to people in need through homeless shelters and community cafes.

In 2021, the company continued to work with the charity Magic Breakfast to offer free educational materials to help children across the UK learn about food origins and the importance of a nutritious breakfast. Through the partnership, the company provides free vouchers for Cravendale milk. During the year 150,000 vouchers were distributed.

Employee-led support

The foundation's Community Challenge initiative allows colleagues to have an input into how the company's community involvement budget is spent. As part of the initiative, the company will match money raised by employees and will also provide funding to causes for which its employees volunteer.

Commercially led support

With each bottle of Arla's Farmers Milk sold, 25p is donated to dairy farmers.

Applications

Contact the correspondent for further information.

Community contributions

We were unable to determine the total figure for community contributions.

Arsenal Holdings plc

Education and training, health, social welfare, sports and recreation

Company registration number: 4250459

Correspondent: Arsenal in the Community, Highbury House, 75 Drayton Park, London N5 1BU (tel: 020 7704 4000; website: www. arsenal.com/community)

Directors: Lord Harris; Stan Kroenke; Josh Kroenke; Timothy Lewis (male: 100%).

Nature of business: Arsenal FC is a professional football club competing in the Premier League.

Financial information

Year end	31/05/2021
Turnover	£328,200,000
Pre-tax profit	(£107,290,000)

UK employees: 703

Main locations: The football club is based in Islington, London.

Community involvement

Arsenal Holdings provides a wide range of sports, social and educational programmes primarily in North London, but sometimes nationally. These programmes are delivered through the club's 'Arsenal in the Community' initiative, which was established in 1985. The initiative is supported by funds from the football club and the Arsenal Foundation, as well as from several external organisations, including the Premier League.

Currently, the club's programmes fall into the following categories:

Sport

Sport has been at the centre of the club's community work, having been developed over the years as a means of engaging young people. The club's sports programmes include a programme for promising players, a female football programme, football sessions designed specifically for people with Down's syndrome and walking football sessions for older people. There are also opportunities to take part in other sports, such as bowls and hockey.

Education and training

The club's educational support spans all aspects of schooling, from basic numeracy and literacy skills to further education and employment. The club runs programmes for reading, modern languages and adult learning, as well as its own sports coaching foundation degree, which is accredited by the London Metropolitan University.

Social inclusion

Arsenal supports young people at risk of crime, substance misuse and other negative influences by offering positive activities that may act as a diversion from such influences. The club's social inclusion programmes include football sessions that promote youth engagement in deprived areas, weekly football and literacy sessions at pupil referral units across North London as well as language and social skills sessions for victims of torture.

Home learning

Arsenal provides home learning materials and resources to young students aged between 7 and 16 years old. Primary materials contain activities that are suitable for children in Key Stage 2 (aged 7–11). Secondary materials contain activities that are suitable for children in Key Stage 3 and 4 (aged 11–16).

Applications

Contact the correspondent for more information.

Corporate charity

The Arsenal Foundation (Charity Commission no. 1145668) – see entry on page 219.

Community contributions

We were unable to determine a figure for the club's charitable contributions.

Artemis Investment Management LLP

Education and training, the environment, health, social welfare

Company registration number: OC354068

Correspondent: Marisa Charosky, Artemis Charitable Foundation Co-ordinator, Cassini House, 57 St James's Street, London SW1A 1LD (tel: 020 7399 6000; website: www.artemisfunds.com/en/about-artemis/artemis-charitable-foundation)

Directors: David Brown; Adrian Frost; Jonathan Loukes; Mark Murray; Raheel Altaf; Matthew Beesley; Lesley Cairney; Jacob De Tusch-Lec; John Dodd; Simon Edelsten; James Foster; Andrew Gray; Peter Leckie; Edward Legget; William Littlewood; Andrew Marsh; Alexandra McAndie; Ross Millar; Graeme Mitchell; Mark Niznik; Antony Page; Jonathan Rigler; Peter Saacke; Nicholas Shenton; Stephen Snowden; Derek Stuart; William Warren; Cormac Weldon; Lindsay Whitelaw; Philip Wolstencroft; Arrow Acquisition LLC; Artemis Strategic Asset Management Ltd (female: 7%; male: 93%).

Nature of business: Artemis is a fund management company.

Financial information

| Year end | 31/12/2021 |
| Turnover | £171,700,000 |

Total employees: 168

Main locations: The company's UK headquarters is in London.

Community involvement

The company's corporate charity, The Artemis Charitable Foundation (OSCR no. SC037857) manages its charitable activities. Each year, Artemis gives a proportion of its revenues to the foundation.

Employee-led support

Staff are encouraged to take part in charitable activities through:

▶ Nominating a Charity of the Year and a Cancer Charity of the Year
▶ Volunteering with the foundation's partner charities
▶ Increasing their charitable donations through a Give As You Earn matched funding scheme

In 2021, 52 (24%) employees volunteered with partner organisations during the year.

Applications

Contact the correspondent for further information.

Corporate charity

The Artemis Charitable Foundation (OSCR no. SC037857) – see entry on page 220.

Community contributions

Cash donations worldwide	£145,000

According to Artemis Investment Management LLP's annual report, it donated £145,000 to charitable causes during the year. We were unable to determine a figure for cash donations to UK causes.

Arup Group Ltd

Community services and development, education and training, emergency response/relief, the environment, general charitable purposes, health, social welfare

Company registration number: 1312454

Correspondent: Phil Walsh, Global Community Engagement Leader, 13 Fitzroy Street, London W1T 4BQ (email: philip.walsh@arup.com or community.engagement@arup.com; website: www.arup.com/our-firm/community-engagement)

Directors: Dr Alan Belfield; Tristram Carfrae; Paul Coughlan; Fiona Cousins; Isabel Dedring; Jerome Frost; Michael Kwok; Dervilla Mitchell; Fergal Whyte; Eva Hinkers; Andy Howard (female: 36%; male: 64%).

Nature of business: Arup is an independent firm of planners, designers, engineers and consultants working across the built environment.

Financial information

Year end	31/03/2021
Turnover	£1,717,000,000
Pre-tax profit	£54,000,000

Total employees: 16,000

Main locations: The group's head office is in London and it has various offices around the UK, in Belfast, Bristol, Cardiff, Edinburgh, Glasgow, Leeds, Liverpool, Manchester, Newcastle, Nottingham, Sheffield, Solihull, Winchester and York. The group also operates in a further 35 countries around the world.

Community involvement

According to the website, Arup's community engagement programme aims to 'produce a more sustainably developed world, focusing on food security, clean and renewable energy, water and sanitation, improved shelter and social mobility'.

The group's areas of interest are relatively broad, as it ultimately seeks to improve the lives of those living in the most vulnerable communities. Examples of funded causes/projects include: tackling homelessness, designing products to improve hand washing and utilising digital tools in disaster recovery.

During the year, the group has worked in collaboration with 200 partners ranging from international NGOs, local governments, CICs and local community organisations. The group's website states that it is 'always open to new, long-term strategic relationships'.

In-kind support

Employees can undertake pro bono work which is sponsored by Arup. Arup then makes contributions towards the costs of approved projects.

Employee-led support

According to the 2020/21 community engagement report, 1,070 employees volunteered over 41,000 hours to this programme.

Applications

Contact the correspondent for more information.

Corporate charity

Ove Arup Partnership Charitable Trust (Charity Commission no. 1038737) – see entry on page 221; The Ove Arup Foundation (Charity Commission no. 328138) – see entry on page 220.

Community contributions

Cash donations worldwide	£3,700,000

According to its 2020/21 community engagement report, the group contributed £3.7 million to an estimated 55,000 beneficiaries. In this same year, over 200 projects were supported in 40 countries. Ove Arup Partnership Charitable Trust received £616,200.

Asda Stores Ltd

Community services and development, education and training, general charitable purposes, health, sports and recreation

Company registration number: 464777

Correspondent: Local Community Champion, Asda House, Southbank, Great Wilson Street, Leeds, West Yorkshire LS11 5AD (website: www.asda.com/creating-change-for-better)

Directors: John Fallon; Mohsin Issa; Zuber Issa; Manjit Dale; Gary Lindsey (male: 100%).

Nature of business: Asda is a food, clothing and general merchandise retailer with stores and services throughout the UK and online. In 1999 ASDA became part of Wal-Mart Stores, Inc.

Financial information

Year end	31/12/2020
Turnover	£22,743,700,000
Pre-tax profit	(£33,600,000)

UK employees: 145,000

Main locations: Asda has locations throughout the UK.

Community involvement

A proportion of Asda's charitable giving is made through its charity, The Asda Foundation (Charity Commission no. 1124268), which makes grants to grassroots charities nominated by employees. The general public can nominate a local voluntary organisation to receive a donation of £500 or £200 through the Green Token scheme in stores. In 2020, the company donated over £1 million through this initiative.

Partnerships

Asda's partnerships have been established as part of its Creating Change for the Better initiative. They include a partnership with The Trussell Trust and FareShare called Fight Hunger Create Change, to which Asda has committed to donate £20 million over three years.

Through the Tickled Pink programme, Asda raises funds for breast cancer research. Over the last 25 years, customers, employees and suppliers have helped to raise over £71 million for this cause. Currently, Asda supports research projects in 22 locations across the UK. Asda has also donated over £5 million to help create the UK's first tissue bank, making research faster and more reliable.

Asda is a supporter of the Bright Future programme, which helps victims of modern slavery secure employment.

In-kind support

Asda stores donate surplus food to local charities and community groups.

Employee-led support

Asda employees are encouraged to fundraise for various causes. Staff can claim up to £300 per year in matched funding for bake sales, marathons, raffles and any other fundraising activities.

Commercially led support

Asda has implemented various cause-related practices, primarily in relation to its own-brand products.

Applications

Applicants should approach the Community Champion at their local store to see if they are eligible for support.

Corporate charity

The Asda Foundation (Charity Commission no. 1124268) – see entry on page 221.

Community contributions

Cash donations UK	£8,460,000

In 2020, the company donated £5 million to its partners, The Trussell Trust and FareShare. The donation was used to support communities made vulnerable as a result of the COVID-19 pandemic. In addition, the company donated £3.46 million to its corporate charity, The Asda Foundation.

Ashmore Group plc

🔍 General charitable purposes, health, housing and homelessness

Company registration number: 3675683

Correspondent: The CSR Team, 61 Aldwych, London WC2B 4AE (tel: 020 3077 6000; email: ashmail@ashmoregroup.com; website: https://saudi.ashmoregroup.com/uk-en/home)

Directors: Mark Coombs; Tom Shippey; Clive Adamson; Jennifer Bingham; Helen Beck (female: 40%; male: 60%).

Nature of business: Ashmore Group is a specialist emerging markets fund manager across six core investment themes: external debt, local currency, special situations, equity, corporate high yield and multi-strategy.

Financial information

Year end	30/06/2021
Turnover	£292,900,000
Pre-tax profit	£282,500,000

Total employees: 310

Main locations: The group's UK head office is in London. It also has several other locations worldwide.

Community involvement

The majority of the group's charitable activity is channelled through its corporate charity, through which the group provides both financial and in-kind support.

The Ashmore Foundation (Charity Commission no. 1122351)

According to its website, the foundation seeks to make a 'positive and sustainable difference' to disadvantaged communities in the emerging markets in which Ashmore operates.

Annual donations

Outside its foundation, the group makes direct annual donations to the homelessness charity Crisis in support of its Christmas card campaign.

In-kind support

The group donates computers that are going out of use to Computer Aid International, a charity that aims to reduce poverty through practical IT solutions. Computers are sent to areas in Africa and South America.

The provision of free office space and administrative support is available through The Ashmore Foundation.

Employee-led support

Employees are encouraged to engage in voluntary work by taking one day's paid leave per year to support charitable projects. Staff take part in a wide range of activities supporting disadvantaged communities in their local area, as well as supporting the work of The Ashmore Foundation.

Applications

For further information, contact your local office's CSR team.

Corporate charity

The Ashmore Foundation (Charity Commission no. 1122351) – see entry on page 222.

Community contributions

Cash donations worldwide	£600,000

According to its 2020/21 accounts, the group made charitable donations totalling £600,000.

Ashtead Group plc

🔍 Community services and development, education and training, employment advice

Company registration number: 1807982

Correspondent: The CSR Team, 100 Cheapside, London EC2V 6DT (tel: 020 7726 9700; website: www.ashtead-group.com)

Directors: Paul Walker; Brendan Horgan; Michael Pratt; Angus Cockburn; Jill Easterbrook; Tanya Fratto; Renata Ribeiro; Lucinda Riches; Lindsley Ruth (female: 44%; male: 56%).

Nature of business: Ashtead plc is an international equipment rental company.

Financial information

Year end	30/04/2021
Turnover	£5,420,000,000
Pre-tax profit	£998,000,000

UK employees: 14,711

Total employees: 19,386

Main locations: The group's head office is in London but it has 193 locations nationwide. It also operates in Canada and the USA.

Community involvement

The group mainly provides its charitable support through partnerships. Currently, the group's UK partners include The Prince's Trust, Teach First and CRASH. Partners receive financial and in-kind support from Ashtead.

In-kind support

Sunbelt Rentals, a subsidiary of the group, donates equipment for local community events.

Employee-led support

According to the group's website, employees are encouraged to:
- Donate equipment
- Volunteer time and expertise for local initiatives and projects (staff can apply for up to 500 fully paid volunteer days)
- Raise funds for community projects close to their heart
- Work with disadvantaged groups in society to develop opportunities

Applications

Contact the correspondent for further information.

Community contributions

Cash donations worldwide	£1,220,000

According to the group's 2020/21 annual report, charitable donations totalled £1.22 million for this year. This figure includes donations made to causes outside the UK.

Associated British Foods plc

🔍 Community services and development, education and training, general charitable purposes, human rights, humanitarian aid, social welfare, women's rights

Company registration number: 293262

Correspondent: Corporate Responsibility Team, Weston Centre, 10 Grosvenor Street, London W1K 4QY (tel: 020 7399 6500; email: online contact form; website: www.abfoods.com)

Directors: Michael McLintock; George Weston; John Bason; Emma Adamo; Ruth Cairnie; Wolfhart Hauser; Richard

ASSOCIATED

Reid; Graham Allan; Dame Heather
Rabbatts (female: 33%; male: 67%).

Nature of business: The activities of the
group principally concern the processing
and manufacture of food worldwide and
textile retailing in the UK, Europe and
the USA. Associated British Foods plc
has five key business areas: sugar,
agriculture, retail, grocery and
ingredients. The group's brands include:
Primark, Twinings, AB Sugar, AB World
Foods, The Silver Spoon Company and
Ryvita.

Financial information

Year end	12/09/2021
Turnover	£13,900,000,000
Pre-tax profit	£908,000,000

UK employees: 46,066

Total employees: 128,000

Main locations: The group is
headquartered in London and operates
in 53 countries worldwide.

Community involvement

The group's brands support a variety of
causes through cash and in-kind
donations, partnerships, and employee
volunteering and fundraising. Grants are
also made to a wide range of causes and
charities through the group's Garfield
Weston Foundation (Charity
Commission no. 230260). Each of the
group's brands has its own CSR
activities, two examples of which are
provided below.

British Sugar

British Sugar's 'One Team, One
Community' scheme enables each of its
five sites to donate up to £5,000 per year
to local charitable causes. The company
provides matched funding (up to £250)
for employees through its 'Supporting
You to Support Others' scheme. The
company also has an annual Charity of
the Year. Beneficiaries have included:
Magpas Air Ambulance (2017); Anna's
Hope (2018); Peterborough Foodbank
and Peterborough Soup Kitchen (2019).

Garfield Weston Foundation

Established by the founder of Associated
British Foods, W. Garfield Weston, the
foundation makes grants to small and
large organisations in most fields apart
from animal welfare. The foundation
owns a majority stake in Wittington
Investments Ltd, the ultimate holding
company of Associated British Foods plc,
and receives its income from Wittington
Investments Ltd by way of dividends. In
2020/21 the foundation awarded 2,000
grants, worth £98 million. Project
funding, capital costs and core costs are
all considered.

In-kind support
In-kind donations

The group donates surplus food to food
banks and one-off volunteering events.
In 2020/21 the group's UK grocery
businesses donated 316 tonnes of food to
FareShare. Since 2010, Primark has
donated unsold merchandise to Newlife,
a charity that supports children who
have a disability or are terminally ill and
their families across the UK. The group
also supports global disaster relief efforts
through donations of emergency
equipment, tents and drinking water.

Employee-led support

The group's brands have their own
employee-led fundraising events and
volunteering initiatives. In 2021,
employees raised £4,100 for the British
Asian Trust emergency appeal and
Oxygen for India.

Commercially led support
Education and empowerment

The group's UK businesses have a variety
of initiatives and partnerships worldwide
which aim to tackle social issues in the
group's supply chain, such as gender
inequality, housing and working
conditions. For example, Twining
partnered with the Work and
Opportunities for Women programme,
an initiative funded by the UK's
Department for International
Development to prevent harassment and
gender-based violence on tea estates in
India.

Applications

Corporate responsibility enquiries
relating to ABF plc can be made using a
contact form on the group's website.

For further information on the CSR
activities of the group's brands, see the
individual websites. A full list of group
brands and locations can be found on
the group's 'About Us' website.

Application and eligibility guidelines for
the Garfield Weston Foundation can be
found on its website. Applications
should be submitted through the
website.

Community contributions

We were unable to determine a figure for
the group's total community
contributions for the 2020/21 year.

Associated British Ports

Arts, culture and heritage, community
services and development, education
and training, the environment, general
charitable purposes, health, heritage

Company registration number:
ZC000195

Correspondent: The CSR Team,
25 Bedford Street, London WC2B 4HN
(tel: 020 7430 1177; website: www.
abports.co.uk/about-abp/supporting-
our-communities)

Directors: Dr Phil Nolan; Henrik
Pedersen; Marina Wyatt (female: 33%;
male: 67%).

Nature of business: The principal
activities of the company comprise the
ownership, operation and development
of port facilities and the provision of
related services in the UK.

Financial information

Year end	31/12/2021
Turnover	£592,500,000
Pre-tax profit	(£80,900,000)

UK employees: 2,245

Main locations: The ABP group has 21
ports across the UK.

Community involvement

The ABP Group is engaged in all kinds
of charitable activities, from fundraising
for local charities and good causes to
helping young people pursue maritime
careers.

According to its 2020/21 annual review,
the group supports both national and
local charities, including Macmillan
Cancer Support, Hull Children's
University, Yorkshire Wildlife Trust and
Scouts.

Partnerships

Maritime UK – In partnership with
Maritime UK, the group has launched
the Women in Maritime Charter. The
initiative strives to promote greater
diversity in the maritime workforce by
consulting a wide range of women's
rights organisations for information and
advice. Additionally, several female
employees will be trained in interviewing
candidates, to join an 'interviewing pool'
to be used by smaller organisations
within the industry that have few or no
female interviewers available.

Macmillan Cancer Support – In 2021,
teams from ABP raised money for
Macmillan Cancer Support by competing
in the annual Houses of Parliament Tug
of War competition.

Hull Children's University – The
charity provides disadvantaged children
in Hull and East Yorkshire access to
good educational support. In 2020/21,

the charity delivered 817 laptops and tablets and 8,759 well-being packs and education packs to local families to ensure children could have access to their school's remote learning programme during periods of lockdown.

Yorkshire Wildlife Trust and Scouts – ABP partners with the Yorkshire Wildlife Trust to organise regular beach cleans at Spurn to help protect the local environment from marine plastic. In 2021, its team at the Port of Barrow supported the Great British Spring Clean event, bringing together the local community to help litter pick.

In-kind support

In-kind support includes staff volunteering and the provision of free access to some of the group's facilities.

Employee-led support

A team drawn from across ABP's 21 ports competes in the annual Houses of Parliament Tug of War competition in support of Macmillan Cancer Support.

In 2021, ABP employees at the Port of Southampton raised £12,074 for its Charity of the Year, Southampton Sight.

Commercially led support

The group sponsors various marathons across the country annually, where tens of thousands of runners take part to raise money for a wide range of charities. During the financial year, ABP sponsored the Teignmouth Carnival for the second year in a row, in line with its commitment to support communities surrounding its ports and beyond.

The group's ports often accommodate tours from local schools. In South Wales, ABP has partnered with Engineering Education Scheme Wales to host 'girls into STEM' activities to inspire the next generation of female engineers.

Applications

Contact the correspondent for more information.

Community contributions

The group did not disclose its contributions in the accounts.

Assura plc

General charitable purposes, health, mental health and well-being, sports and recreation

Company registration number: 9349441

Correspondent: CSR Team, The Brew House, Greenalls Avenue, Warrington WA4 6HL (tel: 01925 420660; email: info@assura.co.uk; website: www. assuraplc.com/making-a-difference)

Directors: Ed Smith; Johnathan Davies; Jonathan Murphy; Jayne Cottam; Louise Fowler; Emma Cariaga; Noel Gordon; Dr Sam Barrell (female: 50%; male: 50%).

Nature of business: Assura plc is a British-based property business that designs, builds, invests in and manages healthcare buildings in the UK.

Financial information

Year end	31/03/2022
Turnover	£136,500,000
Pre-tax profit	£58,200,000

UK employees: 66

Main locations: Assura plc is based in Warrington and has over 570 healthcare properties across the UK.

Community involvement

The group's CSR activities are focused on supporting the health and well-being of people of all ages. The group provides funding to UK-based charities and organisations through its community fund and charity partnerships. Employees also take part in fundraising and volunteering activities.

Assura Community Fund

The fund was established in 2020 to support health and well-being projects run by charities and local groups within 15 miles of an Assura healthcare building. The fund builds on the work of the group's Healthy Communities grants scheme (2017–20) and aims to benefit 1 million people by 2026. Initial funding of £2.5 million was provided by the group. The fund is being delivered by Cheshire Community Foundation.

Grants of between £1,000 and £5,000 are awarded to UK-registered charities, constituted community groups and other charitable organisations, including social enterprises and CICs. Grants can be used towards mental health and well-being projects for vulnerable people, education, employability and skills.

Partnerships

Dementia UK – Assura plc's partnership with Dementia UK funds its Admiral Nurse helpline on Sundays as well as some salary costs. In response to the COVID-19 pandemic, the group donated a further £25,000 to help the charity mobilise additional nurses to the helpline.

Onside Warrington Youth Zone – the group is a founding patron of Warrington Youth Club's new Youth Zone building. The group provides annual funding to support the club's work with thousands of children and young people in Warrington.

Employee-led support

In 2021, in support of the group's partnership with Warrington Youth Club, ten employees volunteered to wrap 335 Christmas hampers for families living in poverty across Warrington.

Exclusions

The Assura Community Fund's 'Guidance for applicants' document provides the following information about what it cannot fund:

- Organisations generating private profit.
- Statutory organisations including schools, universities, or hospitals.
- National organisations, unless the application is submitted by a local office with a separate management committee, bank account and governing documents.
- Organisations promoting religious or party political activity.
- Funding costs retrospectively, i.e. anything that has already been paid for or has already taken place or any costs incurred prior to receipt of a grant offer and signed terms and conditions.
- Applications from individuals.
- Applications seeking a contribution towards major building work, infrastructure, or capital refurbishment work.
- Any costs incurred when putting together the application.
- The programme is open to faith-based organisations. However, [it] cannot fund the practice of religion or any activities that actively promote a religion or belief systems (or the lack of belief). This is because these activities could exclude people from accessing an activity on religious grounds.

Applications

Information on eligibility criteria and applications to the Assura Community Fund can be found on Cheshire Community Foundation's website: http://cheshirecommunityfoundation. org.uk/apply-for-funding/#grant7. For enquiries, email assura@cheshire communityfoundation.org.uk.

For general enquiries about the group's CSR activities, contact the correspondent or use the contact form available on the group's website.

Community contributions

Cash donations UK	£190,000

According to its 2021/22 annual report, Assura donated £190,000 to the Assura Community Fund.

AstraZeneca

Community services and development, education and training, health, housing and homelessness, humanitarian aid, medical research, STEM, work outside the UK

Company registration number: 2723534

Correspondent: Corporate Responsibility Team, 1 Francis Crick Avenue, Cambridge Biomedical Campus, London W1K 1LN (tel: 0800 783 0033; website: www.astrazeneca.com/ sustainability.html)

Directors: Leif Johansson; Pascal Soriot; Aradhana Sarin; Philip Broadley; Euan Ashley; Michel Demaré; Deborah DiSanzo; Diana Layfield; Sheri McCoy; Tony Mok; Nazneen Rahman; Andreas Rummelt; Marcus Wallenberg (female: 38%; male: 62%).

Nature of business: The group's principal activities are the research, development and marketing of medicines for serious health conditions.

Financial information

Year end	31/12/2021
Turnover	£31,330,000,000
Pre-tax profit	(£221,990,000)

UK employees: 7,897

Total employees: 81,300

Main locations: AstraZeneca has various locations throughout the UK and overseas.

Community involvement

The group's community investment strategy focuses on community healthcare and STEM education. It also supports disaster relief.

The group offers the following types of support:

- Educational sponsorships/grants
- Sponsorship/collaborations
- Fellowships
- Corporate memberships
- Community investment/charitable contributions

Patient assistance programmes

In 2021, the group donated products to more than 11 million people in connection with patient assistance programmes around the world, the largest of which is its AZ&Me programme in the USA.

Partnerships

The group also has a number of partnerships to deliver its three healthcare programmes, which are:

Healthy Heart Africa (HHA) – aims to tackle hypertension and the increased burden of cardiovascular diseases. This programme is operating in eight countries in East and West Africa. In 2021, the HHA programme trained over 9,000 healthcare workers, activated over 950 sites and conducted over 23 million blood pressure screenings

Health System Sustainability and Resilience (PHSSR) – aims to strengthen global health systems, through the COVID-19 pandemic and beyond.

Young Health Programme (YHP) – supports young people aged between 10 and 24 to take control of their physical and mental health. In 2021, the YHP programme trained over 53,000 advocates in 30 countries and helped over 1.1 million young people with health information.

In-kind support

The group provides product donations to charitable organisations.

Employee-led support

Employees can take a day's paid leave per year to volunteer and AstraZeneca matches employees' fundraising efforts.

Commercially led support

The group is open to sponsorships and collaborations which advance health and science where AstraZeneca has involvement or receives benefit/recognition.

Applications

Contact the correspondent for further information. Applications for grants and sponsorships can be made online via the group's website.

Community contributions

Total contributions worldwide	£94,570,000

According to AstraZeneca's 2021 annual report, the group gave more than £94.57 million through its community investment activities to more than 1,220 non-profit organisations across 74 countries. This amount includes more than £19.27 million in product donations that were given in support of public heath needs and disaster relief. The financial information has been converted from USD to GBP using the exchange rate at the time of writing (July 2022).

Autotrader Group plc

General charitable purposes, social welfare

Company registration number: 9439967

Correspondent: Christos Tsaprounis, Head of People and Culture, 1 Tony Wilson Place, Manchester M15 4FN (tel: 0161 669 9888; email: Christos. tsprounis@autotrader.co.uk; website: https://plc.autotrader.co.uk/responsibility)

Directors: Jasvinder Gakhal; Ed Williams; Nathan Coe; Catherine Faiers; Jamie Warner; David Keens; Jill Easterbrook; Jeni Mundy; Sigga Sigurdardottir; Claire Baty (female: 60%; male: 40%).

Nature of business: Auto Trader is an automotive classified advertising business.

Financial information

Year end	31/03/2022
Turnover	£432,700,000
Pre-tax profit	£301,000,000

UK employees: 960

Main locations: The company has offices in Manchester and London.

Community involvement

The company provides support through its community fund, sports kits donations and match funding initiatives.

The Auto Trader Community Fund

The Auto Trader Community Fund, administered by Forever Manchester, awards up to £1,000 to grassroots projects across Greater Manchester. The fund also supports projects for Saint Pancras Community Association in London, Camden Giving, New Horizon Youth Centre and Shelter. The annual income of groups applying to the fund must be of less than £50,000. According to the Forever Manchester impact report, for the financial year 2021/22, the amount donated was £49,300.

Christmas gifts

Instead of giving Christmas gifts to employees and customers, the company offers donations to charities of their choice. In 2021, the Christmas party was cancelled due to the COVID-19 pandemic; however, Auto Trader employees still worked with Forever Manchester to deliver Christmas presents to the community with the Forever Manchester camper van, which is also funded by Auto Trader.

Ben Automotive Charity

In 2021, Auto Trader entered into a two-year partnership with Ben, an automotive charity that aims to improve health and well-being within the automotive industry. Auto Trader made a contribution of £55,000 to start the partnership.

Employee-led support

Employee volunteering

Employees are offered two volunteering days per year to support worthy causes across the UK. Although physical volunteering decreased after the arrival of COVID-19, employees continued to volunteer with charities like Omega Chatterbox, with the aim to help those isolated by the pandemic.

Employee fundraising

Funds raised by employees can be matched by 'AT sponsorships' matched funding.

Applications

The Auto Trader Community Fund is administered by Forever Manchester – visit the website for further information: www.forevermanchester.com/auto-trader-community-fund.

For all other enquiries, contact the correspondent.

Community contributions

Total contributions UK	£356,000

In 2021/22 the company's charitable contributions totalled £356,000. This included charitable donations, employee matched funding and sponsorships. Other donations included IT equipment and Christmas gift donations.

AVEVA Group plc

Education and training, general charitable purposes, health

Company registration number: 2937296

Correspondent: CSR Team, High Cross, Madingley Road, Cambridge CB3 0HB (tel: 01223 556655; email: sustainability@aveva.com; website: www.aveva.com)

Directors: Philip Aiken; James Kidd; Christopher Humphrey; Olivier Blum; Ron Mobed; Peter Herweck; Paula Dowdy; Ayesha Khanna; Hilary Maxson; Anne Stevens (female: 40%; male: 60%).

Nature of business: The principal activities of the group are the marketing and development of computer software and services for engineering and related solutions.

Financial information

Year end	31/03/2022
Turnover	£1,185,300,000
Pre-tax profit	(£18,600,000)

Total employees: 6,500

Main locations: AVEVA has offices in more than 40 countries across the world. The group's UK offices are in Cambridge, Chesterfield, Derry, Manchester and London.

Community involvement

In 2018, AVEVA launched its 'Action for Good', designed to encourage employees to take part in activities that support local communities and society. As part of the initiative, the company joined the 'Pledge 1%' movement and has committed to donating the equivalent of 1% of its net profits. It delivers this through a combination of matched funding, direct donations to charitable organisations and offering employees paid volunteering leave.

In previous years the group has made financial donations to organisations such as the British Red Cross, Arthur Rankin Hospice, Guide Dogs for the Blind and Alzheimer's Society.

The AVEVA Forest

The AVEVA Forest is a tree-planting initiative that supports a variety of reforestation projects around the world. As part of the initiative, employees are able to recognise a colleague's contributions by 'planting' a tree in their honour. Tree planting is also included as part of the welcome package for new team members.

Education

AVEVA continues to build relationships with academic organisations across the world through a variety of campaigns and initiatives. It aims to support students looking to start a career in the technology industry.

The group works with BP and the University of Cambridge to fund doctoral studentships at over 50 universities.

In-kind support

The group has ongoing relationships with over 750 universities and higher education organisations to which it provides free software and training for use on engineering and computer-aided design degree courses.

Employee-led support

Employees are offered three days of paid leave per year to enable them to support charitable causes as part of the Action for Good initiative. They are also encouraged to take part in fundraising events and other charitable activities. In 2021/22, 1,244 employees volunteered through the initiative.

The group also operates a matched funding scheme in which it matches employee fundraising efforts up to £300 for individual activities and £500 for team activities.

Commercially led support

AVEVA, in partnership with Schneider Electric, runs a global Student partnership competition, 'Go Green'. In 2021/22, AVEVA sponsored the category of 'Decoding the Future,' calling for students around the world to reimagine future technology approaches to design, engineering and intelligent operation of critical assets and infrastructure.

Applications

Contact the correspondent for further information.

Community contributions

Cash donations worldwide	£530,000
Total contributions worldwide	£1,000,000

In 2021/22, AVEVA contributed £1 million to charitable causes through its Action for Good initiative. This figure includes £530,000 donated to charitable organisations.

Aviva plc

Climate change, community development, financial literacy, disaster relief, social welfare.

Company registration number: 2468686

Correspondent: CSR Team, St Helen's, 1 Undershaft, London EC3P 3DQ (email: communityfund@aviva.com or avivafoundation@aviva.com; website: www.aviva.com/sustainability/communities)

Directors: Amanda Blanc; George Culmer; Patrick Flynn; Michael Mire; Andrea Blance; Michael Cranston; Shonaid Jemmett-Page; Mohit Joshi; Pippa Lambert; Jim McConville; Martin Strobel (female: 36%; male: 64%).

Nature of business: The company transacts life assurance and long-term savings business, fund management and all classes of general insurance through its subsidiaries, associates and branches in the UK, Europe, Asia and Canada.

Financial information

Year end	31/12/2021
Turnover	£33,180,000,000
Pre-tax profit	£801,000,000

UK employees: 16,000

Total employees: 22,000

Main locations: The company has offices across the UK, as well as in several countries worldwide.

Community involvement

The Aviva Foundation (not a registered charity)

The Aviva Foundation was established in 2018 and is funded by Aviva's dormant assets from the shareholder registry and donations from the Aviva business. It is administered by the Charities Trust (Charity Commission no. 327489). Since its inception, the foundation has committed more than £7 million in grants, supporting organisations in the UK and internationally.

In 2021, the Aviva Foundation received £1 million from the Aviva Share Forfeiture Programme and donated over £800,000 to 14 initiatives, benefitting 838,000 people. The foundation's main areas of focus are climate action, financial capability and inclusion and community resilience. Also in 2021, the foundation won Best Corporate Foundation at the Business Charity Awards.

Aviva Community Fund

Through its community fund, Aviva supports community projects across the UK. Every three months Aviva splits £250,000 among its employees for them to donate to the causes that matter to them most. Applications are open to projects that are aiming to raise up to £50,000. Full eligibility criteria can be found on the company's website.

The company has partnered with the fundraising platform Crowdfunder to allow charities and organisations to develop sustainable fundraising. Successful applicants will have a Crowdfunder page created for their cause, which will be shared with networks of supporters and the public.

There is a separate set of awards for projects submitted and supported by an insurance broker. The broker awards are open to any UK-based insurance broker. Applicants do not need to have an existing account or relationship with Aviva to enter into the broker awards.

Partnerships

Aviva has worked in partnership with the British Red Cross (BRC) since 2016. The company is a member of the Disaster Relief Alliance and invests in the BRC's work in preparedness, response, recovery and innovation. It also sponsors the BRC's Emergency App, which provides advice on how to deal with a range of emergencies, among several other features. The company also supports the BRC Community Reserve Volunteer project, which aims to create a network of 10,000 people to help when disaster strikes their local community. Aviva regularly repeats its Aviva Global Mapathon, which creates digital up-to-date maps, helping aid organisations to reach families who live in remote areas of countries such as Indonesia. The company also offers its expertise in risk management, employee volunteering and matched funding for employee fundraising.

In 2021, Aviva and the BRC won the Charity Times Awards Corporate Social Responsibility Project of the Year Award for their COVID-19 Response and UK Hardship Fund supporting those financially at risk during the pandemic.

In 2021, through its partnership with the BRC, Aviva donated £500,000 to the Disasters Emergency Committee's Ukraine Humanitarian Appeal and stated it would match donations by adding £1 for every £1 donated up to the value of a further £500,000.

In 2021, Aviva launched a climate-focused partnership with WWF (World Wide Fund for Nature), which aims to build healthier and more resilient ecosystems.

In-kind support

On its website, Aviva runs a 'Knowledge Library' which offers expertise, support and skills to charities in an attempt to build their capability. The library boasts a range of articles, videos, templates and checklists.

The company also has several International Coaching Federation (ICF)-trained coaches who offer their expertise free of charge.

Employee-led support

Aviva employees decide how money from the Community Fund is distributed. They are also encouraged to get involved with fundraising, skill-sharing and volunteering. Each year, Aviva offers its employees 21 hours of paid time to volunteer in the community.

In 2021, Aviva employees globally contributed more than 19,000 volunteering hours to support their local communities. They also donated and fundraised over £1.03 million.

Exclusions

A full list of exclusions from the Aviva Community Fund is provided on the fund's website.

Applications

Visit Aviva's website for more information on how to apply to the Community Fund and the Aviva Foundation.

Community contributions

Total contributions worldwide £31,800,000

According to its 2021 sustainability report, Aviva contributed £31.8 million in community investment during the financial period, including the value of skills.

Avon Cosmetics Ltd

Education and training, health, support services, women's rights

Company registration number: 592235

Correspondent: UK Causes Team, Lancaster House, Nunn Mills Road, Northampton NN1 5PA (tel: 01604 232425; email: use the contact form on the website; website: www.avon.uk.com/Causes)

Directors: Louise Scott; Anna Tolley (female: 100%).

Nature of business: Avon distributes and sells beauty, gift and decorative products. Core trading continues to be the marketing of products through an established network of active sales representatives.

Financial information

Year end	31/12/2020
Turnover	£558,250,000
Pre-tax profit	(£494,760,000)

Main locations: The company operates in a number of countries worldwide. In the UK, Avon's head office is in Northampton and the global head office is in London.

Community involvement

Avon's community involvement is primarily focused on causes that are more likely to affect women, such as breast cancer and domestic violence. The company supports these causes through a combination of fundraising, events, product sales and the promotion of information and resources.

Breast cancer awareness

Avon has launched its Breast Cancer Promise, a multi-year pledge to educate women about breast health. As part of this, it has established partnerships with CoppaFeel! and Look Good Feel Better. The company also regularly supports

Breast Cancer Awareness Month, running fundraising events and raising money through product sales. The Avon Breast Cancer Promise aims to educate 100 million women each year and ensure that every woman knows the risks and signs of breast cancer.

Gender-based violence

In 2019, Avon launched its 'Promise to Help End Violence Against Women and Girls'. Through this, the company aims to encourage conversations about gender-based violence as well as provide information to help people recognise and respond to violence safely. It also supports local and global organisations that work within this area. In the UK, Avon has partnered with Refuge and Women's Aid.

The Avon Foundation for Women has launched a new partnership with the World Association of Girl Guides and Girl Scouts to encourage more people to speak out against signs of violence, harassment and abuse. As part of the partnership, a new training and awareness programme will launch in 2020, in South Africa, the Philippines and Argentina.

In 2020 the company launched the #SpeakOut campaign, attempting to put an end to pejorative words and phrases used to silence women.

Other partnerships

The company has also established a partnership with Changing Faces, a UK charity supporting people with a visible difference. It has also committed to supporting the charity's #PledgeToBeSeen campaign and is working to include people with visible differences in its own beauty campaigns.

Avon has also partnered with Women Start-up Competition (WSC), a not-for-profit organisation that aims to inspire, educate and unite female entrepreneurs to help them grow their businesses.

The Avon Foundation for Women

The Avon Foundation for Women is a charity based in the USA that was established in 1955. The foundation aims to improve the lives of women and their families. The foundation makes grants and raises awareness for charitable causes across the world, in line with Avon's promises. Previous beneficiaries have included Breast Cancer UK, Charities Aid Foundation and the Nature Conservancy. Avon's website notes that organisations are invited to apply for funding; therefore, unsolicited requests are not accepted.

The foundation operates a Global Scholarship programme to enable children and grandchildren of Avon representatives to access education.

Within the UK, Avon also offers support to causes local to Northamptonshire, the location of its head office and distribution centre.

In 2020 the company made donations to organisations including Children Are Butterflies, Crazy Hats, Kettering General Hospital, Refuge and Women's Aid.

In-kind support

Avon promotes its breast cancer awareness message by providing resources and information in its brochures.

Employee-led support

Employees and Avon representatives are encouraged to take part in fundraising activities.

Commercially led support

Avon sells a range of products from which 50% of the profits are donated to one of its charity partners.

Applications

Contact the correspondent for further information.

Community contributions

Cash donations UK	£322,800

In 2020 the company raised over £514,000 for its UK charity partners. Additionally, it contributed £322,800 toward its breast cancer and domestic abuse campaigns and other activities, including donations to a number of charities.

Axis Europe plc

Social welfare

Company registration number: 1991637

Correspondent: CSR Team, 3 Tramway House, Tramway Avenue, Stratford E15 4PN (email: info@axiseurope.com; website: www.axiseurope.com)

Directors: John Hayes; Sally Hayes; Timothy Hayes; Yusef Ibrahim; Rickardo Santana (female: 20%; male: 80%).

Nature of business: Axis Europe is a property improvement and maintenance contractor.

Financial information

Year end	31/03/2021
Turnover	£147,880,000
Pre-tax profit	£8,249,999

Total employees: 952

Main locations: The company has nine offices throughout London and in Liverpool, Cardiff, Oldbury and Sittingbourne.

Community involvement

The company's community contributions are made primarily through donations to its corporate charity, the Axis Foundation (Charity Commission no. 1126117).

Employee-led support

Employees are encouraged to volunteer and fundraise for local charities and community projects.

Applications

See the company's corporate charity entry for further information.

Corporate charity

Axis Foundation (Charity Commission no. 1126117) – see entry on page 222.

Community contributions

Cash donations UK	£200,000
Total contributions UK	£221,500

In 2020/21, the company donated £200,000 to its corporate charity, the Axis Foundation. Total contributions, including time given up by employees to support community projects, were valued at £221,500.

BAE Systems plc

Community services and development, education and training, health, social welfare

Company registration number: 1470151

Correspondent: CSR Team, 6 Carlton Gardens, London SW1Y 5AD (tel: 01252 373232; email: use the contact form on the company's website; website: www. baesystems.com)

Directors: Roger Carr; Charles Woodburn; Brad Greve; Tom Arseneault; Chris Grigg; Dame Elizabeth Corley; Nicole Piasecki; Stephen Pearce; Jane Griffiths; Nick Anderson; Crystal Ashby; Ewan Kirk (female: 33%; male: 67%).

Nature of business: The main activity of the group is defence, including the design and manufacture of civil and military aircraft, surface ships, submarines, space systems, radar, communications, electronics and guided weapon systems.

Financial information

Year end	31/12/2021
Turnover	£19,520,000,000
Pre-tax profit	£2,110,000,000

UK employees: 39,000

Total employees: 89,600

Main locations: BAE Systems has offices throughout the UK, Sweden, Australia, India, the Middle East and the USA.

Community involvement

BAE Systems aims to strengthen relationships and invest in the communities in which it operates by offering support to charities and organisations that align with its business.

Through its Community Investment Programme, the group provides support in the following areas:

- **Armed forces** – supporting active service personnel, veterans and their families
- **Education and skills** – inspiring young people to consider STEM subjects and careers
- **Local community** – working to support the communities in which BAE operates

Education

BAE supports STEM education and skills development in schools in many of its locations across the world. Recently, the group partnered with Blackburn Youth Zone to deliver a new programme designed to inspire young people in the community to consider careers in STEM industries.

In 2021, the group's education activities were delivered virtually and together with the Smallpeice Trust, the Royal Air Force and the Royal Navy, it launched 'Coding for Success', an initiative that helps educators and students develop confidence with coding and robotics. The initiative was delivered in 600 schools.

Armed forces

In the UK, BAE has an ongoing partnership with multiple armed forces charities such as ABF – The Soldiers' Charity, Combat Stress, the RAF Benevolent Fund and the Royal Naval and Royal Marines Charity. In addition, the group supports the Open University's Disabled Veterans' Scholarships Fund, which aims to help further the education of individuals who have acquired a disability as a result of military service.

Unclaimed Asset programme

In 2020, a proposal for an unclaimed asset programme was approved, with the net proceeds (£3.6 million) from any shares sold to be used to support the local communities in which the group operates. Projects and initiatives suitable for funding are identified by the group.

In-kind support

Volunteering is considered an important part of the career journey at BAE and the company offers volunteering opportunities to its employees that can be pursued as a personal development goal.

As part of its ongoing support for the armed forces, BAE also offers paid time off to support employees who are reservists, military families and adult Cadet Force volunteers.

Employee-led support

The group operates a matched funding scheme and encourages its employees to fundraise and volunteer for charity partners and local communities. Employees may also volunteer as Education Ambassadors in schools through the group's STEM education programmes. The group also operates a payroll giving scheme which allows employees to donate to charities of their choice.

Each year, in the run-up to National Armed Forces Day, the group runs the 'Proud to Support Week' campaign. During this week, employees are encouraged to volunteer and raise funds for armed forces charities. The week also includes 'Reserves Day' in which the contribution made by reservists to the armed forces is celebrated and employee reservists are able to wear their uniforms to work.

Commercially led support

Every year the group sponsors the National Armed Forces Day event. It also sponsors Invictus UK.

Exclusions

Funding and support is not provided to third-party fundraisers or individuals.

Applications

Contact the correspondent for further information.

Community contributions

Total contributions worldwide	£11,000,000

During 2021, the group contributed more than £11 million to local, national and international charities and not-for-profit organisations. This figure includes sponsorships, donations, employee fundraising and volunteering. The contributions were distributed among the following areas: education (34%); armed forces (30%); community (19%); other (11%); and heritage (6%). The group made donations to more than 40 local food banks during the period.

Baillie Gifford and Co. Ltd

🔍 General charitable purposes

Company registration number: SC069524

Correspondent: Philanthropy Team, Calton Square, 1 Greenside Row, Edinburgh EH1 3AN (email: philanthropy@bailliegifford.com; website: www.bailliegifford.com/en/uk/about-us/corporate-citizenship)

Directors: Katharine Bolsover; Dean Buckley; Evan Delaney; Colin Fraser; Derek McGowan; Andrew Telfer; Michael Wylie; Lucy Haddow (female: 25%; male: 75%).

Nature of business: Baillie Gifford and Co. Ltd is an investment management company.

Financial information

Year end	31/03/2022
Turnover	£398,880,000
Pre-tax profit	£33,780,000

Total employees: 1,000+

Main locations: The company is based in Edinburgh and operates throughout the UK. It also has several international offices.

Community involvement

Baillie Gifford and Co. Ltd supports the community in a number of ways including through charitable donations, volunteering and mentoring. According to its website, the majority of the company's support is focused on charities working in Scotland, where it is headquartered. However, the company's international offices in Amsterdam, Dublin, Frankfurt, Hong Kong, Krakow, New York, Shanghai, Toronto and Zurich all support local causes chosen by their staff. The company's website notes:

> As Baillie Gifford's Philanthropy Team, we manage its community engagement. We work in partnership with a committee of staff subgroups spanning:
> - arts
> - communities
> - grassroots sports
> - health and education
> - international
> - land, air and sea
> - social

The company prefers to work with charities on a long-term basis, helping them to make sustainable changes.

Community Awards

Three times each year, employees nominate a charity of their choice to receive an award of £1,000. The initiative runs three times a year, with up to 50 grants being approved each round. Since launching in 2017, the initiative has helped 490 charities across the world.

Charity of the Year

Employees can vote for a Charity of the Year to help raise funds and to offer in-kind support. At the time of writing (July 2022), the company's Charity of the Year was Vocal, a charity that supports unpaid carers in Edinburgh and Midlothian. The Charity of the Year also benefits from employee-led support, design and printing services and technological support.

Employee-led support

Employees are entitled to take two days' paid leave per year to volunteer or undertake charity work.

Commercially led support

The company provides sponsorship to local and international organisations and events, such as museum exhibitions. The sponsorship committee is made up of Baillie Gifford employees, who are

responsible for selecting organisations to be supported by the company.

Applications

Submit a proposal for support by email to philanthropy@bailliegifford.com. Guidance on what to include in the proposal can be found on the company's website and should be consulted in the first instance.

Community contributions

We were unable to determine a figure for the company's charitable contributions for 2021/22.

Balfour Beatty plc

🔍 Community enterprise and social entrepreneurship, education and training, general charitable purposes

Company registration number: 395826

Correspondent: Sustainability Team, 5 Churchill Place, Canary Wharf, London E14 5HU (tel: 020 7216 6800; email: sustainability@balfourbeatty.com; website: www.balfourbeatty.com/how-we-work/sustainability)

Directors: Stephen Billingham; Stuart Doughty; Anne Drinkwater; Philip Harrison; Michael Lucki; Barbara Moorhouse; Leo Quinn; Lord Allen of Kensington; Louise Hardy (female: 33%; male: 67%).

Nature of business: Balfour Beatty is an international infrastructure group involved in construction and infrastructure investments.

Financial information

Year end	31/12/2021
Turnover	£7,185,000,000
Pre-tax profit	£87,000,000

Total employees: 24,500

Main locations: The group operates across the UK. Its head office is in London.

Community involvement

Balfour Beatty is engaged in a wide range of charitable activities including donations, fundraising and employee volunteering.

The group's charitable work focuses on the following:
- Supporting skills in infrastructure
- Supporting people and families with health and well-being
- Regenerating local communities
- Inspiring the future workforce
- Supporting employee-led Affinity Networks
- Supporting national charity partners

The group seeks to support the local community in locations in which it operates.

The group delivers on these objectives via various channels, such as The 5%

Club (Charity Commission no. 1179354), of which Balfour Beatty is a long-standing member. The organisation strives to address the skills gap by encouraging more young people into apprenticeships. By joining the club, members aspire to have at least 5% of their workforce in 'earn and learn' roles, including apprentices, sponsored students and graduates on formalised training schemes.

The group has longstanding partnerships with The Prince's Trust, Project Reece and Groundworks.

Employee-led support

Employees are entitled to 16 hours' paid volunteering leave per year. In 2021, employees contributed over 23,000 hours of volunteering. The group has also set aside £100,000 to match any funds that employees raise for the charity partners.

Applications

Contact the correspondent for further information.

Community contributions

Cash donations UK	£461,400
Total contributions worldwide	£1,020,000

In the UK, the group donated £461,400 to charity in 2021. The group's 2021 annual report states that its total charitable contributions amounted to £1.02 million.

BAM Construct UK Ltd

General charitable purposes, health

Correspondent: CSR Team, Breakspear Park, Breakspear Way, Hemel Hempstead, Hertfordshire HP2 4FL (tel: 01442 238300; email: online contact form; website: www.bam.co.uk/what-we-do/sustainability)

Directors: James Wimpenny; Andrea Singh, Neil McGruer (female: 33%; male: 67%).

Nature of business: Construction.

Financial information

Year end	31/12/2021
Turnover	£918,000,000
Pre-tax profit	£20,400,000

UK employees: 2,033

Main locations: BAM has operations throughout the UK.

Community involvement

BAM provides charitable support through its charity partnerships and its Enhancing Lives programme.

Charity partners

The company's national charity two-year partnership for 2020/22 was with the British Heart Foundation. It is also a patron partner of CRASH Charity.

Enhancing Lives

The company's Enhancing Lives programme aims to have a positive impact on people's lives by supporting and delivering projects that make a real difference. The programme includes pro bono or in-kind support, fundraising or donations and volunteering.

Employee-led support

Employees are given two days of paid leave per year to volunteer. In addition to this, employees can apply for a £1,000 grant for a team voluntary project, allowing them to purchase materials and resources. Employees also fundraise for the company's national charity partner, Young Lives vs Cancer (formerly CLIC Sargent).

Applications

Contact the correspondent for further information.

Community contributions

According to its 2020 sustainability report, BAM generated £339,300 of community investment. This figure may include employee fundraising.

Bank of Ireland (UK) plc

Arts, culture and heritage, community services and development, health, social welfare

Company registration number: 7022885

Correspondent: The Responsible Business Team, Group Head Office, Baggot Plaza, 27–33 Upper Baggot St, Dublin D04 VX58 (tel: + 353 1 661 5933; email: responsiblebusiness@boi.com; website: https://personalbanking.bankofireland.com/campaigns/begin-together)

Directors: Ian Buchanan; Alison Burns; Peter Herbert; Edna Johnson; Thomas McAreavey; Ian McLaughlin; Philip Moore; Clare Salmon; Richard Sommers; Mark Spain (female: 30%; male: 70%).

Nature of business: Bank of Ireland provides an extensive range of banking and other financial services.

Financial information

Year end	31/12/2021
Pre-tax profit	£1,198,670,000

Main locations: The bank has offices throughout the UK and worldwide.

Community involvement

The group provides charitable support through Begin Together, a three-year, €4 million programme that supports communities in which the group operates. The programme has three main funds:

Begin Together Community Fund

The fund supports initiatives that will enable the financial, mental, or physical well-being of vulnerable groups.

Begin Together Fund for Colleagues

The Begin Together Fund for Colleagues provides support for causes which are important to employees across the group. Employees can nominate local causes for a donation of €500 in their name.

Begin Together Arts Fund

The fund provides grants of between €5,000 and €15,000 to artists and art groups.

Commercially led support

The group sponsors all four rugby provinces – Connacht, Leinster, Munster and Ulster – and the Football Association of Ireland

Applications

See the group's website for the latest information on grants programmes.

Community contributions

Cash donations worldwide	£1,040,000

According to its Responsible and Sustainable Business Report 2021, the group donated £1.04 million to charities. This was broken down as follows: Begin Together Community Fund (£438,700); Fund for Colleagues (£307,100); Begin Together Arts Fund (£289,600).

All financial information has been converted from EUR using the exchange rate at the time of writing (October, 2022).

The Banks Group Ltd

Community services and development, education and training, the environment, general charitable purposes

Company registration number: 2267400

Correspondent: The Community Team, Inkerman House, St John's Road, Meadowfield, Durham, County Durham DH7 8XL (tel: 0191 378 6100; email: enquiries@banksgroup.co.uk; website: www.banksgroup.co.uk/corporate-responsibility)

Directors: Harry Banks; Richard Dunkley; Andrew Fisher; Christopher Gill; David Martin; Gavin Styles (male: 100%).

Nature of business: The Banks Group develops land for a variety of uses including surface coal mining, property and renewable energy.

Financial information

Year end	29/09/2021
Turnover	£6,852,000
Pre-tax profit	£52,193,000

Total employees: 300+

Main locations: The group's main office is in County Durham. The group also operates in Scotland, Yorkshire, the North East and the North West.

Community involvement

The group makes grants to voluntary organisations and environmental projects through the Banks Community Fund (not a registered charity) which is administered by the County Durham Community Foundation. Preference is given to educational projects and organisations working to alleviate poverty in the areas where the group has a presence.

Employee-led support

Employees are encouraged into fundraising through the staff-nominated Charity of the Year initiative.

Commercially led support

The group sponsors regional awards and attractions.

Applications

Information about how to apply and application forms can be found on County Durham Community Foundation's website.

Community contributions

The group did not disclose its charitable contributions in the 2020/21 accounts.

J. Barbour and Sons Ltd

🔍 The environment, housing and homelessness

Company registration number: 124201

Correspondent: CSR Team, Simonside Industrial Estate, South Shields, Tyne and Wear NE34 9PD (website: www.barbour.com/uk/corporate-social-responsibility)

Directors: Helen Barbour; Dame Margaret Barbour; Ian Beattie; Ian Bergin; Joseph Bernhoeft; Owain Llewellyn-Pace; Ian Sime; Paul Wilkinson; Stephen Buck (female: 22%; male: 78%).

Nature of business: J. Barbour and Sons (Barbour) is a British luxury and lifestyle brand that designs, manufactures and markets clothing, footwear and accessories.

Financial information

Year end	30/04/2021
Turnover	£218,020,000
Pre-tax profit	£36,330,000

Total employees: 916

Main locations: The company's head office and main production site is in South Shields.

Community involvement

Much of Barbour's charitable activity is channelled through its corporate charity, The Barbour Foundation (Charity Commission no. 328081).

In-kind support

The company donates clothing to charities that share its values. Organisations previously supported by the company include:

▷ The Prince's Countryside Fund
▷ Centrepoint
▷ Smartworks
▷ The Dry Stone Walling Association
▷ The Broads Reed and Sedge Cutters Association
▷ Upper Teesdale Agricultural Support Services
▷ Freshwater Habitats Trust
▷ Groundwork

Employee-led support

Staff are regularly involved in fundraising events, such as bake-offs and dress-up days.

Applications

Contact the correspondent or see the company's corporate charity entry for more information.

Corporate charity

The Barbour Foundation (Charity Commission no. 328081) – see entry on page 224.

Community contributions

According to the 2020/21 annual report for The Barbour Foundation, it received dividend income from J. Barbour and Sons totalling £410,900. The company also donated £1,100 to the foundation in the form of goods. However, we were unable to determine a figure for the company's total charitable contributions.

Barclays plc

🔍 Education and training, general charitable purposes

Company registration number: 48839

Correspondent: Community Affairs Team, 1 Churchill Place, Canary Wharf, London E14 5HP (tel: 020 7116 4451; email: community.investment@barclays.com; website: https://home.barclays/society/investing-in-our-communities)

Directors: Stephen Shapiro; Michael Ashley; Robert Berry; Timothy Breedon; Angela Cross; Dr Mohamed El-Erian; Dawn Fitzpatrick; Mary Francis; Crawford Gillies; Dr Brian Gilvary; Nigel Higgins; Diane Schueneman; Coimbatore Venkatakrishnan; Julia Wilson (female: 36%; male: 64%).

Nature of business: Barclays is a British multinational investment bank and financial services group. Barclays is organised into four core businesses: personal banking, corporate banking, wealth management and investment management.

Financial information

Year end	31/12/2021
Turnover	£6,482,000,000
Pre-tax profit	£2,163,000,000

Main locations: Barclays is headquartered in London and has branches across the UK. The group has a presence in over 50 countries worldwide.

Community involvement

Barclays plc supports communities by partnering with NGOs, social enterprises and charities.

LifeSkills programme

The Barclays LifeSkills programme has supported youth employment since 2013 by aiding young people's move from education to work. The programme helps young people develop transferrable skills that workplaces need. In 2019, the programme was made available to people of all ages across the UK.

Partnerships

Barclay plc's partnership with Age UK has helped the charity deal with the increased demand for its National Advice Line and Telephone Friendship service during the COVID-19 pandemic. Other UK partnerships include NHS Charities Together, Street Soccer Scotland, The Felix Project, The Hygiene Bank, Turn2us and UK Community Foundations.

Employee-led support

In 2021, 12,930 employees donated to charity via the UK payroll giving programme. A total of £950,000 was matched by Barclays plc.

Over 5,900 employees took part in the matched giving scheme with a total of £10.9 million being matched by Barclays plc.

Exclusions

According to the group's website, Barclays does not sponsor the following:

▷ Political or religious associations
▷ Sponsorship properties which have already given significant exposure for our competitors in banking
▷ Sponsorship properties which are perceived to have or encompass a dangerous or violent nature (e.g. boxing)
▷ Sponsorships where Barclays or its employees have or are perceived to have a conflict of interest
▷ Sponsorships of teams (by exception only)
▷ Sponsorship of individuals (by exception only)
▷ An event which is due to commence in the next two months.

Applications

Barclays Community Affairs
Enquiries about charitable or community sponsorship should be made by email to Barclays Community Affairs at community.investment@barclays.com or 020 7116 4451.

Event sponsorship
Enquiries about event sponsorship should be made by email to sponsorshipenquiries@barclays.co.uk. Consult the 'Applying for sponsorship' section on the group's website for eligibility and application details.

Community contributions

Cash donations worldwide	£35,040,000
Total contributions worldwide	£43,800,000

In 2021, Barclays spent £43.8 million in community investment worldwide, of which cash donations totalled £35.04 million (80%). The total contributions figure includes charitable giving, management costs and monetised work hours of Barclays employees.

A. G. Barr plc

Community services and development, the environment, health, mental health and well-being, social welfare, sports and recreation

Company registration number: SC005653

Correspondent: CSR Team, Westfield House, 4 Mollins Road, Westfield, Cumbernauld, Lanarkshire G68 9HD (tel: 01236 852400; email: online contact form; website: www.agbarr.co.uk)

Directors: Roger White; Stuart Lorimer; Jonathan Kemp; Robin Barr; David Ritchie; Susan Barratt; Nick Wharton; Mark Alan; Zoe Howorth; Julia Barr (female: 30%; male: 70%).

Nature of business: The group trades principally as a manufacturer, distributor and seller of soft drinks.

Financial information

Year end	30/01/2022
Turnover	£268,600,000
Pre-tax profit	£41,500,000

Total employees: 895

Main locations: The group has offices and distribution centres across the UK, in Bolton, Cumbernauld, Dagenham, Forfar, London, Manchester, Milton Keynes, Newcastle, Sheffield and Wednesbury.

Community involvement
The group supports local and national charities through cash donations, in-kind support and long-term partnerships. According to the group's website, support is focused on three main areas:

- Encouraging health, wellbeing and physical activity
- Protecting the environment and championing sustainability
- Tackling social inequality

Partnerships
A charity partner is selected through a group-wide vote every three years. The chosen charity partner benefits from a £150,000 corporate donation over three years as well as employee fundraising. Each employee sets out to raise £27 in each year of the partnership. Between 2019 and 2022, Mental Health UK was A. G. Barr employees' chosen charity partner.

The group has a long-term partnership with Keep Scotland Beautiful and is one of the founding funders of the charity's Roadside Litter Campaign.

The group's water brand Strathmore is the official partner of The Prince's Trust and support is given through investment in community programmes and in-kind donations.

In-kind support
In-kind support is normally provided through donations of products. Strathmore donates bottles of water for the fundraising activities of The Prince's Trust as well as various sporting events across the UK.

Employee-led support
Employees are encouraged to fundraise and volunteer for the group's partner charities.

IRN-BRU 32 charity fundraiser
The fundraiser was inspired by the 32 ingredients within the IRN-BRU secret recipe essence. In June 2021, teams made up of IRN-BRU employees took part in the fundraiser challenge. The teams had 32 days to complete a challenge of their choosing every day and fundraise £32 per person for the group's charity partner, Mental Health UK. In total, the IRN-BRU 32 challenge raised over £16,000 for Mental Health UK.

Applications
Requests for support can be made through the Community and Charity Enquiries section of the group's website: www.agbarr.co.uk/contact-us/community-charity-enquiries/.

Community contributions

Cash donations UK	£100,000

According to its 2021/22 annual report, the group donated £100,000 to charitable causes. This represents the group's final corporate donation to its charity partner Mental Health UK (£150,000 over three years).

Barratt Developments plc

Community services and development, general charitable purposes

Company registration number: 604574

Correspondent: Local CSR Team, Barratt House, Cartwright Way, Forest Business Park, Bardon Hill, Coalville, Leicestershire LE67 1UF (email: cr@barrattplc.co.uk; website: www.barrattdevelopments.co.uk)

Directors: John Allan; David Thomas; Steven Boyes; Mike Scott; Jock Lennox; Nina Bibby; Katie Bickerstaffe; Chris Weston; Sharon White; Tina Baines (female: 40%; male: 60%).

Nature of business: The group's principal activities comprise housebuilding and commercial development. Its brands include Barratt Homes, David Wilson Homes and Barratt London.

Financial information

Year end	30/06/2021
Turnover	£4,822,700,000
Pre-tax profit	£812,200,000

Total employees: 6,329

Main locations: The group's head offices are in London and Leicestershire. It also has 27 divisional offices across the UK.

Community involvement
The group provides financial support to a variety of charitable causes through its community fund, employee fundraising and a large number of charity partnerships and sponsorships.

Barratt and David Wilson Community Fund (not a registered charity)
The group's community fund allows each division to donate £1,000 each month to a local charity or organisation.

Partnerships
The group has partnerships with a large variety of charities, most of which are three-year commitments. Examples of charity partners include Highground, Mates in Mind, St Mungo's RBLI, RSPB and Whizz-Kidz.

The Barratt Developments plc Charitable Foundation (Charity Commission no. 1188447)
The foundation was established in 2020 and draws together all of the company's charitable work under one body. The foundation supports a wide range of causes throughout the UK.

Employee-led support

Matched funding
The group's divisional charity matching scheme matches pound for pound the money that divisions raise for their nominated Charities of the Year (up to

£15,000 per year). The group also offers an individual charity matching scheme which provides matched funding for any employee that raises £1,000 for a registered charity. In 2020/21 the company provided matched funding totalling £363,500.

Payroll giving
Employees have the option to make regular, tax-free donations to their chosen charity through payroll giving.

Volunteering
Employees are entitled to one day of paid leave per year to volunteer in their local community.

Applications
For further information contact your local division. A list of addresses and phone numbers for each division is available on the group's website.

Barratt and David Wilson Community Fund
Local groups and charities are encouraged to apply for a £1,000 grant by contacting their local division's charity team. The company's website states: 'Applicants should make clear where their charity is based and what the £1,000 will be used for. The division's charity representative will then be in touch if the application is successful.'

Corporate charity
The Barratt Developments plc Charitable Foundation (Charity Commission no. 1188447) – see entry on page 225.

Community contributions
According to its 2020/21 annual report, the group raised and donated £4.3 million to charities during the year. We were unable to determine the proportion donated directly by the group.

Bayer plc

Community services and development, education and training, the environment, health, medical research, nutrition and diet, sports and recreation, STEM

Company registration number: 935048

Correspondent: Corporate Grants Committee, 400 South Oak Way, Green Park, Reading, Berkshire RG2 6AD (email: communications.ukireland@ bayer.com; website: www.bayer.co.uk/en/ commitment-and-sustainability/ collaboration/community)

Directors: Colin Barker; Thorsten Gerdau; Vinit Jindal; Ramon Payano Baez (male: 100%).

Nature of business: Bayer plc is part of the global company Bayer AG, based in Leverkusen, Germany. In the UK and Ireland, Bayer plc sells and markets

pharmaceutical and consumer health products and crop solutions and services.

Financial information

Year end	31/12/2021
Turnover	£750,622,000
Pre-tax profit	£42,015,000

Main locations: The company's locations in the UK and Ireland are in Newbury (headquarters), Cambridge and Dublin. Bayer AG is based in Germany and has operations worldwide.

Community involvement
Bayer has been involved in social, community and environmental programmes across the UK and Ireland for several years. It supports numerous social responsibility programmes, often in partnership with other organisations. The company supports activities that are local to its operations and that are linked to employees' community activities or connected to the company's products or services.

Community support programme
According to its website Bayer's community support programme provides support and funding to activities which are aligned to:

Science for a Better Life

Support of frontier research in the life sciences for example through science achievement awards or unrestricted research grants.
- Development of science talents, e.g. through fellowship programmes or talent awards
- Science education in schools among children and teenagers, by supporting science teacher projects, science summer schools or hands on lab sessions.
- Science and Society, e.g. external activities to engage with general public and raise scientific awareness

Health for all, Hunger for None
- Food availability for vulnerable groups, food loss, food quality
- Climate Change, biodiversity, water and waste management
- Health for All – public health and child health

Community engagement and sport/ cultural activities
- Serving basic social needs in communities near Bayer sites with a focus on better health, sustainable nutrition or empowerment through nutrition
- Support of direct general public education
- Promotion of sports for people of all ages with disabilities

Community development and support
- Serving basic social needs in the communities near Bayer sites.

Education
Bayer operates a free laboratory called Baylab for schools in the UK. Based in Green Park, Reading, it offers pupils in Key Stages 1 to 5 the opportunity to use equipment, conduct experiments, solve tasks and develop solutions.

Since 2001, Bayer's Crop Science business in the UK has collaborated with long-term partners that are committed to the future of farming. The business organises educational events and award schemes to support these partnerships.

International Bayer Foundations
Bayer AG's CSR activities are channelled through its three foundations that operate worldwide: The Bayer Science and Education Foundation (Germany), The Bayer Cares Foundation (Germany) and The Bayer Fund (USA). These foundations fund a variety of projects aimed at science and education, community development and social innovation. Details of the international programmes are available online and in the group's Sustainability Report.

Employee-led support
The company encourages employee volunteering and works with Berkshire Community Foundation to use its local knowledge to connect staff to the groups and communities they want to help.

Commercially led support
Sponsorship
The company sponsors the Cultivate Programme in the Thames Valley which helps young people to develop their business ideas. The programme is run by the West Berkshire Education Business Partnership and involves young people attending workshops and working with assigned mentors. Shortlisted students then take their idea to the final and compete for the Cultivate trophy and a prize fund to help develop their idea further.

Exclusions
According to the company's website, Bayer is unable to support:
- individuals rather than group activities
- religious, political or racially aligned movements
- projects or activities bridging a gap in government or local authority funding
- sporting or recreational activities
- entries in log books, year books or support advertising
- projects of a local nature which are outside key locations of Berkshire, Cambridge and Dublin
- conferences, lectures, trips, respite breaks or holidays
- donations to online charity sites

Applications
The company's website states: 'In the first instance please contact us, preferably by email, with details of your organisation, your proposed project, the

amount you would be applying for and any other relevant details to communications.ukireland@bayer.com.'

Community contributions

Total contributions UK £648,000

The company's 2020 annual accounts state that it spent £648,000 on its corporate social responsibility programmes during the year.

BC Partners Ltd

Arts, culture and heritage, community services and development, education and training, the environment, general charitable purposes

Company registration number: OC404426

Correspondent: The CSR Team, 40 Portman Square, London W1H 6DA (tel: 020 7009 4800; email: london@ bcpartners.com; website: www. bcpartners.com)

Nature of business: BC Partners is an international investment firm.

Financial information

Year end	31/12/2020
Turnover	£109,684,306
Pre-tax profit	£34,358,000

Main locations: BC Partners has offices in London, Hamburg, New York and Paris.

Community involvement

The firm's charitable giving is channelled through its corporate charity, the BC Partners Foundation (Charity Commission no. 1136956), which is funded by the group.

The foundation primarily focuses on supporting charities proposed by the employees of BC Partners or trustees of the foundation.

Employee-led support

Staff are central to the firm's charitable activities, since the charities supported by the firm are nominated by staff themselves.

The firm also provides matched funding to employees engaging in fundraising for their chosen causes.

Applications

Contact the correspondent for further information, or see the corporate charity entry on page 225.

Corporate charity

BC Partners Foundation (Charity Commission no. 1136956) – see entry on page 225.

Community contributions

Cash donations UK	£384,000

During this financial year, the firm awarded £384,000 to its corporate charity.

Beazley plc

Arts, culture and heritage, community enterprise and social entrepreneurship, education and training, emergency response/relief

Company registration number: 9763575

Correspondent: The Charity Committee, 22 Bishopgate, London EC2N 4BQ (tel: 020 7667 0623; email: info@beazley. com; website: www.beazley.com/ responsible_business.html)

Directors: Christine Oldridge; Rajesh Agrawal; Adrian Cox; Pierre-Olivier Desaulle; Nicola Hodson; Sally Lake; Christine Lasala; Fiona Muldoon; Anthony Reizenstein; Dr Cecilia Reyes Leuzinger; David Roberts; Robert Stuchbery (female: 50%; male: 50%).

Nature of business: Beazley is a specialist insurance company.

Financial information

Year end	31/12/2021
Turnover	£3,789,200,000
Pre-tax profit	£302,880,000

Main locations: The group operates in Europe, Asia, North America, Latin America and Australia. Its UK offices are located in London and Birmingham.

Community involvement

The group's charitable activities are focused on supporting its charity partners, donating to disaster relief efforts and match funding its employees' fundraising activities.

Partnerships

The group has an ongoing partnership with Renewable World. The charity aims to tackle poverty in Nepal and Kenya through the provision of affordable renewable energy services.

Employee-led support

Employees are given 2.5 days' paid volunteering leave per year. The company also organises an annual Make a Difference month, where there is particular focus on encouraging employees as individuals and teams to support charity and community initiatives.

Applications

Contact the correspondent for further information.

Community contributions

We were unable to determine a figure for the group's charitable contributions. However, the group's 2021 responsible business report states that donations totalling £311,500 were made by the group and employees in 2021. According

to the report, support was broken down as follows:

Economic development	71%
Education	23%
Emergency relief	5%
Arts/culture	1%

All financial figures have been converted from USD to GBP using the exchange rate at the time of writing (August, 2022). We have used gross written premiums in place of turnover.

AJ Bell plc

The environment, general charitable purposes, health, social welfare

Company registration number: 4503206

Correspondent: CSR Team, 4 Exchange Quay, Salford Quays, Manchester M5 3EE (tel: 0345 408 9100; email: enquiry@ajbell.co.uk; website: www. ajbell.co.uk)

Directors: Andy Bell; Michael Summersgill; Roger Stott; Baroness Helena Morrissey; Eamonn Flanagan; Evelyn Bourke; Margaret Hassall; Simon Turner (female: 38%; male: 63%).

Nature of business: AJ Bell provides online investment platforms and stockbroker services.

Financial information

Year end	30/09/2021
Turnover	£145,830,000
Pre-tax profit	£55,080,000

Total employees: 1,065

Main locations: The group is headquartered in Manchester and has offices in London and Bristol.

Community involvement

The group's CSR activities are mostly channelled through the AJ Bell Trust. Employees also volunteer and fundraise for a variety of charities each year and are supported by a matched funding programme.

In 2020/21 AJ Bell launched a partnership with the University of Salford, with the aim to support undergraduate students completing computing degrees.

AJ Bell Trust (Charity Commission no. 1141269)

The trust aims to help disadvantaged people, particularly young people, by donating to national and local causes and funding its own charitable initiatives. Each year, the group donates a percentage of its profits to the trust. In 2021, the group donated 0.5% of its profit before tax (£272,000).

In-kind support

The AJ Bell Trust provides in-kind donations to charities working to prevent or relieve financial hardship.

Employee-led support

In 2021, employees raised £30,000 for foodbank services near AJ Bell's Manchester and London offices via FareShare and Salford CVS.

Commercially led support

In 2021, the company sponsored the 'AJ Bell Technology Award', awarded to top performing students in the University of Salford's computing school.

Applications

Contact the correspondent for further information. For enquiries related to the AJ Bell Trust, email moorhall@outlook.com.

Corporate charity

AJ Bell Trust (Charity Commission no. 1141269) – see entry on page 225.

Community contributions

Cash donations UK		£272,000

In 2020/21, the group made a charitable donation of £272,000 to its corporate charity, the AJ Bell Trust.

Bellway plc

Community services and development, the environment, general charitable purposes, health, housing and homelessness

Company registration number: 1372603

Correspondent: Charities Team, Woolsington House, Woolsington, Newcastle upon Tyne, Tyne and Wear NE13 6BE (email: charities@bellway.co. uk; website: www.bellwayplc.co.uk/ corporate-responsibility/society-and-economy/charitable-giving)

Directors: Simon Scougall; Keith Adey; Jill Caseberry; Jason Honeyman; Denise Jagger; Ian McHoul; John Tutte (female: 29%; male: 71%).

Nature of business: Bellway is a property development company specialising in the building of new homes.

Financial information

Year end	31/07/2021
Turnover	£3,122,500,000
Pre-tax profit	£479,000,000

Main locations: Bellway has several locations throughout the UK. The company's head office is in Newcastle upon Tyne.

Community involvement

Bellway supports the communities in which it operates by making donations to both local charities and causes, as well as engaging in partnerships with national charities.

Areas of work

The group looks to support charities connected with the construction industry and/or charities connected to its staff in some way. According to its charity policy on its website, the group's primary aim is to 'support causes which can make a real difference to local communities across the country' and it meets this aim by supporting the following causes:

▌ Health
▌ Young people
▌ Older people
▌ Housing and homelessness
▌ Environment
▌ Community welfare

Each of Bellway's divisions has an annual charitable budget, which is used to support causes within their area of operation.

National charity partners

Bellway's current charity partner is Cancer Research UK, which will receive direct financial contributions from the group, as well as employee matched funding.

Employee-led support

The group offers match funding to its staff engaging in fundraising activities for their chosen causes.

Exclusions

Bellway does not support:

▌ Religious organisations (unless it can be demonstrated that their services are provided to the wider community)
▌ Organisations that operate discriminatory practices (with respect to employment or the provision of services)
▌ Political organisations/candidates/ programmes

Applications

Requests from charities seeking small donations of around £500 should be sent by email to charities@bellway.co.uk. These will be considered on a quarterly basis. Requests for anything over this amount should be directed to the correspondent.

Community contributions

Cash donations UK		£300,000

During this financial year, the group's charitable donations totalled £300,000. A further £237,400 was raised by employees.

Benefact Group plc

Community services and development, general charitable purposes, religion, social welfare

Company registration number: 1718196

Correspondent: Chris Pitt, Group Impact Director, Benefact House, 2000 Pioneer Avenue, Gloucester Business Park, Gloucester, Gloucestershire GL3 4AW (email: information@benefactgroup.com; website: https://benefactgroup.com/ responsible-business)

Directors: Rachael Hall; Rita Bajaj; Francois-Xavier Boisseau; Denise Cockrem; Robert Henderson; Mark Hews; Sir Stephen Lamport; Neil Maidment; Andrew McIntrye; Chris Moulder; Stephanie Whyte; Angus Winther (female: 33%; male: 67%).

Nature of business: Benefact Group is a diverse family of financial services businesses that provide specialist insurance, investment management, broking and advisory services. The group is owned by a charity, Benefact Trust, and all its businesses are united by a common purpose to give all available profits to charity and good causes. Together, businesses in the group aim to provide responsible and sustainable investment, protection of iconic buildings and world heritage sites, and trusted advice to people and businesses.

Financial information

Year end	31/12/2021
Turnover	£486,218,000
Pre-tax profit	£81,855,000

Main locations: Benefact Group plc's head office is in Gloucester. Businesses in the group have offices across the UK, plus offices in Ireland, Australia and Canada.

Community involvement

The Benefact Group is owned by the Benefact Trust and gives a large proportion of its profits to the trust each year. The trust makes grants to churches, Christian charities and the communities they support.

The Benefact Group plc and its businesses also support charitable causes in their own right through a range of programmes, partnerships and employee giving.

Key initiatives include:

▌ Benefact Group's Movement for Good awards distribute £1 million annually. Five hundred charities receive grants of £1,000 and a number of charities receive larger grants of £10,000+. As part of the Movement for Good awards, the group's 12 Days of Giving scheme awarded grants of £1,000 to 120 charities in December 2021.

- Ecclesiastical Insurance's Closer to You grants programme gives the insurer's closest broker partners the chance to donate £2,500 to charities of their choice.
- Partnerships with key charities tackling issues important to Ecclesiastical's customers and communities. Ecclesiastical supports The Prince's Foundation's Building Arts and Crafts Programmes, which give students the opportunity to learn heritage skills from master craftspeople.

The group is working to find more ways to provide support charities and enable them to be more successful and sustainable. It has launched a range of fundraising resources including free webinars and resources on its website.

Employee-led support

The group's MyGiving programme supports volunteering and enables employees to give small grants to causes they care about. The programme also matches employee fundraising and payroll giving.

Applications

Funding – visit www.movementforgood.com.

Advice and support for charities – visit the group's website.

General queries – contact the correspondent for further information.

Corporate charity

Benefact Trust Ltd (Charity Commission no. 263960) – see entry on page 226.

Community contributions

Cash donations UK	£28,100,000
Cash donations overseas	£400,000
Total contributions UK	£28,435,000

According to the group's annual report, cash donations totalled £28.5 million in 2021. This included a grant of £26 million to the Benefact Trust and further £2.5 million to other causes. The group also made in-kind contributions of £335,000 in respect of employee volunteering time and investment in services to support charities.

Berkeley Group plc

🔍 Education and training, social welfare

Company registration number: 1454064

Correspondent: The CSR Team, Berkeley House, 19 Portsmouth Road, Cobham, Surrey KT11 1JG (tel: 01932 868555; email: info@berkeleyfoundation.org.uk; website: www.berkeleygroup.co.uk/about-us/sustainability)

Directors: Ann Dibben; Robert Perrins; Richard Stearn; Justin Tibaldi; Paul Vallone; Karl Whiteman (male: 100%).

Nature of business: Berkeley is a property developer, specialising in building new homes.

Financial information

Year end	30/04/2021
Pre-tax profit	£496,600

Main locations: Berkeley mainly operates in London, Birmingham and the south of England.

Community involvement

Berkeley channels all its charitable and community giving through its corporate charity, The Berkeley Foundation (Charity Commission no. 1152596). The foundation mainly supports organisations that help children and young people.

Employee-led support

The group's website states that 53% of Berkeley staff have been involved with the foundation's work in some way.

Applications

Contact the correspondent for more information.

Corporate charity

The Berkeley Foundation (Charity Commission no. 1152596) – see entry on page 226.

Community contributions

Cash donations UK	£2,120,000
Total contributions UK	£2,460,000

In 2020/21 the group awarded £2.12 million to its corporate charity. A further £339,400 was given in the form of donated services.

Matched funding and Give As You Earn totalled £121,500, which was awarded to the foundation. We were unable to determine how much of this figure came directly from the company, or from employees.

Bestway Group Ltd

🔍 Education and training, emergency response/relief, health

Company registration number: 11003305

Correspondent: CSR Team, 2 Abbey Road, Park Royal, London NW10 7BW (tel: 020 8453 1234; email: use the contact form on the website; website: www.bestwaywholesale.co.uk)

Directors: Zameer Choudrey; Dawood Pervez; Haider Choudrey; Mohammed Pervez; Rizwan Pervez; Mohammed Sheikh (male: 100%).

Nature of business: Bestway Group Ltd is a family-owned business with operations in the wholesale, cement, banking, real estate and pharmacy sectors.

Financial information

Year end	30/06/2021
Turnover	£3,748,680,000
Pre-tax profit	£332,720,000

Total employees: 28,000+

Main locations: The group has locations throughout the UK and South Asia (particularly Pakistan).

Community involvement

According to our previous research, Bestway donates 2.5% of its yearly profits to charitable causes, which is channelled through the group's charities, The Bestway Foundation (Charity Commission no. 297178) and the Bestway Foundation Pakistan. Bestway's website states that the group's CSR programme is focused on education and health in the UK, humanitarian aid for victims of natural disasters and the relief of poverty in Pakistan.

Applications

Contact the correspondent for further information.

Corporate charity

The Bestway Foundation (Charity Commission no. 297178) – see entry on page 227.

Community contributions

We were unable to determine a figure for the group's total charitable contributions for 2020/21.

Bettys and Taylors of Harrogate Ltd

🔍 Education and training, the environment, general charitable purposes

Company registration number: 543821

Correspondent: CSR Team, 1 Parliament Street, Harrogate, North Yorkshire HG1 2QU (tel: 01423 814000; email: HR@bettysandtaylors.co.uk; website: www.bettysandtaylors.co.uk)

Directors: Paul Cogan; Rachel Fellows; Rimla Akhtar; Fiona Gunn; Philip Hanson; Clare Morrow; Andrew Wildsmith (female: 57%; male: 43%).

Nature of business: The company owns the Yorkshire Tea and Taylors of Harrogate brands and runs a small chain of tea rooms in Yorkshire.

Financial information

Year end	31/10/2021
Turnover	£252,000,000
Pre-tax profit	£14,622,000

UK employees: 1,441

Main locations: The company's headquarters is in Harrogate.

Community involvement

Support is given to charities in Yorkshire through the Good Cause Awards programme. The company also runs tree-planting and environmental education schemes for schoolchildren.

Trees for Life

The long-running Trees for Life campaign launched in 1990 with a pledge to plant 1 million trees. Since then, the company has planted over 5 million trees around the world. The programme supports tree-planting activities, environmental education in schools and conservation projects in the UK and in tea and coffee growing regions around the world. In the past, the company has worked with organisations such as the Woodland Trust, Oxfam, Groundworks and the Rainforest Foundation UK.

In 2020, £100,000 was allocated to the Woodland Trust for the planting of 10,000 trees in the Yorkshire Dales, as well as the restoration and maintenance of Nidd Gorge woodland.

Partnerships

The company has an ongoing partnership with cricket charity Chance to Shine.

The Cone Exchange

The company owns the Cone Exchange, a community scrap store. The store provides several benefits for the community, including:

- Encouraging schoolchildren to recycle in exchange for Cone Exchange rewards
- Supporting social enterprises by providing waste from its own and other businesses to use for crafts
- Providing meaningful work experience and placements for young people with additional learning needs
- Raising funds through sales of waste for local good causes

In 2020/21, £11,000 was raised for local charities through the Cone Exchange.

Bettys and Taylors Community Coronavirus Fund

In 2021, Bettys and Taylors partnered with Two Ridings Community Foundation to provide grants to local charities struggling from the impact of the COVID-19 pandemic. Grants awarded through the Bettys and Taylors Community Coronavirus Fund totalled £135,000.

Employee-led support

Employees are encouraged to take part in community activities such as planting trees and sharing skills with young people via school visits. Staff also fundraise for charities which the company matches through the Good Cause Awards.

Employees in 2021 partnered with charity Teach First, which aims to address educational inequality in England and Wales. Employees provided coaching for new teachers on the programme, as well as producing careers films and hosting a week-long virtual work experience for students from disadvantaged backgrounds.

Applications

Contact the correspondent for further information.

Community contributions

Cash donations UK	£50,600
Total contributions UK	£425,200

In 2020/21 the company's UK charitable contributions totalled £425,200. This figure includes financial donations and in-kind support and was measured in accordance with the London Benchmarking Framework. Cash donations totalled £50,600.

A total of £73,600 was raised through staff fundraising, the Cone Exchange and customer fundraising activity.

BGL Group Ltd

General charitable purposes, sports and recreation

Company registration number: 2593690

Correspondent: The Community Team, Pegasus House, Bakewell Road Orton Southgate, Peterborough, Cambridgeshire PE2 6YS (email: csr@bglgroup.co.uk; website: www.bglgroup.co.uk/csr/community)

Directors: Dominic Platt; Allison Hewitt; Mark Bailie (female: 33%; male: 67%).

Nature of business: BGL Group Ltd is a financial services company specialising in vehicle and home insurance.

Financial information

Year end	30/06/2021
Turnover	£208,200,000
Pre-tax profit	(£26,700,000)

Total employees: 2,643

Main locations: In the UK, the group has offices in London, Peterborough, Sunderland and Wakefield. It also has an office in Paris.

Community involvement

BGL Group provides support to charities in the UK and overseas through funding, matched funding, payroll giving and volunteering.

Partnerships

The group's partnerships are designed to empower people and encourage education and entrepreneurship. Support is given to charities local to its offices in Peterborough, Sunderland, Wakefield,

London and Paris. BGL Group Ltd has also worked in partnership with Build It International for several years, creating opportunities for young people and their communities in Zambia through skills training, work experience and essential community-building projects.

Community Teams

The group has dedicated Community Teams at each of its offices that encourage, support and review applications for funding and volunteering each month. The teams allocate BGL resources to worthy causes and establish partnerships with local charities. Organisations that have previously been supported include Inspire Peterborough, Peterborough Soup Kitchen, Railworld, St Cuthbert's Hospice in Sunderland and Wakefield Baptist Church.

Employee-led support

Employee volunteering

The group runs an employee volunteering programme through which employees are able to volunteer during the year for charitable causes

Matched funding

BGL Group will match any funds raised by employees up to £1,000. Those fundraising as part of a group can each claim up to £1,000 of matched funding.

Payroll giving

The group also operates a payroll giving scheme allowing employees to make a monthly donation to a charity of their choice. The group currently holds the Silver Payroll Giving Quality Mark to recognise the number of employees participating.

Commercially led support

The group operates a sponsorship programme that is focused on promoting grassroots sports in its communities. Support is given to a range of local sports teams, clubs and events.

Applications

Contact the correspondent for further information. To enquire about sponsorship, contact the group via email at sponsorship@bglgroup.co.uk.

Community contributions

We were unable to determine a figure for the group's charitable contributions.

Bibby Line Group Ltd

General charitable purposes

Company registration number: 34121

Correspondent: CSR Team, 3rd Floor, Walker House, Liverpool L2 3YL (tel: 0151 708 8000; email: info@ bibbylinegroup.co.uk; website: https:// bibbylinegroup.co.uk)

Directors: Sir Michael Bibby; David Anderson; Geoffrey Bibby; Jonathan Lewis (male: 100%).

Nature of business: Bibby Line Group Ltd is the parent company of a group of trading businesses. Bibby Financial Services, Bibby Distribution, Bibby Marine, Costcutter and Garic are its constituents.

Financial information

Year end	31/12/2020
Turnover	£832,527,000
Pre-tax profit	(£26,592,000)

Total employees: 4,000

Main locations: The group's head office is in Liverpool and its areas of operation span the UK and overseas.

Community involvement

Bibby Line Group Ltd provides support to communities in the UK and abroad primarily through its Giving Something Back programme, which encourages employees take part in volunteering and fundraising events. The group also makes financial contributions to the programme.

In-kind support

Through the Hive Youth Zone, Bibby Line Group and Bibby Financial Services provide support and expertise through skill-sharing. This includes employees teaching young people about finance and CV skills.

Employee-led support

The Giving Something Back programme supports employees to volunteer and fundraise for a cause of their choice. Bibby Line Group then match funds employee efforts. Since the programme's creation in 2007, the group and its employees have donated over £10 million to good causes. Each year the company holds the Giving Something Back Awards ceremony to celebrate the top fundraisers of that year.

Payroll giving

Employees can support their favourite charities through the group's payroll giving scheme.

Applications

Contact the correspondent for more information.

Community contributions

Cash donations UK	£84,000

According to its annual report the company made charitable contributions of £84,000 in 2020.

Biffa

Community services and development, the environment, sports and recreation

Company registration number: 10336040

Correspondent: The CSR Team, Coronation Road, Cressex, High Wycombe HP12 3TZ (website: www. biffa.co.uk/sustainability)

Directors: Sarah Parsons; Carol Chesney; Kenneth Lever; David Martin; Claire Miles; Linda Morant; Richard Pike; Michael Topham (female: 50%; male: 50%).

Nature of business: Waste management.

Financial information

Year end	26/03/2021
Turnover	£1,042,000,000
Pre-tax profit	(£40,500,000)

UK employees: 9,157

Main locations: Biffa has over 100 depots in 49 counties across the UK.

Community involvement

Support is provided through employee fundraising and volunteering, Biffa's charity partnership with WaterAid and funding through the Biffa Award.

Biffa Award

The Biffa Award makes grants to community projects near Biffa landfill sites. Grants are made under three themes: Community Buildings, Recreation and Rebuilding Biodiversity.

Education

Biffa provides a range of educational resources for schools on its website. It also runs workshops and educational visits.

Employee-led support

Employees engage in volunteering and fundraising activities.

Applications

Biffa Award – visit www.biffa-award.org to apply for a grant. The website has a postcode checker to determine whether projects are near enough to a site to be eligible.

Educational visits – contact the company via its website to arrange a visit.

Corporate charity

Biffa Award (not a registered charity) – see entry on page 227.

Community contributions

We were unable to determine a figure for the company's charitable contributions.

Birketts LLP

Community services and development, general charitable purposes, legal advice, social welfare

Company registration number: OC317545

Correspondent: CSR Team, Providence House, 141–145 Princes Street, Ipswich, Suffolk IP1 1QJ (tel: 0808 169 4320; website: www.birketts.co.uk/about-us/ corporate-social-responsibility)

Directors: Jonathan Agar; James Austin; Tim Sarson; Chris Schwer; Adrian Seagers; Alex Davey; Jack Royall; Shaun Savory; Belinda Moore; Tom Wagstaff; Sarah Ralph; Shaun Folan; Marian Squire; Russell Edwards (female: 21%; male: 79%).

Nature of business: Birketts is a law firm based in the East of England.

Financial information

Year end	31/05/2021
Turnover	£69,200,000
Pre-tax profit	£22,450,000

UK employees: 790

Main locations: Birketts has offices in Cambridge, Chelmsford, Ipswich, Norwich and London.

Community involvement

The firm's community involvement focuses on providing support to voluntary and community groups in Suffolk, Norfolk, Cambridgeshire and Essex whose primary aim is to improve the quality of people's lives. It does this through a combination of donations, fundraising and in-kind contributions.

Birketts Charitable Fund (not a registered charity)

The Birketts Charitable Fund, established in 2006, is administered by the community foundations in Suffolk, Norfolk, Cambridgeshire and Essex. Donations to the fund are made annually by the partners of the firm (currently £80,000 per year) and grants are awarded twice a year by a committee made up of employees and partners of the firm. In 2020/21, £105,000 was distributed through the fund to 29 charities.

In-kind support

Birketts is a member of the Suffolk, Norfolk and Cambridgeshire branches of the Pro-Help Group, a network of businesses that provide a broad range of professional services, free of charge, to local charities and community groups.

Employees are also encouraged to take part in local pro bono initiatives with the object of providing legal assistance and support to small local groups, principally those concerned with the interests of ethnic minorities and disadvantaged people. According to the firm's 2020/21 annual report, 367 pro bono hours were provided by employees during the year.

Employee-led support

Employees are entitled to one paid day's leave a year to volunteer with a community project. Throughout the year, employees also take part in several fundraising activities to raise money for charities and good causes. One example is the firm's regular involvement in the Cumbrian Challenge in aid of Walking With The Wounded.

Commercially led support

The firm also provides support to local causes through the sponsorship of events. In 2021, Birkett sponsored several initiatives including the Charity Today Awards and the firm's 12th annual Save the Children Golf Day. The firm also sponsored Power2Inspire, a Cambridge-based sports charity, for its Rugby Power House Games. Volunteers from the firm took part in inclusive and adapted games such as boccia, New Age Kurling and touch rugby.

Applications

Contact the correspondent for further information. For information on how to apply for a Birkett's Charitable Fund grant, visit the Suffolk, Norfolk, Cambridge or Essex Community Foundation website.

Community contributions

Cash donations UK	£105,000

In the 2020/21 annual report, the firm declared cash donations of £105,000 for charitable purposes. Of this amount, £81,100 was awarded to the Birketts Charitable Fund.

Birmingham International Airport Ltd

Arts, culture and heritage, community enterprise and social entrepreneurship, community services and development, education and training, the environment, health, social welfare, sports and recreation

Company registration number: 2078273

Correspondent: Abigail Redmond, Sustainability Assistant, Diamond House, Birmingham Airport, Birmingham, West Midlands B26 3QJ (tel: 0871 222 0072; email: abigail.

Redmond@birminghamairport.co.uk; website: www.birminghamairport.co.uk)

Directors: Nicholas Barton; Timothy Clarke; Simon Richards (male: 100%).

Nature of business: The principal activity of the company is the operation and management of Birmingham International Airport and the provision of associated facilities and services.

Financial information

Year end	31/03/2021
Turnover	£24,080,000
Pre-tax profit	(£67,870,000)

UK employees: 434

Main locations: The company's head office is in Birmingham.

Community involvement

Birmingham Airport's charitable giving is mainly directed through its Community Trust Fund and to its long-term charity partners. However, the company also provides small-scale support to other good causes through small donations and employee fundraising. The company also runs a number of education and employment programmes.

The Birmingham Airport Community Trust Fund (Charity Commission no. 1071176)

Birmingham Airport's charitable involvement is focused on disadvantaged communities in the area where it operates. It operates a 30–30–40 policy to target its investments in East Birmingham (30%), Solihull (30%) and other areas impacted by the airport's activities (40%). This support is distributed through the airport's corporate charity, The Birmingham Airport Community Trust Fund, which received £88,500 of investment from the company in 2021.

Partnerships

In February 2020, the company began a three-year partnership with Solihull Mind, as nominated and voted for directly by employees.

The company has a decade-long partnership with Acorns Children's Hospice, which is supported through employee fundraising. The company also works in partnership with the Solihull Council to deliver the Arden Free Tree Scheme, a free tree-planting scheme that can be accessed by individuals and groups in Solihull. The company provides around £10,000 towards tree-planting schemes every year.

Education and training

The company has a dedicated education facility, The Learning Hub, for activities such as workshops with partner schools, school holiday projects and continued professional development sessions for teachers. The airport also works with

Enabling Enterprise, to deliver free education support programmes for children and young people. The company has a long-term partnership with The Prince's Trust and its Get into Airports programme, which provides vocational experiences for young people aged 16 to 25.

In-kind support

Through its partnership with Newlife – the Charity for Disabled Children, the company donates empty suitcases discarded by passengers to Newlife's stores to be resold and reused.

Employee-led support

Employees fundraise for the company's nominated charity partner and other charities on a smaller scale where appropriate. Employee-led activities include dress-down days and bucket collections in the airport's terminals.

Commercially led support

The company sponsored Coventry UK City of Culture 2021. In 2022, the company sponsored the Birmingham Commonwealth Games.

Applications

Requests for charity support can be made using the online form available at: https://birminghamairport.custhelp.com/app/applications/charities/p/51.

There is also a form on the website for arranging educational visits. Visits are free but booking is essential.

Information on how to apply for a grant from the airport's corporate charity can be found in the entry in this guide.

Corporate charity

The Birmingham Airport Community Trust Fund (Charity Commission no. 1071176) – see entry on page 228.

Community contributions

Cash donations UK	£110,000

According to its 2020/21 sustainability report, the company donated more than £110,000 to over 50 local community projects.

A. F. Blakemore and Son Ltd

Community services and development, education and training, the environment, general charitable purposes, health, sports and recreation

Company registration number: 391135

Correspondent: Kate Senter, Community Affairs Officer, Long Acres Industrial Estate, Rosehill, Willenhall, West Midlands WV13 2JP (tel: 0121 568 2910; email: ksenter@afblakemore.com; website: www.afblakemore.com/our-community)

Directors: Peter Blakemore; Jerry Marwood; Scott Munro-Morris; Ian Diment; Caoire Blakemore; Tomas Blakemore; Charlie Blakemore (female: 14%; male: 86%).

Nature of business: The principal activity of the group is the wholesale and retail distribution of grocery products and the operation of grocery convenience stores, such as SPAR.

Financial information

Year end	24/04/2021
Turnover	£1,000,979,000
Pre-tax profit	£6,117,000

Total employees: 7,493

Main locations: The company's head office is in Willenhall.

Community involvement

All of the company's community giving is distributed through its corporate charity, the Blakemore Foundation (Charity Commission no. 1015938). The foundation supports general charitable purposes in the area the company has a presence.

In-kind support

In-kind donations are given in the form of food, drink or supplies from Blakemore Retail SPAR stores.

Employee-led support

Employee fundraising

Employees are encouraged to fundraise through a range of activities. The company's website states that employees spent 4,491 hours fundraising during the year. A total of £20,800 was raised for local good causes, and SPAR employees raised over £234,000 for the NSPCC.

Branching Out

Branching Out is an educational programme established with the aim of engaging and motivating young people into the world of work. It is made up of five key themes:

- Reading partnerships
- Workplace insights
- Employability workshops
- Career support
- Work experience

The programme is led by employees who volunteer their time to help deliver the programme to local young people.

Employee volunteering

The company's volunteering programme gives employees the opportunity to take part in a variety of projects including practical regeneration projects, mentoring, study tours of sites and employability-based workshops for students. The key themes of the community volunteer programme include, education, employability and enterprise.

Applications

There are different application forms and processes depending on the type of support being requested. All information, including upcoming deadlines, can be found on the 'Our Community' section of the company's website.

Corporate charity

Blakemore Foundation (Charity Commission no. 1015938) – see entry on page 228.

Community contributions

Cash donations UK	£313,300

According to its accounts, the company donated £313,300 through its corporate charity in 2020/21. We have taken this figure as the total cash contribution from the company.

Bloomsbury Publishing plc

🔍 Literature and literacy; the environment

Company registration number: 1984336

Correspondent: CSR Team, 50 Bedford Square, London WC1B 3AT (tel: 020 7631 5600; email: contact@bloomsbury. com; website: www.bloomsbury.com/uk)

Directors: Richard Lambert; Nigel Newton; Penny Scott-Bayfield; Leslie-Ann Reed; Baroness Lola Young of Hornsey; John Bason; Maya Abu-Deeb (female: 57%; male: 43%).

Nature of business: Bloomsbury Publishing is a publisher with offices in London, New York and Sydney.

Financial information

Year end	28/02/2022
Turnover	£230,110,000
Pre-tax profit	£26,730,000

Total employees: 719

Main locations: In the UK, the group has offices in London and Oxford.

Community involvement

The group focuses on supporting causes relating to literacy, literature and education through partnerships and corporate donations.

Partnerships

National Literacy Trust (NLT) – In 2019, Bloomsbury entered into a three-year partnership with the NLT to support its activities aimed at developing literacy in Hastings. To date, the company has donated over 80,000 books to libraries, schools, community centres and food banks in co-operation with the NLT. During 2021/22, Bloomsbury donated £50,000 and 800 books to the NLT to support an array of reading events.

EmpathyLab – Bloomsbury is one of the publishers that have signed the EmpathyLab Manifesto, pledging to publish and promote the books that support the CIC's mission.

The Woodland Trust – Bloomsbury aims to reduce carbon emissions through its partnership with The Woodland Trust. In 2021/22, Bloomsbury donated £19,200 to The Woodland Trust to support the management and care of trees and the engagement of young people to learn about nature.

In-kind support

In the UK, the USA and Australia, the group donates, or provides at a reduced cost, a substantial quantity of books and games each year. This includes donations of mainstream titles to schools, libraries and organisations supporting education. Charities, such as Barnardo's, Oxfam, the Red Cross and smaller organisations local to the group's offices also receive in-kind support and discounted books.

Employee-led support

According to the Bloomsbury's website, employees, both through a Bloomsbury co-ordinator and privately, are involved in formal volunteer reading schemes. Employees also attend schools and colleges to deliver talks on careers in publishing, reading skills in the workplace, and to assist with practice interviews and producing school magazines.

Commercially led support

Reforest'Action – This sponsorship aims to restore the ecosystems by planting trees. In 2021/22, Bloomsbury sponsored the preservation of over 8,000 trees by donating £9,998. In addition, all Bloomsbury employees are given a code to plant eight trees each via the Reforest'Action projects.

Applications

Contact your local office for further information. A general enquiries form can be found on the company's 'Contact Us' web page.

Community contributions

Cash donations UK	£328,900
Total contributions UK	£576,200

According to the company's 2021/22 annual report, cash donations totalled £328,900 with a further £247,300 in in-kind donations of books.

Beneficiaries of corporate donations included: Book Aid and the National Literacy Trust (£50,000 each); The Woodland Trust (£19,200); Reforest'Action and The David Nott Foundation (£10,000 each); ARU Foundation (£1,000).

BMW UK Ltd

🔍 Community services and development, education and training, health

Company registration number: 1378137

Correspondent: BMW Group Sustainability Team, Summit One, Summit Avenue, Farnborough, Hampshire GU14 0FB (tel: 0800 325 6000; website: www.bmw.co.uk/en/footer/experience-bmw/about-us.html)

Directors: Christopher Brownridge; Bernhard Kuhnt; Tomas Ribes (male: 100%).

Nature of business: The principal activity of the company is the importation, storage, distribution, repair and maintenance of BMW Group products in the UK.

Financial information

Year end	31/12/2021
Turnover	£4,682,660,000
Pre-tax profit	£66,900,000

UK employees: 412

Main locations: BMW Group operates 30 production and assembly facilities in over 14 countries and has a global sales network in more than 140 countries. In the UK, BMW Group has operating plants in Oxford, Birmingham and Swindon.

Community involvement

In the UK, the group has partnerships with a number of charities. In 2021 these included Ben – Motor and Allied Trades Benevolent Fund, The Community Matters Partnership Project and Alzheimer's Society.

In 2022, the group began a partnership with Campaign Against Living Miserably through which it pledged to raise £200,000 to support the charity's helpline.

The group has a long-standing partnership with the British Heart Foundation Clothes Bank.

BMW has a long-standing commitment to supporting education across the UK through the BMW Education initiative, the details of which have been taken from the group's website:

> BMW Group Education provides teachers and students with free, curriculum-linked and award-winning educational resources. The comprehensive resources for primary and secondary schools cover topics including:
> ▸ Road safety and the benefits of travelling actively
> ▸ Sustainable mobility, technology and design
> ▸ Understanding sustainable living in urban environments
> ▸ Careers information

Employee-led support

According to the group's 2021 annual report, employees completed over 500 hours of volunteering over the year including painting projects in local schools and other local initiatives.

Applications

Contact the correspondent for more information.

Community contributions

Cash donations UK	£228,000

In 2021, the group made charitable donations of £228,000, of which £218,000 was awarded to Ben – Motor and Allied Trades Benevolent Fund.

Boeing United Kingdom Ltd

🔍 Community services and development, education and training, social welfare, STEM

Correspondent: Katerina Giannini, Communications Manager and Community Investor, 25 Victoria Street, London SW1 0EX (tel: 020 7340 1900; email: katerina.giannini@boeing.com; website: www.boeing.co.uk/boeing-in-the-uk/community.page)

Directors: Brent Bishop; Daniel Drake; Maria Laine (female: 33%; male: 67%).

Nature of business: Boeing United Kingdom Ltd is a subsidiary of The Boeing Company. The Boeing Company is an aerospace manufacturer and defence contractor. Its other subsidiary in the UK is Boeing Defence UK.

Financial information

Year end	31/12/2021
Turnover	£56,970,000
Pre-tax profit	£3,280,000

Main locations: Boeing has sites across the UK.

Community involvement

In the UK, the company provides support through partnerships, sponsorship, grants, employee volunteering and advocacy. Its community engagement efforts are focused on the following three areas:

▸ **Our Future: Tomorrow's Innovators** – educational and support programmes with a particular focus on inspiring young people in the areas of science, technology, engineering and mathematics (STEM) through hands-on experience.

▸ **Our Heroes: Veterans and Families** – support for Service members transitioning to civilian life, veterans and their families.

▸ **Our Homes: Dynamic Communities** – grant funding is provided to regional charities in areas in which the company has a presence. These areas are:
  ▸ Scotland
  ▸ Republic of Ireland
  ▸ Northern Ireland
  ▸ Yorkshire
  ▸ South West England

Partnerships

The company has national partnerships with The Prince's Trust, The Air League, The Royal Academy of Engineering, the Open University and SSAFA. Regionally, partners include Aoibheann's Pink Tie, a children's cancer charity, and the Golddigger Trust, which supports young people in and around Sheffield.

Employee-led support

Employees take part in volunteering activities.

Commercially led support

The company supports organisations close to its sites by sponsoring fundraising events or community programmes. Applying organisations should align with the company's three programmes – Veterans and Families, Tomorrow's Innovators and Dynamic Communities.

Applications

Grants

Proposed projects should first be discussed with a local community investor. More information on grants can be found on Boeing's global website at: www.boeing.com/principles/community-engagement.page#/seeking-support.

Event sponsorship

To apply for sponsorship for an event, contact a local site at least six months prior to the event.

Employee volunteering

For volunteering opportunities that align with the company's strategy, contact the correspondent.

Community contributions

We were unable to determine a figure for the company's charitable contributions.

Boodle & Dunthorne Ltd

🔍 General charitable purposes

Company registration number: 472968

Correspondent: The CSR Team, 178 New Bond Street, Liverpool, Merseyside L2 9SQ (tel: 0151 224 0580)

Directors: Nicholas Wainwright; Michael Wainwright; Frances Wainwright; Harold Wainwright; Diana Wainwright; Elizabeth Wainwright;

James Amos; Jonathan Wainwright (female: 25%; male: 75%).

Nature of business: Boodles is a family-owned luxury jewellers.

Financial information

Year end	05/04/2021
Turnover	£49,540,000
Pre-tax profit	£5,360,000

Total employees: 104

Main locations: Boodles has stores in Chester, Dublin, Liverpool, London and Manchester. The head office is in London.

Community involvement

The majority of the company's charitable giving is channelled through its corporate charity, The Boodle & Dunthorne Charitable Trust (Charity Commission no. 1077748).

Employee-led support

Employees fundraise for the company's partner charity and corporate charity.

Applications

Contact the company for further information.

Corporate charity

The Boodle & Dunthorne Charitable Trust (Charity Commission no. 1077748) – see entry on page 229.

Community contributions

Cash donations UK	£161,100

In 2020/21 the company declared charitable donations totalling £161,100, of which £119,600 was given to The Boodle & Dunthorne Charitable Trust.

Boots UK Ltd

Community services and development, education and training, health

Company registration number: 928555

Correspondent: The CSR Team, 1 Thane Road West, Nottingham, Nottinghamshire NG2 3AA (tel: 0345 070 8090; website: www.boots-uk.com/corporate-social-responsibility)

Directors: Andrew Thompson; Benjamin Horner; Sebastian James; Michael Snape (male: 100%).

Nature of business: The company's principal activity is pharmacy-led health and beauty retailing. Boots UK is part of the Retail Pharmacy International Division of Walgreens Boots Alliance, Inc. (NASDAQ: WBA).

Financial information

Year end	31/08/2021
Turnover	£5,812,000,000
Pre-tax profit	(£58,000)

Main locations: The company has offices across the UK and its head office is in Nottingham.

Community involvement

Much of the company's CSR strategy focuses on the local area around its head office in Nottingham. It awards grants through its corporate charity, The Boots Charitable Trust (Charity Commission no. 1045927), which is wholly funded by the company.

Boots has partnerships with Macmillan Cancer Support and The Prince's Trust. The company also has a partnership with The Hygiene Bank, which aims to provide affordable hygiene products to those who cannot afford them.

Boots UK is also a part of the Walgreens Boots Alliance (WBA). In 2020, the WBA helped provide 250 million women and children with medicine through its partnership with Vitamin Angels, as well as helping to provide 60 million vaccines in the Global South.

Employee-led support

Employees, customers and suppliers fundraise and campaign for the company's charity partners. Employees also volunteer to support different Macmillan initiatives.

Applications

Contact the correspondent for more information.

Corporate charity

Boots Charitable Trust (Charity Commission no. 1045927) – see entry on page 229.

Community contributions

Total contributions UK	£266,800

We were unable to find details of the company's charitable giving for 2021. However, The Boots Charitable Trust's accounts state that it received £266,800 from the company during this period.

AFC Bournemouth Ltd

Education and training, health, social welfare, sports and recreation

Company registration number: 6632170

Correspondent: Andrew Battison, Community Operations Co-ordinator, Vitality Stadium, Dean Court, Bournemouth BH7 7AF (tel: 01202 726300; email: community@afcb.co.uk; website: www.afcb.co.uk/community-sports-trust)

Directors: Neil Blake; Jeffrey Anthony; Nicholas Rothwell; Rico Seitz (male: 100%).

Nature of business: AFC Bournemouth is a professional football club competing in the English Premier League.

Financial information

Year end	30/06/2021
Turnover	£71,690,000
Pre-tax profit	£16,950,000

Total employees: 339

Main locations: The football club is based in Bournemouth.

Community involvement

AFC Bournemouth Ltd supports sport, education and community projects in Bournemouth, Poole and Dorset. Many of the club's community activities are delivered through its charity, AFC Bournemouth Community Sports Trust (Charity Commission no. 1122693). Support is provided through sports and educational programmes, charity partnerships, and in-kind and cash donations.

Charity partners

Each year, the club partners with local registered charities whose work benefits people living in the Dorset and Hampshire areas. According to its website, AFC Bournemouth's chosen charities benefit from:

- Increased awareness
- Fundraising through selected club events
- Signed football club merchandise
- Engagement with AFC Bournemouth corporate partners and AFC Business members
- Match tickets
- Player appearances

The club's chosen charities for the 2022/23 season are Hope For Food, Lewis-Manning Hospice Care, Mytime Young Carers and The Isabel Baker Foundation.

Player appearances

Members of AFC Bournemouth's first team regularly make appearances at local schools and events.

Cherries Community Fund (not a registered charity)

The Cherries Community Fund was set up by the club in 2016 and provides grants of up to £1,000 to community groups and charities supporting young and vulnerable people, sport and healthy living in Dorset. The fund is financed by the Cherries Community Draw and other donations received by the club.

Applications

Charity partners

Each season charities can nominate themselves to be one of AFC Bournemouth's chosen charities. Application and selection processes are announced on the club's website in spring.

Player appearances

Groups can request an appearance by a player using an online form on the club's website: www.afcb.co.uk/community-sports-trust/player-appearance-requests

Cherries Community Fund

Applications to the Cherries Community Fund should be submitted via email to cherriescommunityfund@afcb.co.uk. Funding is allocated in March, June, September and December of each year, with the application deadline set at the end of the month prior to the next panel meeting.

Community contributions

AFC Bournemouth Ltd's total charitable contributions were not declared in its 2020/21 accounts.

BP plc

Education and training, the environment, sports and recreation, arts and culture, disaster relief, STEM

Company registration number: 102498

Correspondent: The UK Social and Community Affairs Team, International Headquarters, 1 St James's Square, London SW1Y 4PD (tel: 020 7496 4000; email: use the 'UK community and investment and sponsorship enquiries' form on the group's website; website: www.bp.com/en_gb/united-kingdom/home/community.html)

Directors: Helge Lund; Bernard Looney; Murray Auchincloss; Pamela Daley; Melody Meyer; Tushar Morzaria; Paula Rosput Reynolds; Sir John Sawers; Amanda Blanc; Karen Richardson; Johannes Teyssen (female: 45%; male: 55%).

Nature of business: BP plc is a multinational oil and gas company headquartered in London.

Financial information

Year end	31/12/2021
Turnover	£144,069,980,000
Pre-tax profit	£13,362,460,000

Total employees: 64,000

Main locations: BP plc operates in Europe, North and South America, Australasia, Asia and Africa. In the UK, the group has offices and operations in London, Milton Keynes, Pangbourne, Hull, Sunbury and the North Sea.

Community involvement

Globally, the group's CSR strategy focuses on economic development, education, environmental programmes, sport, and arts and culture.

The group has a corporate charity, the BP Foundation, which is based in the USA and works to benefit communities around the world by making donations to charities that support STEM education and humanitarian relief.

Education

In the UK, the group has a particular focus on encouraging young people into STEM careers. It achieves this through a range of educational initiatives and employee-led volunteering programmes. The group partners with a range of organisations to deliver these projects, including national charities and universities. For example, BP works with the charity Education and Employers to encourage students to pursue STEM careers and pathways.

Partnerships

The group has a partnership with the mental health charity Mind, through which it is working to improve workplace mental health.

In-kind support

The group provides free STEM resources for schools, colleges and home learning on its BP Educational Service website.

In the UK, employees support local community organisations and small businesses by sharing their expertise through project-specific support and leadership roles.

Employee-led support

Employees volunteer and fundraise for charities of their choice. In the UK, employees also volunteer for the group's educational programmes, through which they take part in careers fairs and talks, CV workshops, mock interviews and mentoring. For example, employees support primary and secondary schools in the UK through the group's Schools Link volunteering programme, which aims to inspire young people with STEM and business activities.

Matched funding

The BP Foundation administers matched funding through its Employee Matching Fund. Employees across the group can access up to £4,400 of matched funding per year for personal contributions, volunteer time and funds raised in sponsored pledge events. The fund includes a Matching Team Time scheme which encourages team volunteering.

Commercially led support

Sponsorship

In the UK, the group supports arts and culture by sponsoring the activities of major institutions with which it has long-standing relationships. These include the British Museum, the Royal Opera House and the National Portrait Gallery.

The group has also supported Paralympic sports for over 13 years and is a partner of the International Paralympic Committee and several national committees around the world.

Applications

Contact the correspondent for further information.

The BP Foundation in the USA does not accept unsolicited proposals.

Community contributions

Total contributions worldwide	£44,700,000

In 2021, the group's total community spend worldwide was £44.7 million. In the UK, the group invests in STEM projects; however, we were unable to determine the value of this investment during 2021.

In the UK, the group does not make arbitrary charitable donations. However, it matches UK employee contributions to charities through its Employee Matching Fund, which is administered by the US-based BP Foundation. We were unable to determine the exact value of UK matched funding provided by the group in 2021.

All financial figures have been converted from USD to GBP using the exchange rate at the time of writing (November 2022).

BPI (British Recorded Music Industry)

Arts, culture and heritage

Company registration number: 1132389

Correspondent: Corporate Responsibility Team, Level 21, 40 Bank Street, Canary Wharf, London E14 5DS (tel: 020 7803 1300; email: general@bpi.co.uk; website: www.bpi.co.uk/about-bpi)

Directors: Kairon Whitehead; Selina Webb; Geoffrey Taylor; Henry Semmence; Stefania Passamonte; Mhari-Jean Olaore; Fredrick Jude; David Joseph; Jason Iley; Nicholas Hartley; Anthony Harlow; Patricia Hammond; Alice Dyson; Jessica Carsen; Yolanda Brown (female: 43%; male: 57%).

Nature of business: BPI acts as a trade association, representing the producers and sellers of recorded music, including by devising and implementing strategies to protect digital and physical music content.

Financial information

Year end	31/12/2020
Turnover	£16,660,000
Pre-tax profit	(£70,700)

UK employees: 42

Main locations: The company's head office is in London.

Community involvement

Through the staging of the annual BRIT Awards and Classical BRIT Awards shows, BPI contributes substantially to its corporate charity the BRIT Trust (Charity Commission no. 1000413). According to the company website, to date, the BRIT Trust has donated over £20 million to fund charitable, social, environmental and ethical initiatives.

Partnerships
Nordoff Robbins is a charity that uses music therapy to help people struggling with a range of challenges including dementia, learning difficulties, autism, stroke, mental health and depression. BPI's partnership with Nordoff Robbins aims to provide financial support to artists and live music communities in the UK.

Julie's Bicycle is a non-profit organization that aims to make environmental sustainability essential to the business, art and ethics of the creative industries. BPI's partnership with Julie's Bicycle aims to reduce CD packaging emissions by at least 95%.

Applications
For further information see the company's corporate charity entry.

Corporate charity
BRIT Trust (Charity Commission no. 1000413) – see entry on page 230.

Community contributions

Cash donations UK	£1,490,000

According to the company's 2020 annual report, it donated £1.04 million to its corporate charity, the BRIT Trust, £341,000 to Help Musicians, £54,000 to The Musicians Benevolent Fund and £54,000 to Stagehand.

Brewin Dolphin Holdings

Education and training

Company registration number: 2135876

Correspondent: The CSR Team, 12 Smithfield Street, London EC1A 9BD (website: www.brewin.co.uk/corporate-responsibility)

Directors: Robin Beer; Susan Beckett; Siobhan Boylan; Richard Buxton; Charlie Ferry; Nick Fitzgerald; Sarah Houlston (female: 43%; male: 57%).

Nature of business: Brewin Dolphin is a British investment management and financial planning firm.

Financial information

Year end	30/09/2021
Turnover	£404,080,000
Pre-tax profit	£72,530,000

Total employees: 2,000

Main locations: The company has offices across the UK.

Community involvement
Each office has a nominated corporate responsibility ambassador who helps to organise a calendar of activities throughout the year and encourages staff to get involved in a variety of ways including fundraising, sponsorships and volunteering.

Partnerships
The company has charitable partnerships with the School for Social Entrepreneurs, Social Entrepreneurs Ireland, The Brokerage and onHand to try and improve young people's educational attainment and employability.

Small grants programme
Employees are invited to nominate local charities that they are personally involved with for a small grant.

In-kind support
Every employee is offered one day's paid leave per year to volunteer for the charity or organisation of their choice. A total of 225 employees volunteered for local charitable organisations during the year.

Employee-led support
The company has a matched payroll giving scheme and also matches funds raised by employees.

Applications
Contact your local office for more information.

Community contributions

Cash donations UK	£150,700

In 2020/21, the company gave £85,500 in matched payroll giving, £39,700 in matched fundraising and £25,500 in small grants.

Bristol Airport Ltd

The environment, general charitable purposes, health, social welfare

Company registration number: 2078692

Correspondent: Community Fund Administrator, Bristol Airport, Bristol BS48 3DY (tel: 0371 334 4444; email: communityfund@bristolairport.com; website: www.bristolairport.co.uk/about-us/community)

Directors: Daves Lees; Andrew Goodenough; Simon Earles; Andrew Griffiths; Debbie Hartshorn; Graeme Gamble (female: 17%; male: 83%).

Nature of business: Bristol Airport is a commercial airport.

Financial information

Year end	31/12/2020
Turnover	£28,200,000
Pre-tax profit	(£37,800,000)

Total employees: 2,500

Main locations: The airport is located in Lulsgate Bottom in North Somerset and serves Bristol and the surrounding areas.

Community involvement
Bristol Airport makes grants to community groups in the local area most affected by the airport's operations through Bristol Airport Environmental Improvement Fund.

Bristol Airport also has a Charity of the Year programme. In 2022, the airport supported the Teenage Cancer Trust.

Bristol Airport Environmental Improvement Fund
This fund focuses on a number of core local parishes including the villages of Winford, Wrington, Backwell, Brockley, Cleeve and Barrow Gurney. Its main purpose is to mitigate the environmental and social impact of the airport's operations. The following information was taken from the company's website:

> The fund will support projects in the following areas:
> - Initiatives to mitigate the impact of aircraft and ground noise on the local community which may include but not be limited to noise insulation for schools and homes in affected areas, the construction of additional noise insulation barriers and the funding of school trip
> - The on-going improvement of transport infrastructure and services to and from Bristol Airport with an emphasis on reducing the impact of airport traffic in the community and villages surrounding the Airport which may include but not be limited to road improvements, public transport initiatives and measures to reduce community severance; and
> - Nature conservation, educational projects and sustainability initiatives in the locality of the Airport.

Employee-led support
Employees take part in various fundraising activities on behalf of the airport's Charity of the Year.

Applications
Bristol Airport Environmental Improvement Fund
Applicants can apply using the online application form available at: www.bristolairport.co.uk/about-us/community/local-community.

Community contributions

Cash donations UK	£173,000

According to its 2020 annual report, the airport donated £173,000 to the Bristol Airport Local Community Fund.

Brit Ltd

 General charitable purposes

Company registration number: 8821629

Correspondent: Social Committee, The Leadenhall Building, 122 Leadenhall Street, London EC3V 4AB (tel: 020 3857 0000; website: www.britinsurance.com)

Directors: Matthew Wilson; Christiern Dart; Gavin Wilkinson; Jesseman Pryor; Joy Ferneyhough; Lorraine Denny (female: 33%; male: 67%).

Nature of business: Brit provides global specialty insurance and reinsurance.

Financial information

Year end	31/12/2021
Turnover	£1,650,000,000
Pre-tax profit	£1,870,000,000

Total employees: 854

Main locations: Brit's head office is in the City of London.

Community involvement

Brit supports charities chosen by its employees and the communities in which it operates. According to the 'Social and community' section of the annual report for 2021, the group supports causes based on the following three criteria:

> Projects should be for a good cause and operate in an area relevant to us, financial involvement should be for the benefit of the good cause, projects should offer alignment with our strategic priorities

Brit employees select the charities that receive support. The charities benefit from an initial one-off donation and support continues throughout the year in the form of fundraising activities and events.

The ten charities employees chose for 2021 were: Anthony Nolan, Best Buddies International, Coppafeel, Cry in the Dark, Grief Encounter, Haven House, Huntington's Disease Association, Leukemia and Lymphoma Society, Mind and Rukhsana Khan Foundation.

Employee-led support

The company's Social Committee organises a range of community and charitable events for employees, including volunteering days. In 2021, Brit employees completed 19.5 volunteering days.

Employees can support good causes through a payroll giving scheme. Money raised by employees through charitable activities is matched by Brit.

Applications

Only charities chosen by employees are supported.

Community contributions

Cash donations UK	£9,030,000

The financial information has been converted from USD using the exchange rate at the time of writing (July 2022). According to its 2021 annual report, Brit donated £9.03 million ($1.1 million) to charitable organisations.

British Airways plc

 Community services and development, education and training, the environment, health

Company registration number: 1777777

Correspondent: The Sustainability Team, Waterside, PO Box 365, Harmondsworth UB7 0GB (email: community.branch@ba.com; website: www.britishairways.com/en-gb/information/about-ba/ba-better-world/planet)

Directors: Andrew Fleming; Alison Brittain; Sean Doyle; Lynne Embleton; Carolina Martinoli; Rebecca Napier; Alison Reed (female: 71%; male: 29%).

Nature of business: British Airways plc is a UK-based international airline.

Financial information

Year end	31/12/2021
Turnover	£3,693,000,000
Pre-tax profit	(£2,104,000,000)

Main locations: British Airways plc is headquartered in London, with its main hub being Heathrow Airport.

Community involvement

British Airways plc supports charities through matched funding, in-kind donations and its BA Better World Community Fund.

BA Better World Community Fund

The crowdfunding programme provides funding of up to £50,000 (or 50% of the project target) to charitable organisations in the UK. Preference will be given to projects that demonstrate an ability to create positive impact across several categories:

- Environment
- Diversity, inclusion and well-being
- Education and employability
- Thriving communities
- Crisis support
- Employee engagement

Partnerships

British Airways has worked in partnership with Comic Relief since 2010. In 2021, over £1 million was raised for the charity.

British Airways also works with the Disasters Emergency Committee to deliver aid to areas where it is needed.

In-kind support

In 2021, British Airways donated over 633,000 end-of-range products such as blankets, amenity kits and t-shirts to over 80 charities across the UK. These organisations included Surplus to Supper, London and Slough Run, Giving World and the Trussell Trust.

Employee-led support

Employee volunteering

In 2021, 4,500 employees volunteered, including 3,100 for Project Wingman. Employees also volunteered at NHS vaccination centres.

Payroll giving

In 2021, 2,913 employees donated more than £900,000 to 566 charities through British Airways' payroll giving scheme.

Match funding

The group's match funding programme allows employees to request up to £250 for a charity they are supporting. In 2021, 120 applications were successful, with £24,700 being match funded.

Applications

Applications to the BA Better World Community Fund can be made via the fund's website (https://bacommunityfund.co.uk).

Contact the correspondent for all other enquiries.

Community contributions

We were unable to determine a figure for British Airways plc's charitable contributions.

British American Tobacco plc

 The environment

Company registration number: 3407696

Correspondent: The CSR Team, Globe House, 4 Temple Place, London WC2R 2PG (tel: 020 7845 1000; website: www.bat.com/csi)

Directors: Luc Jobin; Sue Farr; Jack Bowles; Tadeu Marroco; Kandy Anand; Karen Guerra; Holly Koeppel; Savio Kwan; Dimitri Panayotopoulos; Darrell Thomas (female: 30%; male: 70%).

Nature of business: The group's principal activities are the manufacture, market and sale of cigarettes and other tobacco products.

Financial information

Year end	31/12/2021
Turnover	£25,680,000,000
Pre-tax profit	£8,670,000,000

Total employees: 52,000

Main locations: The group's headquarters is in London and it has various locations worldwide.

Community involvement

The group's approach toward corporate social investment (CSI) is focused on two key themes. The following information has been taken from the company website:

The **sustainable agriculture and rural communities** theme covers contributions to the social, economic and environmental sustainability of agriculture, farmers' livelihoods and wider environmental issues. It includes activities such as efforts to improve biodiversity and access to water, afforestation, programmes to prevent child labour and tackle rural poverty, grants for agricultural research and training to help farmers grow non-tobacco crops.

This theme directly aligns with SDG 15: **Life on the Land**, as well as with the Productivity area of our Group Strategy, and the Sustainable Agriculture and Farmer Livelihoods area of our Group Sustainability Agenda. This recognises that tobacco leaf is the most essential part of our products, so advancing sustainable agriculture practices, supporting farmer livelihoods and protecting the environment, is a pragmatic, commercial approach to ensuring we have an efficient, responsive, productive and secure agricultural supply chain, ensuring the integrity and quality of our products to satisfy our consumers.

Applications

Contact the correspondent for further information.

Community contributions

Cash donations worldwide	£12,600,000
Total contributions worldwide	£19,000,000

According to its 2021 annual report, the company donated £12.6 million to charitable causes worldwide. In-kind donations totalled £6.4 million.

British Land Company plc

Arts, culture and heritage, community services and development, education and training, employment advice

Company registration number: 621920

Correspondent: Anna Devlet, Head of Community, York House, 45 Seymour Street, London W1H 7LX (email: sustainability@britishland.com; website: www.britishland.com/sustainability)

Directors: Tim Score; Simon Carter; Bhavesh Mistry; Preben Prebensen; Mark Aedy; Lynn Gladden; Irvinder Goodhew; Alastair Hughes; Laura Wade-Gery; Loraine Woodhouse; Brona McKeown (female: 45%; male: 55%).

Nature of business: British Land is a real estate investment trust with a portfolio of office and residential properties in London and retail and leisure properties across the UK.

Financial information

Year end	31/03/2021
Turnover	£468,000,000
Pre-tax profit	£20,400,000

Total employees: 790

Main locations: The company's head office is in London but it operates across the UK.

Community involvement

British Land supports national, regional and local initiatives in the areas around its properties and developments.

Regent's Place is a mixed-use retail, business and residential quarter in London. The Regent's Place Community Fund supports smaller community organisations. The company has donated nearly £200,000 to 30 community projects since this partnership's inception. It also has a partnership with the National Literacy Trust.

In-kind support

The company makes in-kind contributions of equipment and allows community organisations to use spaces owned by British Land. According to its 2021 sustainability report, the company donated more than 3,600 educational materials to disadvantaged families and also supported local food banks.

Employee-led support

Staff are encouraged to engage in the company's skills-based volunteering programme, which trains and matches employees with third-sector organisations that may benefit from their professional skills.

The company also provides matched funding to staff engaging in fundraising up to £500 per person per year. It offers payroll giving to staff wanting to make direct financial contributions to their chosen causes.

According to the company's 2021 sustainability report, British Land staff raised £170,400.

Applications

Contact the correspondent for more information.

Community contributions

Cash donations UK	£1,480,000
Total contributions UK	£1,631,000

The company's 2021 sustainability report states that cash donations totalled £1.48 million. The company also made in-kind donations totalling £53,500 and contributed employee time valued at £102,500.

Britvic Soft Drinks plc

Community services and development, education and training, health, housing and homelessness

Company registration number: 5604923

Correspondent: Sustainable Business Team, Breakspear Park, Breakspear Way, Hemel Hempstead, Hertfordshire HP2 4TZ (tel: 00441217111102; email: givingback@britvic.com; website: www. britvic.com/sustainable-business/ healthier-communities/charity-community)

Directors: Emer Finnan; Susan Clark; John Daly; Christopher Eccleshare; Peter Litherland; Euan Sutherland; Joanne Wilson; Alexandra Thomas (female: 50%; male: 50%).

Nature of business: Britvic supplies branded soft drinks in Great Britain, Ireland and Europe.

Financial information

Year end	30/09/2021
Turnover	£1,405,100,000
Pre-tax profit	£142,900,000

Total employees: 4,113

Main locations: Britvic has various locations throughout the UK and worldwide.

Community involvement

The company is involved in the communities in which it operates.

Britvic Community Fund (not a registered charity)

This fund is one of the means through which the company's charitable giving is channelled. The fund is administered by Essex Community Foundation and focuses on supporting charities and voluntary groups in Essex.

Partnerships

The company's 2021 report states that as part of its three-year partnership with Diabetes UK, Britvic reached its 2019 goal of raising £500,000. In its first year, the company raised over £190,000 in corporate donations and employee fundraising.

Britvic is a gold supporter of GroceryAid in the UK. The charity provides support to those who work in grocery stores. This includes support and guidance on health and well-being, personal issues, benefits, careers, housing and legal issues.

The company's Irish branch, Britvic MiWadi, has continued its support for the Temple Street Foundation for the ninth year. Staff engage in various fundraising activities such as 'Trick or Treat for Temple Street' to help generate funds for life-saving equipment at Temple Street Children's Hospital.

In France, Britvic is partnered with Apprentis d'Auteuil. In 2021, charitable activity was focused on providing face masks and hand sanitiser to family centres.

In-kind support

The company's surplus stock is donated to charities and community organisations.

The company also supports local community events taking place within the immediate vicinity of its offices and manufacturing sites, by supplying drinks donations. In 2021, Britvic supplied Only a Pavement Away, a charity supporting people facing homelessness, with soft drinks for the charity's training cafés.

Employee-led support

Employees are encouraged to engage in charitable activities through volunteering, Give As You Earn and matched funding. Equally, the company encourages employees' volunteering efforts to support local communities by offering three days' paid leave for volunteering each year.

In 2021, employees in Great Britain and Ireland took 256 days to volunteer in local communities. This included activity such as working with The Rivers Trust to improve water flow and biodiversity in the River Aire catchment, as well as volunteering for West Midlands Autism to maintain the grounds of a residential home close to the Britvic Solihull office.

Applications

The company's website states: 'Relevant requests should be sent to givingback@britvic.com and will be considered on a case by case basis.'

Community contributions

We were unable to find a figure for Britvic's total charitable contributions for 2020/21.

N Brown Group plc

🔍 General charitable purposes

Company registration number: 814103

Correspondent: ESG Team, Griffin House, 40 Lever Street, Manchester M60 6ES (tel: 0161 236 8256; email: ethicaltrading@nbrowngroup.co.uk; website: www.nbrown.co.uk/sustainability/our-people)

Directors: Ron Macmillan; Steve Johnson; Rachel Izzard; Lord Alliance of Manchester; Richard Moross; Gill Barr; Michael Ross; Vicky Mitchell; Joshua Alliance; Dominic Platt (female: 30%; male: 70%).

Nature of business: N Brown Group plc provides internet and catalogue shopping, specialising in clothing, footwear, household and electrical goods.

Financial information

Year end	08/07/2022
Turnover	£715,700,000
Pre-tax profit	£19,200,000

Total employees: 1,894

Main locations: The group is headquartered in Manchester.

Community involvement

According to its website, the group's current charity partner is Maggie's, which offers free practical and emotional support to people with cancer and their families and friends.

The group's brands support a wide range of charities that are important to its customers. Recent examples include a campaign with Campaign Against Living Miserably (CALM), where 100% of net profits from the sale of certain Jacamo hoodies were donated to the charity. In 2022, Jacamo renewed its partnership with CALM and launched a new campaign.

The group also supports NHS Charities Together through the donation of profits from clothing ranges and face coverings.

Employee-led support

The group's Make a Difference volunteering programme is designed to encourage staff to support a charity or a local cause.

During 2021, the employee-led partnership with Maggie's reached its fundraising target of £100,000 and the partnership was extended to spring 2022.

Exclusions

No support can be given for political appeals.

Applications

Contact the correspondent for further information.

Community contributions

We were unable to determine a figure for the group's community contributions for 2021/22.

Bruntwood Group Ltd

🔍 Arts, culture and heritage, community services and development, education and training, the environment, health, medical research

Company registration number: 2825044

Correspondent: Communities Team, Union, Albert Square, Manchester M2 6L (tel: 0333 323 2239; email: contact form on the website; website: https://bruntwood.co.uk/sustainability)

Directors: Christopher George Oglesby; Katherine Jane Vokes (female: 50%; male: 50%).

Nature of business: Bruntwood is a family-owned and run property investment, development and management group with over 100 properties in four UK cities and provides workspaces, serviced offices, meeting rooms and retail premises to companies across a range of business sectors.

Financial information

Year end	30/09/2021
Turnover	£122,563,000
Pre-tax profit	£44,862,000

UK employees: 669

Main locations: The group operates in Birmingham, Cheshire, Greater Manchester, Leeds and Liverpool.

Community involvement

The group is committed to having a positive impact on local communities in which it operates. It does this through its grant-making corporate charity, the Oglesby Charitable Trust (Charity Commission no. 1026669).

The group also has a partnership with City of Trees, a programme established by the Oglesby Charitable Trust and the Community Forest Trust, with the aim to create a greener living space in cities by planting more trees.

Employee-led support

Through the Bruntwood Cares scheme, staff are allocated two days each year to volunteer for community projects. In the past, staff have helped school leavers with mock interviews, renovated community health centres as well as making board-level commitments to various organisations.

In 2021, Bruntwood employees gave 1,645 hours of their time through the Bruntwood Cares scheme.

Commercially led support

Sponsorship

A list of organisations that the group sponsors, or has sponsored, can be found on its website.

The group has, for the past decade, provided a platform to showcase creative talent by encouraging writers through The Bruntwood Prize for Playwriting. The prize came about through a long-standing partnership between the group, the Oglesby Charitable Trust and the Royal Exchange Theatre.

Applications

Contact the correspondent or see the group's corporate charity entry for more information.

Corporate charity

Oglesby Charitable Trust (Charity Commission no. 1026669) – see entry on page 264.

Community contributions

Cash donations UK	£3,070,000

The 2021 accounts state that the Bruntwood Group and the Oglesby family shareholders donated 10% of distributable profit to charitable causes. The total contribution for 2021 was £3.07 million.

BT Group plc

Community services and development, education and training, social welfare, sports and recreation

Company registration number: 4190816

Correspondent: Jasmine Whitbread, Chair of BT's Digital Impact and Sustainability Committee, 81 Newgate Street, London EC1A 7AJ (tel: 020 7356 5000; email: contact form on the website; website: www.bt.com/about/digital-impact-and-sustainability)

Directors: Adam Crozier; Adel Al-Saleh; Sir Ian Cheshire; Iain Conn; Isabel Hudson; Phillip Jansen; Matthew Key; Allison Kirkby; Simon Lowth; Sara Weller (female: 30%; male: 70%).

Nature of business: BT provides fixed lines, broadband, mobile and TV products and services and networked IT services.

Financial information

Year end	31/03/2022
Turnover	£20,845,000,000
Pre-tax profit	£2,351,000,000

UK employees: 79,000

Total employees: 98,400

Main locations: The group has offices throughout the UK and across the world.

Community involvement

BT supports communities in the UK and overseas by sharing skills, supporting fundraising and providing in-kind donations of technology. It works with various organisations and schools through its Digital Impact and Sustainability strategy, which includes programmes such as:

- **Skills for Tomorrow:** BT is partnered with some of the UK's leading digital skills organisations to offer free courses and guidance on topics such as staying safe online and digital skills for working lives.
- **Barefoot Computing:** this programme involves training teachers to deliver lessons that teach digital concepts in an easy format, suitable for primary schoolchildren. The programme has now helped over 70,000 teachers and 2 million students.
- **Work Ready:** this programme is designed for young people aged between 18 and 24 to learn practical and tech-related skills, all while gaining valuable work experience at BT. Over 3,000 students have graduated from Work Ready since 2014.

Partnerships

In 2022, BT employees voted for Home-Start UK as the company's UK charity partner.

Over the last few years, the group began a partnership with Do-it.org, to create a new platform – Doit.life. This platform will enable people to connect to charities, schools and other non-profit organisations to find volunteering opportunities.

BT Group partners internationally with British Asian Trust and UNICEF.

In-kind support

BT buildings have been used to organise food collections for UK food banks through the Trussell Trust.

Through the Skills For Tomorrow programme, the BT group has prepared over 180 free courses and resources for people looking to improve their digital literacy, with new webinars available each week.

Employee-led support

BT staff make donations to the charities of their choice through payroll giving. In 2022, colleagues in the UK and overseas raised £2.3 million for 1,368 charities through payroll giving schemes.

Through the Festive Give campaign, employees collected over 30,000 gifts for 9,000 children.

Employee fundraising reached £60,000 for UNICEF's VaccinAid appeal and employees also donated to UNICEF's emergency fund for children in Ukraine.

Employees are entitled to take up to three volunteering days per year. Staff are also widely involved in delivering BT's charitable programmes. In 2022, employees gave over 51,000 hours to support the group's charity partners.

Applications

Contact the correspondent for more information.

Community contributions

| Cash donations UK | £300,000 |

We were unable to determine a figure for the group's community contributions. However, the ESG Addendum to the 2022 BT Group plc manifesto states the company topped up colleague fundraising by £300,000. We have taken this amount as the figure for the group's cash donations.

Bupa Ltd

Health, medical research, mental health and well-being

Company registration number: 3956433

Correspondent: The CSR Team, 1 Angel Court, London EC2R 7HJ (website: www.bupa.com/corporate/what-we-do/crs)

Directors: Gareth Evans; Stephanie Fielding; James Lenton; Martin Potkins (female: 25%; male: 75%).

Nature of business: Bupa is an international healthcare group offering health insurance and medical subscription products. It runs care homes, retirement villages, hospitals, primary care and diagnostic centres and dental clinics. Bupa also provides workplace health services, home healthcare, health assessments and long-term condition management services.

Financial information

Year end	31/12/2021
Turnover	£12,300,000,000
Pre-tax profit	£440,000,000

Total employees: 85,000

Main locations: Bupa has locations throughout the UK; details can be found on its website. Bupa also has a presence in Australia, New Zealand and across Europe and Latin America.

Community involvement

Much of the group's charitable activity in the UK is channelled through its corporate charity, the Bupa UK Foundation (Charity Commission no. 1162759). The foundation supports projects that promote good health, such as those supporting carers, empowering young adults living with ongoing health challenges and projects striving to improve mental heath.

The group also has foundations in Australia (Bupa Health Foundation) and in Spain (Sanitas Foundation), which support health care projects and medical research.

Bupa's associate business in Saudi Arabia provides free healthcare and insurance to orphans living in foster homes across the country.

Global Community Grants Scheme

Bupa Global, the group's international health insurance business, provides grant funding for community projects. In the past, the scheme has funded a shelter for young people experiencing homelessness in the UK and given support to repair flood-damaged housing in Sri Lanka.

Health Communities Fund (not a registered charity)

In 2020, Bupa launched its new Health Communities Fund. According to the group's website, the fund constitutes a 'multi-year commitment to support national flagship programmes which promote mental well-being and resilience'. Any programmes supported by the fund will be delivered in partnership with Bupa's existing foundations in the UK, Australia and Europe.

Partnerships

In the UK, Bupa is partnered with the charity Mind, to support better mental health for young people.

Employee-led support

Bupa provides matched funding to its staff engaging in fundraising activities. Previously, employees have helped take phone calls for Sports Relief donations and hosted a Strictly Come Dancing-inspired fundraiser which raised £15,000 for Make-A-Wish Foundation.

In addition, according to the Bupa Ltd 2021 annual report:

> BGUK's employees are empowered to play an active role in their communities through the Bupa Foundation Community Committees and volunteering. This includes volunteering as wellbeing coaches to schools, mentoring via our Career Ready partnership, and supporting Dentaid to offer free dental care to those in need.

Applications

Contact the correspondent or see the group's corporate charity entry for more information.

Corporate charity

Bupa UK Foundation (Charity Commission no. 1162759) – see entry on page 230.

Community contributions

Total contributions UK	£1,500,000
Total contributions worldwide	£7,700,000

According to Bupa's 2021 annual report, the group donated a total of £1.5 million to charitable causes in the UK.

Bupa's global contributions totalled £7.7 million.

Burberry Group

Education and training, social welfare

Company registration number: 3458224

Correspondent: CSR Team, Horseferry House, Horseferry Road, London SW1P 2AW (tel: 020 7806 1328; email: corporate.responsibility@burberry.com; website: www.burberryplc.com)

Directors: Gerry Murphy; Jonathan Akeroyd; Julie Brown; Orna Nichionna; Fabiola Arredondo; Ron Frasch; Matthew Key; Danuta Gray; Debra Lee; Sam Fischer; Antoine Saint-Affrique; Gemma Parsons (female: 56%; male: 44%).

Nature of business: The company designs, develops, makes and sells products under the Burberry brand. Product design and development are centred in Burberry's London headquarters. Fabrics and other materials are bought from, and finished products manufactured at, company-owned facilities in the UK and through an external supplier network, predominantly located in Europe.

Financial information

Year end	28/03/2021
Turnover	£2,830,000,000
Pre-tax profit	£511,000,000

Total employees: 9,234

Main locations: Burberry is headquartered in London and has various locations throughout the UK and in 34 countries worldwide.

Community involvement

The majority of the company's community involvement is carried out through its corporate charity, The Burberry Foundation (Charity Commission no 1154468). Burberry donates 1% of its group adjusted profits before tax to charitable causes each year. This includes disaster relief, scholarships and long-term community programmes led by The Burberry Foundation.

The company has long-term, strategic NGO partnerships with organisations like Oxfam and London Youth.

Partnerships

Burberry announced a partnership with the international footballer and youth advocate Marcus Rashford in November 2021. According to the company website, this partnership aims to provide:

> support for organisations in the UK committed to helping disadvantaged children develop their literacy skills. Honouring the house's founder Thomas Burberry's legacy of using creativity to open spaces, Burberry will provide funding to transform school libraries and donate books, ensuring children have access to safe environments and resources to develop their potential. Burberry will also support organisations in the United States and Asia to create new libraries and provide books to underserved communities.

Other partnerships include:

Oxfam – over the past five years, the group and Oxfam have collaborated on programmes that help foster social inclusion and community cohesion among local communities.

London Youth – Burberry began its partnership with London Youth in 2020. Burberry supports this charity by providing a donation to help fund programmes for young women and girls. According to the London Youth website, Burberry awarded funding to 15 youth clubs in 2021.

In-kind support

Burberry donates non-trademark fabric and materials to assist young people enrolled in creative courses. As well as this, it donates smart business clothing to support vulnerable people who are enrolled in employability programmes and preparing for interviews.

In 2020/21, the company donated 3,000 items to selected charities to enhance their employability programmes and help their clients to improve their confidence as they prepare to re-enter the job market. The company donated 20,000 blankets to its supply chain partners in Italy, 8,000 books to Marcus Rashford's Book Club and 500 books to youth centres in Hong Kong.

Employee-led support

Employees worldwide are encouraged to get involved in their local communities and are entitled to three days' paid volunteering leave per year. Volunteering activities include career inspiration events, employability workshops, long-term mentoring, programmes and charity events. In 2020/21, Burberry employees participated in volunteering and fundraising activities and collectively contributed almost 7,000 hours to charitable causes.

Applications

Contact the correspondent or see the company's corporate charity entry for more information.

Corporate charity

The Burberry Foundation (Charity Commission no. 1154468) – see entry on page 231.

Community contributions

Cash donations worldwide	£5,110,000

Burberry continues to donate 1% of group adjusted profit before tax to charitable causes. We have therefore taken the figure of £5.11 million as the company's overall worldwide charitable contribution.

Business Design Centre Group Ltd

Education and training, social welfare

Company registration number: 532103

Correspondent: CSR Team, Business Design Centre, 52 Upper Street, Islington Green, London N1 0QH (tel: 020 7288 6475; email: info@bdc. london; website: www. businessdesigncentre.co.uk)

Directors: Dominic Jones; Andrew Morris; Gerald Morris; Jack Morris; Paul Morris; Philip Morris; Joseph Mullee (male: 100%).

Nature of business: The Business Design Centre (BDC) is a conference and exhibition venue.

Financial information

Year end	31/03/2021
Turnover	£1,940,000
Pre-tax profit	£244,200

UK employees: 10

Main locations: The BDC is in Islington.

Community involvement

The company's community involvement is focused on improving the community around its venue in Islington. It does this through a combination of fundraising, volunteering, mentoring and donations. Financial support is also available from its corporate charity, The Morris Charitable Trust (Charity Commission no. 802290).

Partnerships

Islington Giving – this partnership aims to alleviate the effects of poverty in the borough.

The Brain Tumour Charity – through this partnership, the company funds pioneering research into brain tumours, to find new treatments, improve understanding and increase survival rates.

London Village Network – through this partnership, the company allows London Village Network to use its workspace as a base.

In-kind support

The company offers seminars and one-to-one mentoring for local sixth-form students over the course of a year, helping them with employability and social skills. Space in the venue is also offered to the London Village Network, a grassroots charity aiming to create a platform for young people of all backgrounds to access careers advice based on their interests.

The company's 'Donate Not Waste' scheme allows event organisers to arrange for their waste, such as card, stationery, novelty goods, fabrics and so on, to be collected and donated to charities, schools and play centres.

Employee-led support

Employees are encouraged to take part in fundraising and volunteering activities.

Applications

Contact the correspondent or see the company's corporate charity entry for more information.

Corporate charity

The Morris Charitable Trust (Charity Commission no. 802290) – see entry on page 259.

Community contributions

Total contributions UK	£294,600

The 2020/21 accounts state that the total value of voluntary and charitable support offered by the company through cash and in-kind donations amounted to £294,600 (£94,500 in in-kind donations).

Cadbury

Community enterprise and social entrepreneurship, community services and development, education and training, social welfare

Company registration number: 52457

Correspondent: Kelly Farrell, Community Affairs Manager Northern Europe, Cadbury House, Sanderson Road, Uxbridge, Middlesex, West Midlands UB8 1DH (tel: 0121 458 2000; website: www.cadbury.co.uk/cadbury-foundation)

Directors: Adrian Arrighi; Michael Foye; Thomas Gingell; Darren Redhead; Jason Vickery; Hannah O'Brien; Sunil Sehgal (female: 14%; male: 86%).

Nature of business: Cadbury is one of the largest confectionery brands in the world. In 2010, it was acquired by US-based Kraft Foods Inc., which was later restructured into two companies: the 'spin-off' company became Kraft Foods Group Inc., specialising in grocery products, and the remaining company was renamed Mondelez International Inc., focusing on confectionery and snacks. Cadbury is now owned by Mondelez International. Given Cadbury's historical and recognisable links to philanthropy, we have made the decision to name this record using the brand name 'Cadbury', rather than the name of the Mondelez holding company whose annual report and accounts declared charitable donations for 2020. See 'Community involvement' for more information.

Financial information

Year end	31/12/2020
Turnover	£35,000,000
Pre-tax profit	£31,000,000

UK employees: 5,000

Main locations: Cadbury's head office is in Uxbridge. Mondelez International also has sites in Birmingham, Wrexham, Devon, Herefordshire, Berkshire, Sheffield and the Republic of Ireland.

Community involvement

Cadbury carries out its philanthropic activities through its corporate charity, The Cadbury Foundation (Charity Commission no. 1050482). The foundation is funded by cash donations from Mondelez UK Holdings and Services Ltd (formerly named Cadbury Holdings Ltd).

Employee-led support

Cadbury employees are encouraged to volunteer their time and skills, as well as take part in fundraising activities for the local community. Support is also given to causes close to employees' hearts

through the company's 'cashmatch' scheme.

Applications

See the company's corporate charity entry for more information.

Corporate charity

The Cadbury Foundation (Charity Commission no. 1050482) – see entry on page 231.

Community contributions

Cash donations UK	£603,500

The 2020 annual report for Mondelez UK Holdings and Services Ltd states that the company donated £603,500 to the Cadbury Foundation during the year. We have taken this figure as the charitable contribution for Cadbury.

Cadent Gas Ltd

Community services and development, the environment, housing and homelessness, social welfare

Company registration number: 10080864

Correspondent: CSR Team, Pilot Way, Ansty Park, Coventry CV7 9JU (email: enquiries@cadentfoundation.com; website: https://cadentgas.com/about-us/responsibility/corporate-social-responsibility)

Directors: Abdulla Al-Ansari; Catherine Bell; Mark Braithwaite; Simon Fennell; Eduard Fidler; Steven Fraser; Richard Greenleaf; Deven Karnik; Jaroslava Korpancova; Mark Mathieson; Sir Adrian Montague; Perry Noble; Hua Su; David Xie; Anthony Bickerstaff; Neil Corrigall; Howard Forster; Andrew Marsden; Paul Smith; Minzhen Wang; Desmond Wilkins (female: 14%; male: 86%).

Nature of business: Gas distribution.

Financial information

Year end	31/03/2022
Turnover	£1,984,000,000
Pre-tax profit	£368,999,998

UK employees: 4,000

Main locations: Cadent Gas is headquartered in Coventry and has an operations centre in Leicester. It also has training centres in Manchester, Birmingham and Hitchin.

Community involvement

Cadent Gas Ltd provides support through charity partnerships, matched giving, volunteering and via its corporate charity, the Cadent Foundation (Charity Commission no. 327489).

Partnerships

In 2022 the company launched a partnership with Emmaus, a charity working to end homelessness.

Employee-led support

Volunteering

Employees are given two days' paid leave per year to volunteer in their local communities. The company partnered with Neighbourly to create an online, interactive platform that provides an accessible and inclusive range of volunteering opportunities.

Matched giving

Employees can claim up to £400 per year in matched funding for any UK-registered charity.

High Five Award

The High Five Award enables employees to be recognised for their work. As part of the award, a financial donation can be made at the employee's request to the company's charity partner.

Applications

See the company's corporate charity entry for more information.

Corporate charity

Cadent Foundation (Charity Commission no. 327489) – see entry on page 232.

Community contributions

Cash donations UK	£134,000

According to its 2021/22 annual report, the company made charitable donations totalling £134,000.

Cadogan Group Ltd

Education and training, general charitable purposes, health, housing and homelessness, religion

Company registration number: 2997357

Correspondent: CSR Team, 10 Duke of York Square, London SW3 4LY (tel: 020 7730 4567; email: info@cadogan.co.uk; website: www.cadogan.co.uk)

Directors: The Hon. James Bruce; Viscount Chelsea Edward Cadogan; Charles Ellingworth; John Gordon; Harry Morley; Sanjay Patel; Francis Salway; Hugh Seaborn; Dame Alison Nimmo (female: 11%; male: 89%).

Nature of business: Cadogan Group Ltd is the holding company for the UK property investment business of the family of Earl Cadogan. The company is ultimately owned by several charitable and family trusts.

Financial information

Year end	31/12/2021
Turnover	£168,920,000
Pre-tax profit	£113,840,000

UK employees: 91

Main locations: The group is responsible for the stewardship of the Royal Borough of Chelsea and its charitable work is for the benefit of this area.

Community involvement

Cadogan provides support to local charities, community projects and educational and religious organisations as well as hosting a programme of community events.

The group hosts an annual sleepout to raise funds for Glass Door, a local homelessness charity. Previously, Cadogan partnered with LandAid, a charity working to end youth homelessness.

Cadogan also has a partnership with and is the principal funder of The Kensington and Chelsea Foundation (Charity Commission no. 1125940). The foundation aims to help local charities operating at grassroots level. Support is also given through The Cadogan Charity (Charity Commission no. 247773).

Pathways to Property

The group supports the Pathways to Property initiative, which is run by Reading Real Estate Foundation (Charity Commission no. 1092627). The initiative works with young people in schools and colleges to show them what a career in property would be like, as well as providing work experience.

In-kind support

The group's land and buildings around Chelsea may be made available for charitable and community purposes. This has included churches, schools and social housing. Each year, £1.1 million is committed as rental subsidies for affordable, community and key worker housing.

Employee-led support

Cadogan's employees volunteer and fundraise for local charities.

Applications

Contact the correspondent or see the group's corporate charity entry for more information.

Corporate charity

The Cadogan Charity (Charity Commission no. 247773) – see entry on page 232.

Community contributions

Cash donations UK	£273,000
Total contributions UK	£291,500

Cadogan's 2021 annual report states that the group's direct and indirect social contributions totalled £291,500. Direct charitable contributions totalled £273,000; we have taken this as the figure for UK cash donations.

Calor Gas Ltd

Community services and development

Company registration number: 303703

Correspondent: CSR Team, Athena House, Athena Drive, Tachbrook Park, Warwick, Warwickshire CV34 6RL (email: Responsible.business@calor.co.uk; website: www.calor.co.uk/about-us/responsible-business)

Directors: Nia Fortune; Paul Instrell; Shaun MacDonald; Thomas Dillon; Rogerio Lopes (female: 20%; male: 80%).

Nature of business: The principal activity of the company is the processing, marketing and distribution of liquefied petroleum gas in the UK.

Financial information

Year end	31/12/2021
Turnover	£471,800,000
Pre-tax profit	£71,800,000

Main locations: The company has various sites throughout the UK.

Community involvement

Calor carries out its community involvement through a combination of donations, volunteering, fundraising and partnerships.

Calor Rural Community Fund (not a registered charity)

The company established the Rural Community Fund to help communities off the gas grid to raise money for local projects, such as an outdoor gym or village hall repairs. Three levels of funding are available – £1,000, £2,500 and £5,000 – depending on the size of the project. The amount of funding applied for must equate to 50% or more of the total project cost. Projects must be connected with a community organisation or charity and benefit the wider community. Visit https://communityfund.calor.co.uk for more information.

Partnerships and Charity of the Year

The company's charity partners are chosen by its employees. Recently, it has partnered with the mental health charity Mind and its Scottish counterpart, SAMH.

Helping Hands Community Project

The company has worked with the charity for a number of years. The charity supports local people in need. In 2021, the company provided the charity with a donation of £10,000 to enable it to create a multi-purpose space to help women who have been victims of domestic violence.

Employee-led support
Employee volunteering
The Start From the Heart programme enables employees to spend one paid day a year volunteering in their community.

Exclusions
Community grants are not available for projects or organisations that are political or discriminatory, or that do not meet the 'off-grid' requirement. Individuals are not supported.

Applications
Contact the correspondent for more information. For the Rural Community Fund, visit https://communityfund.calor.co.uk to find further eligibility details and submission opening dates.

Community contributions
The annual report and accounts for 2021 did not provide a figure for charitable contributions. The company's website states that each year £50,000 is donated to a variety of projects across the UK through the Calor Rural Community Fund.

The Cambridge Building Society

General charitable purposes

Company registration number: 157223

Correspondent: The Marketing Team, PO Box 232, 51 Newmarket Road, Cambridge CB5 8FF (tel: 0345 601 3344; email: marketing@cambridgebs.co.uk; website: www.cambridgebs.co.uk)

Directors: Jonathan Spence; Stephen Jack; Peter Burrows; Pauline Holroyd; Fiona Hotston Moore; Andrew Jones; Andrew Morley; Victoria Stubbs; Richard Brockbank; Carole Charter; Dr Andrew Rice (female: 36%; male: 64%).

Nature of business: The Cambridge Building Society is a UK mutual building society.

Financial information
Year end	31/12/2021
Turnover	£27,000,000
Pre-tax profit	£11,830,000

UK employees: 225

Main locations: The society has 13 branches across Cambridgeshire, Suffolk and Hertfordshire. Its headquarters is in Cambridge.

Community involvement
The society supports a wide range of charities and community groups working in the Cambridge area. Support is provided through cash donations, partnerships and employee volunteering and fundraising.

Community Partnership programme
Through its Community Partnership programme, the society works closely with four charities throughout the year (each for a three-month period). According to the society's website, participating charities each receive:
- 'Hands on help' from Society employees
- A cash donation
- Promotion via the society's social media channels
- Fundraising opportunities
- Access to the society's locations for promotional purposes.
- Access to Team leaders from the Society to help build successful partnership

Applications are accepted from charities that operate within a 30-mile radius of Cambridge or national charities that can guarantee the funds will benefit the area.

According to the society's website, charities that are not selected for partnership will be considered for other aspects of the community programme, including a donations initiative.

Community donations scheme
The society makes monthly cash donations to charities voted for by its members in branches and online.

In 2021, the society supported the following charities: Cambridge Re-Use, Maggie's, East Anglian Air Ambulance, Winter Comfort and YMCA Trinity Group.

Employee-led support
Employees are encouraged to participate in fundraising and volunteering activities in support of charities participating in the Community Partnership programme. According to the society's 2021 impact report, 1,035 volunteering hours were donated by employees to charitable causes in the local area.

Commercially led support
The society regularly sponsors local community events. It has an ongoing partnership with the Perse School and sponsors its Community Lecture Series. The series is part of the school's far-reaching community programme, bringing speakers to share their expertise with a local audience.

In 2021, the society continued to sponsor 'Bridge The Gap', a fundraising walk through the colleges and historic buildings of Cambridge that takes place every September. The event raised £15,000 for Arthur Rank Hospice Charity and Romsey Mill.

Applications
Contact the correspondent for more information. Invitations for applications to the Community Partnership programme are usually announced on the society's website.

Community contributions
Cash donations UK	£206,200

According to its 2021 impact report, the society provided charitable donations of £206,200 during the year.

Capita plc

Education and training

Company registration number: 2081330

Correspondent: The CSR Team, 30 Berners Street, Westminster, London W1T 3LR (tel: 020 7799 1525; website: www.capita.com/responsible-business)

Directors: Clare Denton; Dr Nneka Abulokwe; John Cresswell; Neelam Dhawan; Janine Goodchild; Georgina Harvey; Dr Jonathan Lewis; David Lowden; Brian McArthur-Muscroft; Timothy Weller (female: 50%; male: 50%).

Nature of business: The group provides a range of white-collar integrated professional support services to clients in local and central government, education and the private sector. Services include: administrative services, consultancy, IT and software services and human resource provision.

Financial information
Year end	31/12/2021
Turnover	£3,182,500,000
Pre-tax profit	£285,600,000

Main locations: The group's head office is in London and it has various locations worldwide.

Community involvement
Capita's charitable activities focus on equipping young people with skills for the workplace and enabling better digital access in the communities it serves.

Youth skills and jobs
Capita partners with schools, colleges and charities to improve young people's employability and entrepreneurial skills.

For example, it has developed online workshops which will be delivered in schools to help young people prepare for the world of work.

Digital inclusion
Capita seeks to facilitate digital inclusion in the areas in which it operates. For example, during the COVID-19 pandemic, the company partnered with Google and Microsoft to support the Department for Education's Platform Provisioning Programme to fund and deploy digital learning platforms to every school that needed them. During the pandemic the company also partnered with Business2Schools and its corporate charity partner, Teach First, to donate laptops and IT equipment to schools to

support children to continue their learning while at home.

Partnerships

Capita's 2020 charity partners were Teach First and Young Enterprise, which were supported through corporate donations and employee fundraising. According to the 2020 Responsible Business report;

> Our donation to Teach First funded the recruitment and training of 25 teachers in 2020, who will in turn teach 3,000 students, while our donation to Young Enterprise has supported 2,500 young people.

Employee-led support

Employee volunteering

Employees are encouraged to provide pro bono work and volunteer in their local communities.

Employee fundraising

Employees can apply for matched funding from the group. In 2020, matched funding totalled £83,100. Employees also donate through the group's payroll giving scheme. In 2020, employees donated £250,400 in this way.

Applications

Contact the correspondent for further information.

Community contributions

Cash donations worldwide	£1,498,200
Total contributions worldwide	£1,720,000

Capita's 2020 Responsible Business Report was the latest available at the time of writing. It notes that Capita's community investment totalled £2.05 million during the year. This includes charitable spending (£1.5 million), in-kind gifts (£105,000) and the value of volunteering hours (£116,800). A further £83,100 was donated to charity in the form of employee-raised funds (including matched funding from Capita) and payroll giving totalling £250,400.

Capital One (Europe) plc

Education and training, money and debt advice

Company registration number: 3879023

Correspondent: The CSR Team, Trent House, Station Street, Nottingham, Nottinghamshire NG2 3HX (website: www.capitalone.co.uk/aboutus/corporate-social-responsibility.jsf)

Directors: James Aron; Lucy Hagues; Robert Harding; Kathryn Kasper; Rupert MacInnes (female: 33%; male: 67%).

Nature of business: Capital One provides a range of financial services, primarily credit card lending.

Financial information

Year end	31/12/2021
Turnover	£465,342,000
Pre-tax profit	£159,733,000

Main locations: Capital One has offices in London and Nottingham.

Community involvement

The majority of the company's CSR activity is focused on supporting social mobility, financial education and digital inclusion in the UK. This is achieved through partnerships with national charitable organisations, such as The Sutton Trust, Rethink Mental Illness and Business in the Community.

Financial and digital literacy

The company aims to help communities understand the world of credit. Its CSR work in this area aims to ensure that communities are equipped with financial knowledge and skills.

Employability

The company works alongside primary and secondary schools, as well as colleges and universities, to deliver mentoring programmes that inspire and encourage students to think about work.

Applications

Contact the correspondent for further information.

Community contributions

Cash donations UK	£600,000

According to its 2021 accounts, Capital One made charitable contributions of £600,000.

Capricorn Energy plc

Arts, culture and heritage, community services and development, education and training, health

Company registration number: SC226712

Correspondent: Louise Henderson, Charities Committee, 50 Lothian Road, Edinburgh EH3 9BY (tel: 0131 475 3000; email: louise.henderson@capricornenergy.com; website: www.capricornenergy.com/working-responsibly/charitable-giving)

Directors: Erik Daugbjerg; Nicoletta Giadrossi; Peter Kallos; Catherine Krajicek; Keith Lough; James Smith; Simon Thomson; Alison Wood; Luis Araujo (female: 33%; male: 67%).

Nature of business: Capricorn Energy plc is an independent oil and gas exploration and development company.

Financial information

Year end	31/12/2021
Turnover	£49,730,000
Pre-tax profit	£760,930,000

UK employees: 178

Total employees: 186

Main locations: Capricorn Energy plc has its headquarters in Edinburgh. It also has operational offices in London, Mexico, Mauritania and Egypt.

Community involvement

Capricorn Energy plc provides support to local communities.

Charitable giving programme

The group's annual charitable giving programme supports a range of areas including young people, communities, health, the environment, arts and culture, and education and learning. The group's website notes the following guidelines:

- We consider applications from registered charities only.
- Our support is primarily limited to charities operating in Edinburgh and Lothians.
- Previous applicants are welcome to reapply, regardless of whether they were successful or not in previous rounds.
- We do not provide details of average funding and minimum/maximum donations.
- We cannot provide any specific feedback if an application is unsuccessful.
- We are unable to provide any information in addition to what is available on this webpage regarding our donations and charitable giving process.
- We often make partial donations.
- We will consider multi-year support.

Commercially led support

The group sponsors local events that promote STEM subjects.

Exclusions

The group's website states that it will not fund the following:

- charities with religious or political affiliations;
- political parties;
- places of worship;
- labour unions;
- organisations where there is a potential conflict of interest;
- organisations that discriminate; or
- individual sponsorship.

Applications

Application forms can be downloaded from the website and should be submitted via email to the correspondent. Check the group's website for current application deadlines. All applications will be considered by the Charities Committee at its next meeting.

Community contributions

Cash donations UK	£328,300

According to Capricorn Energy's 2021 Sustainability Data Appendix, the group's charitable giving in the UK totalled £328,300. The following breakdown was provided:

Education and innovation	£200,200
Community health	£71,800
Community protection and climate adaption	£28,500
Community development and environmental benefit	£27,800

Note: the group's financial information (other than the grant totals) was converted from USD using the exchange rate at the time of writing (September 2022).

Card Factory plc

Community services and development, general charitable purposes

Company registration number: 9002747

Correspondent: The CSR Team, Century House, Brunel Road, 41 Industrial Estate, Wakefield, West Yorkshire WF2 0XG (website: www. cardfactoryinvestors.com/foundation)

Directors: Nathan Lane; Ciaran Stone; Kristian Lee; Robert McWilliam; Paul Moody; Octavia Morley; Roger Whiteside; Darcy Willson-Rymer (female: 13%; male: 88%).

Nature of business: Card Factory plc is a greeting card and gift retailer.

Financial information

Year end	31/01/2022
Turnover	£364,400,000
Pre-tax profit	£11,100,000

Main locations: The company has stores throughout the UK.

Community involvement

The company supports charities through its corporate charity, the Card Factory Foundation (Charity Commission no. 1180081), partnerships and cause-related marketing.

Partnerships

Card Factory has had a partnership with Macmillan Cancer Support since 2006. In 2021/22 over £399,700 was raised through employee and customer fundraising and card sales.

Commercially led support

The group supports Alzheimer's Society, Make-A-Wish Ireland, Macmillan Cancer Support, Mind and the Teenage Cancer Trust through the sale of charity Christmas cards.

Applications

Contact the correspondent for further information.

Corporate charity

Card Factory Foundation (Charity Commission no. 1180081) – see entry on page 233.

Community contributions

We were unable to determine a figure for the company's charitable contributions.

CareTech Holdings plc

Health, mental health and well-being

Company registration number: 4457287

Correspondent: The CSR Team, 5th Floor, Metropolitan House, 3 Darkes Lane, Potters Bar, Hertfordshire EN6 1AG (tel: 01707 601800; email: info@caretech-uk.com; website: www. caretech-uk.com)

Directors: Christopher Dickinson; Michael Adams; James Cumming; Christopher Dickinson; Dr Moira Livingston; Farouq Sheikh; Haroon Sheikh; Adrian Stone (female: 13%; male: 88%).

Nature of business: The group delivers care across the whole social care spectrum for children and adults below retirement age.

Financial information

Year end	30/09/2021
Turnover	£489,100,000
Pre-tax profit	£68,300,000

Main locations: CareTech's head office is in Hertfordshire and the group has operations across the country.

Community involvement

The group's charitable giving is predominantly channelled through its corporate charity, CareTech Foundation (Charity Commission no. 1182567).

Employee-led support

Through its foundation, the group provides matched funding for staff engaging in various fundraising efforts.

Also through the foundation, staff can apply for funding under the Community Grants programme to support causes in their communities.

Applications

See the group's corporate charity entry for more information.

Corporate charity

CareTech Charitable Foundation (Charity Commission no. 1182567) – see entry on page 233.

Community contributions

Cash donations UK	£1,200,000

According to its 2020/21 annual accounts, the group donated £1.2 million to its corporate charity.

Cargill plc

Climate change, the environment, health, nutrition and diet

Company registration number: 1387437

Correspondent: Cargill Cares Council, Velocity V1, Brooklands Drive, Weybridge, Surrey KT13 0SL (tel: 01932 861000; website: www.cargill.co.uk)

Directors: Dena Lo'bue; Jonathon Kingston; Samina Kosar; Melanie Pollard; James Timewell; Federico Urquidi Negron (female: 50%; male: 50%).

Nature of business: The group trades commodities and processes and distributes foodstuffs.

Financial information

Year end	31/05/2021
Turnover	£1,136,400,000
Pre-tax profit	£26,000,000

Main locations: In the UK, the group has operations in Bathgate, London, Dalton, Manchester, Farnborough, Weybridge, Hereford, Witham St Hughes, Hull, Wolverhampton, Lichfield, Worcester, Liverpool, Worksop and York.

Community involvement

Cargill's community engagement programme supports local communities through economic development, partnerships and donations combined with the volunteer efforts of its employees. Support is given to select national and global non-profit organisations and NGOs that serve communities in the areas the group operates. Cargill has three focus areas around food security, nutrition and sustainability.

Cargill Cares Councils

Cargill businesses and employees give through employee-led Cargill Cares Councils. The councils provide support for local charitable and civic organisations and programmes such as food relief agencies, schools and youth programmes, and local environmental projects.

Partnerships

The group works with a range of different partners worldwide to deliver its corporate responsibility programmes.

In the UK Cargill has been working in partnership with the charity FareShare since 2009.

Employee-led support

Employees volunteer with activities to support projects local to the area they work in.

Applications

The following information was taken from the Cargill website:

> If your program or project is in a Cargill community contact the Cargill manager or Cargill Cares Council. They are typically responsible for reviewing local grant requests and making funding decisions.

For corporate giving, Cargill's grant application is an invite-only process.

Community contributions

Cash donations UK	£203,600

The group's 2020/21 accounts state that charitable contributions during the year totalled £203,600.

Carr's Group plc

Community enterprise and social entrepreneurship, community services and development, education and training, social welfare

Company registration number: 98221

Correspondent: Ellen Clements, Fund Manager, Old Croft, Stanwix, Carlisle CA3 9BA (tel: 01900 825760; email: ellen@cumbriafoundation.org; website: www.carrsgroup.com)

Directors: Matthew Ratcliffe; Neil Austin; Shelagh Hancock; Stuart Lorimer; Peter Page; Ian Wood; John Worby (female: 14%; male: 86%).

Nature of business: Carr's Group has two divisions: agriculture and engineering

Financial information

Year end	29/08/2021
Turnover	£4,173,000,000
Pre-tax profit	£12,100,000

UK employees: 1,153

Main locations: Carr's head office is in Carlisle.

Community involvement

The group provides support through its fund with Cumbria Community Foundation for rural communities, young people and people who are disadvantaged. It also supports other charitable activities through partnerships and employee engagement.

Carr's Group Fund

During 2015, the group established a grant-making fund with Cumbria Community Foundation. According to the website, the fund was created to invest in the well-being and future of Cumbria's communities.

The following organisations are eligible:

- Charitable groups that support residents throughout Cumbria
- Groups supporting rural communities
- Groups focusing on the needs of disadvantaged people
- Groups that raise the aspirations of young people and people wanting to develop their skills

Grants range from £500 to £1,000 and are awarded on a one-off basis. The fund made £10,000 available in its first year of grant-making.

Partnerships

In 2021, the group continued its partnership with the Yorkshire Dales Millennium Trust to help create a legacy for agriculture in the Yorkshire Dales and surrounding areas. The programme provides support for people, innovation and the environment by delivering sustainable farm improvements.

The group has a partnership with WellChild, a charity that supports seriously ill children in the UK. In 2021, the group raised £45,000 for WellChild through various initiatives including the sale of purple bale wrap.

Employee-led support

The group's 2020/21 annual report states that employees engage in the group's community activities through volunteering, mentoring and fundraising.

Commercially led support

Carr's continues to be part of Zeus Packaging Group's global initiative to support children's charities in Ireland, the UK, Spain, Portugal, New Zealand and Australia. Carr's support goes to WellChild.

Exclusions

The Carr's Group Fund will not provide grants for: the purchase of computers, photocopiers or vehicles, individuals, political purposes, or the promotion of religion.

Applications

Carr's Group

Apply in writing to the correspondent.

Carr's Group Fund

Applications for the fund can be made using the form on Cumbria Community Foundation's website, where deadlines and guidelines are also provided.

Enquiries should be directed to Ellen Clements on 01900 825760 or ellen@cumbriafoundation.org.

Community contributions

Cash donations UK	£52,000

In 2020/21, Carr's Group plc donated £52,000 to charitable causes.

CEMEX UK Operations Ltd

Community services and development, the environment

Company registration number: 658390

Correspondent: CSR Team, CEMEX House, Evreux Way, Rugby, Warwickshire CV21 2DT (tel: 01788 517000; website: www.cemex.co.uk/cemexfoundation.aspx)

Directors: Emma Ashenden; Philip Baynes-Clarke; David Beck; Laurence Dagley; David Hart; Stephanie Horn; Michael Lynn; Carl Platt; Vishal Puri; Lex Russell; Craig Williamson (female: 18%; male: 82%).

Nature of business: CEMEX is a global building materials company with a presence in more than 50 countries. CEMEX UK Operations Ltd is the principal CEMEX trading company in the UK.

Financial information

Year end	31/12/2020
Turnover	£649,098,000
Pre-tax profit	(£20,588,000)

Main locations: CEMEX UK has sites throughout the UK. A searchable list can be found at: www.cemexcommunities.co.uk

Community involvement

The company channels its charitable contributions through the CEMEX UK Foundation (not a registered charity). It was created to provide a single point of focus for the company's charitable donations, community support and employee engagement activities. Both in-kind and financial support is available. The foundation will consider supporting small community and environmental projects within a three-mile radius of a CEMEX site.

Rugby Group Benevolent Fund (Charity Commission no. 265669)

This fund was established in 1955 with the aim of supporting employees and former employees of Rugby Group Ltd and their dependants. The Rugby Group is now a part of CEMEX UK but the fund has kept its independence and is managed by a group of employees and former employees.

Partnerships

The company foundation works with Groundwork UK to improve communities where the company operates. CEMEX UK has also had a partnership with the RSPB since 2009.

Matched funding

The company foundation matches CEMEX employees' fundraising efforts up to £200 maximum per year.

Employee-led support

In the UK, employees from local CEMEX sites volunteer through the Lend-A-Hand initiative to help carry out practical projects for local charities, schools, youth and other community centres.

Applications

CEMEX UK Foundation

At the time of writing (August 2022) the company was not accepting applications. There is a contact form for CEMEX communities on the company's website.

Corporate charity

The Rugby Group Benevolent Fund Ltd (Charity Commission no. 265669) – see entry on page 270.

Community contributions

Cash donations UK	£72,900

In 2020 CEMEX UK donated £72,900 to charitable organisations.

Central England Co-operative

Arts, culture and heritage, community services and development, education and training, emergency response/relief, the environment, general charitable purposes, health, religion, sports and recreation

Company registration number: IP10143R

Correspondent: Community Dividend Selection Committee, Central House, Hermes Road, Lichfield, Staffordshire WS13 6RH (tel: 01543 414140; email: enquiries@centralengland.coop; website: https://communities.centralengland.coop)

Directors: Jane Avery; Dave Ellgood; Jody Meakin; Bradley Tuckfield; Danny Douglas; Suzanne Bennett; Mark Grayling; Marc Bicknell; John Chillcott; John Howells; Maria Lee; Tanya Noon; Sue Rushton (female: 46%; male: 54%).

Nature of business: Central England Co-operative's principal business activities are retail food stores (responsible for around 70% of total turnover), petrol filling stations, funeral services and property investment. The society also has trading interests in travel shops, coffin manufacture and optical services. Central England Co-operative is independent from The Co-operative Group but is part of the wider co-operative movement.

Financial information

Year end	25/01/2022
Turnover	£847,400,000
Pre-tax profit	£13,420,000

UK employees: 4,668

Main locations: The geographical area where support is given can be broken down into three regions: western (the West Midlands, Staffordshire, Warwickshire and Worcestershire), central (Leicestershire, Derbyshire, Nottinghamshire, South Yorkshire and West Yorkshire) and eastern (East and South Leicestershire, Lincolnshire, Northamptonshire, Cambridgeshire, Norfolk and Suffolk).

Community involvement

Central England Co-operative (the society) invests in communities where it has a trading presence, redistributing 1% of its trading profit each year. The society supports local charities and community causes through financial support, volunteering and partnerships.

Community Dividend Fund (not a registered charity)

Through the fund, the society makes charitable donations of between £100 and £5,000 to a wide range of local community groups in its trading area. The fund guarantees that at least 1% of the society's trading profit is reinvested in local communities in a bid to help projects to thrive across its trading area of 16 counties from the Midlands to the east coast. Grants are awarded every three months. Examples of projects recently supported are given on the website. The Community Dividend Fund was temporarily paused during the COVID-19 pandemic to help support causes affected but was reintroduced in 2022. During the pandemic, the fund awarded £175,000 to 116 causes.

Partnerships

As well as making charitable donations to local community groups, the society also holds events to help raise money for its colleague-nominated corporate charity partner. The society's current partner is Dementia UK, which it has supported from 2017. We were unable to find a figure for total contributions to the charity for 2022, although the annual reports state that donations have surpassed £1.7 million since the beginning of the partnership.

In-kind support

The society donates items of unsold food to FareShare East Midlands for redistribution to local charities.

In 2022, the society allocated storage space for Newlife, a charity that supports children with disabilities in the UK.

Employee-led support

Employees nominate and fundraise for the society's corporate charity partners as well as volunteering for local organisations.

Exclusions

The website states that support cannot be given for:
- Vehicles
- Large-scale projects
- Core costs
- Individuals

Applications

Applications for grants should preferably be made online, where further information on eligibility criteria and application deadlines can be found.

Community contributions

Cash donations UK	£170,000

The 2022 annual report states that 136 community dividend grants were awarded to local organisations and totalled £170,000. The report states that investment in community and co-operative affairs totalled £1.34 million, which included membership and community funding, support for other co-operatives, grants, funds raised for charity and colleague volunteering.

Centrica plc

Community enterprise and social entrepreneurship, community services and development, education and training, the environment, housing and homelessness, money and debt advice

Company registration number: 3033654

Correspondent: Abi Robins, Director of Responsible Business, Millstream, Maidenhead Road, Windsor, Berkshire SL4 5GD (tel: 01753 494000; email: responsibility@centrica.com; website: www.centrica.com)

Directors: Scott Wheway; Nathan Bostock; Katherine Ringrose; Rt Hon. Amber Rudd; Chris O'Shea; Carol Arrowsmith; Heidi Mottram; Kevin O'Bryne (female: 50%; male: 50%).

Nature of business: Centrica's principal activities are the provision of gas, electricity and energy related products and services. The group also operates gas fields and power stations.

Financial information

Year end	31/12/2021
Turnover	£14,700,000,000
Pre-tax profit	£613,000,000

Total employees: 19,700

Main locations: Centrica operates in various locations throughout the UK, Ireland and overseas.

Community involvement

Centrica invests in the local communities in which it operates through cash donations and employee volunteering. Centrica's support focuses on the following areas:

- Climate change and the environment – particularly energy efficiency and investing in renewable power
- Social inclusion – by working with public and voluntary sector partners to support Centrica's most vulnerable customers
- Education, skills and employability – by investing in education to promote learning about energy-related issues as well as supporting skills and training development
- Employee involvement – by encouraging charitable giving and volunteering

Grants

In 2020, Centrica announced the launch of a new not-for-profit social impact grant scheme, Energy for Tomorrow. Centrica has allocated £600,000 annually for grants, provided over three years, with up to £100,000 available for each grant. Centrica welcomes applications from charities, CICs, not-for-profit and for-profit companies and social enterprises. Priority is given to smaller organisations with a turnover of less than £1 million and to projects focused in the UK.

The British Gas Energy Trust

The British Gas Energy Trust (Charity Commission no. 1106218) was established by Centrica's British Gas brand to award grants to organisations and individual customers.

Partnerships

Centrica has several partnerships including:

- **Carers UK** – A three-year partnership that began in 2018 which builds on Centrica's previous 15 years of work with the charity. Centrica helps to develop policies that support employees with caring responsibilities. According to the annual report, the partnership ended in 2021, having reached a donation total of £1.5 million. The partnership with Carers UK won the 'Best Partnership with a National Charity' prize at the Better Society Awards.
- **Focus Ireland** – Centrica's Bord Gáis Energy company established a partnership with Focus Ireland in 2015. The company has raised over €2.5 million for over 7,000 families since 2015 to support the charity's work with people who are homeless or at risk of losing their home in Ireland.
- **The Trussell Trust** – During the COVID-19 pandemic, Centrica partnered with The Trussell Trust to provide support to over 400 foodbanks in the UK. The company donated £125,000 to the trust to support people facing food and fuel poverty.

Support for vulnerable customers

Each year, the group makes voluntary and mandatory contributions in support of its vulnerable customers. These contributions fund a range of initiatives including support programmes, advice and specialist products, the UK government's Warm Home Discount scheme and the group's North American 'Neighbor-to-Neighbor' bill assistance programme.

Employee-led support

Employees volunteer and fundraise for partner charities and local organisations. In 2021, employees ended their partnership with Carers UK, having raised £225,000 for the charity. Over 2,000 employees also volunteered with The Trussell Trust to support food banks in the UK. Employees also raised €200,000 in support of Focus Ireland. According to the annual report, volunteering days dropped by 96% in 2021 due to the COVID-19 pandemic's limiting of opportunities to volunteer.

Exclusions

The company is unable to provide assistance for projects that fall outside its Community and Local Impact Policy. This policy is available to view under the 'Sustainability' heading under the 'Contacts' section of the website.

Applications

Contact the correspondent or see the company's corporate charity entry for more information.

Corporate charity

British Gas Energy Trust (Charity Commission no. 1179578) – see entry on page 230.

Community contributions

Cash donations UK	£754,000

In 2021, Centrica's community contributions totalled £305.8 million. This comprised £304.9 million in mandatory contributions and £4,000 in voluntary contributions to help vulnerable customers with their energy bills. Charitable donations totalled £960,000, which included £210,000 in contributions from third parties such as employees.

Channel 4 Television Corporation

Arts, culture and heritage, education and training, media (including tv, film, publishing and radio), technology and engineering

Correspondent: Corporate Responsibility Team, 124 Horseferry Road, London SW1P 2TX (tel: 020 7396 4444; website: www.channel4.com/corporate/operating-responsibly/community)

Directors: Alex Mahon; Jonathan Allan; Ian Katz; Charles Gurassa; Lord Chris Holmes; Paul Geddes; Roly Keating; Sir Ian Cheshire; Dawn Airey; Tess Alps; David Kogan; Michael Lynton; Andrew Miller; Sarah Sands (female: 29%; male: 71%).

Nature of business: Channel 4 is a publicly owned, commercially funded public service broadcaster. Channel 4 works across television, film and digital media to deliver its public service remit, as outlined in the 2003 Communications Act and the 2010 Digital Economy Act.

Financial information

Year end	31/12/2021
Turnover	£1,164,000,000
Pre-tax profit	£101,000,000

Total employees: 1,044

Main locations: The group's head offices are in Leeds and London. The group also has offices in Bristol, Glasgow and Manchester.

Community involvement

The group focuses on supporting education, training and equal opportunities in the creative, film, television and media industries. Support is provided through funding, partnerships and in-kind support. Employees are also encouraged to fundraise and volunteer for charitable causes.

According to the group's website, 'the bulk of charitable donations made by Channel 4 are aimed at providing training that will improve the overall expertise of television staff within the industry, such as Creative Skillset and the National Film and Television School (NFTS).' The group also helps to fund the Royal Television Society's Technology Bursary scheme, which supports undergraduates from low-income backgrounds.

In-kind support

Channel 4 has worked in partnership with the Disasters Emergency Committee for several decades, broadcasting international crisis appeals free of charge.

The group provides local charities and community groups with meeting room space, tours of its buildings and donations of surplus furniture and technical equipment.

Employee-led support

The group encourages staff to fundraise for charities by offering matched funding for charitable fundraising efforts.

Channel 4's network group 4Pride supports LGBTQ+ communities by raising money for charities including the

Terrence Higgins Trust, Mermaids and Just Like Us, and donates airtime to Pride in London.

Applications
Contact the correspondent for further information.

Community contributions
We were unable to determine a figure for the group's charitable contributions in 2021.

Chelsea FC Holdings Ltd

Community enterprise and social entrepreneurship, education and training, health, social justice, sports and recreation

Company registration number: 2536231

Correspondent: Simon Taylor, Chelsea Foundation, Stamford Bridge, Fulham Road, London SW6 1HS (tel: 0371 811 1955; email: Community.Enquiries@ chelseafc.com; website: www.chelseafc. com/en/chelsea-foundation)

Directors: David Barnard; Todd Boehly; Barbara Charone; Behdad Eghbali; José Feliciano; Lord Daniel Finkelstein; Jonathan Goldstein; James Pade; Mark Walter; Hansjorg Wyss (female: 10%; male: 90%).

Nature of business: Chelsea FC is a professional football club competing in the English Premier League.

Financial information

Year end	30/06/2021
Turnover	£434,863,000
Pre-tax profit	£155,939,000

Total employees: 817

Main locations: The football club is based in West London. The Chelsea FC Foundation works across the UK with a preference for the south of England. It also supports organisations overseas (a full list of locations is available on the foundation's website).

Community involvement
Chelsea FC supports a wide range of issues including social inclusion, education, sport, disability and equality and diversity. Support is provided through the Chelsea FC Foundation, the Chelsea Past Players Trust, partnerships, campaigns and matchday collections.

The Chelsea Foundation (Charity Commission Number: 1129723)
The Chelsea Foundation works on a broad range of initiatives focused on employment and education, social inclusion, crime reduction and disability. The foundation also delivers several football development programmes in the UK and overseas and is involved in anti-discrimination projects aimed at improving equality and diversity in football. The foundation's UK focus is in the south of England, covering more then 125 towns and cities. Full details of the foundation's current programmes are available on the club's website.

The Chelsea Players' Trust (Charity Commission Number: 1120214)
The Chelsea Players' Trust makes grants to current and former members of Chelsea FC's playing, coaching, medical or scouting staff at first team, reserve team or youth academy level. In 2020/21, the charity received a £50,000 donation from the club.

No to Hate Campaign
In 2021, Chelsea FC launched its No to Hate campaign, pledging to direct funds towards the aim of eliminating racism and prejudice in football. The campaign is built on several pillars of education, social media, support, opportunity and awareness. The campaign aims to work with schools to deliver education on racism and hate speech, to identify perpetrators of racism in the stadium, to provide increased support for victims of racism at Chelsea FC and to develop diversity in its work force. The campaign runs parallel to the club's Say No to Antisemitism campaign and the Chelsea FC Equality Action Plan.

Partnerships
Beginning in 2015, the club worked in partnership with the international children's charity Plan International to help support its Champions of Change programme in Colombia, Latin America, which encourages both boys and girls to become involved in tackling gender inequality. The partnership was terminated in 2022 by Plan International, citing the Russian invasion of Ukraine and economic sanctions against the club's owner, Roman Abramovich.

Matchday collections
Fans have the opportunity to vote on which charities they would like to see collecting at Stamford Bridge on match days. Charities can come under four categories: armed forces, medical, children's and community. Examples of beneficiaries include: Blesma, Breast Cancer Haven, Children with Cancer UK and Help for Heroes.

In-kind support
The club considers requests for signed merchandise from registered charities. However, the club states that due to high demand it is not possible to meet all requests.

Applications
Chelsea Foundation
General enquiries to the foundation can be made by emailing Community.Enquiries@chelseafc.com or calling 01932 596193.

Charity requests
A request form for signed merchandise is available through the 'Contact Us' heading of the club's website. All requests need to be supported by a letter of authority to fundraise from the registered charity you are supporting.

Community contributions

Cash donations UK		£50,000

We were unable to determine a figure for the club's total charitable contributions for 2020/21. However, the 2020/21 accounts of The Chelsea Players' Trust show that the club made a donation of £50,000. We have taken this figure to represent the club's UK cash donations.

We were unable to determine the donation made by the club to the Chelsea FC Foundation in 2021.

Clarkson plc

General charitable purposes, health, mental health and well-being

Company registration number: 1190238

Correspondent: The Foundation Team, Commodity Quay, St Katharine Docks, London E1W 1BF (email: foundation@ clarksons.com; website: www. theclarksonfoundation.com/the-clarkson-foundation)

Directors: Deborah Abrehart; Peter Blackhouse; Martine Bond; Andrew Case; Susan Harris; Laurence Hollingworth; Dr Timothy Miller; Birger Nergaard; Heike Truol; Jeffrey Woyda (female: 40%; male: 60%).

Nature of business: Clarkson plc is a shipping services provider.

Financial information

Year end	31/12/2021
Turnover	£443,300,000
Pre-tax profit	£69,100,000

Total employees: 1,693

Main locations: Clarkson plc has offices throughout the world. In the UK it has offices in Aberdeen, Great Yarmouth, Newcastle, Harwich, Avonmouth, Belfast, Avonmouth, Birmingham, Invergordon, Blyth, Bristol, Ipswich, Ledbury, Southampton, Liverpool, London, Tilbury and Forth.

Community involvement
The group provides charitable support through in-kind donations, employee fundraising and The Clarkson Foundation.

The Clarkson Foundation (Charity Commission no. 1191357)

The foundation was established in 2020 and supports organisations local to Clarkson sites. In 2021 causes supported included mental health, children's health, maritime causes, poverty and homelessness. Grants are also made to charities nominated by employees.

In-kind support

In 2021 the group donated 70 computers and 200 webcams to children's charities.

Employee-led support

Employees make donations to charity via payroll giving. They also take part in sponsored challenges to raise money for local charities and The Clarkson Foundation.

Applications

See the group's corporate charity's entry for more information.

Corporate charity

The Clarkson Foundation (Charity Commission no. 1191357) – see entry on page 234.

Community contributions

Cash donations UK	£250,000

In 2021 the group made a donation of £250,000 to The Clarkson Foundation.

Clifford Chance LLP

Community services and development, education and training, legal advice, money and debt advice

Company registration number: OC323571

Correspondent: Tom Dunn, Global Pro Bono and Community Director, 10 Upper Bank Street, London E14 5JJ (tel: 020 7006 2951; email: use the contact form on the firm's website; website: www.cliffordchance.com/about_us/responsible-business/community-and-pro bono.html)

Nature of business: Clifford Chance LLP is a multinational law firm headquartered in London.

Financial information

Year end	30/04/2022
Turnover	£1,969,000,000
Pre-tax profit	£812,000,000

Main locations: The firm has offices in London and Newcastle, as well as offices across the world.

Community involvement

The firm has a varied programme of community outreach and pro bono activities focused on widening access to education, justice and finance. The firm's lawyers and business services professionals dedicate their time, expertise and resources to a variety of schemes and initiatives, such as giving pro bono legal advice and representation to individuals and NGO clients. NGO clients are also supported financially by the Clifford Chance Foundation.

The Clifford Chance Foundation (not a registered charity)

The foundation makes grants at a global and local level to NGO clients and other charitable projects. Funding can include long-term commitments or one-off payments. In 2021/22, 21 grants from the Clifford Chance Foundation were used to support disaster relief in Yemen, Afghanistan and Ukraine.

United Nations Sustainable Development Goals (UN SDGs) Award

Recently, the firm launched the global United Nations Sustainable Development Goals (UN SDGs) Award. The firm's website states the following:

> In 2022 we are welcoming applications for the award from non-governmental organisations (NGOs) and educational institutions, including schools and universities, around the world, whose work contributes towards the achievement of SDG 4, which is to ensure inclusive and equitable quality education and promote lifelong learning opportunities for all. The judges are particularly interested in award submissions that demonstrate a commitment to innovative approaches towards the achievement of SDG 4 and those which show potential to be replicated and scaled.

The winning organisation will receive a £50,000 donation and 500 pro bono hours.

Education

The film delivers a number of education initiatives. In the UK, this has included the Raising Aspirations programme, which invited 30 to 50 students each month to its London office for a series of interactive sessions. The firm regularly partners with its clients to provide varied sessions.

Widening access to education for adults is also an important part of the firm's strategy. For example, the firm partners with local organisations in the UK to help refugees and economic migrants develop their English skills and improve their job prospects.

In-kind support

Pro bono

The firm's employees participate in a wide range of pro bono activities including mentoring young people, supporting refugees with their asylum applications, providing financial and legal advice and representing people and NGOs in court that cannot afford to pay for it. Advice and representation is also given to parents of autistic children. In 2021/22, over 73,100 pro bono hours were worked by employees.

The firm in London has previously represented The National Autistic Society and Mind in a UK Supreme Court case.

Applications

Clifford Chance Foundation

According to our previous research, applications to the Clifford Chance Foundation are welcome but must be championed by a member of the firm. All employees are able to download the application form from the firm's intranet site.

United Nations Sustainable Development Goals (UN SDGs) Award

Check the firm's website for updates on when applications open.

Community contributions

Total contributions worldwide	£36,400,000

We were unable to determine a figure for the firm's total charitable contributions for 2021/22. However, the value of the firm's pro bono work carried out by employees was £36.4 million.

According to our previous research, the firm also awards around £1.2 million every year to its foundation.

Close Brothers Group plc

Education and training, general charitable purposes, health

Company registration number: 520241

Correspondent: Rebekah Etherington, Group Head of Human Resources, 10 Crown Place, London EC2A 4FT (email: enquiries@closebrothers.com; website: www.closebrothers.com/charity)

Directors: Mike Biggs; Adrian Sainsbury; Mike Morgan; Bridget Macaskill; Lesley Jones; Tracey Graham; Oliver Corbett; Peter Duffy; Sally Williams; Mark Pain; Tesula Mohindra; Patricia Halliday (female: 50%; male: 50%).

Nature of business: Close Brothers is a merchant banking group that provides lending, deposit taking, wealth management services and securities trading.

Financial information

Year end	31/07/2021
Turnover	£270,000,000
Pre-tax profit	£265,200,000

Total employees: 3,000

Main locations: The group has more than 50 offices in the UK. The group's main offices are in Doncaster, East Sussex, London and Manchester.

Community involvement

Partnerships

UpReach helps disadvantaged students secure graduate jobs and internships. Close Brothers runs a summer internship programme as part of this partnership. This involves a six-week work placement at the company for second and final-year university students from disadvantaged backgrounds.

Make-A-Wish Foundation was selected as the community charity partner in 2018. Close Brothers has helped to grant 49 wishes through the Make-A-Wish Foundation by donating over £122,000 between 2020 and 2021.

Cancer Research UK continues to be the group's health charity partner. Close Brothers raised over £500,000 for this charity between 2013 and 2021.

Funds raised from group-wide activities are split equally between the two charities. Several additional charities are also supported by the group's local businesses.

Apprenticeships and training

The Close Brothers SME Apprentice Programme is part of the group's long-term commitment to supporting small and medium-sized enterprises in its local communities. The programme is in its fifth phase and contributes to fund new apprenticeships in the manufacturing and transport sectors.

Employee-led support

Employee volunteering

Employees are entitled to one day's paid volunteering leave per year. In 2021, employees delivered voluntary reading sessions through the Bookmark programme. Employees are actively encouraged to participate in a range of events held during the group's designated charity week and throughout the year, including sponsored sports matches, silent auctions, cake sales and pub quizzes

Matched funding

The Close Brothers Matched Giving scheme matches 50% of funds raised by employees or donates £8 per hour of voluntary time given by employees. It also matches funds raised by local offices' fundraising activities, encouraging employees to work together to raise money for local causes.

Close Brothers also matches contributions made by employees through its payroll giving scheme. Around 13% of employees across the group signed up for the scheme in 2020/21.

Commercially led support

Sponsorship

Close Brothers is the exclusive sponsor of two Dogs for Good assistance puppies. The group's sponsorship helps support the puppies during their socialisation and training. This includes breeding and welfare costs, equipment and support for the volunteer socialisers. The puppies may go on to be autism assistance dogs, working with a child with autism and their family, or highly trained assistance dogs helping an adult or a child with disabilities.

Exclusions

No support is provided for political appeals.

Applications

Contact the correspondent for further information. The group's CSR committee is chaired by the head of human resources and is supported by employees across the group. There are also several local CSR committees which run initiatives to raise funds for charity.

Community contributions

Cash donations UK	£100,000

According to its 2020/21 annual report, the company donated £100,000 to Bookmark.

CMC Markets plc

Community services and development, general charitable purposes

Company registration number: 5145017

Correspondent: Stephen Cox, CSR Manager, 133 Houndsditch, London EC3A 7BX (email: s.cox@cmcmarkets.com; website: www.cmcmarketsplc.com/sustainability)

Directors: Peter Cruddas; David Fineberg; Matthew Lewis; Euan Marshall (male: 100%).

Nature of business: CMC Markets provides online financial trading.

Financial information

Year end	31/03/2021
Turnover	£409,800,000
Pre-tax profit	£220,000,000

Total employees: 945

Main locations: The group's UK office is in London. The group also has locations across the world.

Community involvement

The group is committed to supporting The Peter Cruddas Foundation (Charity Commission no. 1117323), established by the chief executive and founder of CMC Markets. The foundation seeks to provide pathways into education, training or employment for young people.

Charity of the Year

In 2021, the group's Charity of the Year was Action for Children. The group planned fundraising events in aid of the charity.

Worldwide partnerships

CMC in Sydney will enter its sixth year of partnership with its corporate charity Learning Links in 2023. As well as financial contributions, the group provides in-kind donations in the form of maths tutoring for children with learning difficulties delivered by CMC staff.

In-kind support

In 2021, CMC donated over 200 PCs to educational bodies and community charities.

Employee-led support

Employees are entitled to take one day's paid leave per year to volunteer. As part of its partnership with Action for Children, employees volunteer to mentor young people in care. CMC staff commit to mentoring a child for a period of two years.

Staff social events are often used as opportunities to raise funds for their chosen charities. CMC provides £4 of matched funding for every £1 raised by employees.

Commercially led support

Together with The Peter Cruddas Foundation, the group continues to sponsor Making the Leap Employment Fair. The event attracts around 200 students each year. Some students are provided with internships at CMC following the event.

Applications

Contact the correspondent or see the group's corporate charity entry for more information.

Corporate charity

The Peter Cruddas Foundation (Charity Commission no. 1117323) – see entry on page 236.

Community contributions

We were unable to determine a figure for the group's charitable contributions.

Compass Group plc

Community services and development, education and training, the environment, health

Company registration number: 4083914

Correspondent: The CSR Team, Compass House, Guildford Street, Chertsey, Surrey KT16 9BQ (tel: 01932 573000; email: contact form on the website; website: www.compass-group.com/en/sustainability/people/supporting-local-communities.html)

Directors: Carol Arrowsmith; Dominic Blakemore; Gary Green; Palmer Brown; John Bryant; Ian Meakins; Stefan

Bomhard; Arlean Isaacs-Lowe; Anne-Francoise Nesmes; Sundar Raman; Nelson Silva; Ireena Vittall; Alison Yapp (female: 36%; male: 64%).

Nature of business: Compass provides contract food services to business and industrial organisations around the world. It also provides support services such as building maintenance, cleaning and reception services.

Financial information

Year end	30/09/2021
Turnover	£18,130,000,000
Pre-tax profit	£700,000,000

Total employees: 478,070

Main locations: The group's UK head office is in Chertsey. The group also has around 45 locations across the world.

Community involvement

Each of the group's business sectors is responsible for choosing a charity, school or community group with which to create a long-term partnership. The group makes direct financial contributions, as well as organising various fundraising opportunities in aid of the charities it supports.

According to the group's annual report, its areas of work are:
- The environment
- Education
- Health and well-being
- Community engagement
- Responsible business practice

Partnerships
In the UK, the company has partnerships with FareShare, Plan Zheroes, Too Good To Go and Olio. The company donates unsold food to these organisations. In 2021, it donated more than 250,000 surplus meals to them.

Applications
Contact the correspondent for further information.

Community contributions

Total contributions worldwide	£11,000,000

According to its 2020/21 annual report, the group's charitable donations totalled £11 million. This figure includes amounts raised through employee fundraising.

Computacenter plc

General charitable purposes, health

Company registration number: 3110569

Correspondent: Charity Committee, Hatfield Avenue, Hatfield Business Park, Hatfield, Hertfordshire AL10 9TW (tel: 01707 631000; email: contact form on the website; website: www.computacenter.com/uk)

Directors: Peter Ryan; Philip Hulme; Mike Norris; Tony Conophy; Peter Ogden; Dr Ljiljana Mitic; Rene Haas; Dr Ros Rivaz; Pauline Campbell (female: 33%; male: 67%).

Nature of business: Computacenter is an independent provider of IT infrastructure services, offering services and solutions at every stage of infrastructure investment.

Financial information

Year end	31/12/2021
Turnover	£6,730,800,000
Pre-tax profit	£248,000,000

Total employees: 18,000

Main locations: The group has offices across the UK and the Republic of Ireland. It also has locations in Asia, Africa, North America and across Europe.

Community involvement

Computacenter supports the communities in areas in which it operates by working with charities selected by employees.

Partnerships
According to its 2021 annual report, the group supported three charity partners during the year: Make-A-Wish Foundation, British Heart Foundation and Dementia UK.

Community programmes
Bravo! – The group's peer-to-peer recognition tool (Bravo!) allows staff to immediately recognise the contributions of their peers and thank them. The tool allows managers to award points for exceptional performance and behaviours, which can be redeemed at selected retailers or donated to the group's charity partners.

Community Education Outreach programme – The company works with potential future talents to deliver social value to its communities. Over the last few years, the Computacenter has developed strong partnerships with a number of schools, universities and charities in the UK. In 2021, this programme won the 'Best Community Outreach Programme' in UK tech and has reached over 5,000 students and young adults.

Employee-led support
The group runs a Give As You Earn scheme, allowing staff to make monthly contributions to charities of their choice.

Employees also organise various fundraising efforts for the group's charity partners through the staff-led charity committee.

Applications
Contact the correspondent for more information.

Community contributions

Cash donations worldwide	£21,100

According to its 2021 sustainability report, the company gave £21,100 in charitable donations during the year.

Co-operative Group Ltd

Community services and development, education and training, general charitable purposes, mental health and well-being

Company registration number: IP00525R

Correspondent: Local Community Fund Team, 1 Angel Square, Manchester M60 0AG (tel: 0800 023 4708; email: communityteam@coop.co.uk; website: https://causes.coop.co.uk)

Directors: Allan Leighton; Shirine Khoury-Haq; Sir Christopher Kelly; Paul Chandler; Simon Burke; Stevie Spring; Margaret Casely-Hayford; Lord Victor Adebowale; Rahul Powar; Sarah McCarthy-Fry; Kate Allum (female: 45%; male: 55%).

Nature of business: The Co-operative Group is the UK's largest mutual business, owned by over six million consumers. The group conducts business in the following sectors: food retail and convenience store operation, financial and legal services, funeral care, travel, property investment, electrical products and banking.

Financial information

Year end	01/01/2022
Turnover	£11,151,000,000
Pre-tax profit	£57,000,000

Total employees: 70,000+

Main locations: The group has branches throughout the UK.

Community involvement

The Co-operative Group (Co-op) supports communities through various grant schemes, in-kind donations and its corporate charity, the Co-operative Community Investment Foundation (Charity Commission no. 1093028).

Co-op Local Community Fund (not a registered charity)
Every 12 months, the group chooses new community causes to support. Funds raised through shopping bag sales, as well as 2% of every purchase made by Co-op members, are donated to these causes. Most applications come from charities or local community groups, but any organisation that is not run for private profit can apply. According to the group's website, organisations may make an application if the project:
- brings people together to access food
- helps improve people's mental wellbeing

- creates opportunities for young people to be heard and make a difference
- helps people protect local biodiversity or tackle change by reducing carbon emissions

Priority is given to local charities and other organisations with an income of less than £1 million a year.

The Co-op Academies Trust

The trust provides an education based on co-operative values and principles to over 17,000 young people. Currently, 27 schools across the country have decided to become Co-op Academies.

Farming Pioneers

The group continues to invest in its Farming Pioneers programme. The programme teaches business skills, as well as exploring important issues like mental health, to aspiring farmers and growers. Since its inception, 100 'pioneers' have progressed through the programme.

Community Partnerships Fund (not a registered charity)

Launched in 2020, the fund has allowed the group to build on existing relationships and partner with new organisations to support communities. Through the fund, the Co-operative Group Ltd works with organisations to provide fairer access to food, mental health support and opportunities for young people.

The group has partnerships with Mind, the SAMH (Scottish Association for Mental Health) and Inspire, through which it aims to raise £8 million. It plans to achieve this by engaging its colleagues, members and customers in a range of national and local fundraising activities. In 2022 the group launched a partnership with bereavement support charity Cruse.

In 2021 the group partnered with environmental charity Hubbub to fund 500 community fridges by the end of 2023. Community fridges are run by community groups in shared spaces such as schools, community centres and shops; their main purpose is to save fresh food from going to waste.

The group also has a partnership with the Youth Endowment Fund which will, alongside the #iwill Fund, invest £5.2 million into research to help young people make their communities safer, fairer places to live through a Peer Action Collective.

Co-operate

The group's online community centre, Co-operate, helps to connect people across the UK. It has over 13,500 groups and activities and in 2022, the platform launched a volunteering service which matches community groups with volunteers.

In-kind support

Through Co-op Food Share, the supermarket donates unsold food to local causes across the country. Any incorrect deliveries at Co-op depots that cannot be used in-store are donated to FareShare, who distribute the food to local charities. According to the group's 2021 sustainability report, 88% of stores now have a Food Share partner.

Employee-led support

Employees take part in volunteering and fundraising opportunities. According to the group's 2021 sustainability report, employee time contributed to good causes amounted to 47,518 hours.

Commercially led support

When Co-op members buy selected Co-op-branded products and services, they get 2p back for every pound spent and the same goes to local communities. The funds raised are split between the Local Community Fund and the Community Partnerships Fund

All money raised from shopping bag sales is also donated to charitable causes.

Exclusions

The group's website states the following regarding the Local Community Fund:

We will not consider any applications which involve:

- promoting any political activities or causes
- promoting any religious beliefs (but we will consider projects led by religious organisations, if they're for the good of the whole community)
- funding salaries and overheads that are not directly related to delivering the Project you are applying for
- giving our grant to other people or organisations (onward grant making)
- projects that have already happened or will be finished before the giving period ends
- projects that public authorities (for example, the council) are responsible for, by law
- sponsored events
- overseas projects
- projects which, in our opinion, could harm the reputation of the Co-op or the Local Community Fund

Applications

Contact the correspondent for more information. Applications to the Local Community Fund can be made on the group's website.

Corporate charity

Co-operative Community Investment Foundation (Charity Commisson no. 1093028) – see entry on page 234.

Community contributions

Cash donations UK	£20,000,000
Total contributions UK	£28,400,000

Note: the group's cash donations relate to the previous financial year. According to its 2021 Sustainability Report, the Co-Operative Group Ltd's community investment was as follows: cash (£20 million); employee time (£7.1 million); and gifts in kind (£1.3 million). A further £9.2 million in 'leveraged' donations was raised by members, customers partners and suppliers.

Costain Group plc

General charitable purposes

Company registration number: 1393773

Correspondent: James York, Corporate Responsibility Director, Costain House, Vanwall Business Park, Maidenhead, Berkshire SL6 4UB (tel: 01628 842444; email: corporate.responsibility@costain.com; website: www.costain.com)

Directors: Samuel Crockett; Jacqueline De Rojas; Bishoy Gendi; Paul Golby; Fiona MacAulay; Anthony Quinlan; Alex Vaughan; Helen Willis (female: 38%; male: 63%).

Nature of business: Costain provides engineering and technology-led solutions operating in the rail, highway and energy sectors.

Financial information

Year end	31/12/2021
Turnover	£1,135,200,000
Pre-tax profit	(£13,300,000)

UK employees: 3,500

Main locations: The group's head office is in Maidenhead. It also has offices in Manchester, London, Aberdeen and Weston-super-Mare.

Community involvement

Costain provides charitable support through donations, employee volunteering and employee fundraising.

Employee-led support

Employees are encouraged to undertake voluntary work. In 2021, employees volunteered 2,200 hours in their local communities.

Applications

Contact the correspondent for further information.

Community contributions

Total contributions worldwide	£200,000

According to its 2021 annual report, the group valued its charitable giving at £200,000. This figure includes charitable donations and employee volunteering hours.

Countryside Partnerships plc

Community services and development, general charitable purposes, health

Company registration number: 9878920

Correspondent: The Sustainability Team, Countryside House, The Drive, Brentwood, Essex CM13 3AT (email: sustainability@cpplc.com; website: www.countrysidepartnerships.com/sustainable-business/community)

Directors: Gary Whitaker; Amanda Burton; Amanda Clack; Douglas Hurt; Timothy Lawlor; Peter Lee; Sally Morgan, Baroness Morgan of Huyton; William Townsend (female: 38%; male: 63%).

Nature of business: Countryside Partnerships plc is a property development company.

Financial information

Year end	30/09/2021
Turnover	£1,526,200,000
Pre-tax profit	£150,300,000

Main locations: Countryside Partnerships plc is headquartered in Brentwood. It has regional offices in Ealing, Broxbourne, Sevenoaks, Farnborough, Warrington, Leeds, Wolverhampton, Leicester, Solihull and Bristol.

Community involvement

Countryside Partnerships plc provides support to local charities through its community fund and community chests.

Community fund

The £1 million community fund was launched in 2020 in response to the COVID-19 pandemic. In 2021 a further £1 million was added to the fund. Examples of projects that have been funded include three new defibrillator units within the Watford Rural Parish Council area and a holiday hunger programme run by Munch Club.

Community chests

In addition to the community fund, the company has created community chests at a number of its developments. These chests set aside a funding pot for initiatives around health, well-being and community development.

Applications

Contact your local office for further information.

Community contributions

Cash donations UK	£697,800

According to the company's 2020/21 sustainability report, donations to local charities totalled £697,800.

Coutts & Co.

Health, human rights, mental health and well-being, social justice, social welfare, women's rights

Company registration number: 36695

Correspondent: Foundation Administrator, 440 Strand, London WC2R 0QS (tel: 020 7753 1000; email: coutts.foundation@coutts.com; website: www.coutts.com/coutts-foundation.html)

Directors: Lord William Waldegrave; Peter Flavel; Mark Lund; Linda Urquhart; Andrew Kyle; Matt Waymark; Sharmila Nebhrajani (female: 29%; male: 71%).

Nature of business: Coutts is a private bank specialising in supplying wealth management and banking services to high-net-worth individuals and their businesses. Coutts is a subsidiary of NatWest Group plc (formerly The Royal Bank of Scotland Group).

Financial information

Year end	31/12/2021
Turnover	£658,000,000
Pre-tax profit	£254,000,000

Total employees: 1,750

Main locations: The bank's primary location is London but it has offices across the UK.

Community involvement

All of the bank's giving is directed through the Coutts Charitable Foundation (Charity Commission no. 1150784) which supports a small number of organisations that work to tackle the causes and consequences of poverty. The foundation's core focus is supporting organisations working with women and girls in the UK.

Partnerships

Each year, employees can vote for a charity to be supported for up to two years, based on a particular theme such as mental health or poverty. Support includes fundraising and volunteering. In 2021, the bank's charity partner was Future Frontiers, a charity that supports disadvantaged children through education.

In-kind support

According to the foundation's 2020/21 report, Coutts provides direct and indirect pro bono services and expertise to the foundation in several areas, including IT services and staff and volunteer support.

The bank donates food grown in its Skyline Garden on the roof of its London office to The Felix Project, a charity that takes surplus food and ensures it reaches vulnerable people.

Employee-led support

Volunteering and mentoring

Every employee is entitled to three days of paid leave per year to volunteer for their local community or a charity of their choice. Coutts employees regularly volunteer to help the community through The Conservation Volunteers. Activities include gardening, painting fences and building children's play areas.

In addition, employees offer mentoring to teachers and students at St Saviour's and St Olave's School. Employees offer tutoring in Maths and English and volunteer at events such as Sports Day.

Fundraising

In 2021, employees and clients raised a total of £480,000 through the Thank You From Coutts programme. There is also a payroll giving scheme in place.

Commercially led support

Coutts sponsors exhibitions, festivals and events connected to the arts and design industries.

Applications

For further information contact the correspondent.

Corporate charity

Coutts Charitable Foundation (Charity Commission no. 1150784) – see entry on page 235.

Community contributions

Cash donations UK	£250,200
Total contributions UK	£300,400

According to the Coutts Charitable Foundation's 2020/21 annual report, it received donations of £250,200 from the bank. Additionally, the foundation received in-kind support valued at £50,200. This figure includes pro bono services, office space, IT services, staff support from a part-time administrator and volunteer support.

Note: the foundation and the bank have different financial reporting periods.

Coventry Building Society

Community services and development, education and training, general charitable purposes, health, social welfare

Company registration number: FCA 150892

Correspondent: CSR Team, Oakfield House, PO Box 600, Binley, Coventry, Warwickshire CV3 9YR (tel: 0800 121 8899; email: media@thecoventry.co.uk; website: www.coventrybuildingsociety.co.uk/content/cbs/consumer/en/who-we-are/charities.html)

Directors: David Thorburn; Steve Hughes; Iraj Amiri; Catherine Doran;

Peter Frost; Jo Kenrick; Shamira Mohammed; Brendan O'Connor; Lee Raybould; Martin Stewart (female: 30%; male: 70%).

Nature of business: The Coventry Building Society is a building society based in the UK.

Financial information

Year end	31/12/2021
Turnover	£468,200,000
Pre-tax profit	£232,800,000

Total employees: 2,021

Main locations: The society is based in Coventry. It has branches in the following locations: the Midlands, Somerset, Gloucestershire, Monmouthshire, Oxfordshire, Wiltshire and Yorkshire.

Community involvement

The society supports charities, schools and local causes through partnerships, sponsorship, employee volunteering initiatives and the sale of cause-related products. Its corporate charity, Coventry Building Society Charitable Foundation (Charity Commission no. 1072244) is entirely funded by the society and makes donations to charities and community groups that are based or active in the society's branch locations.

Partnerships

In 2021 the society continued to partner with The Royal British Legion, which it has supported since 2008. Since the partnership began, the society has donated nearly £19 million, predominantly as a result of the society's portfolio of savings accounts that offer customers the chance to donate to the charity.

The society has begun working with the Positive Youth Foundation, which empowers young people who experience inequalities to boost their life chances.

The society has a long-standing relationship with Coventry Citizens Advice Centre. In 2021, it provided funding for core services and also used money from dormant accounts to fund two trainee debt advisors to help meet growing demand.

During 2021, the society also supported the Central England Law Centre. In addition to providing funding for specialist debt advice for those at risk of becoming homeless, it provided funding for a mental health caseworker and an additional intensive worker.

Education

In 2021, the society established partnerships with six primary schools and three secondary schools in Coventry to help improve levels of attainment and to help raise the aspirations of young people. For primary schools, it developed the 'Coventry Counts'

initiative, offering a range of numeracy and literacy support, including free online resources, funding for numeracy interventions and volunteer support. In secondary schools, the programme focuses on employability.

Employee-led support

Employees volunteer and fundraise for local causes and every branch of the society is encouraged to choose a local charity or community group to focus this support on. All employees are offered two days of paid leave to volunteer each year. In 2021, colleagues volunteered 3,894 hours and raised £123,800 supporting local charities and community groups.

Employees also provide volunteer support to the local schools that the society supports.

Commercially led support

Sponsorship

The society sponsors a number of events including Coventry Pride and the MOBO Awards.

Applications

Contact the correspondent for more information.

Corporate charity

Coventry Building Society Charitable Foundation (Charity Commission no. 1072244) – see entry on page 235.

Community contributions

Cash donations UK	£700,000
Total contributions UK	£1,600,000

In 2021, the society's community investment totalled £1.6 million. This figure includes donations from affinity accounts, corporate donations, staff grants, and fundraising activities which benefitted from matching schemes. Grants totalling £700,000 were awarded to charitable organisations during the year. This included an amount of £600,000 to The Royal British Legion's Poppy Appeal and £70,000 to the Coventry Building Society Charitable Foundation.

CPFC Ltd (Crystal Palace Football Club)

🔍 Community enterprise and social entrepreneurship, community services and development, education and training, emergency response/relief, health, social welfare, sports and recreation

Company registration number: 7270793

Correspondent: Palace for Life Foundation, Selhurst Park Stadium, Holmesdale Road, London SE25 6PU (email: admin@palaceforlife.org; website: www.palaceforlife.org)

Directors: David Blitzer; Joshua Harris; Steve Parish; John Textor (male: 100%).

Nature of business: Crystal Palace FC is a professional football club competing in the Premier League.

Financial information

Year end	30/06/2021
Turnover	£1,343,800,000
Pre-tax profit	(£40,210,000)

UK employees: 297

Main locations: The club is based in south London and is spread across three different sites: Selhurst Park Stadium, a London office and a training ground/academy in Beckenham.

Community involvement

The club's community activities are primarily channelled through its charitable foundation, which runs activities focusing on community engagement, social inclusion and crime prevention, disability, family health and well-being, young people and employability.

Palace for Life Foundation (Charity Commission no. 1125878)

The foundation operates in the south London boroughs of Bromley, Croydon, Lambeth and Sutton. It works with partners including local councils, schools and the voluntary sector to deliver a wide range of programmes including mental health workshops, free football camps and more. Details of all of the foundation's current programmes can be found on its website.

In-kind support

Palace Kitchen Initiative

The initiative enables the club and Palace for Life Foundation to provide healthy meals to local voluntary groups. It is funded by a combination of shareholder contributions, club funds and supporter donations. In 2020/21, more than 30,000 meals were donated.

Commercially led support

Charities can request items to be used in auctions.

Exclusions

Previous research suggests that the foundation is unlikely to support requests which are:
- Outside the foundation's area of benefit
- From non-registered charities
- For animal charities
- In relation to fundraising for individuals

Applications

To request support or an item for a charity auction, contact charities@cpfc.co.uk with as much information as possible. To contact the foundation, email admin@palaceforlife.org. A contact form is also available on the foundation's website.

Community contributions

We were unable to determine a figure for the club's total community contributions for 2020/21.

Cranswick plc

Education and training, the environment, social welfare

Company registration number: 1074383

Correspondent: CSR Team, Cranes Court Hesslewood Office Park, Ferriby Road, Hessle, East Riding of Yorkshire, UK HU13 0PA (tel: 01482 275000; email: use the form on the company's website; website: https://cranswick.plc.uk/responsibility)

Directors: Helen Allum; John Bottomley; James Brisby; Adam Couch; Pamela Powell; Mark Reckitt; Tim Smith; Elizabeth Barber (female: 38%; male: 63%).

Nature of business: Cranswick is a British food producer.

Financial information

Year end	27/03/2021
Turnover	£2,008,500,000
Pre-tax profit	£129,900,000

UK employees: 10,300

Main locations: The company's head office is in Yorkshire and it has sites across the UK.

Community involvement

The company engages in charitable activities in the UK through food donations, sponsorship and by encouraging employees to engage with their local communities through fundraising and volunteering.

Cranswick has supported several charities, many of which were nominated by employees, including Bluebell Children's Hospice, Yorkshire Air Ambulance and Macmillan Cancer Support.

Cranswick has also previously partnered with local colleges and universities to offer students career advice through its World of Work course and opportunities for industry placements within IT, HR and business administration functions.

The Cranswick Charitable Trust (Charity Commission no. 1192296)
The trust was launched in 2020 and is funded by donations from the group. Since it began, the trust has provided a number of donations to small local charities including ENYP and Exodus, which support children and young people from deprived areas across Norfolk and Barnsley, respectively.

In-kind support

Cranswick donates surplus food to charities local to its sites.

Cranswick began a partnership with the food charity FareShare in 2017 to send surplus food to front-line charities. According to the company's 2020/21 annual report, since the start of the partnership Cranswick has diverted the equivalent of 500,000 meals for vulnerable people.

Cranswick also works with other food charities surrounding its offices, such as Plan Zheroes (Milton Keynes) and GroceryAid, to help alleviate food and fuel poverty.

Employee-led support

Previous research suggested that employees in the UK nominate local and national charities to support via a voting system and are encouraged to fundraise through sponsored events, competitions and cake sales.

In 2020, the company hosted an employee volunteer day to support Plant A Tree Today Foundation's 'One Hull of a Forest' project. Employees planted 500 trees to help regenerate green spaces across Hull.

Commercially led support

Cranswick also provides sponsorship to local projects. Previous examples include a young mothers' unit at Bell Academy which provides childcare facilities for young mothers so they can attend classes, and the Freedom Festival in Hull, where the company educates festival-goers on food poverty and food waste.

Applications

For enquiries, use the contact form available on the company's website or contact your local Cranswick site.

Corporate charity

The Cranswick Charitable Trust (Charity Commission no. 1192296) – see entry on page 235.

Community contributions

Cash donations UK	£500,000

We were unable to determine the figure for total charitable contributions; however, the company's 2020/21 annual report notes that it donated £500,000 to its corporate charity. A large part of the company's charitable giving involves the provision of in-kind food donations to charitable organisations.

Credit Suisse AG

Arts, culture and heritage, community enterprise and social entrepreneurship, community services and development, education and training, the environment, money and debt advice, sports and recreation

Company registration number: FC007227

Correspondent: Corporate Citizenship Team, 1 Cabot Square, Canary Wharf, London EC14 4QJ (tel: 020 7888 8888; email: responsibility.corporate@credit-suisse.com; website: www.credit-suisse.com/about-us/en/our-company/corporate-responsibility.html)

Directors: Axel Lehmann; Mirko Bianci; Iris Bohnet; Clare Brady; Christian Gellerstad; Keyu Jin; Michael Klein; Shan Li; Seraina Macia; Blythe Masters; Richard Meddings; Amanda Norton; Ana Paula Pessoa (female: 46%; male: 54%).

Nature of business: Credit Suisse AG is the principal subsidiary of Credit Suisse Group AG, a global financial services group based in Switzerland. Credit Suisse AG operates as a bank.

Financial information

Year end	31/12/2021
Turnover	£22,696,000,000
Pre-tax profit	£600,000,000

Total employees: 50,110

Main locations: In the UK, Credit Suisse AG is based in London. The group operates in over 50 countries internationally.

Community involvement

Credit Suisse AG's global CSR strategy has three focus areas: financial inclusion, financial education and future skills. This strategy is implemented at a regional level depending on local needs and is delivered in co-operation with local partners. Education and life skills programmes relating to the three themes are delivered worldwide with the support of the group's two foundations.

The group supports a Charity of the Year in the countries in which it operates. In 2021, the UK Charity of the Year was Cancer Research UK. The group raised £750,000 for the Charity of the Year through a charity trading day. This partnership won the UK Charity Award for Partnership of the Year with a Financial Institution.

The group is also a member of the corporate support group for the International Committee of the Red Cross. The group provides financial contributions and expertise in areas such as human resources and IT skills.

Credit Suisse foundations

The group has a global Credit Suisse Foundation, which allocates funds to the group's Global Education and Financial Inclusion initiatives. The foundation also manages the group's disaster relief fund which provides short and long-term financial support to areas affected by disaster.

The group also has a foundation that supports organisations in Europe, the Middle East and Africa, the Credit Suisse EMEA Foundation (Charity Commission no. 1122472). The foundation is funded by Credit Suisse AG bank. It awards small and large grants to organisations that support the education and employability of disadvantaged young people. The foundation also supports a Charity of the Year scheme and other charities nominated by employees.

In 2021, through the Future Skills initiative and the Credit Suisse EMEA Foundation, Credit Suisse AG targeted racial inequalities by supporting access to education and employment for Caribbean communities in the UK.

In-kind support

The group's Global Citizens programme, an international skills-based volunteering scheme, allows employees to contribute their expertise pro bono to projects run by partner organisations, particularly in low and middle-income countries. Employees have completed over 440 assignments in more than 60 countries since the launch of the Global Citizens programme in 2010.

The group also offered financial training and support to smaller financial institutions facing the effects of the COVID-19 pandemic.

The group offers services to charities and other not-for-profit organisations, such as support with developing a grant-making policy or managing the operation of charitable foundations on behalf of clients.

Employee-led support

Each year, all group employees are entitled to four days of paid leave to contribute to partner organisations' projects in the areas of health, education, social issues and the environment. Employees also fundraise for their country's national Charity of the Year.

According to the group's 2021 Corporate Responsibility Report, 10,030 employees volunteered during the year and dedicated over 83,900 hours to volunteering in 80 countries.

Commercially led support

Sponsorship

The group prefers to sponsor sports and arts events and organisations. It has a strong focus on the promotion of young talent. Examples include the Zurich Film Festival and the Lucerne Festival.

Steps to Success Scholarship Programme

In the UK, the group offers scholarships to outstanding year 13 students who are from an under-represented and/or disadvantaged background. The programme includes summer internships in two Credit Suisse businesses.

Applications

Enquiries can be emailed to the group's Corporate Citizenship team at: responsibility.corporate@credit-suisse.com. To apply for the Steps to Success scholarship programme, submit a CV and cover letter through the group's application portal website.

Corporate charity

Credit Suisse EMEA Foundation (Charity Commission no. 1122472) – see entry on page 236.

Community contributions

Cash donations UK	£1,391,000

We were unable to determine a figure for the bank's total contributions in 2021. However, it donated £1.39 million to its corporate charity, the Credit Suisse EMEA Foundation. We have used this figure as the bank's 2021 UK cash donation.

CRH plc

Arts, culture and heritage, community services and development, education and training, the environment

Company registration number: 12965

Correspondent: Group Sustainability Team, Stonemason's Way, Rathfarnham, Dublin D16 KH51 (tel: +353 1 4041000; email: sustainability@crh.com; website: www.crh.com/sustainability)

Directors: Richie Boucher; Albert Manifold; Tim Mintern; Gillian Platt; Johan Karlström; Shaun Kelly; Richard Fearon; Caroline Dowling; Badar Khan; Lamar McKay; Mary Rhinehart; Lucinda Riches; Siobhán Talbot (female: 33%; male: 67%).

Nature of business: CRH manufactures and supplies building materials and products.

Financial information

Year end	31/12/2021
Turnover	£25,519,000,000
Pre-tax profit	£2,753,000,000

Total employees: 77,446

Main locations: CRH is registered in Ireland. The company operates in 30 countries across Europe, North America, South America, Asia and Australia.

Community involvement

The company has 1,300 sites and 88% of sites have community engagement plans in place. As well as providing community investment the company also engages in educational activities, including the provision of career development guidance, work experience and site tours for students.

Operating companies have developed partnerships with organisations to tackle the housing crisis in its communities and donate products, such as concrete blocks, pavers and mulch.

Employee-led support

Employees fundraise and volunteer on projects which the company is involved in. In 2021, employees across the UK and US divisions volunteered with various organisations, including Charity Roots and Habitats for Humanity, as well as other NGOs and educational institutions.

Commercially led support

In 2021, Leviat, CRH's construction accessories business, sponsored a construction-inspired bear sculpture in the city of Sheffield to raise funds for the local children's hospital. This was part of a campaign to raise funds for a new cancer and leukaemia ward at the hospital.

Applications

For further information contact the correspondent.

Community contributions

Cash donations worldwide	£5,850,000

The company's sustainability report detailed that in 2021 it donated £5.85 million to local organisations and initiatives within its communities. Donations were broken down as follows:

Community relations and development	48%
Health and wellness	24%
Education and employment	22%
Environment and conservation	3%
Provision of shelter	2%
Arts and culture	1%

Financial information has been converted from USD using the exchange rate at the time of writing (August 2022).

Cruden Holdings Ltd

General charitable purposes

Company registration number: SC339123

Correspondent: CSR Team, Baberton House, Juniper Green, Edinburgh EH14 3HN (website: www.cruden-ltd.co.uk/group)

Directors: Graeme Bissett; Euan Haggerty; Alexander Hathorn; Kevin Reid (male: 100%).

Nature of business: Cruden is one of Scotland's largest development and construction groups. The financial information and company details are for the holding company – for details of the other companies within the group consult Cruden's website.

Financial information

Year end	31/03/2021
Turnover	£19,500,000
Pre-tax profit	£302,000

UK employees: 587

Main locations: Cruden has offices in Edinburgh and Glasgow.

Community involvement

The majority of Cruden's contributions are given through the Cruden Foundation Ltd (OSCR no. SC004987), a grant-making charity and a shareholder of the group. The group also makes cash donations to other charitable organisations and various community initiative schemes.

In 2021, Cruden Holdings' website reported that the group had made a 'significant donation' to the Disasters Emergency Committee's Ukraine Appeal.

In-kind support

In 2021 Cruden Holdings supported local communities around its sites by providing building materials and expertise. Examples include building new equipment and play areas for primary schools, refurbishing facilities to be used by the Scouts and constructing outdoor garden areas for nurseries.

Employee-led support

Employees fundraise and volunteer for local charities, as well as working on community initiatives.

Applications

Contact the correspondent or see the company's corporate charity entry for more information.

Corporate charity

Cruden Foundation Ltd (OSCR no. SC004987) – see entry on page 237.

Community contributions

We were unable to find a figure for Cruden Holdings Ltd's charitable contributions for 2021.

Cumberland Building Society

🔍 General charitable purposes

Company registration number: 106074

Correspondent: Community Team, Cumberland House, Cooper Way, Carlisle CA3 0JF (tel: 01228 403141; email: communityfund@cumberland.co. uk; website: www.cumberland.co.uk)

Directors: Jackie Arnold; Kelli Fairbrother; Vicky Bruce; Richard Ellison; Eric Gunn; John Hooper; Mark Stanger; Des Moore (female: 38%; male: 63%).

Nature of business: Cumberland Building Society is a building society based in Cumbria.

Financial information

Year end	31/03/2022
Turnover	£47,666,000
Pre-tax profit	£8,613,000

Total employees: 397

Main locations: The society operates branches across Cumbria and the north of Lancashire. Its headquarters is in Carlisle.

Community involvement

The society provides support for a wide range of charitable initiatives in its area of operation. Support is provided through its Community Fund and its corporate charity, the Cumberland Building Society Charitable Foundation (Charity Commission no. 1072435).

Community Fund (not a registered charity)

Each year the society donates £100,000 to local charities, neighbourhood groups, schools and voluntary organisations. The society supports a wide variety of causes but has a particular preference for initiatives which relate to one or more of the following areas:
- Health and well-being
- Vulnerability
- Financial education

Applications for funding of up to £250 are considered by the branch teams, but applications for larger grants may be considered by the society's foundation.

Pledge for Votes scheme

The society operates a Pledge for Votes scheme in which it donates £1 for every vote cast at its annual general meeting, to charity. In 2021/22, voting was restricted due to the COVID-19 pandemic. In response, the society matched the previous year's donation of £19,000.

Schools and Community Ticket Scheme

Through its partnership with Carlisle United Football Club, the society sponsors the Schools and Community Ticket Scheme, whereby 300 free tickets are allocated to the community for home games throughout the season.

Employee-led support

Employees are encouraged to take part in fundraising and volunteering activities.

Exclusions

According to its website, the society will not provide funding for any of the following:
- Organisations outside its operating area
- Applications that have received a donation in the last 6–12 months
- Trips and holidays
- Events that have already occurred
- Sensitive, controversial or harmful requests, or those that could be a conflict of interest
- Political or pressure organisations
- Running costs, including salaries and capital expenditure
- Individuals' further education/tuition/ course fees

Applications

Those wishing to apply for a donation of up to £250 should contact their local branch with an outline of the request in writing. Alternatively, contact the Community Team via email.

Corporate charity

Cumberland Building Society Charitable Foundation (Charity Commission no. 1072435) – see entry on page 237.

Community contributions

Cash donations UK	£188,000

According to the 2021/22 annual report, during the year, charitable donations of £188,000 were awarded. This figure included a £23,900 donation to the Cumberland Building Society Charitable Foundation.

Currys plc

🔍 Social welfare

Company registration number: 7105905

Correspondent: CSR Team, 1 Portal Way, London W3 6RS (website: www. currys.co.uk/corporate-responsibility. html)

Directors: Nigel Paterson; Alexander Baldock; Eileen Burbidge; Antonio Denunzio; Andrea Joosen; Ian Livingston; Bruce Marsh; Fiona McBain; John Murphy (female: 33%; male: 67%).

Nature of business: Currys is an independent retailer of electrical and telecommunications devices and services.

Financial information

Year end	01/05/2021
Turnover	£10,144,000,000
Pre-tax profit	£186,000,000

Total employees: 31,700

Main locations: The group's head office is based in London and the business operates in various locations across the UK and Ireland. Worldwide, the group has business locations in: Denmark, Finland, Greece, Norway, Spain, Sweden and the USA.

Community involvement

Currys works with its partners to combat digital exclusion.

Digital Poverty Alliance

Currys is a founding partner of the Digital Poverty Alliance. The aim of the organisation is to bring about the social change needed to end digital poverty by 2030. In 2021/22 the company made a £1 million donation to the charity which helped provide 1,000 teachers and teaching assistants in the country's poorest areas with the equipment needed to deliver homeschooling to their pupils.

International support

The group established The Elkjøp Foundation to help address the issue of digital exclusion in the Nordic countries. In 2021/22 the foundation committed over £400,00 to a number of strategic partnerships that will help fight digital exclusion in each of the countries in which it operates.

Partnerships

In March 2020 Currys started a two-year partnership with Age UK. In 2021/22 customers and employees raised over £350,000 for its Tech Connected programme, which aims to help digitally excluded older people.

Ukraine

Currys made a donation of £100,000 to the Red Cross to support the people of Ukraine.

Employee-led support

In the UK, employees regularly take part in fundraising events and activities for good causes.

Applications

Contact the correspondent for further information.

Community contributions

Cash donations UK	£1,000,000

In 2020/21 Currys made a donation of £1 million to the Digital Poverty Alliance.

PZ Cussons plc

Community services and development, education and training, health, research

Company registration number: 19457

Correspondent: Good4Business Committee, 3500 Aviator Way, Manchester Business Park, Manchester M22 5TG (tel: 0161 435 1000; email: pzccommunications@pzcussons.com; website: www.pzcussons.com/about-us/our-purpose)

Directors: Kirsty Bashforth; Valeria Juarez; Dariusz Kucz; Jonathan Myers; John Nicolson; Sarah Pollard; Caroline Silver; Jitesh Sodha; Jeremy Townsend (female: 44%; male: 56%).

Nature of business: Principal activities of the group are the manufacture and distribution of soaps, toiletries, cleaning agents, pharmaceuticals, refrigerators and air conditioners.

Financial information

Year end	31/05/2021
Turnover	£603,300,000
Pre-tax profit	£63,200,000

Total employees: 3,000

Main locations: In the UK, the group has offices in Manchester and London. Internationally, it has offices in Africa, Europe, Asia-Pacific and the USA.

Community involvement

As part of its Good4Business strategy, PZ Cussons supports local communities and charities in the areas where it operates. It does this through a combination of donations, staff volunteering and in-kind gifts. The majority of support is given through The Zochonis Charitable Trust (Charity Commission no. 274769), which receives shares from the group.

Partnerships

PZ Cussons has worked in partnership with Seashell Trust, a charity for children, young people and adults with disabilities. The group has also supported the charity FRAME (Fund for the Replacement of Animals in Medical Experiments). It has funded the charity's independent research activities and supports its campaign for better science and the advancement of non-animal methods.

The group is a national partner of Foodbank Australia.

PZ Cussons Nigerian Foundation

The foundation was established in 2007 and supports projects in Nigeria that improve education, health, water access and infrastructure.

In-kind support

PZ Cussons brands donate products to charity. For example, Sanctuary Spa provides regular Christmas donations to the NHS. In 2020/21, it provided an additional 53,000 products to key NHS workers and charities to recognise their efforts during the COVID-19 pandemic.

Employee-led support

Employees take part in fundraising activities.

Commercially led support

Brand charitable support

In 2018, the group's Carex brand again joined forces with United Purpose

(formerly Universal Concern) to support Global Handwashing Day.

Applications

Contact the correspondent or see the group's corporate charity entry for more information.

Corporate charity

The Zochonis Charitable Trust (Charity Commission no. 274769) – see entry on page 288.

Community contributions

Cash donations UK	£70,000

According to the group's 2020/21 annual report, charitable contributions in the UK during the year amounted to £70,000. We were unable to determine a figure for the group's total charitable contributions.

Daejan Holdings plc

Education and training

Company registration number: 305105

Correspondent: Mark Jenner, Company Secretary, Freshwater House, 158–162 Shaftesbury Avenue, London WC2H 8HR (tel: 020 7836 1555; email: mark.jenner@highdorn.co.uk; website: www.daejanholdings.com)

Directors: David Davis; Alexander Freshwater; Benzion Freshwater; Chaim Freshwater; Raphael Freshwater; Solomon Freshwater (male: 100%).

Nature of business: Daejan Holdings is a property investment and trading company. The major part of the group's property portfolio comprises commercial, industrial and residential premises throughout the UK and in the USA.

Financial information

Year end	31/03/2021
Turnover	£162,457,000
Pre-tax profit	£71,974,000

Total employees: 129

Main locations: The group's head office and the vast majority of its properties are located in London. It also has properties across the UK and in the USA.

Community involvement

The group makes cash donations, mainly to educational charities, in the areas in which the business operates.

Applications

Apply in writing to the correspondent. There is no donations or CSR committee.

Community contributions

Cash donations UK	£1,297,300

According to the annual report for 2020/21, the group made donations totalling £183,000 mainly to educational charities. It also passed on dividend payments of £1.11 million.

Daily Mail and General Trust plc

General charitable purposes, health, social welfare

Company registration number: 184594

Correspondent: CR Champions Network, Northcliffe House, 2 Derry Street, Kensington, London W8 5TT (tel: 020 7938 6000; email: enquiries@dmgt.com; website: www.dmgt.com/corporate-responsibility)

Directors: Viscount Rothermere; Paul Zwillenberg; Tim Collier; Kevin Beatty; Andrew Lane; David Nelson; Kevin Parry; Heidi Roizen; Dominique Trempont; François Morin; Jayaprakasa Rangaswami; Fillippa Wallestam (female: 17%; male: 83%).

Nature of business: Daily Mail and General Trust (DMGT) is a British media company and the owner of the Daily Mail and several other titles.

Financial information

Year end	30/09/2021
Turnover	£1,142,000,000
Pre-tax profit	£88,000,000

Total employees: 5,889

Main locations: DMGT's headquarters is in London.

Community involvement

The group channels its charitable giving through its CR Champions network, which focuses on group-level partnerships, support for local community initiatives and disaster relief. The group provides financial and in-kind donations and employee-led support.

CR Champions Network

A network of employees representing each operating business meets by video call each quarter to discuss corporate responsibility at a grassroots level. The CR Champions share ideas and lessons learnt from CR initiatives they have carried out to encourage best practice. They promote group initiatives such as the Community Champions Awards and co-ordinate efforts for unexpected events and disasters in communities where DMGT's businesses operate.

Partnerships

The group has three main charity partnerships:

▌ **Orbis** – a charity which prevents avoidable blindness and provides training to local eye care teams in countries across the world.
▌ **Greenhouse Sports** – a London-based charity that uses sport to engage young people and improve their life chances by placing full-time coaches into schools.
▌ **The Kensington and Chelsea Foundation** – a local charity which addresses local hardship and exclusion.

Mail Force (Charity Commission no. 1189196)

Mail Force is a registered charity launched by DMGT during the first COVID-19 lockdown to address PPE shortages in the UK. Following this, Mail Force supported students struggling to adapt to online learning by donating IT equipment. Since then, the charity has moved on to an appeal for Ukrainian refugees.

In-kind support

According to the 2021 annual report, DMGT worked with Mail Force to donate computers and IT equipment to schools to facilitate online learning for students during the COVID-19 pandemic.

Applications

Contact the correspondent for further information.

Community contributions

Cash donations worldwide	£800,000

The 2021 annual report states that the DMGT's total charitable donations during the year were £800,000. Funds donated included support for CR initiatives carried out at operating companies and donations to Mail Force.

Darlington Building Society

Education and training, health, medical research, social welfare

Company registration number: 205895

Correspondent: CSR Team, Sentinel House, Morton Road, Darlington, County Durham DL1 4PT (email: community@darlington.co.uk; website: www.darlington.co.uk)

Directors: Jack Cullen; Robert Cuffe; Andrew Craddock; Kate McIntyre; Angela Russell; Christopher Hunter (female: 33%; male: 67%).

Nature of business: Darlington Building Society is a UK building society.

Financial information

Year end	31/12/2021
Pre-tax profit	£3,168,000

UK employees: 176

Main locations: The building society operates ten branches in locations across County Durham, North Yorkshire and Teesside.

Community involvement

The society supports a wide range of charitable causes in its area of operation with a particular preference for social welfare, older people and medical research. Support is provided through cash donations, in-kind support, sponsorship and employee volunteering.

Sharing 5%

In 2017, the society pledged to support the communities local to its branches by donating 5% of its net profits after tax to charities and community organisations.

Society members are invited to vote for the charitable causes that they would like to support. The society's areas of focus include:

▌ Mental health and wellbeing
▌ Unemployment and skills development
▌ Staying connected

The society works closely with the Durham Community Foundation to distribute the funds. For more information, see the community foundation's website: www.cdcf.org.uk.

Local 5

The Local 5 campaign gives each of the society's nine branches, plus its head office, the ability to adopt their own five charities, or good causes, to support for a full year. As well as receiving funding through the annual 5% pledge, charities chosen by staff also receive support in other practical ways such as volunteering, fundraising and knowledge sharing.

In-kind support

The society allows local organisations to utilise available space within its branches to help them to promote themselves, meet new audiences or raise funds.

Employee-led support

All society employees are entitled to two days' paid leave per year to volunteer for local organisations.

Applications

Contact the correspondent for further information.

Community contributions

Cash donations UK	£90,000

According to its 2021 annual report, during the year the society awarded over £90,000 in donations to 28 local charities and community organisations.

De La Rue plc

🔍 Community services and development, education and training, social welfare, STEM

Company registration number: 3834125

Correspondent: CSR Team, De La Rue House, Jays Close, Viables, Basingstoke, Hampshire RG22 4BS (tel: 01256 605000; email: appeals.secretary@uk. delarue.com; website: www.delarue.com)

Directors: Kevin Loosemore; Clive Vacher; Rob Harding; Ruth Euling; Margaret Rice-Jones; The Rt Hon. The Baroness Ashton of Upholland; Nick Bray; Mark Hoad (female: 38%; male: 63%).

Nature of business: The group is a commercial security printer and papermaker, involved in the production of over 150 national currencies and a wide range of security documents. The company is also a leading provider of cash handling equipment and solutions to banks and retailers as well as a range of identity systems to governments worldwide.

Financial information

Year end	26/03/2022
Turnover	£375,100,000
Pre-tax profit	£24,200,000

Total employees: 2,236

Main locations: In the UK, the group has offices or operations in Bathford, Basingstoke, Debden, Gateshead, Overton and Westhoughton. There are also sites in Kenya, Malta and Sri Lanka.

Community involvement

The group states in its 2021/22 annual report that its sites tend to focus their support on smaller, local charities where employees can be involved.

The De La Rue Charitable Trust (Charity Commission no. 274052)

The group's corporate charity, The De La Rue Charitable Trust, supports causes both in the UK and abroad, with an emphasis on education, social welfare, international development and sustainability. The trust's income comes from investments: it does not receive any financial contribution from the company. The website states that grants are made to registered charities in the following categories:

- Well-researched causes in under-developed countries, preferably through UK charities to secure both financial control and tax relief
- Educational charities which promote relevant skills and international understanding, particularly for the benefit of disadvantaged and underprivileged students
- Disaster funds
- Local charities or community projects, particularly if employees are involved
- Charities for the benefit, directly or indirectly, of employees or ex-employees

In 2021/22 the trust made grants totalling £56,000. A list of beneficiaries was not provided.

Education

The group works with charities and schools to promote STEM subjects and employability. It also provides a Caribbean scholarship programme, supporting students studying economics, finance and actuarial sciences in Barbados, the eastern Caribbean, Jamaica and Trinidad and Tobago.

Employee-led support

Employees organise fundraising initiatives to support charities chosen by them. The De La Rue Charitable Trust provides matched funding of up to £500 each for employees undertaking their own fundraising initiatives. Employees can also choose to donate through a payroll giving scheme.

In 2021/22 employees from the group's head office in Basingstoke donated essential items to women escaping domestic violence, as well as educational toys for children with special educational needs.

Employees from the group's office in Sri Lanka donated medical supplies to a local hospital in response to the COVID-19 pandemic.

Exclusions

The De La Rue Charitable Trust will not support:

- Party political causes
- Organisations that do not benefit a community in a place where De La Rue does business
- Individuals
- Grant-makers
- National charities
- Military organisations
- Religious organisations

Applications

The De La Rue Charitable Trust

Applications should be made in writing to the Trust Administrator to be considered at the trustees' meetings, which take place around three times a year. Applications should include the information specified on the website: www.delarue.com/about-us/corporate-responsibility/relationships/de-la-rue-in-the-community/charitable-trust

The trust regrets that it is unable to reply to every unsuccessful application.

Community contributions

We were unable to determine a figure for the group's total contributions during the year.

Dechra Pharmaceuticals plc

🔍 Animal welfare

Company registration number: 3369634

Correspondent: Regional Giving Community, Cheshire Business Park, 24 Cheshire Avenue, Northwich, Cheshire CW9 7UA (tel: 01939 211200; email: contact form on the website; website: www.dechra.co.uk)

Directors: Melanie Hall; Lisa Bright; Anthony Griffin; Julian Heslop; Dr Lawson Macartney; Ishbel Macpherson; Ian Page; Elizabeth Platt; Paul Sandland; John Shipsey (female: 40%; male: 60%).

Nature of business: Dechra is involved in the development and marketing of veterinary products.

Financial information

Year end	30/06/2021
Turnover	£114,803,000
Pre-tax profit	£32,623,000

Main locations: In the UK, the group has locations in Skipton, Cheshire and Shrewsbury. It also has several locations across the world.

Community involvement

Dechra supports causes within its areas of operation, by making both financial and in-kind contributions. The group has a particular interest in causes relating to animal welfare.

Regional Giving Communities

The group used to operate a group donations scheme which allowed staff to nominate and select charities to be supported by the group. However, in 2022 this scheme was replaced by Regional Giving Communities. Under this scheme committee members offer suggestions of organisations to support and then vote to narrow the selections to a reasonable number of organisations given the budget.

In-kind support

The group makes donations of veterinary products.

Employee-led support

Each year, employees are entitled to a day's paid leave per year to undertake voluntary work.

Applications

Dechra's individual locations make decisions on which charities to support. Enquiries should be directed to your local Dechra site.

Community contributions

Cash donations worldwide	£72,000
Total contributions worldwide	£382,000

According to the group's 2020/21 accounts, Dechra's cash donations totalled £72,000. The group also donated products to the value of £310,000.

Deloitte LLP

Community enterprise and social entrepreneurship, education and training

Company registration number: OC303675

Correspondent: Kathryn Alsegaf, Global Chief Sustainability Officer, 1 New Street Square, London EC4A 3BZ (email: deloitteglobalcrs@deloitte.com)

Directors: Richard Houston; Stephen Griggs; Paul Stephenson; Anne-Marie Malley; Richard Bell; Andy Morris; Matt Ellis; Pauline Biddle; Richard Hammell; Dominic Graham; Emma Cox; Daniel Barlow; Donna Ward; Simon Kerton-Johnson; Dimple Agarwal; Mark Mullins (female: 31%; male: 69%).

Nature of business: Deloitte provides audit, tax, corporate finance and management consultancy services. In June 2017, Deloitte LLP combined with its Belgian, Danish, Dutch, Finnish, Icelandic, Norwegian and Swedish member firms to create Deloitte North West Europe. The information in this record refers to Deloitte's activities in the UK.

Financial information

Year end	31/05/2022
Turnover	£4,940,000,000
Pre-tax profit	£797,000,000

Main locations: Deloitte has 28 offices located throughout the UK and in over 100 locations across the world.

Community involvement

Deloitte works with various local and national non-profit organisations through its 5 Million Futures initiative. The initiative is the UK group's contribution to Deloitte's 'WorldClass' commitment, which seeks to reach 50 million people globally by helping people develop their job skills and improve their educational attainment.

5 Million Futures

Under this initiative, the group works with a wide range of charity partners across the UK, to help achieve its overall mission of supporting 5 million people in need by 2030.

Each of the group's UK offices provides pro bono services, volunteering and fundraising to schools, charities and social enterprises. Current partnerships include Starting Point, IntoUniversity, the Papworth Trust and Place2Be.

In addition to locally led partnerships, the group also has several national partnerships. These include:

- **Teach First** – Deloitte is currently funding Teach First's National Professional Qualification, which supports teachers into leadership roles in schools facing the biggest challenges.
- **TutorMate** – using the TutorMate platform, Deloitte volunteers are reading weekly with struggling five- to six-year-olds in five Doncaster schools.
- **The Access Project** – Deloitte and The Access Project work together with students from disadvantaged backgrounds to help them access top universities through tutoring and mentoring. Deloitte volunteers help students with their GCSEs and A-levels for an hour a week during the school year.

In-kind support

In 2021/22, 9,727 hours of pro bono work were completed.

Employee-led support

Employees provide pro bono services and volunteer for charities local to their office. In 2021/22, over 31,716 volunteering hours were completed by staff.

Applications

Contact your local office for more information.

Community contributions

Total contributions worldwide	£8,000,000

According to its 2021/22 Business and ESG Performance Metrics report, the group valued its total contributions at £8 million.

Derwent London plc

Community enterprise and social entrepreneurship, community services and development

Company registration number: 1819699

Correspondent: Community Team, 25 Savile Row, London W1S 2ER (tel: 020 7659 3000; email: community@ derwentlondon.com; website: www. derwentlondon.com/responsibility/ social/communities/community-fund)

Directors: David Lawler; Claudia Arney; Lucinda Bell; Mark Breuer; Richard David; Nigel George; Helen Gordon; Emily Prideaux; Sanjeev Sharma; Priscilla Snowball; Paul Williams; Damian Wisniewski (female: 42%; male: 58%).

Nature of business: Derwent London is an office specialist property regenerator and investor. The group's investment portfolio comprises 6.2 million square feet, 98% of which is located in central London, specifically the West End and areas bordering the City of London.

Financial information

Year end	31/12/2021
Pre-tax profit	£252,500,000

Main locations: The group has offices in London and Glasgow.

Community involvement

Derwent London provides financial support to local charities through its Community Fund and Sponsorships and Donations Committee.

Community Fund (not a registered charity)

Funding is divided between Fitzrovia, the West End and the 'Tech Belt' area, defined as extending from Kings Cross to Whitechapel covering a large number of EC1 and E1 postcodes.

Each area constitutes its own 'fund', which has varying grant allowances, as well as different opening and closing dates for applications.

Sponsorships and Donations Committee

The company also provides financial support through its Sponsorships and Donations Committee. In 2021 the committee focused on supporting homelessness and mental health charities. Support was also provided to increase diversity and inclusion within the property sector.

Employee-led support

Staff are encouraged to volunteer for causes supported by the Community Fund.

Exclusions

See the website for a guidance and exclusions for the Fitzrovia and Tech Belt funds.

Applications

Contact the correspondent for further information.

Community contributions

Cash donations UK	£725,000

According to the company's 2021 Responsibility Report, the Community Fund awarded over £105,000 to 19 projects. A further £620,000 was awarded in 'community and sponsorship donations'.

Deutsche Bank AG

Community enterprise and social entrepreneurship, community services and development, education and training

Company registration number: FC007615

Correspondent: The CSR Team, 1 Great Winchester Street, London EC2N 2DB (tel: 020 7545 8000; website: www.db. com/unitedkingdom/responsibility.html)

Directors: Fabrizio Campelli; James Graf von Moltke; Bernd Leukert; Christiana Riley; Christian Sewing; Rebecca Short; Dr Stefan Simon; Olivier Vignron; Karl von Rohr; Gerd von zur Muhlen (female: 20%; male: 80%).

Nature of business: Deutsche Bank is the holding company of a group providing international merchant banking and investment management services.

Main locations: In the UK, the bank's head office is in London. There is also an office in Birmingham.

Community involvement

Deutsche Bank is engaged in a wide range of charitable activities, with a particular interest in young people, employment, entrepreneurship, community development and social cohesion.

Born to Be

The group's Born to Be programme focuses on educational projects that prepare young people for the workplace and improve social mobility. Through partnerships with various organisations, the group funds projects such as those tackling LGBTQ+ bullying in schools, projects inspiring young women to pursue STEM careers and in-school workshops about the works of Shakespeare.

Made for Good

According to its website, the group's Made for Good initiative encourages social and creative enterprise projects. Under this initiative, the group has partnerships with several organisations including the Thomson Reuters Foundation and Women Entrepreneurs in Social Tech. The company's partnership with Cracked It involves ex-offenders and young people at risk of offending performing smartphone repairs at Deutsche Bank offices to help increase their chances of employability.

Charity of the Year

The group partners with small charities chosen by its UK employees for two years at a time. The chosen charities benefit from employee volunteering and fundraising. The group's Charity of the

Year partner for 2020/21 was Hospice UK.

Deutsche Bank Small Grants Fund

This fund is administered by London Community Foundation (Charity Commission no. 1091263). Grants of up to £5,000 are available for projects in London and Birmingham that improve social cohesion.

In-kind support

The group's office space can be used by charities for free.

Employee-led support

Employees are encouraged to volunteer their time in support of the group's various partnerships.

Permanent staff are also entitled to a £4,000 annual matched-giving allowance for donations to UK-registered charities.

Applications

For the Small Grants Fund, see the London Community Foundation website (www.londoncf.org.uk). For any other enquiries, contact the correspondent for more information.

Community contributions

We were unable to determine a figure for the group's community contributions.

DFS Furniture plc

General charitable purposes

Company registration number: 7236769

Correspondent: The CSR Team, 1 Rockingham Way, Redhouse Interchange, Adwick le Street, Doncaster, South Yorkshire DN6 7NA (website: www.dfscorporate.co.uk/esg/sustainability-2021)

Directors: Elizabeth McDonald; Jane Bednall; Joanna Boydell; Ian Durrant; Alison Hutchinson; Stephen Johnson; Loraine Martins; Michael Schmidt; Timothy Stacey (female: 56%; male: 44%).

Nature of business: DFS specialises in the retail of upholstered furniture.

Financial information

Year end	27/06/2021
Turnover	£1,067,700,000
Pre-tax profit	£99,200,000

Total employees: 5,217

Main locations: DFS has stores across the UK, the Republic of Ireland and Europe. Its head office is in Doncaster.

Community involvement

DFS supports its charity partner, BBC Children in Need, as well as various charities and initiatives based locally to its operations in the UK and Europe.

Giving Back

Through the group's Giving Back programme, it has committed to raise and donate up to 1% of its profit before tax, give every employee one day's paid volunteering leave, and donate up to 1% of its products (by volume) each year to charitable causes.

Partnerships

In 2020/21 the group raised £637,000 for Children in Need. All of DFS's manufacturing and warehouse locations, offices and showrooms have partnered with a Children in Need-funded project within ten miles of their location to ensure a connection is established and to help drive local involvement.

Sofology also has a partnership with The Pennies Foundation. Pennies works with Sofology to allow customers to support local charities nominated by Sofology colleagues for each retail region.

In-kind support

The group donates up to 1% of its products to charitable causes each year.

Employee-led support

Employees help to raise funds for DFS's charity partners through various events and challenges.

Applications

Contact your local DFS store for further information.

Community contributions

Cash donations UK	£138,000

In 2020/21 the group made charitable donations totalling £138,000. A further £700,000 was raised by customers and employees.

Direct Line Insurance Group plc

Health, mental health and well-being, social welfare

Company registration number: 2280426

Correspondent: The CSR Team, Churchill Court, Westmorland Road, Bromley, Kent BR1 1DP (website: www.directlinegroup.co.uk/en/sustainability.html)

Directors: Roger Clifton; Tracy Corrigan; Danuta Gray; Mark Gregory; Penelope James; Sebastian James; Adrian Joseph; Neil Manser; Fiona McBain; Gregor Stewart; Richard Ward (female: 36%; male: 64%).

Nature of business: The group specialises in insurance. It owns several brands such as Churchill, Green Flag and Shotgun.

Financial information

Year end	31/12/2021
Turnover	£3,171,600,000
Pre-tax profit	£446,000,000

61

Main locations: The group's head office is in Kent. It has operations across England and Wales.

Community involvement

Direct Line channels much of its charitable activity through the partnerships it holds and through the Direct Line Group (DLG) Community Fund (not a registered charity).

DLG Community Fund

The group makes donations to its charity partners through the fund. Support is provided in the following three priority areas: marginalised groups and loneliness; mental health and well-being; and food poverty. Beneficiaries have included Business in the Community, Carers UK, Envision, Quartet Community Foundation, Stand Up to Cancer and the UK Sepsis Trust.

Community and Social Committees

Local volunteering and community activities at the group's sites are co-ordinated by employee-led charity committees.

Employee-led support

Employees are entitled to take one paid day's leave from work per year to engage in voluntary work of their choice.

Applications

Contact the correspondent for further information.

Community contributions

Cash donations UK	£1,500,000

According to the group's Sustainability Report 2021, the DLG Community Fund donated £1.5 million to charities.

DLA Piper International LLP

Human rights, medical research, social welfare, women's rights

Company registration number: OC305357

Correspondent: CSR Team, 160 Aldersgate Street, London EC1A 4HT (tel: 020 7349 0296; website: www.dlapiper.com/en/uk/aboutus)

Directors: Jon Hayes; Frank Ryan; Simon Levine; Dr Jan Meents; Sandra Wallace; Charles Severs; Dr Olaf Schmidt; Stéphane Lemarchand; Jackie Park; Richard Chesley; Robert Seidel; Diego Martinez; Álvaro Garza-Galván; Marcelo Etchebarne; Fabio Mello; Matias Zegers; Camilo Beltran; Ricardo Escobar; Nikos Buxeda; Miriam Figueroa (female: 20%; male: 80%).

Nature of business: DLA Piper is a global law firm.

Financial information

Year end	30/04/2021
Turnover	£1,164,500,000
Pre-tax profit	£422,100,000

UK employees: 3,900

Total employees: 12,191

Main locations: DLA Piper has offices in more than 40 countries throughout the Americas, Asia-Pacific, Europe, Africa and the Middle East. In the UK, the firm has offices in Birmingham, Edinburgh, Leeds, Liverpool, London, Manchester and Sheffield.

Community involvement

The majority of DLA Piper's community involvement in the UK is channelled through The DLA Piper Charitable Trust (Charity Commission no. 327280), to which it makes regular donations. The firm also supports charitable and not-for-profit organisations local to its offices.

DLA Piper has an ongoing partnership with UNICEF, which as of August 2022, had raised funds of £1.8 million and seen DLA Piper provide more than 27,000 hours of pro bono support.

In-kind support

Employees are encouraged to take on pro bono work under DLA Piper's global initiative, New Perimeter. The initiative focuses on the following areas:

- Migrant rights
- Rule of law
- Child rights
- Access to justice
- Sound legal institutions
- Social and economic development

Applications

Contact the correspondent or see the company's corporate charity entry for more information.

Corporate charity

The DLA Piper Charitable Trust (Charity Commission no. 327280) – see entry on page 268.

Community contributions

Cash donations UK	£158,800

According to the firm's 2020/21 accounts, DLA Piper made £158,800 in corporate donations. It fundraised £276,300 for charitable causes worldwide and donated £194,000 to COVID-19 response projects in 2020/21.

Drax Group plc

Arts, culture and heritage, community services and development, education and training, the environment, sports and recreation, STEM

Company registration number: 5562053

Correspondent: Charity Committee, Drax Power Station, Selby, North Yorkshire YO8 8PH (tel: 01757 618381; email: enquiries@drax.com; website: www.drax.com/sustainability)

Directors: Philip Cox; Will Gardiner; Andy Skelton; David Nussbaum; Nicola Hodson; Vanessa Simms; John Baxter; Erika Peterman; Kim Keating (female: 44%; male: 56%).

Nature of business: Drax Group has three principal activities: the manufacturing and supply of wood pellets from sustainable residues, electricity production, and electricity sales to the wholesale market and business customers. The group has several businesses, including Haven Power and Opus Energy.

Financial information

Year end	31/12/2021
Turnover	£5,090,000,000
Pre-tax profit	£121,500,000

Total employees: 3,022

Main locations: The group has offices in London and Yorkshire. It has operations across the UK in Galloway, Lanark, Daldowie, Rye, Shoreham, Argyll and Blackburn.

Community involvement

The group supports local projects through grants, partnerships and employee fundraising and volunteering. The group also delivers education and employment programmes in schools local to its operations focused on STEM subjects and careers.

Grants

According to the group's website, Drax will consider requests for support from charitable causes or registered charities local to where it operates for the following causes:

- STEM and education outreach
- Skills and employability
- Improving the local community

Partnerships

Teach First – Teach First is a charity that aims to alleviate educational disadvantages in England and Wales. Drax's partnership with Teach First supports the delivery of its activities with schools.

In-kind support

Drax donated 1,173 laptops to 80 schools and colleges during the year.

Employee-led support

Drax's Community and Charity policy allows employees to volunteer for one working day annually. During the year, Drax colleagues undertook a range of volunteering and charitable work. This included personal fundraising efforts, group-wide fundraising days and outreach support to partner schools, for which Drax offers matched funding. Drax also has a payroll giving scheme.

Commercially led support

Educational visitor centres are open at a number of Drax sites. The group engages directly with schools and colleges to offer free access to its site tours in term time. The public can also visit the group's nature reserve in Selby, which is a sanctuary for over 100 species of wildlife. The reserve is specifically designed to help schoolchildren understand more about the natural habitat and ecology of the area.

Exclusions

Applications will not be considered for organisations with interests that do not match Drax's focus or which are located outside the areas where Drax operates.

Applications

Applications for support and donations can be made in writing using the enquiry form on the group's 'Contact us' web page. All requests are considered by the Drax Charity Committee.

Community contributions

Cash donations UK	£421,000

According to its 2021 annual report, the group donated £421,000 to charitable causes during the year. This includes money raised through community partnerships, the group's community fund, matched funding, payroll giving and national fundraising days.

Dunelm Group plc

General charitable purposes, health

Company registration number: 4708277

Correspondent: CSR Team, Watermead Business Park, Syston, Leicestershire LE7 1AD (tel: 0116 264 4400; email: charity.enquiries@dunelm.com; website: https://corporate.dunelm.com/sustainability/people/customers-and-communities)

Directors: Andy Harrison; Will Adderley; Nick Wilkinson; Karen Witts; Dawn Durrant; Ian Bull; William Reeve; Marion Sears; Peter Ruis; Bill Adderley; Arja Taaveniku; Vijay Talwar; Kelly Devine (female: 38%; male: 62%).

Nature of business: Dunelm Group plc is a specialist homewares retailer providing a range of products under the brand name Dunelm Mill.

Financial information

Year end	29/06/2021
Turnover	£1,340,200,000
Pre-tax profit	£157,800,000

UK employees: 6,897

Main locations: Dunelm has stores across the UK and its head office is in Leicestershire.

Community involvement

Dunelm supports charitable and community initiatives local to its stores and business operations.

Charity of the Year

The group adopts a Charity of the Year biennially to which it makes an annual cash donation. The group also facilitates collections in-store, carrier bag sales and employee fundraising events to raise money for the charity. In 2018/19 the group began a two-year partnership with Macmillan Cancer Support. The group donated a total of £1.3 million to the charity during its partnership.

In July 2021 the company announced Mind as its new charity partner. The company will encourage its customers to donate unwanted homewares products for resale in Mind charity shops.

In-kind support

Dunelm works with over 100 charity partners nationwide to donate quilts and pillows that cannot be sold to customers.

Employee-led support

Each year, employees are entitled to one day of paid leave to volunteer for a local charity. Employees are involved in fundraising events and activities and the group matches funds raised with a donation to its Charity of the Year. In 2021, the total raised for charities by the group and its employees was £467,500.

Commercially led support

In 2020/21, funds raised from carrier bag sales were donated to Macmillan Cancer Support.

Delivering Joy

Through this campaign, Dunelm supports people who are vulnerable during the festive season. At the time of writing (August 2022), over 18,000 Christmas gifts had been donated through its stores and support sites.

Applications

For enquiries relating to charity support, email charity.enquiries@dunelm.com.

Community contributions

Cash donations UK	£112,500

In 2020/21 the total value of charitable donations made by the group was £112,500.

DWF Group plc

General charitable purposes, education and training

Company registration number: 11561594

Correspondent: Clare Bevan, Foundation Manager, 20 Fenchurch Street, London EC3M 3AG (email: clare.beavan@dwf.law; website: https://dwfgroup.com)

Directors: Jonathan Bloomer; Chris Sullivan; Sir Nigel Knowles; Chris Stefani; Matthew Doughty; Teresa Colaianni; Samantha Tymms; Luke Savage; Michele Cicchetti; Seema Bains; Darren Drabble (female: 27%; male: 73%).

Nature of business: DWF is an international law firm.

Financial information

Year end	30/04/2021
Turnover	£338,000,000
Pre-tax profit	£31,000,000

Total employees: 3,100

Main locations: In the UK, the group has offices in Belfast, Birmingham, Bristol, Edinburgh, Glasgow, Leeds, Liverpool, London, Manchester and Newcastle.

Community involvement

The group provides charitable support through its corporate charity, The DWF Foundation (Charity Commission no. 1157229) and through education programmes.

5 STAR Futures

As part of the group's 5 STAR Futures programme, volunteers from DWF go into local schools and deliver workshops on topics such as workplace behaviours, communication and resilience.

Employee-led support

According to the DWF's 2020/21 annual report, employees gave up 5,876 hours of volunteering time during the year and helped more than 600 young people to develop their skills.

Applications

For further information see the company's corporate charity entry.

Corporate charity

The DWF Foundation (Charity Commission no. 1191347) – see entry on page 238.

Community contributions

The group's 2020/21 accounts did not provide a figure for charitable contributions.

Dwr Cymru Welsh Water

Community services and development, education and training, the environment

Company registration number: 2366777

Correspondent: CSR Department, Dwr Cymru Welsh Water Linea, Fortran Road, St Mellons, Cardiff CF3 0LT (email: See 'Applications'; website: https://corporate.dwrcymru.com/en/community)

Directors: Alastair Lyons; Peter Perry; Graham Edwards; Joanne Kenrick; Mike Davis; Debra Bowen Rees; Prof. Tom Crick; Jane Hanson (female: 38%; male: 63%).

Nature of business: Dwr Cymru Welsh Water is a company which supplies drinking water and wastewater services to most of Wales and parts of western England.

Financial information

Year end	31/03/2022
Turnover	£810,200,000
Pre-tax profit	(£215,200,000)

UK employees: 3,514

Main locations: The company's headquarters is in Mid Glamorgan.

Community involvement

The company's CSR activities are focused on supporting local groups and projects that make positive contributions to the environment. Support and funding are given through partnerships, community funds, educational programmes and employee fundraising and volunteering.

Charity partners

The company provides regular support and works on projects in partnership with WaterAid and The Prince's Trust.

Welsh Water Community Fund (not a registered charity)

In 2017, the company launched the Welsh Water Community Fund to support projects benefitting health, well-being and the environment in the communities where it operates. Grants of up to £1,000 are available for communities to boost their fundraising efforts for local projects. Priority is given to projects where Welsh Water is or has been working.

The Community Fund also matches funds raised by employees for the company's charity partners to the value of £15,000 each year.

Environment Fund (not a registered charity)

The Environment Fund gives financial support to projects benefitting nature and enhancing biodiversity at or near the company's sites. The fund is designed to help voluntary organisations develop and implement their ideas. The fund is open to any not-for-profit organisation that works near the company's sites in Wales, Herefordshire and Cheshire.

Dwr Cymru Water Framework Directive

The company's Water Framework Directive funding scheme provides financial contributions to not-for-profit organisations for projects that deliver improvements to Welsh rivers, lakes and waterways, thereby creating a more vibrant and healthy environment for people and wildlife.

Examples of previous projects that received funding include:

- **River Schools** – an educational programme run by Groundwork North Wales that aims to raise awareness of the river environment
- **Clear Streams Swansea** – a project aimed at reducing the surface water that enters the Swansea sewerage network
- **Healthy Rivers** – a project by Groundwork Caerphilly that aims to remove barriers to fish migration and facilitate volunteering opportunities

Education

Education continues to be one of the company's main areas of community support. The company runs an educational outreach programme that combines school workshops and site visits to its educational Discovery Centres. The company's website also hosts a range of free primary and secondary education resources. In 2021/22, 46,000 students were supported through this programme.

The company may offer assistance to communities in its areas of operation that are experiencing flooding.

Employee-led support

Employees fundraise for a variety of charities including the company's charity partners. Individual employees can claim up to £200 of matched funding for their own charity efforts.

Employees offer their business and management expertise, mentoring and other skills to their local communities. For example, employees volunteer as mentors in their local Jobcentre to help people develop interview, CV and application skills.

Exclusions

The Welsh Water Community Fund does not support:

- Sponsorships
- The staffing or ongoing costs of a project
- Funding for IT equipment

Applications

Water Framework Directive – for further information, to discuss ideas for projects or to obtain an application form, email wfd@dwrcymru.com.

Welsh Water Community Fund – for information on the application process, visit dwrcymru.com/community-fund, or email communityfund@dwrcymru.com.

Environment Fund – for further information on how to apply for funding from the fund, visit https://corporate.dwrcymru.com/en/community/environment/our-projects/biodiversity-fund.

To book a free educational visit to a Discovery Centre for your school, email education@dwrcymru.com.

Community contributions

Cash donations UK	£100,000

We were unable to determine a figure for Welsh Water's total charitable donations for the 2021/22 financial year. However, according to its annual report, the company made a £100,000 donation to food banks in 2021. It also made matched donations to charities such as Children in Need, WaterAid and The Prince's Trust.

Dyson James Group Ltd

Arts, culture and heritage, community enterprise and social entrepreneurship, community services and development, education and training, health, medical research, STEM

Company registration number: 7086916

Correspondent: Lydia Beaton, Foundation Manager, The James Dyson Foundation, Tetbury Hill, Malmesbury, Wiltshire SN16 0RP (tel: 01666 746802; email: askdyson@dyson.co.uk; website: www.dyson.co.uk)

Directors: Richard Bevan; Martin Bowen (male: 100%).

Nature of business: Dyson manufactures domestic appliances. The company began in 1978, when James Dyson invented the bagless vacuum.

Financial information

Year end	31/12/2020
Turnover	£325,000,000
Pre-tax profit	£312,000,000

Main locations: The UK head office is in Malmesbury, Wiltshire. Dyson also operates internationally in over 65 countries.

Community involvement

The company's community involvement is directed through The James Dyson Foundation (Charity Commission no. 1099709). The foundation exists to advance education in the fields of engineering, design and technology through the provision of resources, the running of workshops in colleges and universities, as well as through bursary schemes and collaborative projects.

In-kind support

The company's design engineers host workshops at schools and universities throughout the country. Through its foundation the company provides free resources to Design and Technology teachers throughout the UK, such as the Dyson Engineering Box, which introduces secondary school students to engineering through Dyson technology. Each year, the company also donates several Dyson vacuum cleaners (for raffle prizes) to charitable causes through its foundation.

Applications

Contact the correspondent for further information.

Corporate charity

The James Dyson Foundation (Charity Commission no. 1099709) – see entry on page 238.

Community contributions

Total contributions UK	£984,500

According to its 2020 annual report, The James Dyson Foundation received £984,500 from Dyson James Group Ltd in cash donations and donated goods and services during the year. Donated services included the foundation's staff costs, which were incurred by the company.

E.ON UK plc

Community services and development, education and training, the environment, money and debt advice, STEM

Company registration number: 2366970

Correspondent: Community Relations Team, Westwood Way, Westwood Business Park, Coventry, Warwickshire CV4 8LG (tel: 024 7619 2000; email: See 'Applications'; website: www.eonenergy.com/about-us/community-matters.html)

Directors: Michael Lewis; Christian Barr; Chris Norbury; Fiona Humphreys (female: 25%; male: 75%).

Nature of business: E.ON UK is an English energy company and a subsidiary of the German company E.ON SE.

Financial information

Year end	31/12/2021
Turnover	£1,552,000,000
Pre-tax profit	£447,000,000

UK employees: 710

Main locations: The company's UK office is located in Coventry.

Community involvement

In the UK, the company supports energy efficiency projects, fuel poverty and energy education and awareness.

Community Relations

Working with partners such as charities, schools and councils, E.ON UK helps people who need support with their energy usage. There are three areas that the company focuses on:

- Reducing fuel poverty
- Improving energy-awareness, education and skills for people of all ages
- Securing funding for local community energy projects

Partnerships

In 2021 E.ON UK ended its partnership with Alzheimer's UK. The partnership started in 2016 and provided support and raised money for the charity. Activities included employee fundraising and Dementia Friends sessions, which help employees understand what it is like to live with dementia. According to the 2020/21 annual report, the company raised £400,000 for Alzheimer's UK over the course of the five-year partnership.

In 2022, E.ON UK began a partnership with Mind UK.

STEM initiatives

The company's Energise Anything! programme provides free resources for schools to help inspire children in STEM. Energise Anything! workshops are also delivered in schools to Key Stages 2 to 4 by STEM experts.

Employee-led support

Over the course of the partnership with Alzheimer's UK, 5,000 employees at E.ON UK have become 'Dementia Friends' to people with dementia.

In 2021, E.ON UK's parent group E.ON SE reported that over 1,000 employees completed over 8,500 hours of volunteering. We were unable to find a total for hours completed by E.ON UK employees.

Commercially led support

In 2021, E.ON UK partnered with Scamp and Dude to create a cape for children, so as to encourage children and parents to walk to school with the aim of lowering air pollution.

Applications

Community Relations

Use the contact form on the company's website to contact the company's Community Relations Team.

STEM

Resources can be found on the Energise Anything! section of the website: www.eonenergy.com/About-eon/Community/energise-anything.

Community contributions

We were unable to determine a figure for the company's total charitable contributions in 2021. The company is a subsidiary of E.ON SE, whose website states that the group's community investments amounted to £10.5 million in 2021. This figure was converted from EUR using the exchange rate at the time of writing (August 2022).

East of England Co-operative Society Ltd

General charitable purposes, health, mental health and well-being, social welfare

Company registration number: IP01099R

Correspondent: Community Cares Team, Wherstead Park, The Street, Wherstead, Ipswich, Suffolk IP9 2BL (tel: 01473 786000; email: enquiries@eastofengland.coop; website: www.eastofengland.coop/community)

Directors: Frank Moxon; Belinda Busling; Joy Burnford; Sally Chicken; Esme Cole; John Cook; Mandy Errington; Nicola Fox; John Hawkins; Emma Howard; Caroline Ley; Judi Newman; Jane Nice; Beverley Perkins; Maria Veronese; Richard Youngs (female: 75%; male: 25%).

Nature of business: The East of England Co-operative Society is the fourth largest consumer co-operative in the UK.

Financial information

Year end	22/01/2022
Turnover	£348,561,000
Pre-tax profit	£7,574,000

Total employees: 3,834

Main locations: The company's headquarters is in Ipswich and it trades in the eastern counties of Essex, Suffolk and Norfolk.

Community involvement

The company channels its charitable activities through its Community Cares Fund (not a registered charity). The fund seeks to support local community groups and charities in the areas in which the company operates. The fund's current areas of interest include:

- Young people's mental health
- Food poverty
- Reducing food waste
- Supporting an ageing population

The Community Cares Fund is financed by Co-operative members and in 2021/22 the fund donated £237,000 to charitable organisations.

Community token scheme

In food stores, members use tokens to vote for causes they wish to support. The scheme allows the company to make financial contributions to local groups. Funding has been awarded towards play equipment, sports kits and organising trips for vulnerable and isolated people.

Community giving scheme

This scheme operates throughout the company's funeral branches, giving those who have used Co-op's funeral services the opportunity to choose which local good causes should receive funding.

In-kind support

Community gift vouchers

Charities and other groups can apply for a community gift voucher, which can be exchanged in-store for goods to support fundraising events and activities, such as a prize for a tombola or raffle.

Employee-led support

According to the latest annual report, employees carry out a variety of fundraising activities for good causes. In 2021/22, employees and customers raised £22,000 for over 25 local food banks. This total also comprises donations from the East of England Co-operative Society Ltd; however, we were unable to determine the amount donated by the company.

Commercially led support

Shop and Share donation bins

In 2021, the company set up Shop and Share donation bins that move around Co-operative stores, directing customers to the products most needed by food banks in the UK.

Applications

Applications must be made by a member of the co-op. These can be made online – see the website for more details.

Community contributions

Cash donations UK	£10,000

In 2022, the East of England Co-operative Society Ltd made charitable donations totalling £10,000.

The Economist Newspaper Ltd

Education and training, literacy, media, journalism and communications

Company registration number: 236383

Correspondent: The CSR Team, The Adelphi, 1–11 John Adam Street, London WC2N 6HT (tel: 020 7576 8448; website: www.economist.com)

Directors: Manvinder Banga; Lord Paul Deighton; Eli Goldstein; Suzanne Heywood; Phillip Mallinckrodt; Susan Minton-Beddoes; Diego Piacentini; Lara

Salames Boro; Mustafa Suleyman (female: 22%; male: 78%).

Nature of business: The Economist Newspaper Ltd is a British multinational media company specialising in international business and world affairs. It is best known as the publisher of *The Economist.*

Financial information

Year end	31/03/2022
Turnover	£346,300,000
Pre-tax profit	£43,614,000

Total employees: 1,578

Main locations: The group's UK offices are based in London. The group also has offices in several other countries.

Community involvement

The group's charitable activities are channelled through its two corporate charities, The Economist Charitable Trust (Charity Commission no. 293709) and The Economist Educational Foundation (Charity Commission no. 1147661).

The Economist Educational Foundation

The foundation's 2021/22 Impact Report states that it seeks to 'develop young people's news literacy by enabling inspiring discussions about current affairs in classrooms and between schools in different communities'.

Its core programme, Burnet News Club, offers teachers the appropriate training and resources to deliver weekly discussions.

The Economist Charitable Trust

The Economist Charitable Trust, according to The Economist's annual report, exists to match funds raised by the company's employees. In March 2022 the trust decided to double-match donations from colleagues to support the UNICEF appeal for families and children affected by the war in Ukraine. In the year to 31 March 2022, the trust was given a £122,000 budget by the company, which was supplemented by £15,300 for the UNICEF double-matching campaign.

Code for Girls

In 2021, The Economist partnered with Code for Girls, a charity that aims to close the gender gap in the technology sector. The company ran a series of eight-week web development courses in October 2021, with over 120 students completing the courses.

Employee-led support

A payroll giving scheme and matched funding are available to Economist staff, which are administered by The Economist Charitable Trust. The company also runs employee volunteering days.

In 2022, over 200 employees donated a combined total of £23,500 to UNICEF's Ukraine appeal, a figure that was double-matched by The Economist Charitable Trust with an additional £47,000.

Commercially led support

In 2021, The Economist auctioned its cover on decentralised finance as a non-fungible token, raising £218,900, which was then donated to The Economist Educational Foundation.

Applications

For further information on The Economist Educational Foundation, email the team (foundationteam@economist.com).

For other information, contact the correspondent.

Corporate charity

The Economist Charitable Trust (Charity Commission no. 293709) – see entry on page 239.

Community contributions

Cash donations worldwide	£282,000

According to The Economist's 2021/22 annual report, the group donated £122,000 to The Economist Charitable Trust. Additionally, the 2021/22 accounts show the group donated £160,000 to The Economist Educational Foundation in the year. We have taken the sum of these amounts as the figure for the group's cash donations for the year.

EDF Energy Holdings Ltd

Community services and development, education and training, the environment, health, money and debt advice, social welfare, STEM

Company registration number: 06930266

Correspondent: The CSR Team, 334 Outland Road, Plymouth PL3 5TU (website: www.edfenergy.com/about/financial-information)

Directors: Robert Guyler; Simone Rossi (female: 33%; male: 67%).

Nature of business: EDF Energy is an integrated energy company. It generates and supplies electricity and gas for the UK from a nuclear, coal, gas and renewable energy portfolio.

Financial information

Year end	31/12/2021
Turnover	£8,720,000,000
Pre-tax profit	(£1,779,000,000)

Total employees: 11,516

Main locations: EDF has offices in Exeter, Sunderland, Plymouth and Brighton and Hove. It also has a division in France.

Community involvement

EDF is engaged in various charitable activities, particularly relating to health, education in sustainable energy, STEM education and debt advice.

Partnerships

EDF's current partner is Prostate Cancer UK. The charity was chosen by EDF employees in 2019, who were aiming to raise a target of £100,000 per year over the course of three years.

Other partnerships

EDF has partnered with Citizens Advice to provide extra help and support to its customers struggling with debt. EDF customers can call the Plymouth Citizens Advice helpline on 0808 156 666, or 0300 330 0519 from a mobile phone.

Educational programmes and partnerships

Through its educational programmes, EDF has partnered with various charities and organisations with the aim to improve the communities in which the company operates.

Partnerships include those with charities like the Greenpower Education Trust, SmartSTEMs and The Cheltenham Science Festival that aim to get young people interested in engineering while kick-starting their careers in the field.

Community funds

The group supports communities near its renewable energy sites through dedicated community funds. Funds are available to communities to spend on improvements to the local area during the development and lifetime of the site. The size of each fund depends on the size of the wind or solar farm and how much energy it produces.

The group's Hinkley Point C Community Fund supports communities in the county of Somerset experiencing the impacts of the construction of Hinkley Point C. The four eligible areas are South Somerset, Sedgemoor, Mendip and Somerset and West Taunton.

Employee-led support

Helping Hands

Through the Helping Hands volunteering programme, EDF staff can take two days' paid leave each year supporting local community and environmental projects.

Commercially led support

Sponsorship

EDF is the headline sponsor of an award-winning education programme, The Pod. The programme aims to teach 2.5 million children about the sustainable use of energy, while promoting STEM education and careers.

Applications

Community funds: For further information please visit: www.edf-re.uk/working-with-communities/the-community-fund/

Hinkley Point C Community Fund: For further information please visit: www.hpcfunds.co.uk/

For all other queries contact the correspondent using the form on the group's website.

Community contributions

Information on the group's community contributions was not available.

Edinburgh Airport Ltd

Education and training, the environment, health

Company registration number: SC096623

Correspondent: The Community Board, Edinburgh Airport, Edinburgh EH12 9DN (website: https://corporate.edinburghairport.com/community)

Directors: Andrea Badiu; Gordon Dewar; Sir John Elvidge; Michael McGhee; Scott Telesz; Linda Urquhart (female: 33%; male: 67%).

Nature of business: Edinburgh Airport Ltd owns and runs Edinburgh Airport.

Financial information

Year end	31/12/2021
Turnover	£63,944,000
Pre-tax profit	£36,358,000

UK employees: 500

Main locations: The airport is in Edinburgh.

Community involvement

Support is mainly provided through the company's community fund.

Edinburgh Airport Community Fund (not a registered charity)

The airport's community fund is managed by its Community Board, which meets quarterly to consider funding applications based around its areas of interest: sport, health and well-being, the environment and education.

According to the 2019 CSR report, the community board is particularly interested in working with organisations that 'demonstrate opportunities for social enterprise in order to allow an organisation or charity to become self-sufficient or fund other improvements'.

In 2020, due to the COVID-19 pandemic, the Community Board was paused and its charitable contributions ceased. The Community Board relaunched in February 2022.

Charity of the Year

The airport selects a Charity of the Year partner, to which it donates funds from staff raffles, fundraising efforts and foreign currency collections.

In 2020/21, the Charity of the Year was SAMH (Scottish Association for Mental Health). At the end of the two-year partnership, almost £100,000 had been raised through employee fundraising, foreign coin collections and in-kind support.

COVID-19 support

In 2020/21, Edinburgh Airport allocated £50,000 to six national and local charities: Age Scotland, Edinburgh Food Project, SAMH, Scran Academy, Shelter Scotland and Simon Community Scotland.

In-kind support

In 2021, Edinburgh Airport worked with Edinburgh Remakery to donate old IT equipment to apprentices of IT refurbishment. The equipment was then either sold or donated to members of the local community.

The company also donated over 300,000 face masks to more than 50 local charity groups and organisations across Edinburgh.

Employee-led support

Staff can apply for matched funding for their fundraising efforts.

In 2020, employees ran 100 miles in 30 days, raising £11,000 for SAMH.

Exclusions

A full list of criteria for applications to the Edinburgh Airport Community Fund can be found on the Edinburgh Airport website.

Applications

Edinburgh Airport Community Fund
Applications for the Edinburgh Airport Community are processed through the company's website. Full details on the application process, including a full list of criteria can be found on the website.

Charity of the Year
Applications for the next Charity of the Year partner tend to open in October. Note that the airport prefers to support charities for two years. Contact the correspondent for further details.

Community contributions

Cash donations UK	£52,000

According to its 2021 sustainability report, the company donated £50,000 to COVID-19-related causes. A further £2,000, awarded to selected charities, was reported in the 2021 annual accounts.

Entain plc

🔍 Health, sports and recreation

Company registration number: 4685V

Correspondent: Jay Dossetter, Head of CSR and Corporate Communications, 32 Athol Street, Douglas, Isle of Man IM1 1JB (tel: 0350 2007 8700; email: JDossetter@gvcgroup.com; website: https://entaingroup.com/sustainability/csr-reports)

Directors: Barry Gibson; Jette Nygaard-Andersen; Rob Wood; Robert Hoskin; Pierre Bouchut; Stella David; Mark Gregory; Peter Isola; Vicky Jarman; Virginia McDowell; David Satz (female: 36%; male: 64%).

Nature of business: Entain plc owns several gaming and sports betting brands including bwin, Sportingbet and Foxy Bingo. In March 2018 the group purchased Ladbrokes Coral.

Financial information

Year end	31/12/2021
Turnover	£3,830,000,000
Pre-tax profit	£527,000,000

Total employees: 25,554

Main locations: The group is headquartered and registered in the Isle of Man. The group has over 7,000 betting shops and outlets in 20 countries worldwide.

Community involvement

The group makes cash and in-kind contributions to responsible gambling charities as well as other good causes. In 2019, Entain launched The Entain Foundation. The foundation now administers the group's existing CSR projects, including its collaborations with organisations such as SportsAid, EPIC Risk Management, Gordon Moody and the US National Council on Problem Gambling.

The foundation is initially focusing on four key areas:

▶ Responsible gambling, sports integrity and gambling regulation research, education and treatment
▶ Grassroots, women's and disability sports
▶ Men's health, with a particular focus on mental health
▶ Projects with a clear link to the local community in Entain's major office locations

Pitching In

In September 2020, the Entain Foundation launched 'Pitching In', a multi-million pound investment programme designed to support and promote grassroots sports. To start the programme, a partnership was established with three football leagues in the UK (the Isthmian, Northern Premier and Southern Leagues). Through the programme, Entain provides financial support and expertise to aid the delivery of educational programmes on responsible gambling and sports integrity to the leagues' clubs. As well as supporting these Trident leagues, Entain has also set up the Trident Community Fund, to enable clubs to receive funding to run community engagement projects.

The Pitching In volunteer scheme is also in place to link UK-based Entain colleagues with their local football clubs. The programme will also incorporate the group's existing partnership with SportsAid.

See the foundation's website for further information on its most recent projects: https://entaingroup.com/entain-foundation

Ladbrokes Coral Trust (Charity Commission no. 1101804)

In 2018, Entain began its acquisition of Ladbrokes Coral. According to the group's 2021 social impact report, the Ladbrokes Coral Trust (LCT) remains central to the group's community engagement activities. The trust was established in 2003 and receives its income from Ladbrokes Coral staff fundraising. The trust also runs national campaigns with selected charity partners. The primary partners of the LCT are Children with Cancer UK and Prostate Cancer UK.

Charity partners

Entain began a three-year partnership with SportsAid in 2018 to support the next generation of British athletes. In 2021, Entain extended this partnership, committing to raising £500,000 by 2024. Fifty athletes in the UK receive direct funding and personal development opportunities each year through the partnership.

Employee-led support

According to its 2021 annual report, the group offers matched funding for employee fundraising.

Applications

The Entain Foundation does not appear to be a registered charity. For further information on the foundation, contact the correspondent.

Corporate charity

Ladbrokes Coral Trust (Charity Commission no. 1101804) – see entry on page 249.

Community contributions

Cash donations worldwide	£15,000,000

The group's 2021 social impact report states that the company made contributions of £15 million for the year.

Of this amount, £12 million came as a commitment of 0.5% of the company's Gross Gaming Yield and was donated to the research, education and training of charities such as GambleAware and other organisations that support those affected by problem gambling.

A further £693,000 was donated to athletes in the UK and Greece through partnerships with sports organisations.

A further £1 million was donated to various other global charitable organisations.

The Entertainer (Amersham) Ltd

🔍 General charitable purposes, health

Company registration number: 2057757

Correspondent: The CSR Team, Teal House Anglo Office Park, 67 White Lion Road, Amersham HP7 9FB (email: contact form on the website; website: www.thetoyshop.com/charity)

Directors: Catherine Grant; Mark Campbell; Duncan Grant; Gary Grant; Stuart Grant (female: 20%; male: 80%).

Nature of business: The Entertainer is a toy retailer.

Financial information

Year end	26/01/2022
Turnover	£201,354,000
Pre-tax profit	£22,554,000

Total employees: 1,800

Main locations: The company's headquarters is in Buckinghamshire. It has over 140 shops throughout the UK.

Community involvement

The Entertainer mainly provides support through donations. Every year, the toy shop donates 10% of its profits to charities supporting children.

The Entertainer launched Pennies, the 'digital charity box' in 2011, which encourages customers to make micro-donations to the company's chosen charities. Currently, these include Alder Hey Children's Charity, Birmingham Children's Hospital Charity, Bristol Children's Hospital Charity's The Grand Appeal and Great Ormond Street Hospital Children's Charity. According to the company website, from 2011 to 2022, customers donated over £3 million through this programme.

In addition, the website states that in 2022, the company donated £25,000 to Christian Aid and a further donation of £50,000 to the Disasters Emergency Committee's Ukraine Humanitarian Appeal.

Operation Christmas Child

The Entertainer is a drop-off location and partner for the Operation Christmas Child campaign.

In-kind support

The Big Toy Appeal

For every toy customers buy and donate to the appeal, the Entertainer will match this contribution by also donating a toy.

Employee-led support

According to the company's website, 46% of Entertainer staff make donations to various charities through payroll giving.

Staff are also involved in various fundraising efforts.

Applications

Contact the correspondent for more information.

Community contributions

Cash donations UK	£1,370,000

According to the 2021/22 accounts, the company made charitable donations totalling £1.37 million.

Everton Football Club Company Ltd

Community services and development, education and training, health, social welfare, sports and recreation

Company registration number: 36624

Correspondent: Everton in the Community, Goodison Park, Goodison Road, Liverpool, Merseyside L4 4EL (tel: 0151 530 5253; email: contact form on the website; website: www. evertoninthecommunity.org)

Directors: Prof. Denise Barrett-Baxendale; Martinus Brands; William Kenwright; Alexander Ryazantsev (female: 25%; male: 75%).

Nature of business: Everton FC is a professional football club competing in the Premier League.

Financial information

Year end	30/06/2021
Turnover	£193,100,000

UK employees: 500

Main locations: The club is based in Liverpool.

Community involvement

The football club's charitable activity is channelled through its corporate charity.

Everton in the Community (Charity Commission no. 1099366)

The club's corporate charity, Everton in the Community, works in partnerships with schools and colleges to deliver a wide range of community projects in education and employment, sport, health and well-being.

The club's charity also works in partnership with charities to deliver specific projects, such as a programme

delivering high-quality football sessions to asylum seekers and refugees in partnership with Asylum Link Merseyside.

Through its charity, the club has recently embarked on a partnership with Sodexo Stop Hunger Foundation and Meals and More to distribute food over the school holidays across Merseyside. Through this partnership, 1,000 nutritious meals will be provided to local children experiencing poverty.

A full list of all current programmes can be seen on the website.

In-kind support

The club may donate merchandise and signed memorabilia to charities to help raise funds.

The club also organises appearances from members of the first-team squad to help raise awareness of various good causes around the city. These activities are organised on behalf of the club, by its charity.

Exclusions

In-kind donations and player visits are available to charities within a 40-mile radius of Goodison Park.

The club does not provide monetary support or sponsorship.

Applications

Applications for in-kind donations or player visits should be submitted using the club's online form: www.evertonfc. com/community/fundraising/the-projects/everton-giving.

For all other enquiries, contact the correspondent for more information.

Community contributions

Cash donations UK	£360,000
Total contributions UK	£846,000

According to the 2020/21 annual report, Everton Football Club Company Ltd donated £360,000 to its corporate charity and contributed £486,000 in in-kind donations during the year,

Experian plc

Community enterprise and social entrepreneurship, education and training, housing and homelessness, money and debt advice, social welfare

Company registration number: 93905

Correspondent: Head of Community Involvement UK and Ireland, The Sir John Peace Building, Experian Way, NG2 Business Park, Nottingham, Nottinghamshire NG80 1ZZ (tel: 0115 941 0888; website: www.experian.co.uk/responsibilities/corporate-responsibility/community-involvement)

Directors: Ronan Hanna; Julia Cattanach; Steven Cooper; Stuart Deane;

Marcus Jehle; Jose Rossi (female: 17%; male: 83%).

Nature of business: Experian plc provides a range of data and analytics software and services across the world. This includes credit services, decision analytics, marketing services and consumer services.

Financial information

Year end	31/03/2021
Turnover	£4,690,200,000
Pre-tax profit	£940,300,000

Total employees: 17,800

Main locations: Experian's UK subsidiary, Experian Ltd, is headquartered in Nottingham and has offices in London, Leeds, Southport and Dublin. The company's parent company, Experian plc, is headquartered in Dublin and operates worldwide.

Community involvement

Experian plc contributes to the communities in which it operates around the world with a strong focus on financial education and support. The group's businesses utilise their products, services and employees' expertise to provide support and work in partnership with community groups and charities.

For example, in the UK, Experian Ltd partners with Big Issue Invest, the social investment arm of the charity The Big Issue Foundation, for its United for Financial Health programme, which according to The Big Issue's website, works 'with a range of experts to share helpful advice and tips on how to keep in control of your money and be in as strong a position as you can be through the pandemic, and beyond'.

According to its website, Experian Ltd supports community partnerships that best fit its strategic objectives. Support is provided through financial donations, employee volunteering and in-kind gifts.

In-kind support

Experian Ltd has developed online and practical resources to provide financial education to young people in the UK and Ireland. For example, it developed and funded Values, Money and Me, a free online financial education resource for teachers and families aimed at children aged 5 to 11. The company also worked with the charity The Mix to launch an online learning tool, Home Truths, to help young people become financially independent at university.

As well as educational resources, the company also has guides and advice on debt management on its website.

Employee-led support

In the UK, employees can take three days of paid leave per year to volunteer for one-off projects, ongoing activities and team challenges.

Across the group, employees also volunteer to help deliver the group's financial education and community programmes. According to Experian Ltd's 2020/21 annual report, its employees donated 54,500 hours of volunteering during the year.

Matched funding is available for UK and Ireland employees who participate in sponsored events to raise money for a registered charity. The company will match funds up to £250 per person per year. In 2020/21, £100,000 was raised through matched funding.

Applications

Contact the correspondent for further information.

Community contributions

Cash donations UK		£170,000
Cash donations worldwide		£12,220,000

Experian plc's worldwide community investment totalled £12.22 million in 2020/21.

All of the financial figures have been converted from USD to GBP using the exchange rate at the time of writing (November 2022). Experian plc is registered in Jersey.

Fenwick Ltd

General charitable purposes

Company registration number: 52411

Correspondent: CSR Team, Elswick Court, Northumberland Street, Newcastle upon Tyne, Tyne and Wear NE99 1AR (tel: 0800 783 1783; email: use the contact form on the company's website; website: www.fenwick.co.uk)

Directors: Karen Dracou; John Edgar; Hugo Fenwick; Mia Fenwick; Sian Westerman; Simon Calver (female: 50%; male: 50%).

Nature of business: Fenwick is a chain of department stores.

Financial information

Year end		29/01/2021
Turnover		£99,250,000
Pre-tax profit		(£111,980,000)

UK employees: 1,631

Main locations: The company has stores located in Bracknell, Brent Cross, Canterbury, Colchester, London, Kingston upon Thames, Newcastle, Tunbridge Wells and York.

Community involvement

The company makes donations in support of causes local to its stores. Fenwick prefers to support social inclusion initiatives that employees can get involved with. It also has the following partnerships: The Tree Council, sponsoring the growth of trees and hedgerows across the UK; Street Zero, to help rough sleepers in Newcastle; and The Prince's Trust, to support young people's development.

Applications

Contact the correspondent for more information.

Community contributions

Cash donations UK		£98,000

In 2020/21 the company made donations of £98,000 to causes in the local areas of its stores.

FIL Holdings (UK) Ltd (Fidelity International)

Arts, culture and heritage, community services and development, education and training, general charitable purposes, health

Company registration number: 6737476

Correspondent: Corporate Citizenship Department, 4 Cannon Street, London EC4M 5AB (email: corporate.citizenship@fil.com; website: www.fidelity.co.uk/corporate-citizenship)

Directors: Michelle Cracknell; Cara Hewitt; Peter Horrell; Anthony Lanser; Dr Teresa Robson-Capps; Romain Boscher; Mark Gotts; Dipi McKernan; Alan Rubenstein (female: 33%; male: 67%).

Nature of business: This is the holding company for a group of companies whose principal business is the management and distribution of collective investment funds, the management of defined benefit pension funds, and the management and administration of defined contribution pension funds.

Financial information

Year end		31/12/2021
Turnover		£1,167,430,000
Pre-tax profit		£137,710,000

Main locations: The group has offices in London, Kent and Surrey.

Community involvement

Fidelity directs its community support through its two foundations and its Corporate Citizenship Programme. In the UK, financial support is given through The Fidelity UK Foundation (Charity Commission no. 327899) which makes grants to UK-registered charities.

Corporate Citizenship Programme

The programme supports local charities and employees in their efforts to contribute to their communities. Employees are encouraged to lend their support to good causes through volunteering, fundraising and payroll giving. The group sponsors charity fundraising events and has a small budget from which grants are made to support local charities that are working to benefit the communities in areas where the group has a presence.

Employee-led support

Employees are given two days of paid leave to volunteer per year. The company will also match funds that are raised by employees.

Commercially led support

The group provides sponsorship to charitable and community events. Its website states:

> Furthermore, we encourage committees to sponsor local events that have wider community outreach and that provide funds to small, locally based organisations who deliver services at a grass roots level.

Exclusions

Our previous research suggests that the group will not support the following:

- religious, political and animal-support charities (except environmental or conservation related animal causes)
- individuals and individual schools
- events for exclusive audiences such as black tie events
- high-risk activities, such as parachute jumps, motor racing and abseiling

Sports events, clubs and teams are not usually supported, nor are advertisements in charity event programmes, diaries or directories.

Applications

Corporate sponsorship and small grants – for more information on these programmes, contact Fidelity's Corporate Citizenship department.

International foundations – information on the international foundations can found on the UK foundation's website.

For all other enquiries, contact the correspondent.

Corporate charity

The Fidelity UK Foundation (Charity Commission no. 327899) – see entry on page 239.

Community contributions

Cash donations UK		£4,580,000

In 2021, the group donated £4 million to The Fidelity UK Foundation. The group also made direct donations totalling £579,000 to a wide range of charities, including through the employee grant-matching scheme. Individual donations were made to, for example, local children's charities, schools and hospitals.

FirstGroup plc

🔍 General charitable purposes

Company registration number: SC157176

Correspondent: CSR Team, 395 King Street, Aberdeen, Aberdeenshire AB24 5RP (tel: 01224 650100; email: communityfirst@firstgroup.com; website: www.firstgroupplc.com/responsibility. aspx)

Directors: David Martin; Ryan Mangold; Sally Cabrini; Ant Green; Myrtle Dawes; Claire Hawkings; Jane Lodge; Peter Lynas; Graham Sutherland (female: 44%; male: 56%).

Nature of business: The group operates in the UK and the USA and provides passenger transport services primarily through bus and coach services and passenger railways.

Financial information

Year end	26/03/2022
Turnover	£4,591,100,000
Pre-tax profit	(£17,700,000)

Total employees: 30,000

Main locations: The group serves areas across the UK and its headquarters is in Aberdeen.

Community involvement

The group supports local and national community and charitable organisations throughout the UK and the USA. Many sites where the group operates have developed community engagement plans and work in partnership with charitable organisations. According to the group's website, community investment is focused on the following:

- Developing long term partnerships with charitable organisations most aligned with the business
- Mobilising employees to support these partnerships through charity committees and charity champion programmes and by encouraging personal commitments like fundraising and payroll giving

Partnerships

The group had a four-year partnership with Action for Children that came to an end in 2022. The partnership generated over £3.5 million in value. At the time of writing (August 2022), the group's website states:

FirstGroup is now taking the opportunity to review its charity partnership approach and explore new ways to complement, support and enhance community investment programmes across its divisions.

Transform Grants

The Transform Grants programme is run by TransPennine Express, which is owned by FirstGroup plc. Applicants can apply for grants of up to £5,000 for projects that seek to tackle youth unemployment, promote social inclusion and improve the environment. Projects should be located within ten miles of any line of route operated by TransPennine Express train services.

In-kind support

The group provides in-kind support such as donations of advertising space, vehicle hire and free travel tickets.

Employee-led support

Employees' fundraising efforts for charitable causes are matched by the group with up to £200 per person per year available. Employees also take part in volunteering for the charity partner.

Commercially led support

The group's 2021/22 annual report states that its community contributions included event sponsorship but no further details were given.

Applications

Transform Grants – further information can be found on: www.tpexpress.co.uk/about-us/community/transform-grants.

Contact the correspondent for all other enquiries.

Community contributions

Total contributions UK	£1,580,000

The group's community contributions in the UK in 2021/22 totalled £1.58 million. These comprised of cash donations, time, in-kind donations and 'leverage' (contributions from other sources such as employees, customers or suppliers). A detailed breakdown was not available.

James Fisher and Sons plc

🔍 Arts, culture and heritage, community services and development, education and training, health, medical research

Company registration number: 211475

Correspondent: The CSR Team, Fisher House, PO Box 4, Michaelson Road, Barrow-in-Furness, Cumbria LA14 1HR (email: info@sirjohnfisherfoundation. org.uk; website: www.james-fisher.com)

Directors: Justin Atkinson; Dr Inken Brauschmidt; Angus Cockburn; Aedamar Comiskey; Claire Hawkings; Duncan Kennedy; Eoghan O'Lionard; Kashyap Pandya (female: 13%; male: 88%).

Nature of business: The group is a provider of marine-related engineering services and has four divisions: marine support, offshore oil, specialist technical and tankships.

Financial information

Year end	31/12/2021
Turnover	£494,100,000
Pre-tax profit	£29,000,000

Total employees: 2,662

Main locations: The group works across 19 countries and has several offices and operations across the UK. Its headquarters is in Barrow-in-Furness.

Community involvement

The Sir John Fisher Foundation (Charity Commission no. 277844)

Most of the group's charitable support is focused through its corporate charity, The Sir John Fisher Foundation.

Community initiatives

According to the annual report for 2021, the group also runs community initiatives in the areas local to its operations. In 2021, the group ran 30 community initiatives, 18 of which were in the UK. The initiatives were divided by theme into four categories:

- Careers and business support
- Education
- Hobbies
- Health and well-being

Employee-led support

Employee support for food banks

In 2021, ten members from the James Fisher and Sons HR division volunteered to support the Living Waters Storehouse, a charity food bank run by volunteers from the Living Waters Church. The team helped to package 500 food parcels and also donated items to help meet the demand for the food bank.

Employee fundraising

Employees are encouraged to fundraise for charitable causes of their choosing, with the following examples highlighted in the annual report:

In 2021, members of the Marine Support Division raised £10,000 for Great Ormond Street Hospital by running, rowing and climbing 556 miles in 33 hours.

James Fisher Nuclear supported Mark Harding, an Army veteran who executed a Walking Home for Christmas campaign to support a wounded veterans' charity in the UK, raising money for those struggling with PTSD.

Commercially led support

In 2021, James Fisher and Sons sponsored a junior motorboat athlete from Lowestoft so that they could compete at an international level.

Applications

For further information contact the correspondent or see the company's corporate charity entry.

Corporate charity

The Sir John Fisher Foundation (Charity Commission no. 277844) – see entry on page 240.

Community contributions

Cash donations worldwide	£971,500

The James Fisher and Sons annual report for 2021 reported that the group donated £48,500 for the year. In 2021 the group's corporate charity, The John Fisher Foundation received £923,000 in dividend income from its shareholding in James Fisher and Sons.

Flutter Entertainment plc

Sports and recreation, health and wellbeing, education and training, humanitarian aid

Company registration number: 16956

Correspondent: CSR Team, Waterfront, Hammersmith Embankment, Chancellors Road (access on Winslow Road), London W6 9HP (tel: 020 8834 8000; website: www.flutter.com)

Directors: Peter Jackson; Jonathan Hill; Pádraig Ó Ríordáin; Paul Cutter; Amy Howe; Conor Grant; Ian Proctor; Dan Taylor; Barni Evans; Phil Bishop (female: 10%; male: 90%).

Nature of business: Flutter Entertainment operates a portfolio of international sports betting and gaming brands. The group's brands include Betfair (UK), Paddy Power (UK and Ireland), Sportsbet (Australia), Adjarabet (Georgia) and TVG and FanDuel (USA).

Financial information

Year end	31/12/2021
Turnover	£6,036,200,000
Pre-tax profit	(£288,400,000)

Total employees: 8,890

Main locations: Flutter Entertainment plc (formerly Paddy Power Betfair plc) is headquartered in Dublin and has an office in London.

Community involvement

The group focuses its support on grassroots sports clubs, health and technology. The group supports organisations through cash donations and employee-led initiatives.

Partnerships

Sport

The group supports projects that enable people to take part in sport. Partnerships have included:

- **Right To Play** – an initiative which uses sport and game to help children stay in education.
- **Made by Sport/Cash4Clubs** – support to help grassroots sports clubs recover from the COVID-19 pandemic.
- **Racing Welfare** – Betfair has a long-term relationship with Racing Welfare, which supports people who work in the racing industry.

Health and well-being

The group partners with organisations that support people in a variety of situations. Partnerships include:

- **Save Her Seat** – an initiative aiming to help girls get back into education after leaving due to the effects of the COVID-19 pandemic.
- **Macmillan Cancer Support** – the charity has a partnership with Sky Betting through which it receives funding. In 2021, the funds raised went towards a support line.
- **Missing People** – the group provides financial support and awareness.

Technology for good

The group supports initiatives that help people to develop digital skills. Partnerships include:

- **Women Who Code** – in 2021, PokerStars partnered with Women Who Code, an organisation dedicated to inspiring women to excel in technology careers.
- **Alpha Hub** – the group's Alpha Hub programme enables it to connect with innovative start-ups to explore opportunities to support them in their journey.

Emergency support

The group supports aid organisations to help them to respond to crises and emergencies. Examples include Americares, which the group first partnered in 2019 following Hurricane Dorian. It also worked with the charity to provide £100,000 of emergency relief in the form of PPE and other provisions to the USA and India during the COVID-19 pandemic.

Responsible gambling

As part of its sustainability strategy, the group is focused on promoting safer gambling. The group regularly supports the charity GambleAware with financial donations.

The group also committed to a four-year funding plan for the Young Gamblers Education Trust, a charity that informs, educates and safeguards young people against problem gambling.

Employee-led support

Employees are given two paid days' leave per year to volunteer. Employees have previously supported homelessness projects and community gardens.

Commercially led support

Sponsorship

The group's brands provide sponsorship to events such as Pride and sports events.

Cause-related marketing

The group uses the power of its brand to raise awareness for its charity partners.

Exclusions

The Cash4Clubs scheme will only accept applications from clubs that are registered with their national governing body or local authority. Grants will only be sent to official club bank accounts.

Applications

More information about eligibility and applications to the Cash4Clubs scheme can be found at www.cash-4-clubs.com/.

Contact the correspondent for further information.

Community contributions

According to its 2021 annual report, the group invested over £3.7 million in community projects and schemes during the year. This included over 1,600 grants to local sports clubs.

The Football Association Premier League Ltd

Sports and recreation

Company registration number: 2719699

Correspondent: Communities Team, Brunel Building, 57 North Wharf Road, London W2 1HQ (email: info@ premierleague.com; website: www. premierleague.com/communities)

Directors: Mark Bullingham; Andy Ambler; Rachel Brace; Mark Burrows; Baroness Campbell; Craig Donald; Louisa Fyans; Joanna Manning-Cooper; Polly Handford; James Kendall; John McDermott; Lucy Pearson; Navin Singh; Kelly Simmons (female: 43%; male: 57%).

Nature of business: The Football Association Premier League operates and promotes the Premier League.

Financial information

Year end	31/07/2021
Turnover	£3,143,800,000
Pre-tax profit	£7,800,000

Total employees: 1,063

Main locations: The company operates throughout the UK.

Community involvement

The company channels most of its charitable support through its corporate charity, The Premier League Charitable Fund (Charity Commission no. 1137208), which delivers a wide range of education and sports programmes. The company also supports grassroots football through The Football Foundation (Charity Commission no. 1079308).

Community and School programmes

Together with The Premier League Charitable Fund, the company delivers a wide range of sports and education programmes. The following examples of the fund's programmes have been taken from its website:

Premier League Kicks – Premier League Kicks is a well-established community programme using the reach and appeal of the Premier League and network of professional football clubs to regularly engage children and young people of all backgrounds and abilities in football, sport and personal development – providing a trusted, positive influence in high-need areas across England and Wales.

Premier League Primary Stars – Premier League Primary Stars supports primary schools across England and Wales with free access to resources, events and competitions to inspire children aged 5–11 to learn, be active and develop important life skills.

Premier League Inspires – Premier League Inspires is a joint programme between the Premier League, the Professional Footballers' Association (PFA) and the Prince's Trust and uses the appeal of football to help children and young people aged 11–25 to fulfil their potential.

Premier League and PFA Community Fund – The Premier League and PFA Community Fund enables CCOs to respond to local need and provides support to develop projects in partnership with others in new strategic areas. Funded projects engage with players and scholars to enhance the impact on participants.

For full details of all current programmes, see the charity's website.

The Football Foundation
The Football Foundation helps communities improve their local football facilities. Grants are available for various football-related purposes, including pitches, changing rooms and large capital projects. Since 2000, the foundation has delivered community sports projects worth over £1.5 billion across the UK. According to its website, in 2021, the foundation awarded grants to the value of £69.9 million to 2,400 charitable projects.

Funding is available across the UK; however, the amount of funding available is dependent on your area. Search for your postcode on the foundation's 'Local Football Facility Plan' web page to see what support is available.

Football Stadia Improvement Fund
The fund's grants are designed to improve stadium safety and enable clubs to satisfy the FA's ground grading requirements.

Applications
Football Stadia Improvement Fund
To apply to the Football Stadia Improvement Fund, visit: https://footballfoundation.org.uk/grant/football-stadia-improvement-fund

The Football Foundation
To apply for a grant visit: https://footballfoundation.org.uk/looking-for-funding

The Premier League Charitable Fund
For further information visit: www.premierleague.com/communities/plcf.

Community contributions

Total contributions UK		£59,000,000

According to its 2020/21 annual report, during the year the company made charitable donations of £59 million to principally football-related charities. In addition, the company committed £187.9 million to wider football causes and other charitable purposes.

Ford Motor Company Ltd

Community services and development, education and training, the environment, health, sports and recreation

Company registration number: 235446

Correspondent: CSR Team, 15-02B D20-B, Ford Dunton Technical Centre, Laindon, Basildon, Essex SS15 6EE (website: www.ford.co.uk/experience-ford/news/ford-britain-trust)

Directors: Monazza Khan; David Robinson; Johan Schep; Jane Skerry; Nicola Walker; Lisa Brankin; Sabine Duerholt; Timothy Slatter (female: 63%; male: 38%).

Nature of business: The Ford Motor Company Ltd is a wholly owned subsidiary of the Ford Motor Company of Dearborn, Michigan. The company's principal activity is the design, engineering and manufacture of low-carbon technologies, commercial vehicles and automotive components, and the sale of motor vehicles and automotive components. The company and its subsidiaries operate principally in the UK and the Republic of Ireland. It is part of an integrated vehicle manufacturing group of Ford companies throughout Europe.

Financial information

Year end	31/12/2020
Turnover	£8,790,000,000
Pre-tax profit	£71,999,999

Main locations: In the UK, Ford is headquartered in Essex. It has sites across the UK.

Community involvement
Ford Motor Company Ltd operates the Ford Britain Trust (Charity Commission no. 269410), which makes grants for projects in communities close to Ford's locations. In particular, it supports projects that focus on education, the environment, children, people with disabilities, youth activities and community projects.

Employee-led support
Ford Motor Company Ltd offers paid time off for its employees to volunteer in the community.

Applications
For further information see the company's corporate charity entry.

Corporate charity
Ford Britain Trust (Charity Commission no. 269410) – see entry on page 241.

Community contributions

Cash donations UK	£50,000

The company's 2020 annual report did not declare a figure for charitable donations during the year. However, the Ford Britain Trust's 2019/20 accounts state that a donation of £50,000 was received from Ford Motor Company Ltd.

Freshfields Bruckhaus Deringer LLP

Education and training

Company registration number: OC334789

Correspondent: CSR Team, 100 Bishopsgate, London EC2P 2SR (tel: 020 7936 4000; email: responsible.business@freshfields.com; website: www.freshfields.com/en-gb/about-us/responsible-business)

Nature of business: Freshfields is an international law firm with offices in Europe, Asia, the Middle East and the USA.

Financial information

Year end	30/04/2021
Turnover	£1,635,100,000
Pre-tax profit	£440,200,000

Main locations: In the UK, Freshfields has offices in London and Manchester.

Community involvement
The company aims to make a positive difference in the communities in which it operates through volunteering activities and pro bono work. The company's community investment programme focuses on access to opportunity with an emphasis on education and offering routes to work and access to the legal profession.

Scholarships
To address the disproportionally small numbers of Black men in large commercial law firms, Freshfields and Doreen Lawrence launched the Freshfields Stephen Lawrence

Scholarship Scheme in 2013. The scheme awards scholarships to exceptionally talented first-year law undergraduates.

Partnerships

The Freshfields Aspiring Professionals Programme is delivered in partnership with the Social Mobility Foundation and supports students in social mobility 'cold spot' areas.

In-kind support

The company provides pro bono legal support to local charities and individuals. Its pro bono work is focused on promoting access to rights for women, children, LGBTQ+ people, trafficking survivors and refugees. In 2020/21 the company contributed 83,976 of pro bono hours.

Employee-led support

In 2020/21, 35% of staff volunteered for community projects giving over 7,800 hours of time.

Applications

Contact the correspondent for further information.

Community contributions

We were unable to determine a figure for the company's community contributions for 2020/21.

Fujitsu Services Holdings plc

🔍 Education and training, general charitable purposes, STEM

Company registration number: 142200

Correspondent: CSR Team, 22 Baker Street, London W1U 3BW (tel: 01235 797711; website: www.fujitsu.com/uk/about/local/corporate-responsibility)

Directors: Rachel Hitching; Hideroni Furuta; William Patterson; Roberto Putland (female: 25%; male: 75%).

Nature of business: Fujitsu Services Holdings is the holding company of the IT services group Fujitsu.

Financial information

Year end	31/03/2021
Turnover	£1,864,100,000
Pre-tax profit	£46,400,000

Main locations: The group's headquarters is in London.

Community involvement

The group supports charitable causes mainly through various partnerships and employee-led support.

The group focuses its community involvement on the following areas:
- Digital inclusion
- Universities and research establishments
- STEM
- Youth employment
- Volunteering
- Charities

Charity partners

Fujitsu has ongoing partnerships with Business in the Community, The Prince's Trust, Autistica and Children in Need.

Impact on Society groups

The group's website states:

> As well as partnerships, we have our own regional Impact on Society (IOS) groups, which manage requests for funding and sponsorship and coordinate local volunteering activities on behalf of the Company. These groups are employee-led and work closely with organisations in the communities in which we are based. Through IOS, employees are encouraged to contribute their time and knowledge to worthy causes. IOS groups also provide financial support for events such as sponsored runs and bike rides and engages with charities and CASC-registered organisations at the request of employees.

STEM

Fujitsu encourages employees to be STEM ambassadors and role models. The group currently has three government-endorsed STEM programmes which are long-term partnerships with schools and businesses.

Applications

Apply in writing to the correspondent. The group has several regional IOS groups, which co-ordinate charitable activities, including responding to requests. We would suggest that local requests are made in writing to the IOS group at the relevant site.

Community contributions

Cash donations UK	£314,000

According to its 2020/21, the group's charitable and educational donations during the year totalled £314,000.

Galliford Try Holdings plc

🔍 General charitable purposes

Company registration number: 12216008

Correspondent: CSR Team, Blake House, 3 Frayswater Place, Cowley, Uxbridge, Middlesex UB8 2AD (email: online contact form; website: www.gallifordtry.co.uk/sustainability)

Directors: Kevin Corbett; Sally Boyle; Marisa Cassoni; Andrew Duxbury; Bill Hocking; Therese Miller; Gavin Slark; Peter Ventress; Alison Wood (female: 44%; male: 56%).

Nature of business: Galliford Try is a housebuilding and construction group operating in the UK.

Financial information

Year end	30/06/2021
Turnover	£1,124,800,000
Pre-tax profit	£11,400,000

Main locations: The group has operations across the UK – see www.gallifordtry.co.uk/contacts for more information.

Community involvement

The group makes charitable contributions at a group, division, business unit and project level. The group donates time, money and materials and there is some focus on supporting the communities in which the group operates.

Partnerships

For 20 years the group has supported the charity CRASH, which assists homelessness and hospice charities with construction-related projects.

Employee-led support

The group has a volunteering policy that entitles employees to two days' paid leave per year to volunteer for charitable causes.

Applications

Contact the correspondent or the division local to where your project is based.

Community contributions

Total contributions UK	£250,000

The group's 2020/21 annual report states: 'We donated £250,000 in time, materials and money to charitable causes.'

Gamesys Group Ltd

🔍 Health advice and support, mental health and well-being

Company registration number: 10303804

Correspondent: The CSR Team, 10 Piccadilly, London W1J 0DD (website: www.gamesysgroup.com)

Directors: John Rowland-Jones; Lee Fenton; Robeson Reeves; Christina Southall; Daniel Talisman (female: 20%; male: 80%).

Nature of business: The group is a gaming operator.

Financial information

Year end	31/12/2020
Turnover	£727,700,000
Pre-tax profit	£68,700,000

Main locations: The group trades or has offices in the UK, Malta, Gibraltar, Sweden, Ukraine, Manilla, the USA, Canada and Hong Kong.

Community involvement

The group's main community involvement is through the Bally's Foundation (formerly known as Gamesys Foundation, Charity Commission no. 1188099) which makes grants to organisations working in the field of mental health.

Employee-led support

The group encourages employee fundraising and volunteering.

Applications

For further information see the group's corporate charity entry.

Corporate charity

Bally's Foundation (Charity Commission no. 1188099) – see entry on page 223.

Community contributions

Cash donations UK	£1,800,000

The group's annual report states that it gives £150,000 to its foundation each month. In 2020 donations totalled £1.8 million.

Mick George Ltd

 Agriculture and farming, community services and development, education and training, the environment, general charitable purposes, social welfare, sports and recreation

Company registration number: 2417831

Correspondent: Sean Feeley, Marketing and E-Commerce Manager, 6 Lancaster Way, Ermine Business Park, Huntingdon, Cambridgeshire PE29 6XU (tel: 01480 499158; email: marketing@ mickgeorge.co.uk; website: www. mickgeorge.co.uk/explore/community)

Directors: Stuart Costello; Karen Farrell; Michael Alexander; Michael George; Joseph Gossage; Neil Johnson; Jonathan Stump; Ryan Ward (female: 13%; male: 88%).

Nature of business: The group provides a wide range of services to the construction industry, including excavation and earth moving, demolition and asbestos removal, skip hire, waste management, aggregate and concrete supply and facility management.

Financial information

Year end	30/09/2021
Turnover	£193,600,000
Pre-tax profit	£12,930,000

Main locations: The group's headquarters is in Huntingdon; a full list of the group's sites is available on its website.

Community involvement

The group supports local charities, sports clubs and community projects through grants, in-kind donations and sponsorship.

The group's website states that it has 'contributed towards many sports, agriculture, education, performance and environmental projects, forming many great partnerships with various charities and groups'.

Mick George Sports Fund (not a registered charity)

Annually, £50,000 is made available to the fund. Grants of between £500 and £2,000 are available to sports projects which are open to the general public in Northampton and the majority of Peterborough postcodes. The fund is run in association with Living Sport and Northamptonshire Sport.

Mick George Community Fund (not a registered charity)

This fund has around £500,000 available each year to give to community projects located in proximity to the group's sites and operating areas. Grants of between £10,000 and £50,000 are available for community projects with a total cost of between £10,000 and £100,000. The fund is managed externally by the charity GrantScape.

In-kind support

Local events, community projects and sports teams are supported with in-kind donations. Support is provided in several ways including time and resources, materials and specialist equipment.

Commercially led support

Safer Roads Scheme

The group delivers road safety workshops in schools and colleges. It also provides road safety displays and demonstrations in high footfall shopping centres and local community events. The group also sponsors a local Community Roadwatch Group to support its work by ensuring that hauliers are compliant with routing and road safety agreements.

Exclusions

Organisations can only apply to the Mick George Community Fund if their total project cost is between £10,000 and £50,000. Applications to the group's funds must come from organisations and projects located in the areas mentioned in the fund's eligibility criteria.

Applications

In-kind support

Requests for in-kind support can be submitted through an online form available on the group's sponsorship web page. An internal team considers all applications at review meetings four times a year.

Mick George Sports Fund and Mick George Community Fund

Each fund has two grant rounds per year. Applications can be made on the group's website.

Community contributions

We were unable to determine a figure for the group's total contributions for 2021. Around £550,000 is made available by the group to its two community funds annually, but we were unable to determine a figure for in-kind donations.

Glasgow Airport Ltd

Education and training, employment advice, the environment

Company registration number: SC096624

Correspondent: The FlightPath Committee, St Andrews Drive, Paisley PA3 2SW (email: flightpath@ glasgowairport.com; website: www. glasgowairport.com/flightpath-fund)

Directors: Pinsent Masons Secretarial Ltd; John Bruen; Andrew Carlisle; Ignacio Castejon; Simon Geere; Derek Provan; Gonzalo Velasco (male: 100%).

Nature of business: Glasgow Airport is owned by AGS Airports Ltd and is Scotland's principal long-haul airport as well as Scotland's largest charter hub. AGS was formed in September 2014 by Ferrovial and Macquarie. The company acquired Aberdeen, Glasgow and Southampton airports in December 2014 from Heathrow Airport Holdings.

Financial information

Year end	31/12/2020
Turnover	£34,316,000
Pre-tax profit	(£48,633,000)

Main locations: The airport is in Glasgow.

Community involvement

Support is mainly provided through the company's FlightPath Fund.

FlightPath Fund (not a registered charity)

The fund supports local charities and community groups as well as the voluntary work and fundraising of employees. Funding is focused on three main areas: employment, the environment and education. The fund makes donations to projects in areas most affected by the airport's operations. Projects are usually located in the relevant parts of Renfrewshire, East and West Dunbartonshire and Glasgow.

Applications

Application forms and guidelines can be downloaded from the company's website. The FlightPath Fund Committee meets every two months to consider funding applications. A list of meeting dates and application deadlines can be found on the website.

Community contributions

We were unable to determine a figure for the company's charitable contributions for 2020.

Global Media and Entertainment Ltd

Health, housing and homelessness, mental health and well-being, social welfare

Company registration number: 6251684

Correspondent: Grants Team, 30 Leicester Square, London WC2H 7LA (tel: 0345 606 0990; email: contact@ makesomenoise.com; website: https:// global.com/global-goodness)

Directors: Michelle Gammon; Charles Allen; Sally Cairns; Cilesta Doorn; Sebastian Enser-Wright; Michael Gordon; David Henderson; Stephen Miron; Richard Park; James Rea; Darren Singer; Ashley Tabor-King (female: 25%; male: 75%).

Nature of business: The group operates several large commercial stations across the UK including Capital, Heart, Smooth, Classic FM, LBC, Radio X and Gold.

Financial information

Year end	31/03/2021
Turnover	£434,158,000
Pre-tax profit	(£226,011,000)

Main locations: The group's head office is in London and it has around 22 broadcast stations across England, Scotland and Wales.

Community involvement

Global's charitable work focuses on supporting small charities working with disadvantaged children and young people across the UK.

Global Charities (Charity Commission no. 1091657)

Global Charities is Global's corporate charity. The charity's flagship grant-giving programme, Global's Make Some Noise, raises money from Global Radio listeners, employees and the entertainment and music industries, which the charity then distributes to small community charities.

Employee-led support

Employees fundraise for Global Charities throughout the year and specifically in October, when there is a dedicated Make Some Noise fundraising appeal.

Applications

For further information contact the correspondent or see the company's corporate charity entry.

Corporate charity

Global Charities (Charity Commission no. 1091657) – see entry on page 242.

Community contributions

Cash donations UK	£100,000

The group's 2020/21 accounts state: 'The Group's donations to charities amounted to £0.1 million (2020: £0.2 million).'

The Go-Ahead Group plc

Community services and development, general charitable purposes

Company registration number: 2100855

Correspondent: Katy Taylor, Group Commercial and Customer Director, 4 Matthew Parker Street, Westminster, London SW1H 9NP (tel: 020 7799 8999; email: communications@go-ahead.com; website: www.go-ahead.com)

Directors: Clare Hollingsworth; Christian Schreyer; Sarah Mussenden; David Blackwood; Dominic Lavelle; Harry Holt; Leanne Wood; Carolyn Ferguson; Mark Anderson; Kanwar Brar; Andrew Clark; Mark Ferriday; Elliot Laurie; Jeremy Marshall; Chris Peaker; Peter Robinson; Phil Southall; Fabian Amini; Andy Edwards; Cathrine Elgin; Nigel Featham; Magnus Hedin; Luke Marion; Richard Stevens; Andy Thompson; John Trayner; Patrick Verwer; Andrew Wickham; Ed Wills (female: 10%; male: 90%).

Nature of business: The principal activity of the group is the provision of public transport services.

Financial information

Year end	27/06/2021
Turnover	£4,058,500,000
Pre-tax profit	(£6,900,000)

Total employees: 30,573

Main locations: The group's head office is in the City of Westminster, but it has operating companies serving a broad geographical area within England. For more information on the group's companies and where they operate, see the operations map on the website (www.go-ahead.com/who-we-are/uk-bus).

Community involvement

At a corporate level, Go-Ahead supports two international but UK-based charities that have a transport focus and therefore have strong links to its business: Railway Children and Transaid. At a local level, each of its operating companies supports

local initiatives that reflect the concerns and priorities of the communities they serve.

In-kind support

According to the group's 2020/21 Sustainability Report, it gave £9,200 worth of in-kind gifts during the year.

Applications

The group's community involvement is co-ordinated at a local level by its operating companies. For more information about these operating companies and the areas they serve, see the operations map on the group's website.

Community contributions

Cash donations UK	£1,040,000

In 2020/21, the group made community contributions totalling £1.04 million in the following categories:

Cash contributions	£315,700
Gifts in kind	£140,100
Value of employee time	£9,200

Management time contributed was valued at £300,700; as is our usual practice, we have not included this figure in our total for the group's contributions.

The group's 2020/21 Sustainability Report also provides a detailed breakdown of community contributions given by individual operating companies.

Goldman Sachs International

Education and training, general charitable purposes

Company registration number: 2263951

Correspondent: Corporate Engagement Team, Plumtree Court, 25 Shoe Lane, London EC4A 4AU (tel: 020 7774 1000; website: www.goldmansachs.com/ citizenship/index.html)

Directors: Catherine Cripps; Lisa Donnelly; Jose Durao Barroso; Richard Gnodde; Samuel Gyimah; Nigel Harman; Therese Miller; Nirubhan Pathmanabhan; Esta Stecher; Marius Winkelman (female: 40%; male: 60%).

Nature of business: Goldman Sachs provides investment banking, trading, asset management and securities to corporations, financial institutions, governments and wealthy individuals.

Financial information

Year end	31/12/2021
Turnover	£6,360,060,000,000
Pre-tax profit	£3,125,000,000

Main locations: Goldman Sachs' head office is in London and it has offices worldwide.

Community involvement

At a global level, Goldman Sachs' philanthropy includes four major initiatives: Goldman Sachs Gives, a donor-advised fund with which former and current senior employees have an input; Community TeamWorks, a worldwide employee volunteering initiative; 10,000 Women, which looks to boost local economies by supporting female entrepreneurs; and 10,000 Small Businesses, which looks to create jobs and economic growth by investing in business education, opportunities and support services for entrepreneurs.

In the UK, Goldman Sachs has established two registered grant-making charities:

- The Goldman Sachs Charitable Gift Fund (UK) (Charity Commission no. 1120148) – set up for the advancement of education, the relief of poverty, the advancement of religion and any other charitable purposes
- Goldman Sachs Gives (UK) (Charity Commission no. 1123956) – a grant-making charity that provides grants to a wide range of charitable projects

Citizenship programmes

10,000 Women – a global initiative that fosters economic growth by providing women entrepreneurs around the world with a business and management education, mentoring and networking, and access to capital.

10,000 Small Businesses – a programme to help entrepreneurs create jobs and economic opportunity by providing greater access to education, capital and business support services. 10,000 Small Businesses is funded by Goldman Sachs and the Goldman Sachs Foundation.

Employee-led support

Community TeamWorks is the company's worldwide volunteering initiative.

Applications

Contact the Corporate Engagement Team for further information.

Corporate charity

Goldman Sachs Gives (UK) (Charity Commission no. 1123956) – see entry on page 243; The Goldman Sachs Charitable Gift Fund (UK) (Charity Commission no. 1120148) – see entry on page 243.

Community contributions

Cash donations UK	£8,910,000
Cash donations worldwide	£10,670,000

In 2021 Goldman Sachs International made donations to charity totalling £10.67 million including a donation of £8.91 million to Goldman Sachs Gives (UK).

The company's charitable contributions have been converted from USD using the exchange rate at the time of writing (October 2022).

Goodwin plc

General charitable purposes

Company registration number: 305907

Correspondent: John Goodwin, Chair, Ivy House Foundry, Hanley, Stoke-on-Trent, Staffordshire ST1 3NR (tel: 01782 220000; email: info@goodwinplc.com; website: www.goodwin.co.uk)

Directors: Jenny Martin; Nigel Brown; John Connolly; Bernard Goodwin; Matthew Goodwin; Simon Goodwin; Timothy Goodwin; Jennifer Kelly (female: 25%; male: 75%).

Nature of business: Founded in 1883 as R. Goodwin and Sons Engineers, the group specialises in mechanical engineering. The group remains under family management and control with over 51% of the voting shares still in the hands of the Goodwin family.

Financial information

Year end	30/04/2021
Turnover	£131,000,000
Pre-tax profit	£16,500,000

Main locations: The group's head office is in Stoke-on-Trent.

Community involvement

The group's charitable support is mainly in the form of cash donations made to the local communities in which it operates.

Applications

Apply in writing to the correspondent.

Community contributions

Cash donations UK	£78,000

According to the 2020/21 annual report donations by the group for charitable purposes amounted to £78,000.

Gowling WLG (UK) LLP

Education and training, general charitable purposes, homelessness, social welfare

Company registration number: OC304378

Correspondent: Lorna Gavin, Head of Diversity, Inclusion and Corporate Responsibility, 4 More London Riverside, London SE1 2AU (email: lorna.gavin@gowlingwlg.com; website: https://gowlingwlg.com/en/corporate-responsibility/uk/corporate-responsibility)

Nature of business: Gowling WLG LLP is an international law firm.

Financial information

Year end	30/04/2021
Turnover	£187,013,000
Pre-tax profit	£53,424,000

Main locations: The firm has two offices in the UK – in Birmingham and London. There are also offices in Belgium, Canada, China, France, Germany, the United Arab Emirates and Russia.

Community involvement

The firm provides support for a range of causes through its corporate charity, the Gowling WLG (UK) Charitable Trust (Charity Commission no. 803009). The firm nominates a Charity of the Year to support and also provides pro bono legal advice to a range of charities.

Charity of the Year

Employees nominate one national charity to support each year. The chosen charity benefits from staff fundraising throughout the year and, where possible, pro bono and in-kind support. In 2022 the Charity of the Year was United By 2022. Previous Charity of the Year partners include Alzheimer's Society, Auditory Verbal UK, Bede House, Beyond Food, Birmingham St Mary's Hospice, Bliss, Cancer Research UK, Dementia UK, Dogs for the Good, Friends of the Elderly, Help Harry Help Others, KidsOut, Macmillan Cancer Support, Make-A-Wish, The Buddy Bag Foundation and Young Minds.

Partnerships

The firm is part of the Legal Social Mobility Partnership, providing work experience opportunities to disadvantaged young people.

In-kind support

The firm provides pro bono legal advice to charities and community groups and through legal clinics, supporting local and national organisations including the NSPCC, Roshni, SIFA Fireside and The Big Issue Foundation.

Employees' volunteering is focused on the key issues of homelessness, education and inner city needs. Employees offer support through activities such as CV and interview workshops to help people who are homeless or disadvantaged to gain employability skills and confidence.

Employee-led support

Employee volunteering

The firm's volunteering programme focuses on homelessness, education and social welfare. Employees volunteer in a range of activities to support these causes.

Social welfare

Employees can donate to food and clothing banks in the firm's offices, supporting The Trussell Trust as well as local charities SIFA Fireside (in

Birmingham) and Spitalfields Crypt Trust and St Giles Trust (in London).

Employee fundraising

Employees raise funds for partner charities and can also donate to charities through a payroll giving scheme. There is also a staff choir which raises money at concerts throughout the year.

Applications

General – contact the correspondent for further information.

Pro bono – for further information on pro bono assistance contact Katie Rothwell (katie.rothwell@gowlingwlg.com) or Amy Tabari (amy.tabari@gowlingwlg.com).

Corporate charity

Gowling WLG (UK) Charitable Trust (Charity Commission no. 803009) – see entry on page 244.

Community contributions

Total contributions worldwide	£140,000

According to the firm's 2020/21 annual accounts its charitable contributions totalled £140,000.

Grainger plc

Community services and development, education and training, housing and homelessness

Company registration number: 125575

Correspondent: CSR Team, No. 1 London Bridge, 3rd Floor East, London SE1 9BG (tel: 020 7940 9500; email: dbutler@graingerplc.co.uk; website: www.graingerplc.co.uk/responsibility.aspx)

Directors: Mark Clare; Helen Gordon; Robert Hudson; Justin Read; Andrew Carr-Locke; Rob Wilkinson; Janette Bell; Carol Hui (female: 38%; male: 63%).

Nature of business: The group owns, acquires and trades regulated and market-let tenanted properties.

Financial information

Year end	30/09/2021
Turnover	£248,900,000
Pre-tax profit	£152,100,000

Total employees: 294

Main locations: Grainger has offices in Newcastle (head office), Altrincham, Birmingham and London.

Community involvement

Grainger looks to improve the social, economic and environmental outlook for the communities in which it operates. Charities have been supported through cash donations, in-kind support, employee fundraising and volunteering time. The company is a partner of the charities LandAid and Age UK.

LandAid First Step Campaign

In 2021, the group supported LandAid's 'First Step' campaign. The campaign aims to support young people facing homelessness by increasing the provision of emergency accommodation. During the year, Grainger plc provided financial support for the campaign, as well as pro bono advice to an accommodation project for YMCA North Tyneside.

In-kind support

The group provides facilities and space for local charities and community organisations.

In addition to the pro bono services provided by the group to LandAid's 'First Step' campaign, Grainger plc signed on to LandAid's pro bono programme, offering further advice and services to three charities during 2021, from lease negotiations to building surveys.

Employee-led support

According to the Grainger plc annual report for 2021, the group's employees fundraise within the group's Diversity Network and organise charity events. We were unable to find details on these events.

Employees are entitled to a day's paid leave for volunteering each year.

Applications

Contact the correspondent for further information.

Community contributions

Total contributions UK	£56,400

According to the group's annual report for 2021, the group donated £56,400 to its two charity partners, LandAid and Age UK. We were unable to find a breakdown for this figure.

Greggs plc

Community services and development, general charitable purposes, social welfare

Company registration number: 502851

Correspondent: CSR Team, Greggs House, Quorum Business Park, Newcastle upon Tyne, Tyne and Wear NE12 8BU (email: getintouch@greggs.co.uk; website: http://corporate.greggs.co.uk/social-responsibility)

Directors: Jonathan Jowett; Nina Richards; Alicia Ryan; Roisin Currie; Matthew Davies; Ian Durant; Mohamed Elsarky; Catherine Ferry; Dr Helena Ganczakowski; Richard Hutton; Sandra Turner; Lynne Weedall (female: 50%; male: 50%).

Nature of business: The principal activity of the group is the retailing of sandwiches, savouries and other bakery products.

Financial information

Year end	01/01/2022
Turnover	£1,229,700,000
Pre-tax profit	£145,600,000

Main locations: Greggs' head office is located in Newcastle. The group operates stores nationwide.

Community involvement

Greggs carries out its community involvement in several ways, including through The Greggs Foundation (Charity Commission no. 296590), in-kind donations and employee involvement through volunteering and fundraising activities.

In-kind support

The group donates unsold food at the end of each working day to charitable organisations. There is now a dedicated page on the foundation's website which charities can use to apply for food donations.

Commercially led support

In-store fundraising

The group encourages fundraising in its nationwide outlets and receives donations from customers for a variety of charitable causes.

Sponsorship

The group is the main sponsor of the annual Children's Cancer Run, which is held in aid of the North of England Children's Cancer Research charity.

Applications

Contact the correspondent for further information.

Food donations – applications can be made via the foundation's website: www.greggsfoundation.org.uk/unsold-food-donations.

Corporate charity

The Greggs Foundation (Charity Commission no. 296590) – see entry on page 244.

Community contributions

Cash donations UK	£1,200,000

In 2020/21 the company donated £1.2 million to The Greggs Foundation. A further £100,000 was donated from the sale of carrier bags and £300,000 from the sale of products.

Alun Griffiths (Contractors) Ltd

🔍 Education and training, general charitable purposes

Company registration number: 1493003

Correspondent: CSR Team, Waterways House, Merthyr Road, Llanfoist, Abergavenny, Monmouthshire NP7 9PE (tel: 01873 857211; email: enquiries@ alungriffiths.co.uk; website: www. alungriffiths.co.uk)

Directors: Nick Mason; Stephen Tomkins; Tarmac Secretaries (male: 100%).

Nature of business: Alun Griffiths is a civil engineering and construction company.

Financial information

Year end	31/12/2021
Turnover	£225,800,000
Pre-tax profit	£11,630,000

UK employees: 1,000

Main locations: The company's headquarters is in Abergavenny. There are also offices in Gwynedd, Carmarthenshire, Swansea and Bristol.

Community involvement

The company engages with local communities via its public liaison officers and donates to local charities and organisations. Additionally, the company runs health and safety and careers programmes in local primary schools. In 2021, the company supported Cardiff Foodbank.

Commercially led support

According to its website, one of the ways in which the company provides support to local charities is through sponsorship.

Applications

Contact the correspondent for further information.

Community contributions

Cash donations UK	£2,000

According to the company's 2021 annual report, it donated £2,000 to local charities, clubs and community groups.

Grosvenor Group Ltd

🔍 Education and training, social welfare

Company registration number: 1265651

Correspondent: CSR Team, The Grosvenor Office, 70 Grosvenor Street, London W1K 3JP (tel: 020 7408 0988; email: online contact form; website: www.grosvenor.com)

Directors: Jonathon Bond; Robert Davis; Mark Preston; Michael McLintock; The Duke of Westminster; Matthew Barzun; Sir Philip Dilley; William Kendall; Barbara Kux; Christopher Pratt; Dame Fiona Reynolds; Alexander Scott; Peter Vernon (female: 15%; male: 85%).

Nature of business: The group's principal activities are property investment, financial services and general management in the UK and Ireland, the USA, Europe and Asia-Pacific.

Financial information

Year end	31/12/2021
Turnover	£193,500,000
Pre-tax profit	£298,500,000

Total employees: 570

Main locations: Grosvenor has UK offices in London and Liverpool.

Community involvement

The group provides support for health and welfare through its two foundations and The Living Cities Community Fund, administered by the London Community Resource Network. It also supports community events, makes cash donations and provides employee matched funding.

The Westminster Foundation (Charity Commission no. 267618)

Most of Grosvenor's community support is given through The Westminster Foundation, which was established in 1974 as the Grosvenor family's charitable foundation. The foundation's grant-making is focused on inspiring children and young people early in life with opportunities to thrive, build confidence and raise aspirations.

The Westminster Foundation has also allocated £12.5 million since March 2020 to provide support for those affected by the COVID-19 pandemic.

Staff charity committees

Each of the group's operating companies has its own staff charity committee. These help by recommending (to The Westminster Foundation trustees) those charities in their local communities that they wish to receive support and by organising staff fundraising activities, volunteering and pro bono support to charities selected by employees.

In-kind support

The group's 2021 annual report states:

> In South Belgravia, a portfolio of approximately 20,000 sq. ft. of office space accommodates around 20 charities in small office units. This portfolio is managed by Grosvenor Britain and Ireland and each charity receives a contribution, typically amounting to 50% of its rent, from the Westminster Foundation. This is funded by the Group and in 2021 totalled £430,000. These charities tell us that they find the central location very helpful.

Employee-led support

The group's 2021 annual report states:

> The Westminster Foundation matches the fundraising efforts of individual members of staff for registered charities of their own choosing up to £1,000 per member of staff in any given year. In 2021, the total figure given by the Westminster Foundation in this way was £4,248 (2020: £9,283). In addition, Grosvenor supports Give As You Earn up to £1,200 for UK-based employees and in 2021 this amounted to £28,419 (2020: £31,483).

Applications

Contact the correspondent for further information.

Corporate charity

The Westminster Foundation (Charity Commission no. 267618) – see entry on page 286.

Community contributions

Cash donations UK	£3,000,000

In 2021 the group made a donation of £2.7 million to The Westminster Foundation. A further £300,000 was given to other charitable causes by the group.

GSK plc

🔍 The environment, health, medical research, STEM

Company registration number: 1047315

Correspondent: Responsible Business Team, GSK House, 980 Great West Road, Brentford, Middlesex TW6 9GS (website: http://uk.gsk.com/en-gb/ partnerships/charitable-partnerships)

Directors: Victoria Whyte; Elizabeth Anderson; Charles Bancroft; Dr Hal Barron; Dr Anne Beal; Dr Harry Dietz; Dr Jesse Goodman; Iain Mackay; Urs Rohner; Dr Vishal Sikka; Sir Jonathan Symonds; Emma Walmsley (female: 33%; male: 67%).

Nature of business: The group's principal activities are the creation, discovery, development, manufacture and marketing of pharmaceutical products, including vaccines, over-the-counter medicines and health-related consumer products.

Financial information

Year end	31/12/2021
Turnover	£34,114,000,000
Pre-tax profit	£5,442,000,000

Main locations: The group's global headquarters is in Brentford. Other UK sites are located in County Durham, Harlow, Irvine, Maidenhead, Montrose, Slough, Stevenage, Ulverston, Uxbridge, Ware, Weybridge and Worthing.

Community involvement

GlaxoSmithKline (GSK) plc's charitable investments are focused in three main areas:

- **Health for people** – strengthening health and well-being systems worldwide to improve the health of vulnerable and marginalised people.
- **Innovators for the future** – investment in STEM to improve educational and career outcomes for those who are under-represented in these areas
- **Health for the planet** – partnerships to improve water quality, reduce carbon emissions, and protect and restore nature.

In the UK, health charities are supported through partnerships, donations and the GSK IMPACT Awards.

GSK IMPACT Awards

The annual GSK IMPACT Awards are run in partnership with The King's Fund (Charity Commission no. 1126980) to recognise and promote excellence in community healthcare.

To be eligible for a GSK IMPACT Award, organisations must be registered, have an annual income of between £120,000 and £3 million, be working in a health-related field, and have been operating in the UK for at least three years. The King's Fund website provides the following information:

- Up to ten winners receive £40,000, in unrestricted funding with the overall winner receiving an additional £10,000.
- Up to five runners-up receive £4,000 in unrestricted funding.
- Award winners are offered free training and development valued at an average of £9,500 for each organisation.
- ou do not need to present a new project, and you decide how to spend the award money.

For further details, visit The King's Fund's website: www.kingsfund.org.uk

Partnerships

The group currently has nine charity partnerships that operate nationally. Details of partnerships in each region of the UK can be seen on the GSK website.

STEM education

The group's science education website offers a range of free curriculum resources for 11- to 14-year-olds.

Grants and donations

GSK makes grants to healthcare organisations and patient advocacy groups for activities that enhance patient care or benefit the NHS.

In-kind support

GSK makes in-kind contributions in the form of product donations and staff time, particularly for financially developing countries.

Employee-led support

Orange United Week

During Orange United Week, GSK employees come together for one week to raise money and awareness for Save the Children.

Employee fundraising

Most employees' fundraising efforts are focused on raising funds for the group's main global charity partner, Save the Children. Donations are then matched by the group.

Applications

Grants and donations

Application forms can be downloaded from: www.gsk.com/en-gb/locations/united-kingdom/#criteria-for-grants-and-donations

GSK IMPACT Award

To apply for a GSK IMPACT Award, read the application guidelines and complete the online form available at: www.kingsfund.org.uk.

Community contributions

Cash donations UK	£545,500
Cash donations worldwide	£83,800,000
Total contributions worldwide	£242,900,000

In 2021, GlaxoSmithKline plc's worldwide community investment totalled £242.9 million and was broken down as follows:

Product and in-kind donations	£158.9 million
Cash	£83.8 million
Time	£200,000

As is our usual practice, we have not included management costs (£17.3 million).

Guardian Media Group plc

Education and training, human rights, journalism, social welfare.

Company registration number: 94531

Correspondent: Richard Kerr, Secretary to the Trustees, Kings Place, 90 York Way, London N1 9GU (tel: 020 3353 2369; email: info@theguardianfoundation.org; website: www.theguardian.com/sustainability)

Directors: Stephen Godsell; Anna Bateson; Emily Bell; Jennifer Duvalier; Charles Gurassa; Yasmin Jetha; Gail Ruth Rebuck; Rene Rechtman; Mary Sieghart; Keith Underwood; Katharine Viner; Coram Williams (female: 58%; male: 42%).

Nature of business: Guardian Media Group is one of the UK's leading media organisations.

Financial information

Year end	03/04/2021
Turnover	£255,800,000
Pre-tax profit	£142,700,000

Total employees: 924

Main locations: The Guardian has offices in London and Manchester.

Community involvement

Guardian Media Group works in partnership with local, national and international charities to raise awareness and run fundraising campaigns.

The Guardian Foundation

Guardian Media Group makes donations to The Guardian Foundation (Charity Commission no. 1153865), an independent charity that aims to empower journalists and communities to report the truth through education, the promotion of human rights and the right to information.

The foundation was registered in 2013 as the successor to The Scott Trust Foundation, which transferred its assets and operations to The Guardian Foundation in September 2014. The foundation's principal source of funding is the Guardian Media Group.

While in the past The Scott Trust Foundation operated as a grant-maker, The Guardian Foundation's current activities are focused on its object of advancing education, research and human rights.

In-kind support

In previous years, the group has given in-kind support such as books and free publishing services to local charities.

Employee-led support

Employees fundraise and volunteer for organisations that are committed to advancing education, research and human rights.

Applications

The group's community contributions appear to be concentrated on The Guardian Foundation. Contact the foundation for more information.

Community contributions

Cash donations UK	£435,000

Guardian Media Group plc's 2020/21 annual report does not detail its charitable contributions during the year. However, according to The Guardian Foundation's 2020/21 annual report, the group donated £435,000 to the foundation during the year.

Hammerson plc

Community enterprise and social entrepreneurship, community services and development, education and training, general charitable purposes, health

Company registration number: 360632

Correspondent: Louise Ellison, Head of Sustainability, Kings Place, 90 York Way, London N1 9GE (tel: 020 7887 1000; email: sustainability@hammerson.com; website: https://www.hammerson.com/sustainability)

Directors: Habib Ibrahim Annous; Mahkameh Brunel; Michael Butterworth; Desmond de Beer; Rita Gagne; Adam Metz; Robert Noel; Alan Olivier; Himanshu Raja; Carol Welch.

Nature of business: Hammerson is an owner-manager and developer of retail and office property in the UK and France.

Financial information

Year end	31/12/2021
Turnover	£134,800,000
Pre-tax profit	£408,000,000

Total employees: 426

Main locations: Hammerson's UK office is located in London and it has properties throughout the UK. For details of the whereabouts of Hammerson properties, see www.hammerson.com/property.

Community involvement

Hammerson looks to develop relationships in the communities where it has a presence, both at a corporate level and through its locations in the UK and France. Support is given to charities in the form of cash and in-kind donations and through employee volunteering and fundraising.

Centre charity bursaries

Every Hammerson plc shopping centre selects one or two charity partners each year. As well as receiving a cash donation, charity partners receive a small space to allow them to fundraise and develop their relationship with the local community.

Local community projects

In addition to having charity partners, Hammerson plc shopping centres engage in projects with local organisations to meet the needs of their local communities. For example, Union Square shopping centre introduced bees to its rooftops in 2021, in partnership with Urban Bee.

Charity partners

The group's employee charity partner is The Outward Bound Trust and its corporate charity partner is LandAid. The group also has number of national charity partners, including LionHeart and Young Enterprise.

Group-wide community programmes

At a corporate level, group-wide programmes are delivered. These programmes are focussed on the following four key thematic areas:
- Employment and skills
- Well-being
- Developing young people
- Enterprise

Employee-led support

Employee volunteering

In 2021, Hammerson plc employees volunteered 2,408 hours of their time.

Community Fortnight

Each year, the group holds a Community Fortnight, during which employees take part in various challenges to raise funds for the group's charity partners.

Applications

Contact the correpsondent for further information.

Community contributions

Cash donations UK	£274,900
Total contributions UK	£2,020,000

According to the group's 2021 sustainability report, its total contributions amounted to £2.02 million, which included £247,500 in cash donations.

Harbour Energy plc

Community services and development, education and training, general charitable purposes, housing and homelessness, social welfare, STEM

Company registration number: SC234781

Correspondent: Sustainability Department, 23 Lower Belgrave Street, London SW1W 0NR (tel: 020 7730 1111; email: info@harbourenergy.com; website: www.harbourenergy.com/safety-esg/social)

Directors: Robert Blair Thomas; Linda Cook; Alexander Krane; Simon Henry; Anne Marie Cannon; George Steven Farris; Alan Ferguson; Andy Hopwood; Margaret Øvrum; Anne Stevens (female: 40%; male: 60%).

Nature of business: Harbour Energy is an international gas and oil exploration and production company.

Financial information

Year end	31/12/2021
Turnover	£3,478,800,000
Pre-tax profit	£314,500,000

Total employees: 1,771

Main locations: In the UK, the group's head office is in London and it has offices in Aberdeen. It also has offices in several locations across the world.

Community involvement

The group invests in community projects to help deliver economic and environmental benefits for communities within its areas of operation.

UK community investment

According to the Harbour Energy plc community engagement web page, the company makes contributions to charitable causes that align with its strategic purpose and core values. The company makes cash contributions as well as contributions through sponsorship of educational programmes and charity events.

STEM in the Pipeline UK

The group is one of the headline sponsors of the STEM programme, which is run in senior schools by the charity TechFest in Aberdeen. As part of the programme, the company supplies mentors to local schools to help deliver oil and gas-related challenges to students.

The River Dee Trust

Harbour Energy plc also sponsors The River Dee Trust's education programme. Based in Aberdeenshire in Scotland, the scheme focuses on connecting young people to the River Dee through activities linked to the Curriculum for Excellence. In 2021, the programme delivered 164 visits to 2,200 children.

Run Balmoral UK

The group is the sponsor of the 5k event at Run Balmoral, where more than 5,000 people take part in a varied programme of races on the Balmoral Estate in Royal Deeside, Scotland over a weekend in April. Harbour Energy plc employees take part in the event to aid charities of their choice.

Employee-led support

Employees of Harbour Energy plc volunteer as mentors for the STEM in the Pipeline UK programme, as well as participating in the Run Balmoral UK event.

Applications

Contact the correspondent for more information.

Community contributions

Total contributions worldwide	£973,200

According to the group's 2021 annual report, Harbour Energy plc contributed £973,200 (USD 1.1 million) to community investment and charitable causes across the world, including in the UK.

All financial information has been converted from USD using the exchange rate at the time of writing (September 2022).

Hargreaves Lansdown plc

Community services and development, education and training, general charitable purposes, money and debt advice

Company registration number: 2122142

Correspondent: CSR Team, One College Square South, Anchor Road, Bristol BS1 5HL (tel: 0117 900 9000; email: HLFoundation@hl.co.uk; website: www. hl.co.uk/corporate-social-responsibility/ community)

Directors: Andrea Blance; Adrian Collins; Christopher Hill; Penelope James; Dan Olley; Deanna Oppenheimer; Roger Perkin; Amy Stirling; Sheik Mansurah Tal-At Mannings; John Troiano (female: 40%; male: 60%).

Nature of business: Hargreaves Lansdown (HL) is a financial service company that sells funds, shares and related products to investors.

Financial information

Year end	30/06/2021
Turnover	£631,000,000
Pre-tax profit	£366,000,000

UK employees: 1,768

Total employees: 1,842

Main locations: The company is based in Bristol.

Community involvement

The company's community involvement is focused locally, around Bristol. The company donates to its corporate charity, The HL Foundation (Charity Commission no. 1167927), and offers financial education to schools and universities and supports local initiatives such as the city-wide campaign to end period poverty.

The HL Foundation

The HL Foundation chose Help Bristol's Homeless as its charity partner for 2020 and plans to fund a new well-being centre at the charity's centre.

As well as company contributions, employees volunteer, donate through payroll giving and fundraise for the charity and customers can also donate. During 2020/21 the foundation distributed £123,000 to local charities.

Financial education

The company delivers a financial education service which teaches organisations about investing and pensions. A team of volunteers make up the company's Financial Inclusion Group, which educates school children and university students on topics such as budgeting, savings and future financial options. The company is looking to expand this service to community groups.

Partnerships

The company has established several partnerships with charitable organisations in Bristol, with an aim to improve the lives of those who live and work in the city. Examples of partnerships include those with Bristol Learning City, Bristol Green Partnership and Bristol Sport Foundation.

The company is also a founding member of the Bristol Equality Charter, a cross-sector collaborative approach to addressing inequality in the city. HL is also a signatory of the Social Mobility Pledge.

In-kind support

In response to the COVID-19 pandemic's effect on education, HL donated 200 laptops to schools and colleges to help close the digital divide.

The company also worked with FareShare to provide food to those facing food poverty. In 2020, the company supported FareShare South West's emergency food operation, FoodStock 2020. The company's volunteering and fundraising helped FareShare to deliver 3.4 million meals to over 350 frontline projects across the region working with the most vulnerable people.

Employee-led support

Employee volunteering

The HL Volunteering Scheme gives employees two days' paid leave to volunteer each year. Employees can volunteer for HL-organised activities or choose their own charity or good cause. In 2020/21, employees volunteered over 1,000 hours.

Payroll giving

Employees can donate to The HL Foundation through Give As You Earn. The company double-matches employee donations. According to the foundation's annual report for 2020/21, the total for funds raised through Give As You Earn in 2021 was £21,000.

Employee fundraising

Employees are encouraged to fundraise for The HL Foundation. Activities include a payday lottery, bike rides, cake sales and sports tournaments.

Commercially led support

The company sponsors Bristol Pride and St Paul's Carnival.

Applications

The HL Foundation – to contact the foundation, email HLFoundation@hl.co.uk.

For all other enquiries, contact the correspondent for further information.

Community contributions

Cash donations UK		£193,000

We were unable to determine the total for the company's charitable giving in 2020/21. However, The HL Foundation's 2020/21 accounts report a donation of £193,000 from the company. We have taken this amount as the figure for the company's total contributions.

Hastings Group Holdings plc

Education and training, general charitable purposes, health, housing and homelessness

Company registration number: 9635183

Correspondent: Tony Leppard, Company Secretary, Conquest House, Collington Avenue, Bexhill-on-Sea, East Sussex TN39 3LW (email: community@ hastingsdirect.com; website: www. hastingsplc.com)

Directors: Knut Arne Alsaker; Thomas Colraine; Pierre Lefevre; Torbjorn Magnusson; Morken Thorsrud; Ricard Wennerklint (male: 100%).

Nature of business: Hastings Group provides general insurance to the UK market. The group has two businesses: Hastings Insurance Services Ltd and Advantage Insurance Company Ltd.

Financial information

Year end	31/12/2021
Turnover	£39,300,000
Pre-tax profit	£28,300,000

Total employees: 2,995

Main locations: The group is headquartered in Bexhill-on-Sea, East Sussex. The group also has operations in Leicestershire, London and Gibraltar.

Community involvement

Hastings supports its local communities through charity partnerships, sponsorship, the sale of cause-related products and employee fundraising and volunteering. The group also provides financial and in-kind support through the Hastings Community Fund.

Hastings Community Fund (not a registered charity)

The fund supports individuals and groups by providing advice, volunteers or small grants to help with fundraising. The scheme supports local charities within a 20-mile radius of Hastings' sites in Bexhill and Leicester.

Charities of the Year

In 2021, the group supported Comic Relief and Macmillan Coffee Morning through company fundraising days. The group also supported Movember, the national fundraising event highlighting men's cancer.

Partnerships

The group maintains partnerships with organisations such as Women in Data, Carers UK and Inclusive Companies. A full list of the group's partners is available on the group's website.

Bexhill Beach Adoption

In 2021, the group gave support to the local council in Bexhill in the form of beach adoption, beach cleaning and the purchase of additional waste bins to help reduce litter on beaches.

In-kind support

Computers for Schools

In 2021, Hastings supported the Computers for Schools scheme by donating old IT equipment to 23 local schools. Also, as part of its environmental sustainability, the group donated any old furniture and IT equipment to local charities.

Employee-led support

Employee fundraising

Employees fundraise for the group's charity partners. For example, in 2019 employees took part in quiz nights, bake sales and sponsored sea swims to raise money for Warming Up The Homeless. They also donated products such as toiletries and non-perishable goods.

Community days

The group offers employees the chance to partake in community days to volunteer or fundraise for charitable causes. In 2021, 975 employees completed community days, raising £21,000 for a range of local charities. Employees also raised a further £9,000 for Macmillan Cancer Support and Comic Relief through national fundraising days.

Future Ready education programme

In 2021, the Future Ready education programme, supported by Hastings employees, reached 128 local students. The mentoring programme is designed to help equip young people with skills for the future.

Commercially led support

Cause-related products

The group offers an insurance policy called insurePink. For every policy purchased, the group donates £10 to the Pink Ribbon Foundation, a breast cancer charity. To date, the group has raised over £1 million through this initiative.

Applications

Contact the correspondent for further information.

Community contributions

Cash donations UK	£198,000

According to the group's 2021 sustainability report, £198,000 was donated to help those affected by the COVID-19 pandemic.

Heart of England Co-operative

Community services and development, general charitable purposes

Company registration number: IP02399R

Correspondent: Jo Dyke, Community and Membership Adviser, Whittle House, Foleshill Enterprise Park, Courtaulds Way, Coventry CV6 5NX (tel: 024 7638 2331; email: jo.dyke@ heartofengland-coop.co.uk; website: www.heartofengland.coop)

Directors: Mark Alexander; Scott Arlidge; Colin Brown; Gary Haigh; Nick Matthews; Chris Newman; Mark Runsey; Andrew Tampion (male: 100%).

Nature of business: The society is a food retailer and funeralcare provider.

Financial information

Year end	18/01/2022
Turnover	£90,928,000
Pre-tax profit	£5,715,000

UK employees: 805

Main locations: The society has stores in Coventry, Warwickshire, South Leicestershire and Northamptonshire.

Community involvement

Partnerships

The society's corporate charity partner is decided by a staff vote every two years. In 2022, the society's partnership with Alzheimer's Society concluded, having raised £33,000. The corporate charity selected for 2022–24 is Coventry and Warwickshire Mind, a local mental health charity.

Helping Hearts Awards

The awards scheme provides small grants to charities and groups in the regions of Coventry, Warwickshire, South Leicestershire and Northamptonshire. The scheme is administered by the Heart of England Community Foundation.

In-kind support

In 2021/22, the society's food division increased the number of food bank donation points in its stores. The society works with FareShare and the Trussell Trust to donate its surplus food to charities and community groups.

Heart of England Co-operative also donated surplus items to FareShare Midlands to help tackle food poverty.

During the year, the society partnered with organisations over the Christmas period to provide Christmas lunches to older people and vulnerable groups.

Commercially led support

In 2021/22, the society organised an in-store promotion for FareShare, donating a proportion of sales to the community.

Applications

Application forms for the Helping Hearts Awards are available in all stores. Forms can also be requested from the correspondent, as can further information on all the society's initiatives.

Community contributions

Cash donations UK	£59,000

The Heart of England's annual report for 2021/22 states that the society contributed a total of £59,000 in grants and donations. Of this total £36,000 was donated through the Helping Hearts Awards Scheme and accounts for 0.9% of the society's annual pre-tax profit.

Heathrow Airport Holdings Ltd (formerly BAA Ltd)

Community enterprise and social entrepreneurship, community services and development, education and training, the environment, health

Company registration number: 5757208

Correspondent: Community Relations Team, The Compass Centre, Nelson Road, London Heathrow Airport, London TW6 2GW (tel: 0800 307 7996; email: communityrelations@heathrow. com; website: www.heathrow.com/ company/community-and-environment/ community)

Directors: Ali Bouzarif; Mark Brooker; Luke Bugeja; Ignacio Fernandez; Ignacio Hernandez; Jessie Jin; Deven Karnik; Joan MacNaughton; Chao Wang; Gonzalo Zabalza; Lord Paul Deighton; Akbar Al Baker; Ahmed Al-Hammadi; Chris Beale; Stuart Baldwin; ; María Casero; Oliver Fortin; Ruth Kelly; Ernesto López Mozo; Mike Powell; David Xie; John Holland-Kaye; Javier Echave (female: 17%; male: 83%).

Nature of business: Heathrow Airport Holdings Ltd (formerly BAA) owns and runs London Heathrow Airport.

Financial information

Year end	31/12/2021
Turnover	£1,214,000,000
Pre-tax profit	£252,000,000

Main locations: The airport is based in London and supports the boroughs of Ealing, Hillingdon, Hounslow, Richmond, Runnymede, Slough, Spelthorne, South Buckinghamshire, Windsor and Maidenhead.

Community involvement

The group's charitable support is focused on the areas surrounding Heathrow Airport. The group's corporate charity makes grants to local projects supporting communities, the environment and sustainability, young people and education. Employees can also volunteer with local projects, and employees and customers contribute to fundraising for the group's partner charities.

Heathrow Community Trust (Charity Commission no. 1183004)

The group channels its charitable support through Heathrow Community Trust. The trust awards between £880,000 and £1 million in grants every year and provides matched funding for employee donations.

The trust also encourages employees to support projects in their local communities. Awards of up to £2,500 are granted to charities for projects involving Heathrow Airport employee volunteering.

Community investment

The group has a community investment programme which aims to support the economic prosperity of the areas surrounding the airport through skills development, careers support and engagement with educational institutions and businesses. For example, the group's Heathrow Academy supports local people with training and employment opportunities. The group also supports children in local schools with education programmes. These initiatives are funded by corporate donations and money raised from noise fines issued to airlines.

Employee-led support

The group provides matched funding for employees engaged in their own charitable fundraising initiatives through Heathrow Community Trust. An additional £5,600 was leveraged from colleague and passenger fundraising, as well as levies from noise fines.

Applications

Contact the correspondent for further information on the community investment programme. See the group's corporate charity entry for further information on how to apply for a grant.

Corporate charity

Heathrow Community Trust (Charity Commission no. 1183004) – see entry on page 245.

Community contributions

Total contributions UK	£440,500

In 2021, the group's contributions totalled £440,500. This consists of a contribution of £315,500 to its corporate charity the Heathrow Community Trust and an additional donation of £125,000.

John Henderson (Holdings) Ltd

Education and training, health, religion, social welfare

Company registration number: NI010588

Correspondent: CSR Team, 9–11 Hightown Avenue, London EC2M 3AE (website: https://henderson-group.com)

Directors: William Whitten; Geoffrey Agnew; John Agnew; Martin Agnew (male: 100%).

Nature of business: John Henderson (Holdings) Ltd is a holding company of the Henderson Group. The group owns retail, property, wholesale, technology and printing businesses in Northern Ireland.

Financial information

Year end	31/12/2020
Turnover	£956,646,600
Pre-tax profit	£28,494,821

Total employees: 4,171

Main locations: The group is based in Northern Ireland.

Community involvement

Ardbarron Trust (NICC no. NIC101111)

The group's charitable giving is directed through its corporate charity, the Ardbarron Trust Ltd. The Ardbarron Trust states its purpose as the advancement of the Christian faith, as well as the provision of education, healthcare, literacy and economic development.

Heart of the Community

The group is working to install 300 defibrillators in the communities in which it operates, as part of its Heart of the Community campaign.

Community Cashback Fund

In 2020, the group allocated £5,000 for its Community Cashback Fund, whereby members of the community could vote for the charities they wished to receive a portion of the fund. The final charities voted for were Parenting NI, Nexus NI, Eating Disorders Association NI and Cruse Bereavement Care.

Applications

See the group's corporate charity entry for further information.

Corporate charity

Ardbarron Trust Ltd (NICC no. NIC101111) – see entry on page 219.

Community contributions

Cash donations UK	£5,000,000

In 2020 the group made a donation of £5 million to its corporate charity.

William Hill plc

Community services and development, education and training, general charitable purposes, health, mental health and well-being

Company registration number: 4212563

Correspondent: Sustainability Team, 1 Bedford Avenue, London WC1B 3AU (tel: 020 7612 3000; website: www.williamhillplc.com/sustainability/supporting-communities)

Directors: Josie-Azzara Havita; Philip Grice; Virtual Internet Services Ltd (male: 100%).

Nature of business: William Hill is a UK-based bookmaker. The principal activities of the group include the operation of licensed betting shops and the provision of telephone, online and interactive television betting services.

Financial information

Year end	31/12/2021
Turnover	£1,241,000,000
Pre-tax profit	£61,600,000

Total employees: 12,000

Main locations: The group operates worldwide and its headquarters is in London.

Community involvement

William Hill supports the communities in which it operates through charitable donations, partnerships with national charities and other charitable initiatives, predominantly through its corporate charity.

The William Hill Foundation (Charity Commission no. 1146270)

Established in 2011, the foundation initially made donations to William Hill staff experiencing hardship, as well as funding various charity programmes. The foundation was re-launched in 2019 with a new and expanded focus on mental health. The trustees' three areas of interest were mental health and well-being, colleagues and employability. However, according to the Charity Commission website, the foundation has now been wound up, with all its funds going to Alzheimer's Society.

Partnerships

According to William Hill plc's 2021 annual report, it continued its partnership with Alzheimer's Society. The group had raised £250,000 for the charity at the time of writing (October 2022).

Employee-led support

Employees engage in various fundraising efforts for the company's charity partner.

Applications

Contact the correspondent for more information.

Community contributions

We were unable to determine a figure for William Hill plc's charitable contributions for the year.

Hiscox Ltd

Arts, culture and heritage, education and training, health, medical research, social welfare, work outside the UK

Correspondent: CSR Team, 1 Great St Helen's, London EC3A 6HX (tel: 020 7448 6000; email: enquiries@hiscox.com; website: www.hiscoxgroup.com/responsibility)

Directors: Robert Childs; Aki Hussain; Joanne Musselle; Colin Keogh; Donna DeMaio; Caroline Foulger; Michael Goodwin; Thomas Hürlimann; Anne MacDonald; Constantinos Miranthis; Lynn Pike; Lynn Pike; Marc Wetherhill (female: 42%; male: 58%).

Nature of business: Hiscox Ltd specialises in insurance and is registered in Bermuda. The group's UK charitable activities are carried out by its UK subsidiaries and The Hiscox Foundation.

Financial information

Year end	31/12/2021
Turnover	£4,270,000,000
Pre-tax profit	£158,090,000

Total employees: 3,000

Main locations: Hiscox Ltd has offices in Birmingham, Colchester, Glasgow, London, York, Maidenhead and Manchester. The group's UK operations are headquartered in London.

Community involvement

In the UK, Hiscox Ltd makes an annual donation to its corporate charity, The Hiscox Foundation (Charity Commission no. 327635). According to the group's website:

> The Hiscox Foundation UK divides its approach to charitable giving into three main pillars; social mobility and entrepreneurship, protecting and preserving the environment, and causes our people are passionate about; and charities aligned with these areas of focus are encouraged to apply.

Employees can nominate charities to support through the Hiscox Gives initiative. This initiative aims to raise awareness for charitable causes and encourage volunteering among staff.

Partnerships

Employees play an important role in choosing the charities that the group supports. In 2021, the London office began a three-year partnership with Bethnal Green Spear Trust. The trust supports disadvantaged 16- to 24-year-olds by placing them in long-term employment. Employees raised £7,400 for the trust in 2021.

In-kind support

According to the 2021 impact report, the group donated 24,984 learning resource boxes to schools.

Employee-led support

Employees can apply to The Hiscox Foundation for matched funding or request support for a good cause. The Hiscox Gives programme creates volunteering opportunities for employees. In 2021, employees logged 1,000 volunteering hours.

Commercially led support

Sponsorship

According to the group website, Hiscox Ltd regularly sponsors the Dive In Festival, which is a global festival that promotes diversity and inclusion in insurance.

Applications

Applications for sponsorship can be submitted to sponsorship@hiscox.com. Hiscox only selects a few sponsorships that fit best with its marketing strategy. Requirements for applications can be found on the 'Sponsorship' page of the group's website.

For more information about The Hiscox Foundation, see the corporate charity entry.

Corporate charity

The Hiscox Foundation (Charity Commission no. 327635) – see entry on page 246.

Community contributions

| Total contributions worldwide | £1,500,000 |

In 2021, the group's charitable contributions totalled £1.5 million. According to its 2021 impact report, this includes donations made to its UK and US Hiscox foundations, corporate charitable contributions, employee fundraising, matched funding and gift aid. We have used this figure as the group's total contributions worldwide.

All the financial figures have been converted from USD to GBP using the exchange rate at the time of writing (August 2022).

C. Hoare and Co.

Animal welfare, arts, culture and heritage, education and training, general charitable purposes, health, social welfare

Company registration number: 240822

Correspondent: Philanthropy Team, 37 Fleet Street, London EC40 4DQ (tel: 020 7353 4522; email: info@hoaresbank.co.uk; website: www.hoaresbank.co.uk)

Directors: Alexander Hoare; Venetia Hoare; Simon Hoare; Bella Hoare; Alex Hoare; Rennie Hoare; Lord Macpherson of Earl's Court; Andrew McIntyre; Johanna Waterous; Giles Andrews; India Gary-Martin; Diana Brightmore-Armour (female: 42%; male: 58%).

Nature of business: C. Hoare and Co. provides banking and ancillary services to a predominantly high-net-worth customer base.

Financial information

Year end	31/03/2022
Turnover	£108,810,000
Pre-tax profit	£16,540,000

UK employees: 386

Main locations: The company's head office is in London.

Community involvement

The company's charitable giving is channelled primarily through its corporate charity, The Golden Bottle Trust (Charity Commission no. 327026), to which the company makes donations.

In addition, the company's Philanthropy Team identifies causes aligned to the bank's values and establishes the most efficient means of supporting them, such as one-off donations or long-term giving.

Each year the partners donate up to 10% of the bank's profits to charity.

Employee-led support

The company double-matches charitable donations made by its employees through its payroll giving scheme.

Employees are entitled to take two days' paid leave a year to volunteer.

Applications

See the corporate charity entry for more information.

Corporate charity

The Golden Bottle Trust (Charity Commission no. 327026) – see entry on page 242.

Community contributions

| Cash donations UK | £1,500,000 |

In 2021/22, the company donated £1.5 million to its corporate charity.

Holland and Barrett Retail Ltd

Education and training, the environment, health

Company registration number: 2758955

Correspondent: CSR Team, Samuel Ryder House, Barling Way, Nuneaton, Warwickshire CV10 7RH (tel: 024 7621 5823; email: corporate@hollandandbarrett.com; website: www.hollandandbarrettcorporate.com)

Directors: Matthew Smith; Robbie Bell (male: 100%).

Nature of business: Holland and Barrett is a chain of health food shops.

Financial information

Year end	15/08/2021
Turnover	£528,590,000
Pre-tax profit	£43,630,000

Total employees: 7,000

Main locations: The company's headquarters is in Nuneaton. There are 792 stores in the UK as well as stores in the Netherlands, Belgium, Sweden and the Republic of Ireland.

Community involvement

The company makes donations to UK-based organisations, often by boosting employees' fundraising efforts.

In-kind support

In 2021, the company donated meals and 2,000 bottles of vitamin D to The Felix Project to be distributed to various churches, shelters and care homes throughout London.

Employee-led support

The company supports its colleagues by donating to their fundraising efforts on completion of an event or activity.

Commercially led support

In 2020, the company introduced the Pennies digital donation scheme, an initiative that gives customers the option to add a 50p top-up donation when purchasing items. Money raised through this initiative goes towards supporting NHS Charities Together. The company raised £75,000 between 2020 and 2022.

Applications

Contact the correspondent for further information.

Community contributions

We were unable to determine a figure for the group's charitable contributions.

Honda of the UK Manufacturing Ltd

Community services and development, education and training, the environment, general charitable purposes

Company registration number: 1887872

Correspondent: CSR Team, 1 More London Place, London SE1 2AF (tel: 01793 831183; email: corporate.communications@honda-eu.com; website: www.hondamanufacturing.co.uk)

Directors: Katshuhisa Okuda; Katsushi Inoue (male: 100%).

Nature of business: The principal activity of the company is the manufacture of motor vehicles, including the manufacture of motor engines and other vehicle parts.

Financial information

Year end	31/03/2021
Turnover	£1,143,000,000
Pre-tax profit	(£394,700,000)

UK employees: 3,400

Main locations: The company's UK manufacturing facility is in Swindon.

Community involvement

Honda of the UK Manufacturing Ltd invests in sustainability initiatives focusing on education, safety, the environment and the community. The company predominantly supports charitable and community initiatives in the area local to its Swindon base. The company also makes quarterly donations to charities voted for by employees.

In-kind support

The 2020/21 annual report states that Christmas hamper donations are made to local organisations.

Employee-led support

The company provides matched funding for fundraising events organised by its associates.

Applications

Contact the correspondent for further information.

Community contributions

Cash donations UK	£57,200

According to its 2020/21 annual report, the company made charitable donations of £57,200.

Hoover Ltd

Education and training, the environment, general charitable purposes, health

Company registration number: 2521528

Correspondent: The Hoover Foundation, Hoover Candy, 302 Bridgewater Place, Birchwood, Warrington, Cheshire WA3 6XG (tel: 0330 041 2345; email: online contact form; website: www.hoover.co.uk)

Directors: Abrar Bokhari; Lawrence Edwards-Smajda; David Meyerowitz (male: 100%).

Nature of business: Hoover Ltd is a manufacturer of major domestic appliances including washing machines, dishwashers, dryers, refrigerators and ovens.

Financial information

Year end	31/12/2020
Turnover	£257,355,000
Pre-tax profit	(£2,388,000)

UK employees: 600

Main locations: Hoover Ltd has its head office in Warrington, Cheshire.

Community involvement

Hoover Ltd directs its charitable giving through The Hoover Foundation (Charity Commission no. 200274), which supports educational, environmental and charitable work in and around the areas of Hoover Ltd locations throughout the UK. According to the company's accounts, Hoover Ltd also works alongside the foundation to support local charitable initiatives.

Commercially led support

Hoover Ltd is a sponsor of Warrington Wolves Rugby League Football Club.

Applications

For further information on The Hoover Foundation, email ggray@hoovercandy.com.

Community contributions

We were unable to determine a figure for the company's total community contributions during 2020.

Howden Group Holdings

Education and training, the environment, health, humanitarian aid, social welfare

Company registration number: 2937398

Correspondent: Clare Ballantine, Foundation Manager, 1 Creechurch Place, London EC3A 5AF (email: info@howdengroupfoundation.com; website: www.howdengroupholdings.com/our-approach/howden-group-foundation)

Directors: Andrew Moore; John Bernstein; Clement Booth; Andrew Collins; Mark Craig; Ralph Friedwagner; David Hodgson; David Howden; Andrew Land; Kelly Lyles; Luis Muñoz-Rojas Entrecanales; James Parry-Crooke; Thomas Stephen; Caroline Woodworth (female: 14%; male: 86%).

Nature of business: Howden Group Holdings is a group of insurance businesses.

Financial information

Year end	30/09/2021
Pre-tax profit	£6,100,000

Main locations: The group has offices worldwide, including more than 100 offices in the UK.

Community involvement

The group provides charitable support through match funding, donations and partnerships. The group's charitable work is co-ordinated through its foundation.

Howden Group Foundation (Charity Commission no. 1156286)

The foundation was established in 2014 and has six charitable objectives:

- Relief of sickness
- Relief of poverty
- Relief of disasters
- Relief of unemployment
- Advancement of education
- Environmental sustainability

The foundation makes one-off donations to charities supported or selected by employees. These are sometimes in response to global initiatives such as disaster relief or annual awareness-raising events.

Investing in the Community Awards

Each year employees nominate local, grassroots charities for one-off grants of £5,000.

Partnerships

The group supports global organisations through strategic long-term partnerships. Strategic partners include The Prince's Trust, Seven Clean Seas, The Nature Conservancy and Care Channels International.

Employee-led support

Employees take part in fundraising events throughout the year. The foundation matches donations of up to £750 per employee, per year.

Applications

See the foundation's website for further information.

Community contributions

Cash donations worldwide	£1,500,000

In 2020/21 the group made cash donations totalling £300,000. The group also issued shares in the Howden Group, with a fair value of £1.2 million, to the Howden Group Foundation for nominal value.

Howden Joinery Group plc

Arts, culture and heritage, community services and development, education and training, general charitable purposes, housing and homelessness

Company registration number: 2128710

Correspondent: Local Howdens Depot, 40 Portman Square, London W1H 6LT (tel: 020 7535 1110; email: guy.stainer@howdens.com; website: www.howdenjoinerygroupplc.com/index.asp#Sustainability)

Directors: Richard Pennycook; Andrew Livingston; Peter Ventress; Karen Caddick; Paul Hayes; Andrew Cripps; Geoff Drabble; Louise Fowler; Debbie White (female: 33%; male: 67%).

Nature of business: Howden supplies kitchens and joinery products to trade customers, principally small builders, in the UK.

Financial information

Year end	28/12/2021
Turnover	£402,000,000
Pre-tax profit	£390,000,000

Total employees: 11,000

Main locations: The company's head office is in London and there are 732 depots throughout the UK. There is a local depot search facility on the website.

Community involvement

Individual Howden's depots, manufacturing sites and distribution and support centres support their local communities through cash and stock donations. Employees take part in a wide range of fundraising initiatives.

Partnerships

Since 2004, Howden's has worked in partnership with Leonard Cheshire Disability. Its work with the charity has mainly focused on installing kitchens in its care homes. According to the 2020/21 sustainability report, Howdens donated and installed 14 accessible kitchens for Leonard Cheshire Disability during the year.

In 2021, Howden began a £100,000 partnership with I Can and I Am, a charity that aims to inspire young people. According to Howden's 2020/21 sustainability report:

> This donation is used to cover the running costs of the bus and enable the 'I can & I am' team to focus on delivering workshops and mentoring. Since May 2021, over 3,300 children have attended workshops on the bus, the majority of whom were between 10 and 15.

Employee-led support

Employees play an active role in supporting their local communities, principally through fundraising activities. Employees also participate in payroll giving and have been recognised by the Charities Aid Foundation with a Gold Award for high staff participation.

Exclusions

Our research indicates that no grants are given for overseas projects, political or religious appeals, science/technology projects or local appeals outside the areas of company presence.

Applications

Direct requests to your local Howden depot, manufacturing site or distribution or support centre.

Community contributions

Total contributions worldwide	£2,000,000

According to its 2020/21 annual report, the company donated £2 million in cash

and in kind to charitable causes in the UK and in Europe.

HSBC Holdings plc

Community services and development, education and training, the environment

Company registration number: 617987

Correspondent: Community Investment Committee, 8 Canada Square, London E14 5HQ (website: www.hsbc.com/who-we-are/our-people-and-communities/supporting-communities)

Directors: Mark Tucker; Noel Quinn; Ewen Stevenson; Geraldine Buckingham; James Forese; Rachel Duan; Dame Carolyn Fairbairn; Steven Guggenheimer; José Kuribreña; Eileen Murray; David Nish; Jackson Tai; Aileen Taylor (female: 38%; male: 62%).

Nature of business: HSBC is one of the largest banking and financial services organisations in the world, with businesses working in the areas of commercial banking, global banking and markets, global private banking and retail banking and wealth management.

Financial information

Year end	31/12/2021
Turnover	£41,214,000,000
Pre-tax profit	£15,729,000,000

Total employees: 232,957

Main locations: HSBC's UK headquarters is in Birmingham. It has branches worldwide.

Community involvement

HSBC has partnerships with charitable organisations, through which the group runs various educational programmes targeted at young people. The group's direct financial contributions are predominantly made in the form of matched funding on monies raised by employees for charities and causes.

According to the website, HSBC's charitable activities in the UK are based around:

- Educating young people to make the most of the opportunities available to them
- Getting involved in our local communities to support those most in need
- Enabling the net zero carbon economy of the future through sustainable finance

Nominated charities

Each year, the group nominates several national charities and encourages its customers and employees to make donations.

Partnerships

HSBC works in partnership with The Prince's Trust to provide young people with opportunities to develop their skills and realise their potential.

The Future Skills 'Get Into' programme helps young people to access the necessary training and work experience to gain employment. The HSBC UK Traineeship programme offers job opportunities with the bank to young people who may not have previously considered it possible to work in financial services. Together with the charity, HSBC has helped over 50,000 young people re-engage with education and secure employment.

The group also supports Young Enterprise's work to help young people successfully earn and manage money. The Company Programme encourages young people to set up and run their own student company by creating a product or service of their own. The Young Money Centre of Excellence in Financial Education programme aims to embed financial education within the curriculum.

HSBC is open to enquiries from schools and universities in the UK looking to get involved in the employability/financial education programmes listed above.

Employee-led support

Staff are encouraged to volunteer their time in aid of local causes in schools, Scout groups, etc. HSBC staff gave 79,000 volunteering hours to community projects in 2021.

Staff are also eligible for matched funding when undertaking various fundraising efforts.

Commercially led support

As part of its partnership with The Prince's Trust, HSBC sponsors the charity's Breakthrough Award which recognises the progress of young people in overcoming barriers.

Applications

For information on how the Financial Well-being Education Team can support schools and universities, contact: financialwell-being@hsbc.com.

For all other enquiries, contact the correspondent for more information.

Community contributions

Cash donations worldwide	£34,770,000

According to its 2021 annual report, the group awarded £34.77 million to charities in the form of matched funding.

All the financial figures have been converted from USD to GBP using the exchange rate at the time of writing (August 2022).

Alan Hudson Ltd

General charitable purposes, health

Company registration number: 613979

Correspondent: The Alan Hudson Foundation, Bevis Lane, Wisbech St Mary, Wisbech, Cambridgeshire PE13 4RR

Directors: David Ball; Stephen Layton; David Wheeler; Sarah Wheeler; Paul Seeley (female: 20%; male: 80%).

Nature of business: Alan Hudson Ltd is a fruit-growing company.

Financial information

Year end	31/07/2021
Turnover	£1,650,000

UK employees: 23

Main locations: The company's head office is in Cambridgeshire.

Community involvement

Alan Hudson Ltd is the principal subsidiary of The Hudson Foundation (Charity Commission no. 280332) and donates its profits to the foundation by way of gift aid.

The objective of The Hudson Foundation is to provide funds for general charitable purposes, with a particular focus on the relief of ill and/or older people in the Wisbech area.

Applications

Contact the correspondent for more information.

Corporate charity

The Hudson Foundation (Charity Commission no. 280332) – see entry on page 246.

Community contributions

Cash donations UK	£240,000

The Hudson Foundation's 2020/21 annual report states: 'The performance of Alan Hudson Ltd over the 2020/21 year will enable it to Gift Aid taxable profit of £240,192. However the severe frosts in early 2021 will result in a loss by Alan Hudson Ltd in 2021/22 and consequently the Foundation will not receive any Gift Aid payment for that year.'

IBM United Kingdom Ltd

Education and training, medical research

Company registration number: 741598

Correspondent: The CSR Team, PO Box 41, North Harbour, Portsmouth, Hampshire PO6 3AU (tel: 0370 542 6426; website: www.ibm.org/responsibility/commitment)

Directors: Sharon Bagshaw; Timothy Eagle; Naomi Hill; William Kelleher; Christopher Cook; Sreeram Visvanathan (female: 33%; male: 67%).

Nature of business: IBM United Kingdom Ltd is the UK subsidiary of IBM Corporation. It is involved in the provision and development of information technology services and solutions.

Financial information

Year end	31/12/2021
Turnover	£2,728,000,000
Pre-tax profit	£194,900,000

Main locations: The company's head office is in Portsmouth and it has offices throughout the UK.

Community involvement

IBM United Kingdom Ltd's community contributions focus on increasing skills and education and making grants through its corporate charity, the IBM United Kingdom Trust (Charity Commission no. 290462).

Education and skills

Globally, IBM delivers its own educational initiatives in the fields of tech and business skills, cybersecurity, software development and more.

IBM SkillsBuild is a free digital training programme that helps students and adults develop skills and explore career options. The programme currently operates in 159 countries and a global network of 90 non-profit partners helps connect learners with local job opportunities. In the UK, employees volunteer in local schools to roll out the programme. IBM United Kingdom Ltd has also partnered with a number of not-for-profit organisations that work with under-served communities such as veterans, refugees and young people who are not in education.

IBM Service Corps

Through this initiative, IBM deploys teams of employees to partner with social enterprises, non-profit organisations and governments working in the areas of education, health, disaster preparedness and economic development.

Volunteer grants

Through this programme, IBM's current and retired staff can apply for funding for organisations. Volunteers are eligible for the programme after having completed a minimum of ten hours of volunteering. Grants can be awarded to any charitable organisation. Staff do not have to volunteer at an organisation in order for an organisation to be eligible. Volunteers can choose to award partial grants to multiple organisations.

In-kind support

IBM Sustainability Accelerator

Launched in 2022, the group provides pro bono delivery of IBM technologies and expertise to non-profit organisations.

Employee-led support

IBM Volunteers programme

The programme supports both current and retired employees to volunteer their skills and assistance to local causes. In 2021, the programme had more than 89,000 registered users, who recorded over 860,000 volunteer hours in 2021.

Applications

Contact the correspondent for more information.

Corporate charity

IBM United Kingdom Trust (Charity Commission no. 290462) – see entry on page 247.

Community contributions

Cash donations worldwide	£35,300,000
Total contributions worldwide	£407,730,000

Globally, the group contributed £407.7 million in 2021, of which £335.9 million was donated technology, £36.5 million was donated services and £35.3 million was cash donations. We were unable to determine how much of this was given in the UK.

Note: the figures have been converted from USD using the exchange rate at the time of writing (November 2022).

IGas Energy plc

Arts, culture and heritage, care and treatment, community services and development, education and training, the environment, health, renewable/ sustainable energy, social welfare

Company registration number: 4981279

Correspondent: Sue Winch, Fund Administrator, IGas Community Fund, 4 The Dell, Vernham Dean, Andover, Hampshire SP11 0LF (tel: 07768 498148; email: contact@igascommunityfund.co. uk; website: www.igasplc.com)

Directors: Chris Hopkinson; Philip Jackson; Frances Ward; Kate Coppinger (female: 50%; male: 50%).

Nature of business: IGas Energy operates onshore oil and gas fields.

Financial information

Year end	31/12/2021
Turnover	£37,920,000
Pre-tax profit	(£12,270,000)

Total employees: 140

Main locations: Igas Energy sites are located in Surrey, Hampshire, West Sussex, Lincolnshire and Nottinghamshire.

Community involvement

The company makes grants to community and voluntary organisations near its sites in Surrey, Hampshire, West Sussex, Lincolnshire and Nottinghamshire.

IGas Energy Community Fund (not a registered charity)

Launched in 2008, the fund supports projects in the communities in which the company operates. Applications are invited from organisations working in a number of areas including children and young people, health, heritage, sustainability, education, vulnerable people, community regeneration and energy. Full details of what can be supported can be found on the community fund's website: www.igascommunityfund.co.uk.

According to the fund's website, the company is keen to support community groups, voluntary organisations and schools undertaking projects that benefit the wider community. IGas stresses that projects should be close to an IGas location.

Exclusions

The community fund does not support salaries or running costs. It does not normally support projects from commercially orientated organisations where there is an element of profit from the proposed project. The community fund cannot consider applications covering a wider area unless they can demonstrate a specific and substantial benefit to the 'host' community (i.e. IGas' operational areas) and its immediate surroundings.

Applications

Applications can be made via the fund's website.

Community contributions

We were unable to determine a figure for the company's charitable contributions for 2021. However, the community fund's website states that it awarded £25,000 in grants to support 17 projects in March 2022, bringing the total awarded to date to well over £1 million.

Informa plc

General charitable purposes

Company registration number: 8860726

Correspondent: The Sustainability Team, 5 Howick Place, London SW1P 1WG (tel: 020 7017 5000; email: sustainability@informa.com; website: http://informa.com/sustainability)

Directors: John Rishton; Stephen Carter; Gareth Wright; Helen Owers; David Flaschen; Mary McDowell; Gill Whitehead; Patrick Martell; Louise Smalley; Joanne Wilson; Zheng Yin (female: 45%; male: 55%).

Nature of business: Informa is an international provider of specialist information and services for the academic, scientific, professional and commercial business communities across more than 40 countries.

Financial information

Year end	31/12/2021
Turnover	£1,800,000,000
Pre-tax profit	£94,000,000

UK employees: 3,200

Total employees: 10,000

Main locations: Informa's head office is in London and it has other offices in Abingdon, Basingstoke, Chobham, Colchester, Macclesfield, Pathhead (Midlothian) and Solihull. There is an office locator facility on the website.

Community involvement

According to its 2021 Sustainability Report, Informa has committed to contributing at least 1% of its profit before tax to community groups by 2025.

Partnerships

BookShare is an online library of accessible ebooks for people with print disabilities such as severe dyslexia and visual impairment. This partnership allows Informa to make 95% of its eBook catalogue available to those most in need.

In-kind support

Informa develops strategic relationships with community partners, both locally and internationally, by making in-kind donations.

Employee-led support

Employees are entitled to four days' paid leave to volunteer each year.

Informa's flagship community engagement and annual charity initiative, Walk the World, involves staff from all offices embarking on walks in their area to raise funds for local charities. In 2021, employees raised £259,000 for charitable causes through volunteering.

Informa provides matched funding of up to £500 to staff engaging in fundraising efforts for registered charities. In 2021, the company and its employees fundraised £132,000 for charities.

Applications

Contact the correspondent for more information.

Community contributions

Cash donations worldwide	£345,000
Total contributions worldwide	£602,000

According to the 2021 Sustainability Report, the company made cash donations totalling £345,000. In-kind donations totalled £257,000.

Innocent Ltd

🔍 Social welfare

Company registration number: 4007092

Correspondent: CSR Team, Fruit Towers, 342 Ladbroke Grove, London W10 5BU (tel: 020 7993 3311; email: hello@innocentfoundation.org; website: www.innocentdrinks.co.uk)

Directors: James Davenport; Nicholas Canney; Douglas Lamont; Nichola Clare (female: 25%; male: 75%).

Nature of business: The company develops, manufactures and distributes soft drinks. Innocent Ltd's immediate parent company and immediate controlling company is Fresh Trading Ltd, a company incorporated in the UK. The ultimate parent company and ultimate controlling party is The Coca-Cola Company, a company incorporated in Delaware, USA.

Financial information

Year end	31/12/2020
Turnover	£187,370,000
Pre-tax profit	£15,460,000

UK employees: 240

Total employees: 849

Main locations: Innocent's head office is in London. It also has offices across Europe.

Community involvement

Innocent donates at least 10% of its annual profits to charitable causes, primarily through its corporate charity, The Innocent Foundation (Charity Commission no. 1104289). The company also supports a range of charities across Europe.

The company is a founding member of a pioneering new plastic initiative led by the environmental charity WRAP and the Ellen MacArthur Foundation.

Partnerships

Innocent began a partnership with FareShare in 1999 to ensure that its surplus of fruit juices and smoothies can be distributed to vulnerable people across the UK.

In-kind support

Innocent Foundation Scholarships

Each year three Innocent employees are given an extra week's holiday to work with one of The Innocent Foundation's projects.

Employee-led support

Innocent employees are entitled to one volunteering day each year to spend supporting their local communities. In 2021, 525 employees used their volunteering days. Employees also volunteer with The Innocent Foundation's charity partners.

Commercially led support

Big Knit Campaign

Innocent customers knit small woolly hats which are then sent to either Innocent or Age UK. The hats are placed on top of the smoothie bottles and sold in shops. Innocent then donates 25p to Age UK for every bottle that is sold as part of the campaign. For more information visit www.thebigknit.co.uk/.

Applications

Contact the correspondent for further information.

Corporate charity

The Innocent Foundation (Charity Commission no. 1104289) – see entry on page 247.

Community contributions

Cash donations worldwide	£228,000

The 2020 annual report was the latest available at the time of writing. In 2020, the company donated £228,000 to charitable causes.

Intercontinental Hotels Group plc

🔍 Community enterprise and social entrepreneurship, community services and development, education and training, the environment

Company registration number: 5134420

Correspondent: CSR Team, Broadwater Park, Denham, Buckinghamshire UB9 5HR (tel: 01895 512000; email: companysecretariat@ihg.com; website: www.ihgplc.com)

Directors: Patrick Cescau; Deanna Oppenheimer; Keith Barr; Paul Edgecliffe-Johnson; Elie Maalouf; Graham Allan; Daniela Soares; Arthur de Haast; Ian Dyson; Duriya Farooqui; Byron Grote; Jo Harlow; Jill McDonald; Sharon Rothstein (female: 43%; male: 57%).

Nature of business: Intercontinental Hotels is multi-national hospitality company.

Financial information

Year end	31/12/2021
Turnover	£2,470,000,000
Pre-tax profit	£306,900,000

UK employees: 6,013

Total employees: 350,000

Main locations: The group has hotels in nearly 100 countries. Its head office is in Denham, Buckinghamshire. There are also regional offices in China, Singapore and the USA.

Community involvement

Intercontinental Hotels Group (IHG) seeks to make a positive contribution to the communities in which its brands operate through its True Hospitality for Good programme. The group works in partnership with charitable organisations that are delivering action in three focus areas: building skills in hospitality, disaster relief and environmental sustainability. Support is also given through employee-led initiatives.

Charitable donations

The group's charitable donations policy, detailed on its website, states that contributions are made to registered charities that support its three focus areas.

Community partnerships

According to its website, the group will consider supporting organisations that:

- exhibit a clear purpose and defined need in one of IHG's three areas of focus
- recognise innovative approaches in addressing the defined need
- demonstrate an efficient organisation and detail the organisation's ability to follow through on its proposal
- explain clearly the benefits to IHG and its hotel communities

Local managers and employees are encouraged to use this list as a guide, along with the group's Code of Ethics, when deciding what is right for local community needs.

Disaster relief

IHG works with several charity partners to deliver support and funds to communities in the event of a natural disaster. In the UK, these charity partners include the British Red Cross and CARE International UK. The group is a member of the British Red Cross Disaster Relief Alliance.

In-kind support

Our previous research indicates that the group can provide free hotel rooms to eligible charities.

Employee-led support

Employees are offered two days' paid leave each year to volunteer for causes of their choosing. In 2021, 260,000 hours were volunteered globally.

Giving for Good programme

Every September, employees are encouraged to get involved in Giving for Good month. The programme enables them to give back and make a positive difference to their local community through volunteering, 'going green' or taking part in an activity focused on health and well-being. Additionally, each employee who participates in the programme can choose from one of four causes – waste reduction, water and sanitation, hospitality skills-building and disaster relief – and IHG donates to its charitable partners working in that area. In 2021, 40,000 employees took part in the programme.

Exclusions

The company's website provides the following information:

We do not support organisations that discriminate on the basis of race, religion, creed, gender, age, physical challenge or national origin. In addition, we will not generally provide contributions for:

- Individuals
- Religious organisations
- General operating support for hospitals and health care institutions
- Capital campaigns
- Endowment funds
- Conferences, workshops or seminars not directly related to our business interests
- Multi-year grants; only the first year of multi-year requests will be assured, with support in subsequent years dependent upon annual evaluation
- Political donations of any kind.

Applications

Contact the correspondent for further information.

Community contributions

The company's 2020/21 accounts did not provide a figure for its charitable contributions.

All the financial figures have been converted from USD to GBP using the exchange rate at the time of writing (August 2022).

Intermediate Capital Group plc

🔍 Education and training

Company registration number: 2234775

Correspondent: The CSR Team, Procession House, 55 Ludgate, London EC4M 7JW (website: www.icgam.com)

Directors: Andrew Skyes; Benoit Durteste; Vijay Bharadia; Antje Hensel-Roth; Rosemary Leith; Matthew Lester; Virginia Homes; Michael Nellingan; Kathryn Purves; Amy Schioldager; Stephen Welton (female: 45%; male: 55%).

Nature of business: The company is specialist asset manager investing in private debt, credit and equity.

Financial information

Year end	31/03/2022
Turnover	£982,100,000
Pre-tax profit	£565,400,000

Main locations: Intermediate Capital Group plc's head office is in London. It also has offices across Europe, North America, Asia-Pacific and the Middle East.

Community involvement

The group's charitable approach focuses mainly on areas of social mobility and the education of young people from disadvantaged backgrounds.

Current charity partners

The group has established a three-year charity partnership with the Education Endowment Foundation. The foundation supports the Nuffield Early Learning Intervention and The Tutor Trust.

New charity partnerships

Alongside its existing charity partnerships, in 2022 the group announced new partnerships with UpReach, The Access Project and Seizing Every Opportunity. The announcement promised a commitment of £3.75 million to the charities over three years.

Other contributions

The group's annual report states that in addition to its charity partnerships, the group supports a number of local initiatives in London and New York that focus on social mobility. In 2022, the group also donated to charities that support victims of the Ukrainian conflict.

Employee-led support

The group supports employee fundraising with matched funding as well as providing two days' paid leave each year for employees who wish to volunteer.

Applications

Contact the correspondent for further information on Intermediate Capital Group's charitable giving.

Community contributions

Total contributions worldwide	£2,000,000

According to the group's annual report for 2021/22, Intermediate Capital Group plc increased its budget for charitable giving to £2 million.

International Personal Finance

🔍 Community enterprise and social entrepreneurship, community services and development, education and training, money and debt advice, social welfare

Company registration number: 6018973

Correspondent: UK Corporate Affairs Team, 26 Whitehall Road, Meadow Lane, Leeds, West Yorkshire LS12 1BE

(tel: 0113 285 6700; email: investors@ ipfin.co.uk; website: www.ipfin.co.uk/en/ sustainability.html)

Directors: Stuart Sinclair; Gerard Ryan; Gary Thompson; Katrina Cliffe; Deborah Davis; Richard Holmes; John Mangelaars (female: 29%; male: 71%).

Nature of business: International Personal Finance is an international home credit business and digital provider of consumer finance.

Financial information

Year end	31/12/2021
Turnover	£549,000,000
Pre-tax profit	£67,700,000

Total employees: 5,600

Main locations: The group's head office is in Leeds. There are also offices in Australia, the Czech Republic, Estonia, Finland, Hungary, Latvia, Lithuania, Mexico, Poland, Romania, Slovakia and Spain.

Community involvement

International Personal Finance aims to support its local communities and promote social and financial inclusion. It does this through a combination of financial education and community investment programmes, volunteering and grant-making.

The following information is taken from the company's 2021 annual report:

We work to forge meaningful relationships in the communities we serve to help support causes and address issues that colleagues and customers care about locally. Building better relationships also helps attract employees and customer representatives to work with us.

Key areas of interest

- Financial literacy
- Social wellbeing
- Volunteering
- Community
- support programmes

How we engage

- Financial literacy programmes
- NGO partnerships
- Financial wellbeing research
- Colleague volunteering
- Supporting causes chosen by colleagues

Employee-led support

The group's Make a Difference in May event enables employees to volunteer in their local communities. The website states that volunteering activities are organised at a local level in co-operation with the group's charity partners. This is to ensure that voluntary work responds to the needs of the communities in which the group operates. According to the group's website, more than 1,200 UK employees volunteered for charitable causes in 2021.

Applications

The group has a Corporate Affairs Group that discusses sustainability issues and new initiatives. However, many activities are organised at the level of each local branch. For contact details of each branch, refer to the website: www.ipfin.co.uk/en/contact-us.html

The head office is the only branch in the UK; this is based in Leeds.

Community contributions

International Personal Finance's 2021 annual accounts did not provide a figure for its charitable contributions.

Investec plc

Community enterprise and social entrepreneurship, education and training, the environment

Company registration number: 3633621

Correspondent: Susie Steyn, Corporate Sustainability Manager, 30 Gresham Street, London EC2V 7QP (tel: 020 7597 3713; email: sustainabilityUK@investec.co.uk; website: www.investec.com/en_gb/welcome-to-investec/corporate-responsibility/our-community.html)

Directors: David Miller; Henrietta Baldock; Zarina Bassa; Philip Hourquebie; Stephen Koseff; Nicola Newton-King; Jasandra Nyker; Vanessa Olver; Nishlan Samujh; Khumo Shuenyane; Philisiwe Sibiya; Brian Stevenson; Fani Titi; Richard Wainwright; James Whelan (female: 33%; male: 67%).

Nature of business: Investec is a specialist bank and asset management company.

Financial information

Year end	31/03/2021
Turnover	£946,400,000
Pre-tax profit	£92,130,000

Total employees: 8,200

Main locations: Investec's head office is in London with offices located across the UK. See the 'Contact us' section on the group's website for the locations of individual offices.

Community involvement

Investec looks to contribute to the communities in which it has a presence in three core areas: education, entrepreneurship and the environment. It does this by making small project grants and by forming partnerships with local charities.

Aside from their volunteering efforts, employees support charitable causes through payroll giving and various fundraising activities.

Partnerships

The group's sustainability report for 2021/22 provides numerous and detailed case studies of Investec's partnerships in the communities in which it has a presence. Examples of partnerships under the three areas of support provided in the report are detailed below.

Education: Arrival Education

Investec has a partnership with Arrival Education, a social enterprise that focuses on talent management with young people from challenging backgrounds and minority ethnic groups. Investec staff volunteer on Arrival Education's programmes, running workshops and becoming coaches to the students.

Entrepreneurship: Bromley by Bow Centre

The Bromley by Bow Centre works to promote economic regeneration in Tower Hamlets and has been a partner of Investec since 2008. Through the partnership, the Beyond Business programme is delivered and helps to support local people who want to set up their own social enterprise, providing successful applicants with funding and skills support. Volunteers from Investec sit on the selection panel and offer advice to shortlisted applicants. Each year, Investec also runs the Beyond Business College programme, providing specialist skills and expertise to entrepreneurs who have benefitted through the programme.

Project grants

As well as supporting its charity partners, Investec also provides grants (normally up to £6,000) to small and medium-sized charities that work in its focus areas of education, entrepreneurship and the environment.

The charity's grant guidelines provide the following information regarding eligibility:

- Charities must be UK, Ireland or Channel Island registered;
- Charities should not be politically affiliated or religious;
- London based schools will not be considered due to our partnership with Morpeth School; and
- Charities should have been established for at least 12 months.

The guidelines further state that there is a preference for:

- project funding rather than requests for core funding;
- charities that are situated in and/or projects targeting communities close to one of Investec's offices; and
- projects presented by small to medium sized charities (less than £3m annual turnover).

Employee-led support

Employee volunteering

All staff in the UK are given two days' paid leave to volunteer with the group's community partners. One partner is the charity Trees for Cities which offers opportunities for staff to plant trees in urban areas across the UK. In 2021/22, employees volunteered 2,020 hours to charitable causes.

Employee fundraising

In 2021/22, £84,000 was raised by staff in the UK.

Payroll giving

In 2021/22, UK staff donated £359,000 to charities through payroll giving.

Commercially led support

Sponsorship

Investec sponsors a range of individuals, teams and organisations from a wide range of sectors from a local to international level.

Applications

Project grants

Apply in writing to the correspondent including a completed summary sheet. Summary sheets, which also contain details of what should be included in the application, can be downloaded from the 'Our Communities' section of the company's website. Applications are reviewed in March and September and proposals should be received three weeks in advance.

Other support

Contact the correspondent for further information.

Community contributions

Cash donations UK	£2,200,000
Total contributions overseas	£7,630,000

The group's 2021/22 sustainability report states that it donated £2.2 million to charities in the UK during the year.

Cash donations in the 'UK and other' regions were broken down as follows:

Environment and other philanthropy	£1.53 million
Education and learnerships	£351,900
Entrepreneurship and job creation	£336,200

Isles of Scilly Steamship Group

Community services and development, education and training, the environment

Company registration number: 165746

Correspondent: The Community Fund Committee, Hugh Town, St Mary's, Isles of Scilly TR21 0LJ (tel: 01736 334220; email: communityfund@issg.co.uk; website: www.islesofscilly-travel.co.uk)

Directors: Stuart Reid; Ian Howard; Judith Piper; Stephen Hicks; Sonya Bassett; Gary Randall; Sam Hicks; Kevin George (female: 22%; male: 78%).

Nature of business: The Isles of Scilly Steamship Company operates the principal air and sea services from mainland UK to the Isles of Scilly

Financial information

Year end	31/03/2021
Turnover	£9,460,000
Pre-tax profit	£712,800

Total employees: 204

Main locations: The company's head office is on the Isles of Scilly. The Community Fund gives in the West Cornwall and Isles of Scilly region.

Community involvement

The company makes grants to organisations in the West Cornwall and Isles of Scilly region through its community fund. Complimentary tickets are also provided to local good causes.

Community Fund (not a registered charity)

Note: at the time of writing (August 2022), the community fund was temporarily suspended – check the company's website for any further updates.

The fund provides around £30,000 per year for community projects in the West Cornwall and Isles of Scilly region. Organisations and individuals can apply for grants of £500 to £3,000 per project and there are three application rounds per year. Projects are supported in the following categories:

- Education (all ages)
- Local projects and skills
- Young people
- Protection for the local environment
- Specific community projects

Applications for projects outside these areas can be considered by the committee if sufficient community or legacy benefits can be identified.

In-kind support

According to our previous research, the company provides complimentary tickets for raffles, events, community groups and other good causes. It also provides some free luggage containers and adult travel for school trips.

Applications

Visit the company's website for updates on the community fund.

Community contributions

We were unable to determine a figure for the company's charitable contributions for the year.

ITV plc

🔍 Arts, culture and heritage, community enterprise and social entrepreneurship, education and training, emergency response/relief, general charitable purposes, health, social welfare

Company registration number: 4967001

Correspondent: Social Purpose Team, ITV Social Purpose, 2 Waterhouse Square, 140 Holborn, London EC1N 2AE (email: socialpurpose@itv.com; website: www.itvplc.com/socialpurpose)

Directors: Sir Peter Bazalgette; Carolyn McCall; Salman Amin; Chris Kennedy; Edward Bonham Carter; Margaret Ewing; Mary Harris; Anna Manz; Duncan Painter; Graham Cooke; Andrew Cosslett; Sharmila Nebhrajani; Gidon Katz (female: 38%; male: 62%).

Nature of business: ITV is an independent television company.

Financial information

Year end	31/12/2021
Turnover	£3,453,000,000
Pre-tax profit	£480,000,000

Total employees: 6,618

Main locations: ITV has offices in Leeds, London and Salford.

Community involvement

ITV plc looks to make a positive social contribution by working in partnership with a range of organisations, charities, NGOs and government. The principal way in which it supports its partners is by contributing airtime for appeals and campaigns.

Soccer Aid

Soccer Aid, in partnership with UNICEF, is ITV's largest fundraising initiative. The event sees celebrities take part in a football match against football legends and has so far raised over £38 million.

Better health

One of the group's social purpose aims is to encourage people to take care of their mental and physical health. ITV runs a number of campaigns, including a mental wellness campaign titled Get Britain Talking, which is supported by Mind, YoungMinds and SAMH (Scottish Association for Mental Health).

In-kind support

Pro bono

ITV employees contribute their skills and expertise to benefit good causes. For example, the legal team provides pro bono legal support.

Airtime

ITV uses its position as an established commercial TV network to provide charitable causes with airtime.

Employee-led support

Employees are able to take three days' paid leave per year for volunteering purposes. In 2021, 276 employees took part in volunteering activities. The group's 2021 annual report states:

From 2020, ITV has focussed on measuring volunteering around our strategic priority of improving diversity and inclusion in the creative industries through school visits and mentoring

In 2021, employees also raised £32,600 for charitable causes via Give As You Earn.

Applications

Contact the correspondent for more information.

Community contributions

Cash donations UK	£1,550,000
Total contributions worldwide	£53,270,000

According to the ITV Social Impact Report 2021, during the year charitable contributions totalled £53.27 million. The donations were broken down as follows: in-kind (£51.71 million) and cash (£1.55 million).

The report provides the following definitions:

In-kind: Includes donations of ITV's programme or marketing airtime.

Cash: Donations to charities including celebrity prize money and other miscellaneous donations.

Ivy Holdco Ltd (Gatwick Airport Ltd)

🔍 Arts, culture and heritage, community services and development, education and training, the environment, general charitable purposes, sports and recreation

Company registration number: 7497036

Correspondent: CSR Team, 6th Floor, Destinations Place, South Terminal, Gatwick Airport, West Sussex RH6 0NP (email: community@gatwickairport.com; website: www.gatwickairport.com/business-community/community-sustainability/local-community)

Directors: Michael McGhee; David Macmillan; Bill Woodburn; Nicolas Notebaert; Olivier Mathieu; Remi Maumon de Longevialle; Pierre-Hugues Schmit; Eric Delobel; Lucy Chadwick; Marten Per Soderbom (female: 10%; male: 90%).

Nature of business: Ivy Holdco Ltd is the ultimate parent company of Gatwick Airport.

Financial information

Year end	31/12/2021
Turnover	£192,700,000
Pre-tax profit	(£368,700,000)

UK employees: 1,752

Main locations: The airport is near Crawley in West Sussex.

Community involvement

Support is mainly provided through The Gatwick Foundation Fund and the Gatwick Airport Community Trust (Charity Commission no. 1089683). The company also provides sponsorship and has several education programmes.

The Gatwick Foundation Fund (not a registered charity)

The fund distributes £300,000 per year in three grant rounds to projects in Kent, Surrey and Sussex. Support is focused on four main areas: employment, training and skills; families; widening horizons (projects which provide young people with opportunities); and older people. It is managed in partnership with the Community Foundations for Kent, Surrey and Sussex, which oversee the programme and assess all applications.

Partnerships

The company has three charity partners with which it works on a longer-term basis. These are: Surrey and Sussex Healthcare NHS Trust; the Kent, Surrey and Sussex Air Ambulance; and the Gatwick TravelCare Charity.

In-kind support

The company's 2021 annual report states:

> In the latter part of 2021 Gatwick donated nearly 200 laptops to 19 local community groups, projects and charities. Colleagues from IT donated around 100 hours of their time on furlough to clear Gatwick data, install clean operating systems and sanitised the cases and keyboards ready for use.

Employee-led support

Employees fundraise for the company's charity partners.

Commercially led support

The company sponsors a range of local events such as festivals, carnivals, awards and local sporting events. According to the company's website, it also sponsors a range of events across the South East. This has included youth activities, national parks and Pride events.

Applications

The Gatwick Foundation Fund

Grants are distributed by Kent, Surrey and Sussex Community Foundations. Further information can be found on their websites. At the time of writing (August 2022), the fund was paused due to the impact of the COVID-19 pandemic – check the foundations' websites for updates.

Sponsorships and partnerships

Contact the correspondent for further information.

Corporate charity

Gatwick Airport Community Trust (Charity Commission no. 1089683) – see entry on page 241.

Community contributions

Cash donations UK	£236,000

The company donated £236,000 to the Gatwick Airport Community Trust in 2021. It also donated nearly 200 laptops to 19 local community groups, projects and charities.

William Jackson Foods Ltd

Agriculture and farming, education and training, the environment, health, mental health and well-being, social welfare

Company registration number: 11273230

Correspondent: Community Giving Team, The Riverside Building, Livingstone Road, Hessle, East Yorkshire HU13 0DZ (tel: 01482 224939; email: info@wjfg.co.uk; website: www.wjfg.co.uk)

Directors: Katie Denyer; Andrea Davis; Sonta Eastaugh; Patrick Mountifield; Mark Oughtred; Monica Turner; James Watson; Roger White (female: 38%; male: 63%).

Nature of business: William Jackson Food Group is a food manufacturer.

Financial information

Year end	27/04/2021
Turnover	£226,290,000
Pre-tax profit	£2,646,000

Total employees: 51

Main locations: The group operates across the UK. Its headquarters is in Hessle in Yorkshire.

Community involvement

According to the group's website, in 2021 it gave 1.5% of its earnings before interest, taxes, depreciation and amortization to charities in the communities in which it is based.

Community Giving programme

The group's Community Giving programme supports charities that encourage health, well-being and education. The programme is administered by the group's Community Giving Team. Long-term beneficiaries have included: Cat Zero, Food for Life, Mires Beck and The Outward Bound Trust.

In-kind support

The group's brands support local communities through donations of food and goods.

Employee-led support

Employees are encouraged to fundraise and volunteer for the group's charity partners. Employees can take one day's paid leave each year to support community projects local to where they work. According to the group's website, in 2021, employees completed 329 days of volunteering during the year.

Applications

Apply in writing to the correspondent.

Community contributions

Total contributions UK	£251,000

The group's total for charitable contributions in 2020/21 was £251,000.

Jaguar Land Rover Automotive plc

Animal conservation, community enterprise and social entrepreneurship, community services and development, education and training, emergency response/relief, general charitable purposes, health, social welfare, sports and recreation, STEM, work outside the UK

Company registration number: 6477691

Correspondent: Kate Birkenhead, Senior Communications Officer, Responsible Business, Abbey Road, Whitley, Coventry, Warwickshire CV3 4LF (email: kbirkenh@jaguarlandrover.com; website: www.jaguar.co.uk/about-jaguar/responsibility/index.html)

Directors: Pathamadam Balaji; Thierry Bolloré; Natarajan Chandrasekaran; Charles Nichols; Al-Noor Ramji; Hanne Sorensen; Dr Ralf Speth (male: 100%).

Nature of business: Jaguar Land Rover designs, develops, manufactures and markets high performance luxury saloons, specialist sports cars, four-wheel drive off-road vehicles and related components. Jaguar Land Rover is a wholly owned subsidiary of Tata Motors Ltd.

Financial information

Year end	31/03/2022
Turnover	£18,320,000,000
Pre-tax profit	£455,000,000

Total employees: 36,031

Main locations: The group operates worldwide, but its headquarters and most of its employees are based in the UK across eight sites in the West Midlands (Castle Bromwich, Coventry, Gaydon, Solihull, Wolverhampton, Warwick and Whitley) and Liverpool.

Community involvement

The group's global CSR programme focuses on the following three areas:

- Education and talent – inspiring the workforce of the future
- Design and technology – applying technological innovation for social good
- Well-being and health – supporting disadvantaged communities

The group supports several partner charities through funding, in-kind donations, employee volunteering, fundraising and pro bono support. For the year ending 31 March 2022, the majority of the group's contributions were either in-kind donations or employee-led fundraising.

In-kind support

The group provides in-kind support to charity partners in the form of vehicle donations. For example, the group supports the International Federation of Red Cross and Red Crescent Societies by developing and supplying vehicles that allow the Red Cross to reach remote and vulnerable communities globally and reduce emergency response times. In the UK, the group also works with the British Red Cross to deliver intensive training to create a community of expert emergency response specialists.

In 2022, Land Rover donated vehicles to be used by the Red Cross and Red Crescent Societies in Ukraine, providing support for those affected by the conflict. Also, 57 donated vehicles were used by emergency services in the UK to deliver medicine and medical aid.

COVID-19 response

During the COVID-19 pandemic, Land Rover Automotive plc produced thousands of pieces of PPE to be donated to the NHS and key workers in the UK. The group also made public its computer-aided design software for other additive-based manufacturing companies to produce more PPE.

Employee-led support

Employee volunteering

Employees are encouraged to volunteer for projects that support education, young people and the environment. Employees are entitled to two days of paid volunteering leave per year. Jaguar Land Rover also encourages all employees to design solutions for the challenges that their local communities and the wider world may face. For example, in the UK a team of advanced apprentices volunteered to design and create hi-tech steps to enable a young girl with cerebral palsy to mount a horse without assistance.

In December 2021, an employee-led donation drive led to 10,000 items of food and £2,000 being raised for local food banks.

Employees also raised the first £5,000 of a £50,000 pledge to charity in 2022. The pledge will deliver £1,000 to 50 different charities and the charities to receive the first £5,000 are:

- Breast Cancer Haven
- Family Care Trust
- The Grove Residential Home
- On The Streets Outreach
- Solihull Down Syndrome Support Group

Inspiring STEM Careers

Jaguar Land Rover employees in 2021/22 led virtual work experience, school visits and tailored programmes to encourage the future generation of engineers and meet the STEM skills shortage. In 2021/22, 213 employee volunteers delivered 881 hours of their time to develop the programme which reached 148 students over the course of the year.

Commercially led support

Sponsorship

The group supports the animal conservation charity Tusk by sponsoring its Conservation Awards. It also supports Tusk's conservation fieldwork in Africa by supplying the charity with vehicles and technology.

Jaguar Land Rover continues to be the partner of the Invictus Games.

Applications

The group provides support for organisations located near its operating sites. Contact the correspondent for more information.

Community contributions

We were unable to determine a figure for the group's total charitable contributions for 2021/22.

Johnson Matthey plc

🔍 Education and training, STEM

Company registration number: 33774

Correspondent: Sustainability Department, 5th Floor, 25 Farringdon Street, London EC4A 4AB (email: group.charity@matthey.com; website: https://matthey.com/sustainability)

Directors: Patrick Thomas; Liam Condon; Stephen Oxley; John O'Higgins; Jane Griffiths; Xiaozhi Liu; Doug Webb; Chris Mottershead; Rita Forst (female: 33%; male: 67%).

Nature of business: Johnson Matthey is a speciality chemicals and sustainable technologies company that focuses on its core skills in catalysis, precious metals, fine chemicals and process technology.

Financial information

Year end	31/03/2022
Turnover	£1,602,500,000
Pre-tax profit	£195,000,000

Total employees: 15,560

Main locations: Johnson Matthey is headquartered in London and has offices across the world. In the UK, the group has sites in Annan, Billingham, Brimsdown, Cambridge, Clitheroe, Edinburgh, London, Reading, Royston, Stockton-on-Tees and Swindon.

Community involvement

Johnson Matthey supports the communities in which it works through donations, the promotion of STEM education and employee-led initiatives.

The group supports science education programmes and has connections with local schools. It also established a new £1 million Science and Me programme aimed at improving access to science education for children and young people.

Science and Me

The aim of the programme is to improve science education for young learners who are often excluded from science education for socio-economic reasons. According to Johnson Matthey's website, the programme will target five key areas that enable better access to science:

- Attitudes of young people and influencers
- Inspiring teachers and training
- Career pathways
- Careers advice
- Diversity, inclusion and social mobility

The Science and Me programme is an employee-led grant scheme. Employees are invited to develop partnerships with local organisations to achieve the programme's goals. They can access funding to run local Science and Me projects in partnership with national charitable/educational delivery partners. Employees can access up to £20,000 per project and can apply four times a year.

Employee-led support

Employees can take two days' paid leave to volunteer each year to support the local community. In 2021/22 employees spent 1,322 days volunteering.

Employees also regularly take part in fundraising activities for charities of their choice. The group operates a matched funding scheme through which it matches up to £1,000 of money raised per employee each year. In 2021/22 Johnson Matthey donated £60,000 to match money raised by more than 400 employees to support the people of Ukraine.

Applications

Science and Me – contact the correspondent for further information.

Community contributions

Total contributions worldwide	£451,000

According to the group's 2021/22 annual report, community investment totalled £451,000.

Jones Lang LaSalle Ltd

🔍 General charitable purposes

Company registration number: 1188567

Correspondent: Sophie Walker, UK Head of Sustainability, 30 Warwick Street, London W1B 5NH (tel: 020 7399 5050; email: buildingabettertomorrow@eu.jll.com or sophie.walker@eu.jll.com; website: http://jll.co.uk/buildingabettertomorrow)

Directors: Siddharth Mehta; Christian Ulbrich; Hugo Bagué; Matthew Carter; Samuel Di Piazza; Tina Ju; Bridget Macaskill; Deborah McAneny; Jeetu Patel; Ann Petach; Larry Quinlan; Efrain Rivera (female: 33%; male: 67%).

Nature of business: Jones Lang LaSalle (JLL) is a professional services and investment management company specialising in real estate. The company's immediate parent company is Jones Lang LaSalle Europe Ltd. The ultimate parent company is Jones Lang LaSalle Incorporated, a company incorporated in the USA.

Financial information

Year end	31/12/2021
Turnover	£19,400,000,000
Pre-tax profit	£1,220,000,000

UK employees: 3,098

Total employees: 98,000

Main locations: The company has around 300 offices across 80 countries, including 28 offices in the UK.

Community involvement

Building a Better Tomorrow is the company's global sustainability strategy. JLL works in partnership with a variety of organisations to address issues related to urban regeneration, housing and homelessness, access to the property profession, and education and skills. Support is provided through pro bono advice and services, cash donations, employee volunteering and fundraising.

Partnerships

The company has an ongoing partnership with the national homelessness charity Crisis. The charity is supported with fundraising, advice, volunteer support and pro bono services. Since the partnership was established, JLL has raised over £1 million for the charity, including £193,000 in 2021.

The company also has an ongoing partnership with the charity Best Buddies. Best Buddies aims to create opportunities for one-to-one friendships, leadership development, integrated employment and inclusive living for individuals with intellectual and developmental disabilities. In 2021. the company expanded on this partnership by providing job placements at JLL for seven people with intellectual and developmental disabilities.

The company also provides support through its corporate charity, the JLL UK Foundation (Charity Commission no. 1170388).

In-kind support

As part of its partnership with Crisis, JLL has developed a bespoke toolkit to help the charity identify potential retail markets and has provided advice on rental values and incentives. In 2021, the company provided £137,700 in in-kind services, which included pro bono work.

Employee-led support

JLL hosts several annual sporting events to raise money for charity. Over the past few years, proceeds have gone to the company's national charity partners.

The company allows its employees to volunteer for charities during work time. In 2021, 6,906 employees volunteered for a total of 4,221 days. Employees also fundraised £1.1 million for charitable causes.

Applications

Contact the correspondent for further information.

Community contributions

Cash donations worldwide	£7,520,000
Total contributions worldwide	£8,462,000

The company's 2021 Sustainability Report states that in 2021 it made cash donations of £7.52 million. The company also contributed £804,900 in staff time and £137,700 in in-kind services, including pro bono work.

All the financial figures have been converted from USD to GBP using the exchange rate at the time of writing (August 2022).

Kentucky Fried Chicken (Great Britain) Ltd

🔍 Social welfare

Company registration number: 967403

Correspondent: The CSR Team, Orion Gate, Guilford Road, Woking, Surrey GU22 7NJ (website: www.kfc.co.uk)

Directors: Michael Williams; Christopher Drew; Matthew McCormick; Neil Morrison; James Whitehorn (male: 100%).

Nature of business: KFC is a fast-food vendor.

Financial information

Year end	27/12/2020
Turnover	£207,573,000
Pre-tax profit	£51,600,000

Main locations: KFC has restaurants throughout the UK.

Community involvement

The company provides support to charities through its corporate charity, the KFC Foundation (Charity Commission no. 1163560).

Applications

For further information see the company's corporate charity entry.

Corporate charity

KFC Foundation (Charity Commission no. 1163560) – see entry on page 248.

Community contributions

Total contributions UK	£56,700

In 2020 the company gave £56,700 in product donations to the KFC Foundation.

Kingfisher plc

🔍 Community services and development, general charitable purposes

Company registration number: 1664812

Correspondent: CSR Team, 3 Sheldon Square, Paddington, London W2 6PX (tel: 020 7372 8008; email: sustainability@kingfisher.com; website: www.kingfisher.com/sustainability)

Directors: Andrew Cosslett; Thierry Garnier; Bernard Bot; Claudia Arney; Jeff Carr; Sophie Gasperment; Rakhi Goss-Custard; William Lennie; Catherine Bradley (female: 44%; male: 56%).

Nature of business: Kingfisher is a home improvement retail group with stores located in nine European countries. The Kingfisher companies in the UK are B&Q and Screwfix.

Financial information

Year end	31/01/2022
Turnover	£13,183,000,000
Pre-tax profit	£1,007,000,000

Total employees: 82,000

Main locations: Kingfisher is headquartered in London and has stores across Europe. The B&Q and Screwfix websites both have store-finder searches.

Community involvement

Kingfisher's community involvement focuses on improving housing and community spaces. Support is provided through partnerships, cash donations, in-kind support and employee-led initiatives.

Foundations

Kingfisher funds a network of foundations that support charities that are providing, maintaining and improving housing and community spaces. The foundations are funded by annual corporate donations as well as employee and customer fundraising.

In the UK, Kingfisher's retail foundations are The Screwfix Foundation (Charity Commission no. 1151375) and the B&Q Foundation (Charity Commission no. 1183275). Each foundation has its own initiatives and application processes.

Partnerships

Kingfisher establishes partnerships with national and local organisations. In the UK, it has partnered with homelessness charity Shelter. Through this partnership, Kingfisher has helped to fund a team of specialist DIY Skills Advisers who provide practical home improvement assistance to people who have experienced or are at risk of homelessness. It has also helped to fund some of Shelter's frontline advice services.

Kingfisher has also partnered with the Red Cross. In the UK, its support has helped the Red Cross respond to incidents and enabled people to attend emergency preparedness workshops. In 2022, Kingfisher also worked with the Red Cross to support vulnerable people following the regime change in Afghanistan, wildfires in Turkey and the COVID-19 pandemic in India, while also partnering with organisations supporting victims of the war in Ukraine.

Improving housing

Kingfisher has seven foundations across Europe that have worked to improve living and public spaces through community projects since 2016. These projects receive funding through annual donations from Kingfisher as well as through commercially and employee-led fundraising. Since 2016, the community projects have reached 1.5 million people, 800,000 of whom were supported in 2021/22.

In-kind support

Kingfisher companies donate products in support of good causes.

Employee-led support

The London Marathon

Employees volunteer for local projects that are working to improve homes and community spaces. In 2021/22, 1,000 employees walked the London Marathon (or an equivalent distance) to fundraise for charitable causes. In total, £45,000 was raised by employees, which was then matched by Kingfisher to bring the total to £90,000.

Payroll giving

There is a payroll giving scheme in place that enables employees to donate to charities.

Ukraine

Kingfisher provided matched funding in 2022 for employees' donations to organisations supporting people affected by the conflict in Ukraine. It also offered paid volunteering leave for employees and financial support for employees sheltering refugees.

Commercially led support

Profits from sales of reusable plastic bags are used to support the network of foundations.

Exclusions

B&Q's website states that it will not provide support for the following:

- Political parties or causes
- Religious organisations whose principle aim is to propagate a particular faith or belief
- Personal appeals by, or on behalf of, individuals

Applications

For further information contact the correspondent or see Kingfisher's corporate charities' entries.

Corporate charity

The Screwfix Foundation (Charity Commission no. 1151375) – see entry on page 273; B&Q Foundation (Charity Commission no. 1183275) – see entry on page 223.

Community contributions

Cash donations worldwide	£3,047,000
Total contributions worldwide	£3,600,000

Kingfisher's Responsible Business report 2021/22 states that its community investment totalled £4 million during the year. This figure includes cash donations, employee time and in-kind contributions. The report provided the following breakdown:

Cash	£3,047,000
In-kind contributions	£405,000
Management costs	£367,000
Employee time	£148,000

In 2021/22 employees and customers raised a further £2.8 million for good causes – this figure is not included in the total of contributions for the year.

KPMG LLP

Community services and development, education and training, literacy, social welfare

Company registration number: OC301540

Correspondent: CSR Team, 15 Canada Square, London E14 5GL (email: corporateresponsibility@kpmg.co.uk;

website: https://home.kpmg.com/uk/en/home/about/corporate-responsibility.html)

Directors: Bina Mehta; Jonathan Holt; Tim Jones; Melissa Geiger; Anthony Lobo; Linda Main; Annette Barker; John Hallsworth; Jonathan Downer (female: 44%; male: 56%).

Nature of business: KPMG provides professional services including audit, tax and advisory.

Financial information

Year end	30/09/2021
Turnover	£2,433,000,000
Pre-tax profit	£670,000,000

Total employees: 15,310

Main locations: KPMG's headquarters is in London and it has 22 offices throughout the UK.

Community involvement

KPMG is focused on improving literacy and numeracy skills and helping to develop opportunities for disadvantaged groups across the UK. These objectives are predominantly met through the firm's corporate charity, The KPMG Foundation (Charity Commission no. 1086518).

Partnerships

The firm's charity partnership with the NSPCC concluded in 2021. Over the course of this partnership, KPMG raised £1.5 million for the charity through various fundraising activities. KPMG colleagues also volunteered at the charity, offering their expertise in cyber safety to help the NSPCC to keep children safe online.

In 2022, the charity partnership with Marie Curie began and will continue until 2024.

In-kind support

Literacy partnerships

In 2022, KPMG partnered with The Marcus Rashford Book Club and The National Literacy Trust to pledge the donation of 62,000 books to schools across the UK.

The firm has been part of the Vision for Literacy pledge since 2015, providing reading material to help close the literacy gap in the UK.

Charity partnerships

According to the firm's corporate social responsibility web page, by the conclusion of KPMG's partnership with the NSPCC in 2021, it had provided £500,000 in pro bono support.

Employee-led support

KPMG encourages employees to volunteer for charitable causes during work hours. In 2021/22, 33% of KPMG employees (4,797) volunteered, providing 45,995 hours of volunteering.

Within this total, 195 employees provided 3,119 hours for the NSPCC.

Employees also volunteered with TutorMate, through the firm's partnership with global education charity Innovations for Learning. The TutorMate programme sees cohorts of KPMG employees in its UK offices, volunteer their time to offer weekly support to five to six-year olds with their reading and literacy skills via a specially designed virtual platform. Six cohorts of ten volunteers are currently supporting students from primary schools in Bradford and Middlesbrough.

Commercially led support

In 2021, KPMG LLG sponsored the Skills Builder Accelerator Programme through the Skills Builder partnership. The programme ran in five schools in the Black Country area, reaching 2,312 pupils and 85 teachers.

Applications

For national charity partner enquiries, contact corporateresponsibility@kpmg.co.uk.

For more information on The KPMG Foundation, contact Jo Clunie at jo.clunie@kpmgfoundation.co.uk.

Corporate charity

The KPMG Foundation (Charity Commission no. 1086518) – see entry on page 249.

Community contributions

Cash donations UK	£630,000

According to The KPMG Foundation's 2020/21 accounts, the firm donated £630,000 to its corporate charity.

KPMG's corporate web page states that it donated £7.6 million to charitable causes through cash donations, in kind support, employee-led support and management costs.

Lancashire Holdings Ltd

🔍 General charitable purposes

Correspondent: Donations Committee, 29th Floor, 20 Fenchurch Street, London EC3M 3BY (tel: 020 7264 4056; website: www.lancashiregroup.com/en/responsibility.html)

Directors: Andrew Birtwistle; Kevin Birtwistle; Sandra Birtwistle; Steven Birtwistle (female: 25%; male: 75%).

Nature of business: Lancashire Holdings Ltd is a global provider of specialty insurance products incorporated in Bermuda.

Financial information

Year end	31/12/2021
Turnover	£747,200,000
Pre-tax profit	£56,800,000

Total employees: 306

Main locations: The group's head office is in the City of London.

Community involvement

Lancashire Holdings Ltd supports communities, predominantly in the UK and Bermuda, through its corporate charity, The Lancashire Foundation (Charity Commission no. 1149184).

Employee-led support

All staff are encouraged to take part in voluntary work. In the past, staff have helped to transform a roof garden for St Giles Trust, volunteered at a day centre for people who are homeless, as well as engaging in various fundraising efforts such as the London and Mid Sussex marathons.

The group offers one day of paid charity leave for all employees and a week of paid charity leave for employees who have been employed full time for over five years. This week then doubles once an employee has been employed full time for six years.

Through its corporate charity, the group takes applications for matched funding for staff up to a limit of £2,000.

Applications

For further information see the group's corporate charity entry.

Corporate charity

The Lancashire Foundation (Charity Commission no. 1149184) – see entry on page 250.

Community contributions

Cash donations worldwide	£636,000

Lancashire Holdings' annual report for 2021 states that the group gave £636,000 in charitable donations. Of this total, £590,000 was donated to The Lancashire Foundation and the remaining £46,000 to Médecins Sans Frontières.

The group annually donates 0.75% of its full-year profits to the foundation with a minimum threshold of £250,000 and a maximum threshold of £750,000.

The total contributions figure has been converted from USD to GBP using the exchange rate at the time of writing (August 2022).

Land Securities Group plc

🔍 Community services and development, education and training, housing and homelessness, social welfare

Company registration number: 4369054

Correspondent: Sustainability Team, 100 Victoria Street, London SW1E 5JL (tel: 020 7413 9000; email: enquiries@landsec.com; website: https://landsec.com/sustainability/creating-jobs-and-opportunities)

Directors: Mark Allan; Edward Bonham Carter; Nicholas Cadbury; Madeleine Cosgrave; Christophe Evain; Cressida Hogg; Colette O'Shea; Vanessa Simms; Manjiry Tamhane (female: 56%; male: 44%).

Nature of business: Land Securities (Landsec) is a property group in the UK involved in both property development and investment, and property outsourcing.

Financial information

Year end	31/03/2022
Turnover	£679,000,000
Pre-tax profit	£875,000,000

Total employees: 610

Main locations: Land Securities (Landsec) owns properties across the UK.

Community involvement

The group aims to support the communities in which it operates by working with charities, as well as delivering its own charitable programmes and initiatives.

Partnerships

The group works with charities addressing issues such as homelessness, poverty, social exclusion, mental health and criminal justice.

One of its partnerships is with LandAid, a charity seeking to end youth homelessness in the UK. The group makes grants for accommodation projects, as well as offering its expertise through pro bono work.

The group also looks to work with small, grassroots charities supporting marginalised communities.

In 2021, the group partnered with John Lewis, Primark and Boots to run the Get Into St David's scheme with The Prince's Trust. The two-week initiative supported local young people aged 16 to 30 with skills required for work. Participants received employability training, interview practice and work experience.

The group also partnered with homeless charity Crisis to launch an initiative to tackle job and home insecurity for vulnerable people. The initiative offered three weeks of employability training to five candidates who had experience of homelessness.

In Lewisham, the group worked with the Youth Construction Trust to deliver a programme focused on inspiring young people from underrepresented backgrounds to pursue a career in the real estate sector.

Community employment

Through this programme, the group provides training, work placements and a direct route into a job for some of the most excluded groups in society.

The group's Prisons Programme operates in partnership with organisations such as Bounce Back and Key4Life, to support ex-offenders in their efforts to secure positive work opportunities.

Education

The group's education programme looks to inspire young people (particularly those not in education, employment or training) into careers in the property industry.

As part of this initiative, the group runs a Future Property School, to educate students in Westminster about the industry. Landsec staff work closely with students over the course of three months on a project to create their own sustainable development proposals.

In-kind support

The group provides pro bono support and space to partner charities.

Employee-led support

The group's volunteering programme encourages employees to use their skills and expertise to support its community partners.

In the past, staff have mentored refugees and ex-offenders to help improve their employability skills and inspired young people to take up careers in property, as well as providing a wide range of pro bono support to charities.

In 2021/22, 117 employees from Landsec spent 848 hours volunteering, to the value of £195,000.

Commercially led support

The group supports ShareGift (Charity Commission no. 1052686), a charity that accepts donations of shares that would be uneconomical to sell, to be used for charitable benefit.

Applications

Contact the correspondent for more information.

Community contributions

Cash donations UK	£150,700
Total contributions UK	£2,000,000

According to its 2022 Sustainability Performance and Data Report, the group generated £2.5 million of social value for charity partners in 2021/22. This figure comprises the value of in-kind space donated to charity partners (£1.73 million), direct financial donations (£150,700) and non-financial donations excluding space (£121,600). In addition, £479,700 was raised through guest donations, while employees donated £45,900. As is our usual practice, we have only included amounts contributed directly by the group in its total contributions figure.

Leeds Building Society

Community services and development, general charitable purposes

Company registration number: FCA 164992

Correspondent: The Charity and Community Team, 105 Albion Street, Leeds, West Yorkshire LS1 5AS (email: contact form on the website; website: www.leedsbuildingsociety.co.uk/your-society/charity-and-community/hub/#)

Directors: Iain Cornish; Richard Fearon; Annette Barnes; Andrew Conroy; David Fisher; Neil Fuller; Andrew Greenwood; Gareth Hoskin; Rob Howse; Lynn McManus; Anita Tadayon (female: 27%; male: 73%).

Nature of business: Leeds Building Society is the fifth largest building society in the UK.

Financial information

Year end	31/12/2021
Turnover	£284,000,000
Pre-tax profit	£160,700,000

Total employees: 1,474

Main locations: The building society is headquartered in Leeds and has branches across the UK.

Community involvement

Leeds Building Society makes donations to registered charities in the areas near its branches, directly and also through its corporate charity the Leeds Building Society Charitable Foundation (Charity Commission no. 1074429).

Partnerships

The building society launched its partnership with Dementia UK with a £25,000 donation in 2020. By 2021, the society had raised £380,000 and aims to reach its target of £500,000 by 2024.

Canal and River Trust Partnership

In 2021, the society formed a partnership with the Canal and River Trust, adopting a mile of waterway outside the society's head office in Leeds. The society pledged funding for the trust until 2023, focusing on heritage, wildlife and environmental efforts.

Yorkshire Dales Millennium Trust

The society also partnered with the Yorkshire Dales Millennium Trust in 2021, offering a children's savings product, dedicating trees for each society colleague and providing volunteering opportunities.

Employee-led support

The society's volunteering scheme offers every staff member up to 14 hours volunteering time per year to support their communities. Staff also deliver workshops on budgeting, saving and the importance of good money management to schools in Leeds. In 2021, the society's financial education and skills programmes, run by employee volunteers, reached 8,000 students.

Applications

For charity partner enquiries, contact the building society directly for further information. For Leeds Building Society Foundation enquiries, contact foundation@leedsbuildingsociety.co.uk.

Corporate charity

Leeds Building Society Foundation (Charity Commission no. 1074429) – see entry on page 250.

Community contributions

Cash donations UK	£231,300

According to its 2021 annual report, the building society donated £141,300 to causes in the local community.

The society also made donations totalling £90,000 to its corporate charity, the Leeds Building Society Foundation.

Legal & General Group plc

Community enterprise and social entrepreneurship, general charitable purposes

Company registration number: 1417162

Correspondent: Jack Roper, Group Head of Sustainability, One Coleman Street, London EC2R 5AA (tel: 07876 482844; email: jack.roper@landg.com; website: https://group.legalandgeneral. com/en/sustainability/supporting-communities/charity-stakeholders-and-collaborative-partners)

Directors: Sir John Kingman; Sir Nigel Wilson; Jeff Davies; Phillip Broadley; Henrietta Baldock; Nilufer Von Bismarck; Carolyn Johnson; Lesley Knox; George Lewis; Ric Lewis; Tushar Morzaria; Laura Wade-Gery (female: 42%; male: 58%).

Nature of business: The group's principal activities are the provision of long-term insurance, investment management and general insurance.

Financial information

Year end	31/12/2021
Turnover	£45,450,000,000
Pre-tax profit	£2,632,000,000

UK employees: 9,705

Total employees: 10,741

Main locations: The group has offices in Birmingham, Cardiff, Hove, Ipswich, London, Kingswood, Surrey, Witham and Essex.

Community involvement

Legal & General employees at each location choose small (mainly local) charities to support. The group also supports several national charities.

Partnerships

The group is a founder patron of the Legacy Youth Zone in Croydon, a purpose-build facility for the borough's young people. As part of its role as founder patron, between 2019 and 2022, the group made an annual £25,000 donation to the charity.

The group is also a partner of FastFutures, a digital collaborative learning programme designed to equip participants with employability advice and skills. In 2021, Legal & General donated £100,000 to the programme, funding three cohorts.

Legal & General is also a partner of the Samaritans and in 2021, was the headline sponsor for the charity's Dawn Walk.

The group also supports the Duke of Edinburgh Awards and in 2021 the group focused on widening access to the programme, particularly in the North East.

In-kind support

In 2021, Legal & General supported the Royal Voluntary Service's £5 million charity appeal by providing advertising for the organisation in the Telegraph newspaper.

Employee-led support

Legal & General staff engage in various fundraising efforts and the group provide matched funding for funds raised. According to the group's 2021 Sustainability Report, the Legal & General matched funding scheme allows employees to claim up to £5,000 per person per calendar year for their chosen cause, and up to £500 in recognition of volunteering time. In 2021, 250 employees claimed matched funding, with an average of £1,284 in fundraising per person matched by the group.

Exclusions

The group makes no political donations.

Applications

Employees in each location choose charities, often local, to support. For further information contact the correspondent.

Community contributions

We were unable to determine a figure for the group's total charitable donations. However, the 2021 Sustainability Report states that £1.3 million was donated to UK charities including group matched funding.

Also during 2021, Legal & General donated £90,000 through its Small Donations campaign to small charities as requested by its staff.

Leicester City Football Club Ltd

Community services and development, education and training, the environment, general charitable purposes, health, sports and recreation

Company registration number: 4593477

Correspondent: Allison Tripney, Community Director, King Power Stadium, Filbert Way, Leicester, Leicestershire LE2 7FL (tel: 0116 291 5223; email: community@lcfc.co.uk; website: www.lcfc.com)

Directors: Shilai Liu; Khun Aiyawatt Srivaddhanaprabha; Khun Apichet Srivaddhanaprabha; Susan Whelan (female: 25%; male: 75%).

Nature of business: Leicester City FC is a professional football club competing in the Premier League.

Financial information

Year end	31/05/2021
Turnover	£226,204,000
Pre-tax profit	£33,097,000

UK employees: 320

Main locations: The football club is based in Leicester.

Community involvement

The club's charitable support is primarily channelled through its two charities, The Vichai Srivaddhanaprabha Foundation and the Leicester City Football Club Trust. Support is provided through education and sports programmes, fundraising and in-kind donations.

The Vichai Srivaddhanaprabha Foundation (Charity Commission no. 1144791)

In 2018, the LCFC Foxes Foundation was renamed The Vichai Srivaddhanaprabha Foundation in honour of the club's late chair. Each year, the foundation raises funds and awards grants to a selected number of local charities chosen by the club. According to the foundation's 2021 annual report, the club made no substantial donation in 2021.

Leicester City Football Club Trust (Charity Commission no. 1126526)

The trust delivers the club's 'Leicester City in the Community' programmes. It works in partnership with the Premier League, Leicestershire Police, and local charities, educational institutions and businesses to provide a broad range of programmes for children, young people and adults in the areas of education, health, social inclusion and sports

participation, with a focus on football projects.

Recent examples of the trust's programmes include:

- **Football Welcomes** – The club has partnered with Amnesty International to create more welcoming communities for refugees and people seeking asylum through football
- **Black History Month** – Leicester City's Wes Morgan joined the campaign to answer questions generated by Premier League Inspires participants. Inspires runs secondary school workshops around racial equality.

For full details of all of the club's current community programmes, see its website.

Commercially led support

The club has several matchday collections each season. Collections for St John Ambulance, the Royal British Legion and the Vichai Srivaddhanaprabha Foundation took place between 2018 and 2020; however, collections were paused in 2021 due to the COVID-19 pandemic.

Exclusions

Charity policy

The charity policy states that the club will only support charities in the East Midlands area. The club is unable to offer signed merchandise or monetary donations.

Applications

The club

Applications for stadium tour vouchers can be made by downloading an application form available at: www.lcfc.com/fans-community/foundation/charity-policy. Forms must be sent by post to Charity Department, King Power Stadium, Filbert Way, Leicester, LE2 7FL.

Leicester City in the Community

For general Leicester City in the Community enquiries email: community@lcfc.co.uk.

Corporate charity

The Vichai Srivaddhanaprabha Foundation (Charity Commission no. 1144791) – see entry on page 278.

Community contributions

Cash donations UK	£78,500

According to its 2020/21 accounts, the club made charitable donations of £78,500 during the year. This includes a donation of £42,500 to the Leicester City Football Club Trust in 2020 and £36,000 in 2021 to other charitable causes. In 2021, the club suspended donations to its corporate charities, the Vivchai Srivaddhanaprabha Foundation and the Leicester City Football Club Trust.

John Lewis Partnership plc

Arts, culture and heritage, education and training, emergency relief, the environment, general charitable purposes, health, housing and homelessness, research

Company registration number: 238937

Correspondent: CSR Team, 171 Victoria Street, London SW1E 5NN (email: See 'Applications'; website: www. johnlewispartnership.co.uk/csr/our-strategy/social-impact.html)

Directors: Rita Clifton; Nishpank Kankiwala; Andrew Martin; Bérangère Michel; Julie Rushworth; Sharon White; Rebecca Wollam; David Wood (female: 63%; male: 38%).

Nature of business: The John Lewis Partnership trades under the names of John Lewis (full line department stores and smaller 'at home' stores) and Waitrose (food shops, including supermarkets and convenience stores). The partnership is a retail business run on co-operative principles.

Financial information

Year end	25/01/2022
Turnover	£10,837,500,000
Pre-tax profit	£26,700,000

Total employees: 79,500

Main locations: John Lewis and Waitrose have stores throughout the UK.

Community involvement

The partnership provides support to a variety of good causes through in-kind donations of food and cash donations made via its Community Matters scheme and corporate charities.

The John Lewis Foundation (Charity Commission no. 1118162)

The John Lewis Foundation is designed to benefit the communities in which those who produce products for the partnership live and work. The John Lewis Foundation funded eight UK-based employability projects to the value of £157,000 during 2021/22.

The John Spedan Lewis Foundation (Charity Commission no. 240473)

The foundation makes charitable contributions which reflect the interests of John Spedan Lewis, the founder of the John Lewis Partnership, particularly entomology, ornithology, horticulture and associated environmental and conservation projects. Preference is given to small projects with an educational content.

Community Matters

Community Matters is a charitable giving scheme that runs throughout John Lewis and Waitrose stores. Each shop has £3,000 per quarter to donate, and every three months, customers choose three community groups or charities to support through a token scheme. The winners can receive support in the form of product donations, volunteering time or cash donations. In 2021/22, £3 million was donated to charities through the John Lewis and Waitrose Community Matters schemes.

Environment

The partnership supports environmental causes, such as the Farming Community Network and Linking Environment and Farming which both support current and future farming.

Charity Partners

The partnership supports various national charity partners including:

▶ The British Red Cross
▶ FareShare Go
▶ Home-Start
▶ The Prince's Countryside Fund
▶ The Trussell Trust

Creative Arts Development Programmes

In 2021, the partnership also worked with the charity Create Not Hate to run development programmes for young people from underrepresented groups to give them an opportunity to experience working in the creative arts.

In-kind support

Food donations

Waitrose stores work in partnership with the FareShare Go scheme to distribute donations of surplus food to charities and community groups. In 2021/22, over 4 million meals were donated to over 3,000 organisations.

Furniture donations

John Lewis' Sofa Reuse scheme collected over 6,500 items from customers' homes which were then reused or recycled by charities and helped over 1,700 households.

Home-Start

During 2021/22, the partnership worked with Home-Start to provide 165 families with Christmas dinners, trees and decorations.

Give a Little Love Campaign

Launched in 2020, the Give a Little Love Campaign was established to support families in the UK by working with charity partners FareShare and Home-Start. In 2021, the second phase of the campaign, the Farm to Family Initiative, began with the aim to support those struggling as a result of the COVID-19 pandemic. In 2021, the initiative donated over 3 million portions of fruit to over 3,000 organisations.

Employee-led support

The Golden Jubilee Trust (Charity Commission no. 1079195)

The Golden Jubilee Trust is the partnership's volunteering charity. Partners have the opportunity to volunteer full or part-time with a UK-registered charity for up to six months, on full pay. Since the trust was established, over 980 partners have participated, equating to over 393,000 hours representing a value of £25 million. In 2021, the John Lewis Partnership Golden Jubilee Trust awarded both virtual and in-person secondments to 31 charities across the country. This equates to 2,392 partner days' work donated.

Commercially led support

Duchy Organic

The total sales of the Waitrose Duchy Organic brand have generated a total contribution of over £30 million for The Prince of Wales Charitable Foundation since its inception in 2011.

Exclusions

The partnership does not support individuals, religious or political groups, or third-party fundraising activities.

Applications

Community Matters

Local charities and not-for-profit organisations can contact the Champion for Community Giving at their local Waitrose store, or the Community Liaison Co-ordinator at their local John Lewis store. Alternatively, email community.matters@waitrose.co.uk.

John Lewis nomination forms can be downloaded from: www.johnlewis.com/our-services/helping-our-community.

Waitrose nomination forms can be downloaded from: www.waitrose.com/content/waitrose/en/home/inspiration/community_matters.htm.

The John Spedan Lewis Foundation

Further information can be found at: https://johnspedanlewisfoundation. wordpress.com. Alternatively, email JSLF@johnlewis.co.uk.

Golden Jubilee Trust

UK-registered charities that would like to highlight a potential secondment opportunity should email the trust manager at golden.jubilee.trust. enquiries@johnlewis.co.uk. A page dedicated to the trust can be found on the partnership's website.

Corporate charity

John Lewis and Partners Foundation (Charity Commission no. 1118162) – see entry on page 250.

Community contributions

Total contributions UK	£6,500,000

According to the John Lewis Partnership's Ethics and Sustainability Report for 2021/22, the partnership donated £6.5 million to charitable causes during the year. This total comprises cash and in-kind donations. The report states that £3 million was donated through the Community Matters Programme. Further information was not available.

Eli Lilly and Company Ltd

🔍 Community services and development, health

Company registration number: 284385

Correspondent: Grant Office, Lilly House, Basing View, Basingstoke, Basingstoke, Hampshire RG21 4FA (tel: 01256 315000; email: UKgrants@ lilly.com; website: www.lilly.co.uk/ responsibility/lilly-grant-office)

Directors: David Ricks; Ralph Alvarez; Katherine Baicker; J. Erik Fyrwald; Jamere Jackson; William Kaelin; Juan Luciano; Marschall Runge; Gabrielle Sulzberger; Jackson Tai; Karen Walker (female: 38%; male: 62%).

Nature of business: The principal activity of the company is the production and supply of pharmaceuticals and animal health products to other subsidiaries and third parties in the UK and other areas of the world. It is a wholly owned subsidiary of Eli Lilly and Company, its US parent company.

Financial information

Year end	31/12/2021
Turnover	£2,341,000,000
Pre-tax profit	£509,000,000

Total employees: 33,625

Main locations: In the UK, the group's headquarters is in Basingstoke and it has other locations across the UK.

Community involvement

In the UK, Lilly supports health-based projects and a wide range of community initiatives local to its sites through its grants programme.

Grants are made to organisations promoting patient care, such as universities (particularly those engaged in life sciences innovation), hospitals and patient advocacy groups.

Eli Lilly also supports community initiatives within its areas of operation. Examples include educational programmes, hospital radio stations and funding for charities supporting adults and children with disabilities.

Cash donations and in-kind support (namely product donations) are available.

Other support

The following activities may be considered for practical support from Lilly but would not be eligible for funding:

- Clinical research
- Exhibition stands
- Projects working in partnership with Lilly such as joint working, or other partnerships (which should be sent to your corporate affairs or marketing team contact)

Partnerships

Lilly works closely with various partners across the UK healthcare system, including the NHS to ensure patients get access to the most effective new medicines as fast as possible.

Lilly's research partners include Dementia Discovery Fund and the Advanced Pain Discovery Platform. Lilly's partnership with Dementia Discovery Fund aims to discover and develop novel therapies for dementia, including Alzheimer's research. Lilly's partnership with the Advanced Pain Discovery Platform aims to improve understanding of the complexity of pain.

Employee-led support

Employees take part in Lilly's annual 'Global Day of Service'. Each year, staff volunteer within their local communities across the world, working in partnership with health organisations. According to the company website, in 2021, employees spent 10,000 hours volunteering.

Applications

Grant applications can be made online through the Lilly website. There are two different application forms for public bodies and NGOs. Any queries should be sent to UKgrants@lilly.com.

Community contributions

We were unable to determine a figure for Lilly's other charitable contributions.

All the financial figures have been converted from USD to GBP using the exchange rate at the time of writing (August 2022).

Lincolnshire Co-operative Ltd

🔍 Community services and development, education and training, general charitable purposes, health

Company registration number: 141R

Correspondent: Community Team, Stanley Bett House, 15/23 Tentercroft Street, Lincoln LN5 7DB (tel: 01522 544632; email: community@lincolnshire. coop; website: www.lincolnshire.coop)

Directors: David Cowell; Claudia Nel; Nicola Berry; Jane Moate; Ian Haldenby; James Scott; Jackie Munn; Stephen Hughes; Julia Romney; Richard Willis (female: 50%; male: 50%).

Nature of business: The company's businesses include food, pharmacy, travel, funerals, florists, post offices and property.

Financial information

Year end	04/09/2021
Turnover	£324,514,000
Pre-tax profit	£13,153,000

Total employees: 2,909

Main locations: The company's head office is in Lincoln and it has stores throughout Lincolnshire.

Community involvement

Support is provided to organisations in Lincolnshire through donations and educational and well-being programmes.

Community Champions

Community Champions are selected by staff and local members' groups in each area. Each time a member shops using their dividend card, a donation is made to the nominated Community Champion in that area. Other fundraising efforts are also incorporated into the donation, such as staff fundraising, carrier bag charge proceeds and collection boxes in outlets. The Community Champions change on a quarterly basis, and charities and good causes can register on a central list for consideration.

During 2020/21, £646,700 was raised for 586 charities through the Community Champions scheme.

Education

There are several staff members who are qualified and experienced in delivering lessons and information sessions in local schools. Topics include, Fairtrade, local produce and healthy living. The company has also developed a range of resources for schools. These services are offered free of charge.

Lincolnshire Co-operative Ltd also partners with The Prince's Trust to deliver a 'Get Into Retail' programme each year, giving participants one week's training, followed by a three week placement in a Co-operative store, where the participant receives two Level 1 qualifications in food hygiene and responsible alcohol retailing.

Health walks

All of the company's health walks are free and give local people the opportunity to learn about their local area and its wildlife and meet new people.

Community Cuppa

Free Community Cuppa events are aimed at those wanting to find out more about their local area and how to get involved. They are designed to build connections between communities in Lincolnshire.

COVID-19 groups

During the COVID-19 pandemic, Lincolnshire Co-operative Ltd established links between all of its pharmacies and food stores with a community group that could help with shopping and collecting prescriptions for people who were isolating or vulnerable.

In-kind support

Local charities can request smaller donations of goods or raffle prizes by taking a written request to their local store.

The company's food stores host collection points for local food banks and community larders (one collection point per store).

Employee-led support

Lincolnshire Co-operative Ltd offers two days' paid leave for employees to volunteer. Staff volunteer on practical projects and also offer professional support and expertise.

Exclusions

Any charity, community group or not-for-profit organisation can apply to Community Champions, providing that the money raised is used locally.

Applications

Application forms for the Charity Champions scheme are available to download on the company's dedicated web page. They are also available to pick up in local Lincolnshire Co-op food stores.

For enquiries about educational resources and other forms of support for schools, complete an online enquiry form on the company's website, or call 01522 544 632.

If you would like to advertise a school governor or trustee vacancy for company staff, email education@lincolnshire.coop.

If you have a project that could be supported by staff volunteers, contact the Engagement Team via busybees@lincolnshire.coop, or complete a volunteering request form online.

Community contributions

Cash donations UK	£375,000

In 2020/21 donations to charities and community groups totalled £375,000.

The Liverpool Football Club and Athletic Grounds Ltd

Community services and development, education and training, social welfare, sports and recreation

Company registration number: 35668

Correspondent: Liverpool FC Foundation, Anfield Road, Liverpool, Merseyside L4 0TH (tel: 0151 432 5675; email: lfcfoundation@liverpoolfc.com; website: https://foundation.liverpoolfc.com)

Directors: Sir Kenneth Dalglish; Michael Egan; Michael Gordon; John Henry; William Hogan IV; Andrew Hughes; Thomas Wener (male: 100%).

Nature of business: Liverpool FC is a professional football club competing in the Premier League.

Financial information

Year end	31/05/2021
Turnover	£487,365,000
Pre-tax profit	(£4,762,000)

Total employees: 853

Main locations: The football club is based in Liverpool.

Community involvement

The club provides most of its support through its charity, the Liverpool FC Foundation (Charity Commission no. 1096572) which delivers a wide range of health, education and sport programmes in the local community.

Liverpool FC Foundation

The club's charity delivers a wide range of community programmes in areas of high-deprivation and need across Liverpool. The foundation also works internationally, supporting the work of charity partners and the Premier League.

The foundation's programmes focus on six key areas:
- Sport and physical activity
- Health and well-being
- Education and life skills
- Employment and training
- Youth interventions
- Community engagement

Recent examples of the foundation's programmes include:
- **Game On:** a collaboration between LFC Foundation and Nike, to provide all children across Merseyside with free sport opportunities, including sports such as netball, tennis and athletics.
- **Works:** Works focuses on employability provision for people aged 16 and over. The foundation currently has six Works programmes with five different funding partners.

- **#iwill:** a youth-led programme that empowers young people to identify, prioritise and tackle the issues that young people feel most strongly about.

Full details of all of the foundation's current programmes can be found on its website.

Partnerships

In addition to delivering its own programmes, the foundation also works in partnership with local charities and non-profit organisations such as Alder Hey Children's Charity, IntoUniversity/Liverpool University, the Owen McVeigh Foundation, NSPCC and Zoë's Place to improve the life and health chances of children and young people.

Red Neighbours

Red Neighbours is a community programme set up by the club in 2017 to support local residents and schools and community groups in the Anfield area. Club staff volunteer their time and expertise to create events and experiences that address four key areas: food poverty and education; support for the older community; encouraging a physically active community; and creating memorable experiences for young people.

Exclusions

According to the club's help centre, the club is unable to support events and charity requests outside its existing programmes and partnerships.

Applications

For more information on Red Neighbours, contact red.neighbours@liverpoolfc.com or see @Red_Neighbours on Twitter.

Community contributions

We were unable to determine a figure for the club's total charitable contributions for 2020/21.

Liverpool Victoria

General charitable purposes, health

Company registration number: FCA 110035

Correspondent: Regional Community Committee, County Gates, Bournemouth, Dorset BH1 2NF (tel: 01202 292333; email: see 'Applications'; website: www.lv.com/about-us/lv-cares)

Directors: Colin Ledlie; Seamus Creedon; Susan McInnes; Simon Moore; Mark Hartigan; Natalie Ceeney; Suzy Neubert; (female: 43%; male: 57%).

Nature of business: The group's formal company name is Liverpool Victoria Financial Services Ltd (formerly Liverpool Victoria Friendly Society Ltd).

The group carries out insurance and financial services business in the UK under the brands LV= and Liverpool Victoria.

Financial information

Year end	31/12/2020
Turnover	£103,000,000
Pre-tax profit	£37,000,000

Total employees: 1,623

Main locations: The group has offices in Bournemouth (head office), Brentwood, Bristol, Croydon, Exeter, Hitchin, Huddersfield, Ipswich, Leeds and London.

Community involvement

The group supports charities and communities in the locations in which it has a presence through donations, community partnerships and by supporting its employees' fundraising and volunteering efforts.

Regional Community Committees

The group has Regional Community Committees made up of employee volunteers who help decide how the group should lend its support in the neighbourhoods surrounding its offices in Bournemouth, Exeter and Hitchin. The committees provide support via donations, fundraising activities or volunteering. In 2021, the committees provided £11,000 to local and national charities.

Member Support Fund

The Member Support Fund was set up in 2001 to help members in financial hardship by awarding grants and practical support.

Employee-led support

Volunteering

Employees can take up to two and a half days of paid leave to volunteer for good causes.

Payroll giving

As of 2021, 61% of employees were donating through the 'Pennies for Charity' scheme. The scheme raised £5,500 in 2021 which was then distributed to a local charity voted for by each office.

Employee fundraising

During the year, employees raised £30,000 for charities and community projects through fundraising. The group matched £12,500 (matched funding is capped at £500 for one employee or £1,000 for a team of colleagues).

In 2021, employees also supported cancer charity Maggie's. By undertaking the Miles for Maggie's challenge, 53 employees raised £3,000, with matched funding included.

Commercially led support

LV=KidZone

This a scheme whereby LV= works with Bournemouth, Christchurch and Poole Council to help keep children safe along Bournemouth's beaches. During the year, 40,000 wristbands were provided to local and visiting families and 190 children were reunited with their families.

Applications

For support, apply in writing or via email to your nearest regional committee. Locations and contact details are available from the website: www.lv.com/about-us/lv-cares/investing-in-communities.

Community contributions

Cash donations UK	£22,500

In 2021, the group raised, donated and invested £87,500 in UK communities. The following breakdown was provided in its 2021 annual report:

Cost of support given via the Member Support Fund	£34,000
Community fundraising	£30,000
Matched funding	£12,500
Community investment	£11,000

We have excluded 'community fundraising' from our figure for UK contributions. This is standard practice as, according to the 2021 annual report, this relates to employee-led activities, including fundraising for charities of the year.

The figure for the company's UK cash donations has been taken from its 2021 CSR report and includes £11,000 in donations made by the Regional Charity Committees and £12,500 in matched funding.

Lloyd's

🔍	Community enterprise and social entrepreneurship, community services and development, education and training, emergency response/relief, the environment, general charitable purposes, health, research, sports and recreation, work outside the UK

Company registration number: FCA 202761

Correspondent: The ESG Team, One Lime Street, London EC3M 7HA (tel: 020 7327 1000; email: responsiblebusiness@lloyds.com; website: www.lloyds.com/about-lloyds/responsible-business)

Directors: John Neal; Sara Gomez; Bob James; Burkhard Keese; David Sansom; Jo Scott; Peter Spires; Patrick Tierman (female: 25%; male: 75%).

Nature of business: Lloyd's is a specialist insurance and reinsurance underwriter.

Financial information

Year end	31/12/2021
Turnover	£39,216,000,000
Pre-tax profit	£2,277,000,000

UK employees: 980

Total employees: 1,280

Main locations: The group's head office is based in London and it has offices worldwide.

Community involvement

Lloyd's focuses its community contributions in the local communities it serves worldwide. It gives support through its grant-making charities. The group supports communities in East London, where it is based, through the Lloyd's Community Programme.

Lloyd's charities

- Lloyd's of London Foundation (Charity Commission no. 207232) – supports local, national and international causes on Lloyd's behalf. It currently supports employability, social mobility, mental health, disaster recovery and climate change.
- Lloyd's Patriotic Fund (Charity Commission no. 210173) – Lloyd's has a long history of providing support to the UK armed forces community. This fund was established to make grants to serving and ex-Service personnel and their families. It also provides support to several armed forces organisations with a particular focus on helping ex-Service personnel into employment and supporting them in developing coping mechanisms for stress.
- Lloyd's Tercentenary Research Foundation (Charity Commission no. 298482) – provides research grants for research into the field of societal risk, with a particular focus on the 'protection gap' (the difference between insured losses and economic losses, or uninsured losses).

Employee-led support

Lloyd's Community Programme (LCP)

LCP is a sub-fund of the Lloyd's of London Foundation. Through the programme, employees are able to contribute their time and skills to community projects.

Lloyd's Market Charity Awards

The Lloyd's website states that anyone who works in the Lloyd's market can apply for a donation for a charity or community organisation in which they are actively involved through the Lloyd's Market Charity Awards scheme.

Applications

All of Lloyd's charities can be contacted by emailing globalcommunity engagement@lloyds.com.

Corporate charity

Lloyd's Patriotic Fund (Charity Commission no. 210173) – see entry on page 253; Lloyd's of London Foundation (Charity Commission no. 207232) – see entry on page 252.

Community contributions

Cash donations UK		£5,000,000

In its annual report and accounts for 2021 the group declared charitable donations of £5 million.

We have used the group's gross written premium in place of turnover.

Lloyds Banking Group

Community enterprise and social entrepreneurship, community services and development, education and training, the environment, health, money and debt advice, social welfare

Company registration number: 2065

Correspondent: Responsible Business Team, The Mound, Edinburgh EH1 1YZ (tel: 020 7626 1500; website: www. lloydsbankinggroup.com/who-we-are/responsible-business.html)

Directors: Charlie Nunn; William Chalmers; Robin Budenberg; Alan Dickinson; Sarah Legg; Lord Lupton; Amanda Mackenzie; Harmeen Mehta; Scott Wheway; Catherine Woods (female: 40%; male: 60%).

Nature of business: Lloyds Banking Group is a leading UK-based financial services group providing a wide range of banking and financial services. Its main activities are retail, commercial and corporate banking, general insurance, and life, pensions and investment provision.

Financial information

Year end	31/12/2021
Turnover	£374,460,000,000
Pre-tax profit	£6,902,000,000

Total employees: 58,000

Main locations: The group's headquarters is in London and it has branches throughout the British Isles.

Community involvement

Lloyds Banking Group (LBG) is one of the UK's largest corporate donors. As part of its 'Helping Britain Prosper Plan', the group provides support through employee volunteering, fundraising, working with community organisations and donations to its independent foundations. Alongside the plan, it also runs several community investment programmes.

Helping Britain Prosper Plan

The Helping Britain Prosper Plan was launched in 2014 and aims to address some of the social, economic and environmental challenges facing the UK. The plan operates across seven key themes, which are outlined on the website as follows:

- Helping the transition to a sustainable low carbon economy
- Helping Britain get a home
- Helping people save for the future
- Supporting businesses to start up and grow
- Tackling social disadvantage across Britain
- Building capability and digital skills
- Championing Britain's diversity

Through the plan, LBG provides regional support across the UK. More information about support in individual regions can be found on the group's website.

Community investment programmes

The Lloyds Bank and Bank of Scotland Social Entrepreneurs Programme – delivered in partnership with the School for Social Entrepreneurs and the Big Lottery Fund, this programme supports entrepreneurs to start and grow social businesses. Since the partnership began in 2012, over 1,800 entrepreneurs have received support.

Financial inclusion – improving the financial inclusion and skills of children and young people. The group has launched a new range of financial capability resources, designed to be an exciting, engaging and informative way of helping children and young people to understand money and financial management.

Digital inclusion – improving the digital skills of individuals, small businesses and charities.

Education and employability – investing in education and employability.

Lloyds Scholars – established in 2011, Lloyds Scholars is an award-winning social mobility programme aimed at UK students. The group works in partnership with nine leading universities across the UK to support progression into graduate-level employment of talented university students from lower-income households. The scholars are given financial support along with access to paid internships within LBG and mentoring for the duration of their time at university. In return, they are asked to complete 100 hours of volunteering for local causes. Partner universities include:

- Queen's University, Belfast
- University College London
- University of Bath
- University of Birmingham
- University of Bristol
- University of Edinburgh
- University of Oxford
- University of Sheffield
- University of Warwick

Supporting credit unions – since 2014, the group has awarded £6 million to support credit unions. Delivered in partnership with the Credit Union Foundation and the Association of British Credit Unions Ltd (ABCUL), the funding has helped 120 credit unions, benefitting communities across the UK.

Foundations

LBG provides support to communities across the UK and the Channel Islands through its four corporate charities, all of which receive annual funding from the group. The foundations provide grants and support to charities that tackle issues such as domestic abuse, mental health, modern slavery, human trafficking and employability.

Together, the foundations are currently funding 294 charities that provide mental health support to people. Over the last four years, the group has donated an additional £2.1 million to the foundations to specifically support the issue of mental health.

The Lloyds Bank foundations are:

- Bank of Scotland Foundation for Scotland (OSCR no. SC032942)
- Lloyds Bank Foundation for England and Wales (Charity Commission no. 327114)
- Halifax Foundation for Northern Ireland (NICC no. NIC101763)
- Lloyds Bank Foundation for the Channel Islands (Charity Commission no. 327113)

Mental Health UK

In 2017, the group launched a partnership with Mental Health UK with the initial aim of raising £4 million. So far, over £12 million has been raised for the charity through employee and customer fundraising. Currently, the focus of the partnership is mental health resilience in young people. The funds raised will be used to expand Bloom, a UK-wide programme that is delivered in schools and colleges. The programme teaches skills and techniques that will help young people deal with challenges such as exam pressure, relationships and managing their time. According to the group's 2021 ESG report, it raised £1.2 million for Mental Health UK in 2021.

The Woodland Trust

The group is working with The Woodland Trust to plant ten million trees over the next ten years to expand the UK's carbon sink. According to the 2021 ESG report, LBG employees planted nearly 50,000 trees at 60 tree-planting events during the year.

Pan's Amies London

The Lloyds Bank Foundation for England and Wales funds Pan's 'Amies London' project with a three-year grant for £75,000. Pan Intercultural Arts is a charity that supports marginalised people in society, including women who have survived trafficking into the UK.

Employee-led support

Lloyds Banking Group's Colleague Volunteering Programme
As one of the group's Community Investment Programmes, the Colleague Volunteering Programme enables employees to spend at least one day per year volunteering for a charity or community project of their choice. Within this, over 50% of volunteering during the year was skills-based, meaning volunteers use their own skills to support charities and community groups or develop the skills of others in those causes. In 2021, 535 volunteered for this programme.

In addition, 1,200 employees volunteered to help The Woodland Trust and 463 colleagues supported 74 charities through Charity Response Forums.

Employee fundraising
Employees participate in fundraising activities for the group's charity partner, Mental Health UK as well as for charities of their choosing. The group's foundations operate a matched giving scheme to support employee fundraising efforts.

Applications
The website notes that queries or comments about the group's responsible business or Helping Britain Prosper activity can be directed to the correspondent in writing.

Corporate charity
Bank of Scotland Foundation (OSCR no. SC032942) – see entry on page 223; Lloyds Bank Foundation for England and Wales (Charity Commission no. 327114) – see entry on page 251; Halifax Foundation for Northern Ireland (NICC no. NIC101763) – see entry on page 245; Lloyds Bank Foundation for the Channel Islands (Charity Commission no. 327113) – see entry on page 251.

Community contributions

Total contributions UK	£46,000,000

According to LBG's 2021 ESG report, it gave almost £46 million in community investment during the year. This figure includes employee time, direct donations and a share of the group's profits given annually to the foundations.

London City Airport Ltd

Community services and development, employment advice, the environment, health, social welfare

Company registration number: 1963361

Correspondent: Anna Boss, London City Airport London, Royal Docks, City Aviation House, London E16 2PB (email: Community.Fund@ londoncityairport.com; website: www. londoncityairport.com/corporate/ responsible-growth/community-fund)

Directors: Rob Holden; Robert Sinclair; Wilma Allan; Eric Machiels; Prateek Maheshwari; Greg Pestrak; Mel Ewell; David Stanton; Jamie Adam; Adam Harbora; Ross Clemmow (female: 9%; male: 91%).

Nature of business: The company operates London City Airport.

Financial information

Year end	31/12/2020
Turnover	£27,690,000
Pre-tax profit	(£48,050,000)

UK employees: 2,000

Main locations: The airport is located in the Royal Docks in the Royal Borough of Newham.

Community involvement
The airport supports charities through its community fund and educational programmes.

London City Airport Community Fund (not a registered charity)
The fund's website states the following:

To qualify for any of the available Grants you will have to be a charity or not for profit organisation and your project is expected to adhere to the following criteria; London City Airports' community focus areas to improve the quality of life in local communities by either:
1 Building stronger, safer and healthier communities
2 Creating more sustainable and greener communities
3 Raising aspirations of East Londoners
4 Creating pathways into employment
Applications from only the local area are eligible for consideration, please see list below:
- Barking & Dagenham, Bexley, Epping Forest District Council
- Greenwich, Hackney, Havering, Newham, Lambeth, Lewisham
- Redbridge, Southwark, Tower Hamlets and Waltham Forest

Education
According to the airport website, its education programme aims to:

Raise levels of aspiration amongst young East Londoners and help them to develop key employability skills by engaging them creatively through a range of activities. These include tailored education programmes, career awareness initiatives,

and tours. The programmes are available for students in primary, secondary, and higher education.

In-kind support
According to the airport's 2020 annual report, it delivered 27,000 pieces of fruit to Newham-based charities during the year.

Employee-led support
Volunteering
Employees are offered two days per year to volunteer for community organisations in East London.

Employee fundraising
The airport has a longstanding relationship with Richard House Children's Hospice and staff regularly participate in various activities to raise funds for the hospice.

Applications
Community fund – applications can be made through the airport's website where the latest application deadlines can also be found.

Volunteering – if you would like the airport to support your organisation, email Anna Boss (Anna.Boss@londoncityairport.com).

Community contributions

Cash donations UK	£85,000

The airport's 2020 annual report states that total contributions for charitable purposes totalled £85,000.

London Luton Airport Ltd

Arts, culture and heritage, education and training, the environment, general charitable purposes, housing and homelessness, social welfare, sports and recreation

Company registration number: 2020381

Correspondent: Mark Turner, Chief Finance Officer, Hart House Business Centre, Kimpton Road, Luton LU2 0LA (tel: 01582 405100; email: communityupdate@ltn.aero or mark. turner@llal.org.uk; website: www.llal.org. uk/LLAL-CorporateSocialResponsibility. html)

Directors: Andrew Malcolm; Waheed Akbar; Javeria Hussain; Khtija Malik; Amy Nicholls; Tahmina Saleem; John Young; Lord McKenzie of Luton; Dr Romano Pagliari; Roy Davis (female: 40%; male: 60%).

Nature of business: London Luton Airport is an international airport located 1.5 miles east of Luton and 28 miles north of central London.

Financial information

Year end	31/03/2021
Turnover	£814,000
Pre-tax profit	(£138,178,000)

Main locations: The airport is based in Luton.

Community involvement

London Luton Airport Ltd (LLAL) provides support to the local community through its Community Funding Programme. The programme consists of four separate funds, each with a specific purpose. Financial support is given to voluntary and community groups providing essential services to the people of Luton and the surrounding areas. Luton Borough Council is the shareholder of LLAL and the airport shares the corporate objectives of its shareholder.

Partnership Fund

The company operates a partnership fund. This fund aims to provide sponsorship and donations to charitable organisations, having a major and key role in contributing to the delivery of priority outcomes in the medium- to long-term. Partnership organisations are chosen by the board of directors from a list of recommendations. In 2021, East Anglian Air Ambulance and Luton Foodbank were chosen as the company's charitable partners from 2021 to 2023.

Luton Community Fund (not a registered charity)

This fund provides small grants that are generally limited to one year. The fund aims to support community and voluntary activity in Luton. Assistance can be given for project work, running costs, support with rent, rates or room hire and capital investment. Funding from this fund may not be continuing; organisations applying are advised to demonstrate that they have explored the potential for finding alternative funding. Applications may also be required to secure matched funding from other sources, support capacity building and innovative ways of working, particularly in partnership with other organisations, and meet emerging or changing needs in the community. In 2021, the fund awarded £213,300 in grants to charitable organisations in the UK.

Near Neighbour Fund

This fund provides small grants that are limited to one year only. The fund aims to support community and voluntary organisations, activities and projects in communities neighbouring Luton, that are most affected by airport operations.

Enterprise Fund

This fund provides small grants that are also limited to one year only. The fund aims to support the start-up of small businesses, including social enterprises, in Luton with a particular focus being given to areas of significant deprivation.

In-kind support

According to the 2021 sustainability report, 218 crates of food and hygiene items worth £4,360 were donated to Luton Foodbank.

Employee-led support

In 2021, some employees volunteered at the local vaccination centre and at Luton Foodbank.

Commercially led support

According to the company's 2021 sustainability report, it sponsored two awards during the year: Community Interest and Love Luton. The awards recognised those in the Luton community that volunteered to support charities and local services in the area.

Exclusions

A detailed list of eligibility criteria and exclusions for both the Luton Community Fund and the Near Neighbour Fund can be found on the Bedfordshire and Luton Community Foundation's website.

Applications

Partnership Fund

For general information about this fund, contact mark.turner@llal.org.uk. Each theme has its own contact information, details of which can be found on the website.

Luton Community Fund

This fund is administered by the Bedfordshire and Luton Community Foundation. More information can be found at www.blcf.org.uk/central-beds/community-trust-fund.php. For more information, applicants can call 01582 522 422.

Near Neighbour Fund

This fund is administered by the Bedfordshire and Luton Community Foundation. Full guidelines and information on how to apply can be found at: www.blcf.org.uk/stevenage-aylesbury-vale-others/near-neighbours.php.

Enterprise Fund

This fund is administered by Wenta. For more information email: info@wenta.co.uk.

Community contributions

Cash donations UK	£8,332,000

According to the company's 2020/21 annual report, it donated a total of £8.33 million through its Community Funding Programme.

London Stock Exchange Group plc

Community enterprise and social entrepreneurship, education and training

Company registration number: 5369106

Correspondent: CSR Team, 10 Paternoster Square, London EC4M 7LS (tel: 020 7797 1000; website: www.lseg.com/about-lseg/lseg-foundation)

Directors: Don Robert; David Schwimmer; Anna Manz; Dominic Blakemore; Martin Brand; Erin Brown; Prof. Kathleen DeRose; Tsega Gebreyes; Cressida Hogg; Dr Val Rahmani; Douglas Steenland; Ashok Vaswani (female: 50%; male: 50%).

Nature of business: London Stock Exchange Group (LSEG) is an international markets infrastructure business. The group has a presence in several locations across the globe.

Financial information

Year end	31/12/2021
Turnover	£4,290,000,000
Pre-tax profit	£222,000,000

Total employees: 24,158

Main locations: The group is headquartered in the City of London.

Community involvement

LSEG supports programmes that are making a positive difference in the communities in which it has a presence. The majority of the group's charitable involvement is channelled through the London Stock Exchange Group Foundation, which was established in 2010 through the Charities Aid Foundation (CAF). Employees are also actively involved in their communities through the foundation's work.

London Stock Exchange Group (LSEG) Foundation

The foundation was established as the single-channel for the group's charitable giving and a focal point for employee engagement with charities. It provides support to the communities in which the group operates. According to the LSEG Corporate Sustainability Report for 2021, the foundation has three main sources of income:

- Employee donations and fundraising events
- LSEG plc donations
- Money raised through fines levied by LSEG

The foundation's giving is based on the group's brand values. Focus is given to projects that help young and disadvantaged people reach their full potential by developing life skills and business enterprises. The foundation also partners with local charities where it can have a long-lasting impact. In 2021, the foundation awarded grants totalling £1.13 million.

Charity partners

Global partner – The group has worked in partnership with UNICEF for over twenty years. Currently, it is supporting the charity's Zambian Girls 2030 project which aims to equip more than 11,000 girls in Zambia with employability skills and help them access formal employment. Support is also given to the UNICEF UK Children's Emergency Fund.

UK partner – In 2017, School-Home Support was announced as the group's UK charity partner. The charity provides support to families and children that face barriers to education and improves engagement in learning and attendance. The group supports the charity through donations, fundraising and volunteering.

In-kind support

The group offers in-kind donations, including free venue hire to charities in the UK and Italy.

Employee-led support

Fundraising

Employees take part in fundraising initiatives and provide one of the three principal sources of funding for the London Stock Exchange Group Foundation.

Volunteering

LSEG employees in the group's various global locations can take two days' paid leave a year to volunteer in their local communities.

LSEG Matching scheme

Money raised by employees through fundraising initiatives is doubled by the LSEG Foundation up to £2,000 per year per person.

According to the 2021 Sustainability Report, more than 400 charities were positively impacted through employee-matched fundraising and volunteering initiatives.

Applications

The LSEG website explains that the foundation's approach is to focus its charitable efforts on a small number of charities in order to make the biggest difference. More information can be found about the work carried out by the foundation by emailing LSEGFoundation@lseg.com.

Community contributions

Cash donations worldwide	£2,000,000

The London Stock Exchange Group's Corporate Sustainability Report for 2021 states that the group's total contribution was £2 million during the year. £1.93 million was awarded to the LSEG

Foundation and £242,000 to other charities.

We were unable to determine how much of the group's community investment was given in the UK.

LondonMetric Property plc

General charitable purposes, social welfare

Company registration number: 7124797

Correspondent: Charities and Communities Working Group, One Curzon Street, London W1J 5HB (tel: 020 7484 9000; email: info@ londonmetric.com; website: www. londonmetric.com)

Directors: Andrew Jones; Martin McGann; Patrick Vaughan; Rosalyn Wilton; James Dean; Andrew Livingston; Suzanne Avery; Robert Fowlds; Kitty Patmore; Alistair Elliott (female: 30%; male: 70%).

Nature of business: LondonMetric is a property development and investment company.

Financial information

Year end	31/03/2022
Turnover	£133,200,000
Pre-tax profit	£738,300,000

Total employees: 32

Main locations: The company has offices in London and Birmingham. It has properties in England, Scotland, Northern Ireland and Wales. For details of the whereabouts of properties, see the properties map on its website.

Community involvement

LondonMetric Property looks to make a positive contribution to the communities in which it operates. In recent years, the company established a Charity and Communities Working Group, which formalised the company's approach to community activities and charitable giving. Support is given in the form of cash donations, events, sponsorship and employee-led initiatives. According to its 2022 responsible business and ESG report, LondonMetric Property aims to allocate £100,000 each year for charitable giving.

In 2021/22, the company supported a number of charitable organisations including:

- LandAid – the company continues to support the property industry charity, donating £10,000 to it during 2021/22. Additionally, 85% of the company's employees took part in the charity's Steptober event.
- The Forest of Marston Vale – a community forest between Bedford and Milton Keynes. The company

funded a number of projects including improving footpaths, signage and seating.
- Food banks – the company supports local food banks. In 2021/22 it donated £6,000 to food banks in the local community.
- Project Turn-Over – a charity that supports vulnerable young people via three-month programmes combining rugby, sports and life skills.

The company also provides support to employee-chosen charitable causes, including Macmillan Cancer Support and kits for young football teams.

Employee-led support

Employees are encouraged to engage in local charity and community events. In 2021/22, five employees hosted an online teach-in for school pupils. The event, organised by Speakers for Schools, aimed to help students better understand what property companies do and how they can start a career in the property industry.

Commercially led support

According to its community policy, the company will sponsor local events and initiatives.

Applications

Contact the correspondent for further information.

Community contributions

Cash donations UK	£66,800

In 2021/22, the company made charitable donations totalling £66,800.

Lush Cosmetics Ltd

Animal welfare, the environment, human rights

Company registration number: 4162033

Correspondent: Charity Pot Team, 29 High Street, Poole, Dorset BH15 1AB (tel: 01202 641001; email: charitypot@ lush.co.uk; website: www.lush.co.uk/tag/ our-policies)

Directors: Mark Constantine, Margaret Constantine; Karl Bygrave (female: 33%; male: 67%).

Nature of business: Lush produces a range of cosmetic products and spa treatments.

Financial information

Year end	30/06/2021
Turnover	£73,170,000
Pre-tax profit	(£18,710,000)

UK employees: 4,057

Total employees: 13,652

Main locations: Lush is headquartered in Poole, Dorset and has stores throughout the UK. There are over 900 Lush stores in 49 countries worldwide.

Community involvement

Lush focuses its charitable giving on supporting small, grassroots organisations working in the areas of the environment, human rights and animal protection. Lush looks to support less popular causes and organisations using education, campaigns and activism as a way to address global issues. Aside from supporting registered charities, Lush also supports non-violent campaign groups and other organisations not registered with the Charity Commission. Lush prefers to support projects looking to create a long-term change that addresses the root causes of social issues. Funding is also given to projects that provide aid and support, such as an animal shelter or refugee support and advice groups. The majority of Lush's funds that are distributed to good causes are raised from the sale of its Charity Pot lotion.

The Re:FUND

According to the company's website, the fund is fully dedicated to funding regenerative projects in the following three fields:

- Protect habitats in partnership with land defenders.
- Regenerate land through meaningful livelihoods.
- Rewild ecosystems while strengthening community.

The biennial award, the Spring Prize, is part of this fund. The company awards £200,000 to groups working toward ecological and social regeneration.

The Lush Spring Prize

Launched in 2017 in a joint venture with Ethical Consumer, this prize for social and environmental regeneration awards those repairing the earth's damaged systems. It seeks to increase the capacity of communities and societies to thrive in harmony with nature and each other, building healthy and resilient ecosystems and livelihoods.

The Lush Prize

The Lush Prize offers a global prize fund to support initiatives to end or replace animal testing. It was launched in 2016 in partnership with Ethical Consumer. It is now a biennial event. In 2022 a total of £250,000 was donated to the winners. There are six award categories:

- Lobbying
- Training
- Public awareness
- Science
- Young researchers
- Political achievement

Charity Pot

Charity Pot is a Lush hand and body cream where 100% of all sales (minus local taxes) are distributed as grants, to groups working in the areas of:

- Animal protection
- The environment
- Human rights (including social justice, peace and equality)

Charity Pot grants range from £100, up to a maximum of £10,000 per project/application. The average Charity Pot grant is between £2,000 and £4,000. Organisations must have an annual income of less than £250,000 to apply.

In-kind support

Individual Lush shops donate unwanted products to charities in their local areas.

Employee-led support

Employees volunteer their time to help the company's charity partners. Staff frequently participate in volunteer days with Charity Pot partners local to their shops or offices.

Commercially led support

The company sells other products to raise money for charities and campaigns.

Campaign products

Campaign products are designed, produced and sold to raise money and awareness for specific causes. According to the company's 2020/21 annual report, a total of £595,000 was raised from various campaign products.

Exclusions

According to the funding guidelines available on its website, Lush does not support organisations that:

- Deny the human rights of others
- Are involved in cruelty/subjugation of animals (incl. farming, testing or research)
- Coerces or forces others to change their beliefs or proselytizes
- Harbour racism or prejudice
- Prevents or impedes the free-speech of others
- Judge others on anything other than their actions
- Have not made every effort to be environmentally responsible
- Promote/support violence, aggression or oppression towards others ([Lush] will only support direct action groups if they are non-violent)

Applications

Charity Pot grants

Applicants are advised to read the full guidelines available at: www.lush.com/uk/en/a/charity-pot-funding-guidelines.

Applicants can then fill out the online application form available at: https://form.jotformeu.com/LushCharityPot/charity-pot-grant-application.

Applications are accepted at any time and there are no cut-offs. However, you should allow at least three months from application to when you need the funds. Applications are assessed on a first-come, first-served basis; however, if your funding is exceptionally urgent, email: charitypot@lush.co.uk for advice.

Lush Spring Prize

The Lush Spring Prize accepts nominations from anywhere in the world. Full eligibility guidelines can be found at: https://springprize.org/regeneration.

The Lush Prize

The prizes are open to organisations, teams or individuals. For full eligibility guidelines, visit: https://lushprize.org.

Community contributions

Cash donations worldwide	£273,000

According to the 2020/21 annual report, Lush donated a total of £273,000 to charities and other good causes. A further £197,000 was committed to be paid out in 2021/22.

M&G plc

Education and training, housing and homelessness, social welfare, urban communities

Company registration number: 11444019

Correspondent: The Sustainability Team, 10 Fenchurch Avenue, London EC3M 5AG (email: info@mandg.co.uk; website: www.mandgplc.com/sustainability/sustainability-report)

Directors: Alan Porter; Clive Adamson; Edward Braham; Clare Chapman; Fiona Clutterbuck; Kathryn McLeland; Paolo Rossi; Debasish Sanyal; Clare Thompson; Massimo Tosato (female: 40%; male: 60%).

Nature of business: M&G plc is a global investment management company.

Financial information

Year end	31/12/2021
Pre-tax profit	£721,000,000

Main locations: M&G plc has offices worldwide. It is headquartered in London and also has UK offices in Chelmsford.

Community involvement

M&G plc's community giving has three strategic pillars: urban regeneration, economic empowerment, and skills and education.

Under the urban regeneration pillar the group has been working with The Tree Council on a programme to plant trees, orchards and fruiting hedgerows in UK schools that would benefit from them most. The group has also been working with Habitat for Humanity to establish a coalition of the public, voluntary and private sectors to re-purpose empty commercial and office spaces to address the social housing crisis in the UK and across Europe.

Under its skills and education programme the group has supported Age

UK's Building Resilience programme. The programme provides a detailed, local advice and information service delivered for older, vulnerable people in need across the UK.

M&G Community Fund (not a registered charity)

The Community Fund is an annual grant programme that supports local charities and projects with small donations. The fund's committee includes 40 employees from across M&G plc's locations. Since its launch in 2019 the fund has awarded grants to almost 200 charities worldwide.

Employee-led support

In 2021, 862 employees gave 7,280 hours of volunteering time. Employees also donated £168,700 through payroll giving.

Applications

Contact your local M&G plc office for further information.

Community contributions

Cash donations worldwide	£3,800,000
Total contributions worldwide	£4,600,000

M&G plc's total community investment for 2021 was £4.6 million, of which £3.8 million was cash. A further £800,000 was donated in in-kind contributions which included 7,280 hours of costed employee volunteering.

Mactaggart and Mickel Group Ltd

 Education and training, general charitable purposes, sports and recreation

Company registration number: SC326355

Correspondent: The Building Communities Fund, 1 Atlantic Quay, 1 Robertson Street, Glasgow G2 8JB (tel: 0141 332 0001; email: contact form on the website; website: https://bcf.macmicgroup.co.uk)

Directors: Alan Hartley; Andrew Mickel; Craig Ormond; David Shaw; Ed Monaghan; Paul McAninch; Ross Mickel (male: 100%).

Nature of business: Mactaggart and Mickel specialises in the building of new homes.

Financial information

Year end	30/04/2021
Turnover	£73,200,000
Pre-tax profit	£5,330,000

UK employees: 200

Main locations: The group's head office is in Glasgow. It mainly operates in Glasgow, Ayrshire, Edinburgh, the Lothians and Oxfordshire.

Community involvement

Mactaggart and Mickel has a long history of supporting good causes and initiatives in areas local to its developments in Ayrshire, Glasgow, Edinburgh, the Lothians and Oxfordshire.

The group created its Building Communities Fund (not a registered charity) to deliver on its charitable objectives. Charities, community groups, schools and sports teams operating within five miles of the group's developments can apply for funding towards equipment, travel costs and so on.

Recent beneficiaries include Cathcart Youth Ministry Partnership, Children's Health Scotland, Heddington Rugby Football Club, Roslin Village Group and RSPB Scotland.

Applications

Applications to the Building Communities Fund can be made using a form on the group's website.

Community contributions

Cash donations UK	£54,500

The group declared charitable donations totalling £54,500 in 2020/21.

Man Group plc

🔍 Education and training, literacy

Company registration number: 127570

Correspondent: The CSR Team, Riverbank House, 2 Swan Lane, London EC4R 3AD (email: charitable.trust@man.com; website: www.man.com/corporate-responsibility)

Directors: John Cryan; Anne Wade; Antoine Forterre; Ceci Kurzman; Dame Katherine Barker; Jacqueline Hunt; Lucinda Bell; Luke Ellis; Richard Berliand; Alberto Musalem; Elizabeth Woods (female: 54%; male: 46%).

Nature of business: The group is a global provider of alternative investment products and solutions.

Financial information

Year end	31/12/2021
Turnover	£1,245,787,580
Pre-tax profit	£496,300,000

Main locations: The group has offices in London, Oxford, York and Dublin. It has a total of 16 offices around the world.

Community involvement

Man Group's charitable activities are channelled through its corporate charity, Man Group plc Charitable Trust (Charity Commission no. 275386).

Employee-led support

The trust's 'ManKind' initiative provides volunteering opportunities to staff. In 2021 staff were offered £400 each to donate to a food bank or a charity focused on homelessness or poverty in their community

Through its charity, the group provides matched funding to employees undertaking fundraising efforts, as well as a Give As You Earn scheme.

Applications

For further information see the company's corporate charity entry.

Corporate charity

Man Group plc Charitable Trust (Charity Commission no. 275386) – see entry on page 253.

Community contributions

Cash donations UK	£3,100,000

According to the trust's 2021 accounts, it received a donation of £3.1 million from the group.

Note: the group's financial information has been converted from USD using the exchange rate at the time of writing (November 2022). The group is registered in Jersey.

Manchester Airport Group plc

🔍 Arts, culture and heritage, community services and development, education and training, the environment

Company registration number: 8353309

Correspondent: Vanda Murray, Chair of CSR Committee, 6th Floor, Olympic House, Manchester Airport, Manchester M90 1QX (website: www.magairports.com/responsible-business/our-responsibility-plans)

Directors: Sir Adrian Montague; Charlie Cornish; Ken O'Toole; Jenny Cochrane; Jan Bramall; Jon Wragg (female: 33%; male: 67%).

Nature of business: The group is comprised of Manchester Airport, East Midlands Airport and London Stansted Airport.

Financial information

Year end	31/03/2021
Turnover	£178,600,000
Pre-tax profit	(£477,600,000)

UK employees: 40,000

Main locations: The group's airports are in the East Midlands, Greater Manchester and Stansted Mountfitchet.

Community involvement

The group has a long-standing commitment to supporting charities, groups, people and projects in the areas in which it operates. The group is particularly interested in education, addressing the skills gap, the environment, and arts and culture.

Each airport owned by the group has its own designated fund, which distributes funds for local projects. See the websites for Manchester Airport, London Stansted Airport and East Midlands Airport for information on specific community funds.

Employee-led support

Employees are encouraged to volunteer their skills in areas such as engineering, accountancy, retail and human resources to local community initiatives. In 2020/21, staff volunteered over 23,000 hours to their local communities.

Commercially led support

The group operates an arts sponsorship programme, which is committed to enriching culture within its operational areas. The approach of the programme is to support a wide range of schemes (from high profile organisations to smaller community initiatives) and to promote art forms to those who would not normally have access to them.

In 2020, the group launched its first ever group-wide Christmas collection. The 'Give and Go' campaign is in partnership with local food banks and charity support groups, and according to the group's 2020/21 Corporate Social Responsibility Report, employees volunteered and donated food and toys to over 1,000 people for this campaign.

Exclusions

Refer to your local airport's website for exclusions.

Applications

Contact your local airport for information on how to apply for funding.

Arts sponsorship applications can be made at: www.manchesterairport.co.uk/ community/working-in-our-community/ sponsoring-the-arts.

Corporate charity

Manchester Airport Community Trust Fund (Charity Commission no. 1071703) – see entry on page 254.

Community contributions

Cash donations UK		£253,000

According to the group's 2020/21 CSR report, £253,000 was awarded to over 130 local projects.

Manchester City Football Club Ltd

Education and training, health, social welfare, sports and recreation

Company registration number: 40946

Correspondent: City in the Community, Etihad Stadium, Etihad Campus, Manchester M11 3FF (tel: 0161 438 7712; email: citc@mcfc.co.uk; website: www.mancity.com/community)

Directors: Khaldoon Al Mubarak; Martin Edelman; Alberto Galassi; John Macbeath; Simon Pearce; Abdulla Khouri; Mohamed Al Mazrouei (male: 100%).

Nature of business: Manchester City FC is a professional football club competing in the Premier League.

Financial information

Year end	30/06/2021
Turnover	£569,850,000
Pre-tax profit	£9,800,000

Total employees: 509

Main locations: The football club is based in Manchester.

Community involvement

The club gives support through its corporate charity, City in the Community (Charity Commission no. 1139229), and makes direct in-kind donations to charities.

City in the Community

Established in 1986, the club's corporate charity delivers a wide range of programmes, focusing on three key areas: health, inclusion and education.

Examples of programmes run by the charity include:

- Kicks: an outreach programme providing free evening, weekend and school holiday provision in the most deprived communities in Greater Manchester
- City Lifestyles: a programme delivered in schools to help children develop social skills, practical cooking skills and hand hygiene knowledge
- Women and Girls Football project: free football training, leadership and mentoring opportunities for girls and young women across Greater Manchester

In-kind support

The club may provide charities with signed merchandise, tickets to matches and stadium tours upon request.

Exclusions

The club does not provide monetary donations or sponsorship to charities upon request.

Applications

Requests for in-kind donations can be made on the club's website using an online form. All other enquiries should be directed to City in the Community at citc@mcfc.co.uk.

Community contributions

Cash donations UK		£3,790,000

The club's 2020/21 annual report states donations to UK charities totalled £3.79 million. This figure includes £2.6 million supporting youth and community development via the Premier League.

Manchester United Ltd

Community services and development, education and training, health, sports and recreation

Company registration number: 2570509

Correspondent: The Manchester United Foundation, Old Trafford, Manchester M16 0RA (tel: 0161 868 8600; email: enquiries@mufoundation.org or enquiries@manutd.co.uk; website: www. mufoundation.org/en/Charity/United-for-UNICEF)

Directors: Avram Glazer; Joel Glazer; Edward Woodward; Richard Arnold; Cliff Baty; Kevin Glazer; Bryan Glazer; Darcie Glazer Kassewitz; Edward Glazer; Robert Leitão; Manu Sawhney; John Hooks (female: 8%; male: 92%).

Nature of business: Manchester United is a professional football club competing in the English Premier League.

Financial information

Year end	30/06/2021
Pre-tax profit	£10,810,000

Main locations: The club supports charitable causes worldwide; however, the majority of its community projects are delivered within Greater Manchester.

Community involvement

The club's community activities are mainly delivered through its corporate charity the Manchester United Foundation, which works with locals and charity partners to deliver a wide-range of education and sport programmes. Support is also provided through in-kind donations.

The Manchester United Foundation (Charity Commission no. 1118310)

According to its website, the foundation 'uses football to engage and inspire young people to build a better life for themselves and unite the communities in which they live'. To achieve its objectives, the foundation creates and develops strategic partnerships with local, regional and national organisations working in the areas of health, education and inclusion.

Full details of all of the foundation's current programmes are available on its website.

Charity partners

Since 1999, the club has been a partner of UNICEF. Each year the club hosts a gala dinner, attended by the first-team players and management staff, to raise funds for its charity partner and its corporate charity.

The Sir Bobby Charlton Foundation is the official charity partner of the club. The foundation supports communities affected by conflict.

In-kind support

The club donates shirts, pennants and photographs signed by its players to charities and organisations for their own fundraising and events. Under this initiative, over 1,000 charities and causes are supported each year.

Applications

Contact the correspondent for further information. Applications for signed items can be made via the Manchester United Foundation's website. .

Community contributions

The club did not declare a figure for its charitable contributions in its accounts.

The Manchester United Foundation states in its most recent accounts:

> The Trustees are grateful to Manchester United Football Club Limited for Gifts in Kind for the services provided in relation to human resources, information technology, payroll and maintenance, together with the provision of kit and equipment, office facilities, goodwill payments to staff and a discretionary staff bonus. This equates to an estimated monetary value of £625,400.

The Mansfield Building Society

Animal welfare, arts, culture and heritage, education and training, the environment, general charitable purposes, health, housing and homelessness, social welfare

Correspondent: Community Support Scheme, Regent House, Regent Street, Mansfield, Nottinghamshire NG18 1SS (email: enquiries@mansfieldbs.co.uk; website: https://mansfieldbs.co.uk)

Directors: Alison Chmiel; Paul Wheeler; Daniel Jones; Nicholas Baxter; Colin Bradley; Lucy McClements; Keith McLeod; Rachel Howarth (female: 38%; male: 63%).

Nature of business: The Mansfield Building Society is an independent mutual building society based in Nottinghamshire.

Financial information

Year end	31/12/2021
Pre-tax profit	£2,879,000

UK employees: 82

Main locations: The society has branches in Nottinghamshire and Derbyshire.

Community involvement

The society supports communities in which it has a presence through its Community Support Scheme and employee volunteering. The society also partners with charities in the local area. The society has a corporate charity, the Mansfield Building Society Charitable Trust (Charity Commission no. 1177151).

Community Support Scheme

The society offers a Community Support Scheme which invites applications for funding of around £100 to £1,000 from charitable groups in Nottinghamshire and Derbyshire that are in need of financial assistance. The society considers applications in several different categories, including those that:

- Work in partnership with organisations assisting people who are disadvantaged
- Promote and encourage sporting activities
- Promote and encourage activities in the arts
- Support education and development
- Benefit the environment

Partnerships

The society's charity partner in 2022 was Mind Nottinghamshire.

In-kind support

The society encourages staff to participate in the Work in the Community Scheme through granting two days' paid leave each year for employees to volunteer.

Employee-led support

Employees fundraise for the society's Charity of the Year. In 2021 employees reached the fundraising target of £5,000 through events such as sponsored walks and a row across the English Channel.

Commercially led support

In 2017, the society launched a range of Community Saver accounts linked to the society's trust. Every year, the society will contribute to the trust based on balances held in the Community Saver account range.

Applications

Community Support Scheme

To apply to the society's Community Support Scheme, applicants should complete the application form found on the society's website. The scheme only accepts applications from groups in Nottinghamshire or Derbyshire.

Partnerships

Contact the correspondent for further information.

Corporate charity

The Mansfield Building Society Charitable Trust (Charity Commission no. 1177151) – see entry on page 255.

Community contributions

Cash donations UK	£98,100

The society's Community Support Scheme contributions totalled £21,600 in 2021. The society also donated £76,500 to the Mansfield Building Society Charitable Trust. We have taken the total of £98,100 as our figure for the society's cash donations.

Marks and Spencer Group plc

General charitable purposes, social welfare

Company registration number: 214436

Correspondent: Carmel McQuaid, Head of Sustainable Business (Plan A), Waterside House, 35 North Wharf Street, London W2 1NW (tel: 020 7935 4422; website: https://corporate. marksandspencer.com/sustainability)

Directors: Archie Norman; Eoin Tonge; Andy Halford; Andrew Fisher; Justin King; Fiona Dawson; Evelyn Bourke; Katie Bickerstaffe; Stuart Machin; Ronan Dunne; Nick Folland; Tamara Ingram; Sapna Sood (female: 38%; male: 62%).

Nature of business: The principal activities of the group are retailing clothes, beauty products, home products and food, and providing financial services.

Financial information

Year end	28/03/2022
Turnover	£10,885,100,000
Pre-tax profit	£391,000,000

Main locations: The group's headquarters is in London. It has stores throughout the UK and overseas.

Community involvement

Marks and Spencer (M&S) supports charities in the areas local to its stores and, at a corporate level, builds strategic partnerships with several fundraising partners. M&S stores can select a 'Local Charity of the Year' to raise funds for. In total, across all stores, this raises approximately £1 million each year. Stores also donate food and clothes to local and national charities. Employees and customers contribute to fundraising, and employees are supported in their community involvement through volunteering time, payroll giving and matched funding initiatives.

Partnerships

The group works with selected charities, offering money, specialist skills, awareness raising and space in stores. In the UK, M&S' national funding partners are:

▸ Breast Cancer Now
▸ Great Ormond Street Hospital Charity
▸ Macmillan Cancer Support
▸ NHS Charities Together
▸ Royal British Legion
▸ Shelter
▸ Together for Short Lives

Marks and Start

Marks and Start is the group's employability programme. It helps people who face barriers getting into work to gain skills and experience through work placements. Single parents, people with disabilities or health conditions, people who are homeless or at risk of homelessness, and disadvantaged young people are eligible to undertake a two to four-week placement along with coaching, enabling them to acquire retail experience.

Make Your Mark

This programme was launched in 2013 and saw the group, together with The Prince's Trust, scale up the existing young people's element of Marks and Start to help unemployed 18 to 24-year-olds, supporting around 1,500 young people each year.

In-kind support

The group manages a nationwide food redistribution scheme which connects its stores with local food charities through the platform Neighbourly.

Employee-led support

Volunteering

M&S has a volunteer week each year. In 2021/22, between 4,000 and 5,000 colleagues volunteered with approximately 450 community organisations across the UK. The group also operates a payroll giving scheme, and groups of employees (of five or more) who are fundraising can apply to have funds matched. The group also offers one day's paid volunteering leave each year to all its employees.

Commercially led support

Sparks card

On registering for the Sparks loyalty card scheme, customers can choose a cause from a selected list of 35 charities. Each time they make a transaction at M&S, their Sparks card can be scanned and M&S makes a donation of 1p to their chosen charity.

The group also ran 'double donation' periods throughout the year, for example

during Black History Month, when the group doubled donations to Sparks partners Blueprint for All and The Black Curriculum.

In 2021/22, the Sparks loyalty card scheme raised £2 million for charity.

Charity products

M&S also sells specific products from which a proportion of the sales goes to charity. For example, 10% of sales of the M&S post-surgery bra are donated to Breast Cancer Now and 10% of sales of certain food lines are donated to the charities Shelter and Together for Short Lives. In 2021/22, £1.6 million was raised through sales of charity products.

Macmillan Cancer Support

In 2021/22, the group was again the headline sponsor for Macmillan's biggest coffee morning.

Ukraine

Through till-point donations, M&S customers donated £1.7 million to UNICEF UK's Ukraine Appeal by March 2022.

Exclusions

According to the group's website, M&S stores are not able to support:

▸ Personal appeals on behalf of individual people, including overseas trips
▸ Advertising or goodwill messages
▸ Political parties
▸ Third party fundraising on behalf of a charity
▸ Religious bodies, except where the project provides non-denominational, non-sectarian support for the benefit of a project
▸ Supplying clothing, other than in exceptional circumstances

Applications

Small store-led donations

Each store has a limited budget from which small donations of up to £50 can be made in support of local community causes. The M&S website advises interested organisations to visit their local store and ask to speak with a manager.

For all other enquiries, contact the correspondent for further information.

Community contributions

Total contributions UK	£5,200,000

According to the Marks and Spencer 2022 sustainability report, the group made community contributions totalling £5.2 million in the UK.

An additional £4 million was raised by employees, customers and suppliers and this amount has not been included in the total for contributions.

Marsh Ltd

Community services and development, education and training, emergency response/relief, general charitable purposes

Company registration number: 1507274

Correspondent: Helen Lam, Head of Social Impact, 1 Tower Place West, Tower Place, London EC3R 5BU (tel: 020 7357 1000; website: www.marsh.com/uk/about-marsh/corporate-social-responsibility.html)

Directors: Jane Barker; James Boyce; Mark Chessher; Thomas Colraine; Jeremiah Flahive; Alistair Fraser-Hawkins; Adrian Girling; Anthony Gruppo; John Hirst; Alisa King; Christopher Lay; Paul Moody; James Nash; Roy White (female: 14%; male: 86%).

Nature of business: Marsh is a global provider of insurance broking and risk management services with a presence in more than 130 countries. The company is a wholly owned subsidiary of Marsh and McLennan Companies, Inc., incorporated in Delaware, USA.

Financial information

Year end	31/12/2021
Turnover	£1,194,000,000
Pre-tax profit	£260,000,000

Main locations: The company has offices throughout the UK.

Community involvement

The theme of Marsh Ltd's and its parent company's (Marsh and McLennan Companies, MMC) corporate social responsibility programmes is 'People and Communities at Risk'. According to Marsh's UK website, philanthropy and employee volunteering are two of the central elements of its CSR programmes.

Donations: Marsh partner charities

The company administers its charitable donations programme centrally. It establishes multi-year partnerships with six UK charities and agrees with each at the beginning of its involvement a specific project or activity that its donation will fund. Marsh then works with its charity to ensure the project or activity is achieved.

Partnerships

Marsh's parent company and the British Red Cross teamed up in 2016 for a five-year strategic partnership. The British Red Cross website states that the two organisations work together through fundraising, volunteering and business collaboration.

Following the conclusion of the five-year partnership, Marsh Ltd has selected Ambitious About Autism as its new charity partner.

National charity beneficiaries for 2016–22 were: Apps for Good, Business in the Community, Help Musicians UK, The Centre of Social Justice, The Silver Line and Tommy's.

Employee-led support

Volunteering

Employees are involved in a range of volunteering activities within their communities. The company's website states:

> Support varies from country to country and is demonstrated in a variety of ways, including the provision of a day's paid leave to assist on a community project and having a portion of employee's charitable fundraising matched by the company.

Matched giving

Marsh supports employee donations to charities by matching up to $1,000 (or equivalent) per person, per year.

Payroll giving

Employees are able to contribute to charities of their choice through the Give As You Earn scheme. Payroll donations are topped up by 10% by Marsh.

Applications

Marsh's charitable donations programme is administered centrally. Contact the correspondent for further information.

Community contributions

We were unable to determine a figure for the company's charitable giving due to it ceasing to declare the amount in its accounts.

Marshall of Cambridge (Holdings) Ltd

Community services and development, education and training, formal sciences, general charitable purposes, health, religion, social welfare, technology and engineering

Company registration number: 2051460

Correspondent: Julie Ingham, CSR Team, Airport House, The Airport, Newmarket Road, Cambridge CB5 8RY (tel: 01223 373737; website: www.marshallgroup.co.uk)

Directors: Alex Dorrian; Kathy Jenkins; Roger Hardy; Justin Read; Doug Baxter; Julie Baddeley; James Buxton; Jonathan Flint (female: 25%; male: 75%).

Nature of business: Marshall of Cambridge is the private holding company of the Marshall family. The Marshall group operates in four business sectors and has three wholly owned businesses – Marshall Aerospace and Defence Group, Marshall Fleet Solutions and Marshall Group Property. It is also a majority shareholder of Marshall Motor

Holdings plc, an independent public company.

Financial information

Year end	31/12/2020
Turnover	£2,488,114,000
Pre-tax profit	£30,460,000

Total employees: 6,256

Main locations: The group is headquartered in Cambridge.

Community involvement

Marshall of Cambridge (Marshall) looks to make an active contribution in the communities in which it operates and principally in the area surrounding its group head office in Cambridge. Marshall's 'Code of Business Ethics' policy explains that support in the form of cash and in-kind donations is directed 'primarily to causes with educational, engineering and scientific objectives, as well as to social objectives connected with our business and our place in the wider community'.

STEM Launch Pad

In 2015, Marshall established LaunchPad, a programme aimed at encouraging more young people between the ages of 8 and 18 to make decisions that could result in opportunities for careers in engineering and related industries. The programme is delivered through local schools in the Cambridge area and is led by a group of young engineers and apprentices from Marshall. Participants benefitted from talks from LaunchPad ambassadors, visits to Marshall and various engineering-themed activities and competitions. In 2020, the programme hosted 170 events and reached over 6,200 students.

Employee-led support

The group's website states:

> We are proud to support the many varied activities pursued by our employees. From bike rides, marathons, sponsored walks, Macmillan Cancer Support coffee mornings, to name but a few, our teams have raised and continue to raise thousands for many worthy causes.

According to the 2020 annual report, the group also encourages employees to participate in local community and charitable activities.

Applications

Contact the correspondent for further information.

Corporate charity

D. G. Marshall of Cambridge Trust (Charity Commission no. 286468) – see entry on page 255.

Community contributions

Cash donations UK	£154,000

In 2020, the group made charitable donations of £154,000, of which

£100,000 was donated to the group's corporate charity, the D. G. Marshall of Cambridge Trust (Charity Commission no. 286468).

Marston's plc

General charitable purposes

Company registration number: 31461

Correspondent: CSR Team, Marston's House, Brewery Road, Wolverhampton, West Midlands WV1 4JT (email: online contact form; website: www.marstons.co.uk/responsibility/community)

Directors: William Rucker; Hayleigh Lupino; Andrew Andrea; Anne-Marie Brennan; Matthew Roberts; Bridget Lea; Octavia Morley (female: 57%; male: 43%).

Nature of business: Marston's is a British brewery, pub and hotel operator. It operates over 1,000 pubs in the UK.

Financial information

Year end	20/12/2021
Turnover	£401,700,000
Pre-tax profit	£171,100,000

Total employees: 12,000

Main locations: Marston's is headquartered in Wolverhampton. There is a local pub finder facility on the Marston's website (www.marstons.co.uk/pubs/finder).

Community involvement

Marston's supports good causes in its local communities through a combination of donations, its corporate charities and supporting its employees' fundraising efforts.

Corporate donations

Marston's makes donations to charities that align with its business.

The company makes an annual donation to Pub is the Hub, a not-for-profit organisation that helps rural pubs adapt and survive under changing economic pressures.

Marston's is a founder patron of the Youth Zone (The Way) in Wolverhampton. The charity offers recreational, sports and developmental activities for over 2,000 young people. In 2019, Marston's took part in the charity's Get a Job Week to provide work experience opportunities for schoolchildren.

Charitable trusts

Marston's Inns and Taverns Charitable Trust (not a registered charity) is funded by donations from the company and its employees. Through the trust, employee fundraising efforts are matched.

Alcohol awareness

Marston's campaigns for responsible retailing of alcohol and supports education to encourage responsible consumption. The company is a corporate donor to alcohol education charity, Drinkaware.

Employee-led support

Community Heroes Week

The company runs Community Heroes Week, a fundraiser that takes place at the end of April. During the week, Marston's offices, breweries and pubs take part in fundraising activities such as car washes, bake sales, sponsored walks and many more. The money raised during the week is donated to different charities chosen by the head office and regional teams. In 2020/21 the Community Heroes Week was paused due to the COVID-19 pandemic and according to the 2021 annual report, the company will review its strategy for charitable donations in 2022.

Payroll giving

According to the website, employees give to the Marston's Inns and Taverns Charitable Trust voluntarily through their 'salary credit'.

Applications

Contact the correspondent for further information.

Community contributions

The company's 2020/21 annual report did not declare a figure for charitable donations.

Dr. Martens plc

Anti-racism, LGBTQ+ rights, mental health and well-being, social justice

Company registration number: 12960219

Correspondent: The Sustainability Team, 28 Jamestown Road, Camden, London NW1 7BY (email: sustainability@drmartens.com; website: www.drmartensplc.com/sustainability)

Directors: Emily Reichwald; Yasmin Alhadeef; Paul Mason; Jon Mortimore; Onyeije Nwokorie; Robyn Perriss; Ian Rogers; Lynne Weedall; Kenneth Wilson (female: 44%; male: 56%).

Nature of business: Dr. Martens plc produces footwear.

Financial information

Year end	31/03/2022
Turnover	£773,000,000
Pre-tax profit	£70,900,000

Main locations: Dr. Martens plc has UK offices in London and Northampton.

Community involvement

The group supports causes that work to advance social justice issues including support for anti-racism, LGBTQ+ rights and mental health initiatives. In 2021/22

it supported a number of global charities through donations including The Trevor Project in the USA, Albert Kennedy Trust, Le Refuge and Jugend gegen Aids in EMEA and ReBit in the Asia-Pacific region.

Dr. Martens Foundation (Charity Commission no. 1194513)

The foundation was established in 2021 and supports causes which exist to advance social justice worldwide.

Employee-led support

Employees are given two days' volunteering allowance each year which they can use to support a charity of their choice.

Applications

Contact the correspondent for further information.

Corporate charity

Dr. Martens Foundation (Charity Commission no. 1194513) – see entry on page 256.

Community contributions

We were unable to determine a figure for the group's charitable contributions for 2021/22.

Mazars LLP

Community services and development, general charitable purposes, social welfare

Company registration number: OC308299

Correspondent: CSR Team, Tower Bridge House, St Katherine's Way, London E1W 1DD (tel: 020 7063 4000; website: www.mazars.co.uk/Home/About-us/Corporate-Responsibility)

Nature of business: Mazars specialises in audit, tax and advisory services around the world.

Financial information

Year end	31/08/2021
Turnover	£234,000,000
Pre-tax profit	£44,000,000

Total employees: 2,339

Main locations: Mazars operates some 300 offices globally, 17 of which are based in the UK.

Community involvement

Mazars LLP wishes to make a positive contribution to the communities in which it operates. Each year the firm donates a proportion of its profits to a range of charities. The firm also engages in charitable activity through its corporate charity, Mazars Charitable Trust (Charity Commission no. 1150459) which it funds. The firm also supports employee fundraising efforts and offers pro bono services.

Charities of the year

Each year, Mazars LLP nominates new national charity partners. In 2021, the firm partnered with Young Minds, a youth mental health charity, as well as Carers Trust, Samaritans and Refuge. The Mazars LLP Sustainability Report 2021 states the firm has a specific focus on skills-based volunteering, alongside its donations to the Mazars Charitable Trust.

The firm also partnered with Young Enterprise, with members from across all of Mazars LLP's offices in the UK volunteering their time to mentor young people in schools local to the firm's areas of operation.

Employee-led support

The firm's volunteering initiative, Mazars Days, allows employees to spend one workday a year participating in community projects.

Employees across the globe are encouraged to take part in volunteering initiatives as well as fundraising. The firm's 2021 sustainability report notes the various ways employees raised funds or volunteered, including:

- Partnership with Young Enterprise: Mazars LLP members volunteer their time in local schools to deliver mentoring sessions to students.
- Notes of Positivity: in 2021, employees of the firm wrote over 300 letters to care home residents who were experiencing isolation due to the COVID-19 pandemic.
- Movember: during the year, employees raised over £22,500 for Movember, with 180 employees walking over 9,000 kilometres collectively.

Applications

Contact the correspondent for further information.

Corporate charity

Mazars Charitable Trust (Charity Commission no. 1150459) – see entry on page 256.

Community contributions

Cash donations UK	£362,000

Mazars LLP did not declare its cash donations or total contributions for the year. The Mazars Charitable Trust annual report 2020/21 notes that it received £362,000 from Mazars LLP. We have taken this figure to be the firm's cash donations for the year.

Sir Robert McAlpine Ltd

Education and training, general charitable purposes, health

Company registration number: 566823

Correspondent: Simon Richards, Sustainability Director, Eaton Court, Maylands Avenue, Hemel Hempstead, Hertfordshire HP2 7TR (tel: 0333 566 3444; email: information@srm.com; website: www.srm.com)

Directors: Edward McAlpine; Hector McAlpine; Paul Hamer; Leighton More; Karen Brookes; Alison Cox; Lynda Thwaite; Steve Hudson; Tony Gates; Mark Gibson; Ian Cheung; Andrew Hunter (female: 25%; male: 75%).

Nature of business: The company provides building construction, civil engineering, design and project development services.

Financial information

Year end	31/10/2021
Turnover	£937,160,000
Pre-tax profit	£9,180,000

Total employees: 2,158

Main locations: The company's head office is in Hemel Hempstead. It also has offices across the UK.

Community involvement

The company provides support to its local communities through donations, volunteering, fundraising and via its corporate charities, The Robert McAlpine Foundation (Charity Commission no. 226646) and The McAlpine Educational Endowment (Charity Commission no. 313156).

Partnership

In 2016 the company committed to raising at least £1 million for Maggie's Cancer Care Centres over ten years. The charity provides free cancer support and information in centres across the UK and online. As well as this, each year the company selects other charities to support through fundraising activities.

Strong Foundations grants

To celebrate its 150th anniversary in 2019, the company provided funding to charitable projects across the UK. As a result of its success, in 2020 the company launched the Strong Foundations grants programme to support grassroots initiatives and charitable organisations, working in partnership with social investment enterprise, Semble, using its ActionFunder platform. The scheme was launched in eight locations across the country: Bristol, London, Oxford, Edinburgh, Manchester, Knutsford, West Hyde and Kettering. In total, the company provided £100,000 in 2020/21 to 40 community projects across the

country. Recipients ranged from organisations working with those with dementia, to groups supporting refugees, victims of domestic abuse and older people, as well as a variety of youth programmes and outdoor projects.

The McAlpine Educational Endowment

The McAlpine Educational Endowment provides bursaries to individual children for educational purposes. The charity's principal source of funding is donations from Sir Robert McAlpine Ltd and investment income.

Education

The company often engages with local schools and colleges to provide activities for students. In addition to employees visiting schools, students are regularly invited to company sites to gain first-hand experience of the construction industry.

Employee-led support

Employees regularly take part in fundraising activities. For example, in 2022, a team of colleagues took part in a sponsored abseil off the ArcelorMittal Orbit Tower in London to raise money for ParalympicsGB.

Commercially led support

The company is a founding partner of the Supply Chain Sustainability School (SCSS) – a free online educational tool for the registered members of the company's supply chain.

Applications

Contact the correspondent for further information.

Corporate charity

The Robert McAlpine Foundation (Charity Commission no. 226646) – see entry on page 256.

Community contributions

Cash donations UK	£108,000

The 2020/21 sustainability report states that the company donated over £108,000 to charitable projects across the UK. We were unable to determine a figure for the company's total community contributions.

McCain Foods (GB) Ltd

Community services and development, education and training, the environment, health, sports and recreation

Company registration number: 733218

Correspondent: Community Team, Havers Hill, Scarborough, North Yorkshire YO11 3BS (tel: 01723 584141; email: online contact form; website: www.mccain.co.uk/about-us)

Directors: Andrew Bates; Alan Bridges; Mark Hodge; Andrew Hoff; Richard

Jones; Allison McCain; Bobby Puri; Howard Snape; Helen Watts; James Young (female: 20%; male: 80%).

Nature of business: McCain manufactures and supplies frozen and ambient potato products.

Financial information

Year end	30/06/2021
Turnover	£528,776,000
Pre-tax profit	£50,236,000

UK employees: 1,284

Main locations: McCain's UK head office is in Scarborough, North Yorkshire. It has UK factories in Hull, Peterborough and Wolverhampton, and a potato seed business in Montrose, Scotland.

Community involvement

McCain supports charities and community organisations in the communities in which it operates. Its community support programme is focused on the following areas: educating the next generation, encouraging healthy, active lifestyles and reducing food waste.

As part of a commitment to promote healthy lifestyles, McCain supports a range of initiatives such as encouraging schoolchildren to grow their own potato crops through the Agriculture and Horticulture Development Board's Grow Your Own Potatoes Scheme and helping to organise the annual McCain Yorkshire Coast 10k and Fun Run.

In 2021, McCain partnered with Family Fund, a charity that helps families in the UK with children with disabilities or serious illness, and has announced a donation of £1 million by 2023.

In-kind support

The company has an ongoing partnership with food re-distribution charity FareShare to which it donates products.

Employee-led support

The company runs 'McCain Community Stars', a grant scheme that supports employee volunteering. No further details as to how this scheme operates were available.

Exclusions

McCain cannot provide individual product donations.

Applications

Contact the correspondent for further information.

Community contributions

Cash donations UK	£93,600

According to the 2020/21 annual report, the company made charitable donations of £93,600.

McDonald's Restaurants Ltd

Community services and development, education and training, the environment, health, sports and recreation

Company registration number: 1002769

Correspondent: CSR Team, 11–59 High Road, East Finchley, London N2 8AW (website: www.mcdonalds.com/gb/en-gb/our-plan-for-change/communities.html)

Directors: Sarah Cole; Rebecca Dodd; Michelle Graham-Clare; Mark Kiernan; Alistair Macrow; John Park; Gareth Pearson (female: 43%; male: 57%).

Nature of business: The principal activity of the company is the franchising and operation of a chain of quick-service restaurants.

Financial information

Year end	31/12/2020
Turnover	£970,266,000
Pre-tax profit	(£23,350,000)

Main locations: McDonald's has stores and franchises throughout the UK and worldwide. Its UK head office is in London.

Community involvement

McDonald's donates a portion of its profits to its corporate charity, the Ronald McDonald House Charities (UK) (Charity Commission no. 802047), which provides free home-away-from-home accommodation for families of children in hospital and hospices across the UK. The company also holds annual fundraising days to raise money for the charity.

Partnerships

In 2020 the company began a three-year partnership with The Prince's Countryside Fund to support UK farming families and rural communities. During the first year of the partnership, the company's funding helped to support farmers to adapt to change and make their businesses more sustainable for the future.

McDonalds, in partnership with four UK football associations, is running 'Fun Football', an initiative that aims to provide 5 million hours of free football sessions with fully trained coaches to centres across the UK.

The company fundraises for Children in Need across its UK restaurants.

In-kind support

The company redistributes surplus food through partnerships with FareShare, Community Shop and the Irish food waste charity FoodCloud.

Commercially led support

McDonald's has worked in partnership with The National Literacy Trust since 2012 as part of its Happy Readers campaign which strives to increase book ownership among families in the UK and Ireland. Through the campaign, McDonald's has offered free book vouchers and book extracts with its Happy Meals. It has now begun the 'Book or Toy' initiative, which will allow families to choose either a book or a toy with their 'happy meal'.

McDonald's stores across the UK have collection boxes for customers to donate to Ronald McDonald House Charities (UK). Since October 2019, customers ordering from McDonald's kiosks are now able to round up their purchase to the nearest pound, or give a donation of 1p, 10p or 20p, 100% of which is given to Ronald McDonald House Charities UK.

Applications

Contact the correspondent for further information.

Community contributions

Cash donations UK	£158,800

The company's 2020 accounts state that it donated £585,000 to Ronald McDonald House Charities (UK) during the year. Of this, £158,800 came directly from the company, the rest was raised through the carrier bag levy in Wales and Scotland.

Medicash Health Benefits Ltd

Community services and development, the environment, health, housing and homelessness, mental health and well-being, social welfare

Company registration number: 258025

Correspondent: Linda Traynor, One Derby Square, Derby Square, Liverpool L2 1AB (email: linda.traynor@medicash.org; website: www.medicash.org/about-us/medicash-foundation)

Directors: Andrew Roberts; Jonathan Brown; Jean Ellis; Paul Gambon; William Tubey; Susan Weir (female: 33%; male: 67%).

Nature of business: Medicash is a health insurance provider.

Financial information

Year end	31/12/2021
Turnover	£34,217,000
Pre-tax profit	£8,524,000

Main locations: Medicash is based in Liverpool.

Community involvement

Support is provided through the company's corporate charity, the Medicash Foundation (Charity Commission no. 257636) which supports health-related charities in the North West.

Partnerships

Medicash has worked alongside Cool Earth since 2010, providing financial support to aid the charity's work protecting at-risk rainforests and the surrounding communities.

Commercially led support

Medicash manages the CardiACT heart safety campaign in Liverpool. Medicash works alongside the Liverpool BID Company and North West Ambulance to increase the number of defibrillators available in Liverpool city centre.

Applications

To make an application to the Medicash Foundation, download an application form from the 'Charity' page of the company's website and email it to linda.traynor@medicash.org.

Corporate charity

The Medicash Foundation (Charity Commission no. 257636) – see entry on page 257.

Community contributions

Cash donations UK	£893,000

In 2021 charitable donations to the company's corporate charity totalled £893,000.

Melrose Industries plc

Community services and development, education and training, health, medical research, STEM

Company registration number: 9800044

Correspondent: Joff Crawford, Company Secretary, 11th Floor, The Colmore Building, Colmore Circus Queensway, Birmingham B4 6AT (tel: 020 7647 4500; website: www.melroseplc.net/sustainability)

Directors: Justin Dowley; Christopher Miller; Simon Peckham; Geoffrey Martin; David Lis; Charlotte Twynig; Funmi Adegoke; Peter Dilnot; Victoria Jarman; Heather Lawrence (female: 40%; male: 60%).

Nature of business: Melrose buys and sells manufacturing and industrial businesses.

Financial information

Year end	31/12/2021
Turnover	£6,883,000,000
Pre-tax profit	(£618,000,000)

Total employees: 48,658

Main locations: The group owns businesses operating in several different geographical regions. In the UK, it has offices in Birmingham, London and North America.

Community involvement

The group encourages employees to contribute to a range of charitable and community projects. The group's businesses also support charitable causes by making cash donations.

The Melrose Skills, Innovation and Productivity Fund (not a registered charity)

The fund was launched in 2019 and the group has pledged to invest £10 million over the next five years. The fund is designed to develop engineering skills in the UK and will create STEM programmes, apprenticeships and degrees as well as investing in employee development.

Employee-led support

The group's 2021 annual report states:

> Our businesses promote the social wellbeing of their employees by encouraging them to actively contribute to local charitable and community projects, and lead by example through the sponsorship of such projects.

Applications

Apply in writing to the correspondent.

Community contributions

Cash donations UK		£703,400

The group made cash donations totalling £703,400 to charitable organisations in 2021.

Melton Building Society

General charitable purposes, social welfare

Correspondent: The CSR Team, Mutual House, Leicester Road, Melton Mowbray, Leicestershire LE13 0DB (tel: 01664 414141; email: online contact form; website: www.themelton.co.uk/community-support)

Directors: Fiona Pollard; Judith Sykes; Simon Thomas; Jonathan Farrington; Sue Douthwaite; Simon Taylor; Andy Lumby; Rita Bullivant; Debbie Flint; Rachel Kolebuk; Nicola Walker (female: 64%; male: 36%).

Nature of business: The society provides savings accounts, mortgages, insurance and other financial services.

Financial information

Year end	31/12/2021
Turnover	£10,575,000
Pre-tax profit	£1,710,000

UK employees: 114

Main locations: The society has branches in Grantham, Melton and Oakham.

Community involvement

The society provides support to the communities in which it operates.

The Melton Mowbray Building Society Charitable Foundation (Charity Commission no. 1067348)

The foundation was launched in 1998 and operates within a 15-mile radius of each of the society's branch offices in Melton Mowbray, Grantham and Oakham. The foundation commits 33% to 50% to kickstart a community project or activity.

Charity of the Year

The society's current Charity of the Year is Rainbows, a children's hospice in the East Midlands. The society supports the charity with fundraising initiatives and volunteering.

Financial education

The society supports local financial education initiatives. It also provides a financial education programme for local secondary schools and sixth forms, together with a Melton School Bank service for local primary schools.

Employee-led support

Employees volunteer for local projects and initiatives.

Commercially led support

Affinity accounts

Through its Affinity accounts, the society raises money for a number of local charities. The accounts give savers an attractive rate of interest, while every year the society donates a percentage of the average daily account balances. In 2021, charities receiving donations from affinity accounts included DLR Air Ambulance, Home-Start, Loros Hospice, Phoenix Children's Foundation and Rainbows.

Sponsorship

The society sponsors local community groups and organisations. For example, it has previously sponsored the CiCLE Classic, Leicestershire County Cricket Club Academy, Melton Band, Melton Town Bowls Club and the Victorian Fayre.

Applications

Details of how to apply to the foundation can be found in its corporate charity's entry.

To apply for sponsorship, contact the society via to marketing@mmbs.co.uk.

Corporate charity

The Melton Mowbray Building Society Charitable Foundation (Charity Commission no. 1067348) – see entry on page 257.

Community contributions

Cash donations UK		£7,500

In 2021, the society donated £7,500 to the Melton Mowbray Building Society Charitable Foundation. However, in previous years, the amount donated by the society has been higher (for example, £18,200 and £15,300 was donated in 2020 and 2019, respectively).

Additionally, over £40,000 was donated through Affinity accounts and £2,500 through staff and customer fundraising; however, we have not included these amounts in the total donations, as is our usual practice.

John Menzies Ltd

Climate change, community services and development, the environment, general charitable purposes

Company registration number: SC34970

Correspondent: Responsible Business Team, 2 Lochside Avenue, Edinburgh Park, Edinburgh EH12 9DJ (tel: 0131 225 8555; email: info@johnmenziesplc.com; website: https://menziesaviation.com/about-overview/corporate-responsibility-and-sustainability)

Directors: Philipp Joeinig; David Garman; Alvaro Gomez-Reino; John Geddes; Silla Maizey; Paul Baines; Christian Kappelhoff-Wulff; Henrik Lund (female: 13%; male: 88%).

Nature of business: John Menzies plc is the holding company of Menzies Aviation, an aviation and logistics support services business based in Edinburgh.

Financial information

Year end	31/12/2021
Turnover	£1,350,000,000
Pre-tax profit	£76,000,000

Total employees: 27,000

Main locations: The group operates in more than 200 locations across 37 countries. In the UK, the group has sites in more than 14 locations.

Community involvement

The group looks to contribute to communities, particularly in places where it has a presence. The group makes charitable donations globally through its two funds, the Charities Fund and the John Maxwell Menzies Fund.

From 2020 to 2025, the group is evolving its charitable framework to focus on two key charity themes: community and climate. According to the company website, the group is seeking new opportunities to link with charities local to its operations which promote sustainable opportunities in the local communities.

Applications

Contact the group for further information.

Community contributions

The company's 2021 accounts did not provide a figure for its charitable contributions.

Merck Sharp & Dohme (UK) Ltd

Education and training, health, medical research

Company registration number: 820771

Correspondent: CSR Team, 120 Moorgate, London EC2M 6UR (tel: 020 8154 8000; email: Grantscommittee@msd.com; website: www.msd-uk.com/partnerships/grants)

Directors: Ebru Temucin; Samuel Pygall; Benjamin Lucas (female: 33%; male: 67%).

Nature of business: Merck Sharp & Dohme (UK) Ltd (MSD) is the UK subsidiary of Merck and Co., Inc., which is headquartered in New Jersey, USA, and specialises in discovering, developing, manufacturing and marketing pharmaceutical products for human and animal use.

Financial information

Year end	31/12/2021
Turnover	£652,720,000
Pre-tax profit	£26,500,000

Main locations: MSD has a number of sites in the UK.

Community involvement

MSD supports academic, charitable and government organisations, with the aim of improving health outcomes for patients.

MSD UK Therapy Area Community Grants Programme

In July 2020, the company launched the MSD UK Therapy Area Community Grants Programme aimed at funding projects that tackle health challenges and reduce health inequalities. The programme is open to a range of organisations such as charities, patient organisations and healthcare organisations.

Neighbour of Choice community grant programme

This programme supports the work of local non-profit organisations that strive to improve people's quality of life and to preserve the environment in communities in which MSD has a presence. Support is given through partnerships, financial donations and employee volunteering.

MSD for Mothers

This global initiative focuses on improving the health and well-being of mothers during pregnancy and childbirth. In the UK, support is given to organisations such as Baby LifeLine, to run training courses that help pregnant women and unborn babies. Additionally, MSD, with the help of its employees, creates 'Mumma Kits' containing essentials for neonatal care for vulnerable mums and babies. These include nappies, sanitary products, muslin cloths and so on. More information on the initiative can be found at www.msdformothers.com.

Disaster relief

MSD provides support to countries affected by disasters in the form of financial aid and product donations.

In-kind support

Employees from across the group have the opportunity to take part in a three-month, field-based pro bono programme called the MSD Fellowship for Global Health. In 2021, 251 employees from 39 countries took part in the programme.

MSD also donates products, for example in the first half of 2022, it committed donations of more than $93 million in products and funds to various organisations in response to the war in Ukraine.

Employee-led support

Employees are entitled to 40 hours of paid volunteering each year. Previous projects have included school education programmes, beach cleans, gardening and support for food banks. Globally, in 2021, over 1,700 employees volunteered for a total of 68,300 hours.

Commercially led support

Sponsorship

MSD sponsors research programmes, conferences, events and partnerships. Previous sponsorships have included

- **Alzheimer's Disease International** – annual corporate partnership (£38,000)
- **Institute for Public Policy Research** – the Lord Darzi Review research programme (£25,000)
- **Alzheimer's Research UK** – annual conference (£10,000)
- **Positively UK** – the National Conference of People Living with HIV (£7,000)
- **Terrence Higgins Trust** – the Terrence Higgins Trust World AIDS Day Parliamentary Reception (£3,000)

Applications

Contact the correspondent for further information.

Community contributions

We were unable to determine a figure for MSD's total charitable contributions in

2021; however, a list of organisations that received donations in 2021 can be found on the company's website.

Merlin Entertainments Ltd

Animal conservation, education and training, the environment, general charitable purposes, health, social welfare

Company registration number: 8700412

Correspondent: CSR Team, Link House, 25 West Street, Poole, Dorset BH15 1LD (tel: 01202 666900; email: See 'Applications'; website: www. merlinentertainments.biz)

Directors: Nick Varney; Alistair Windybank; Matt Jowett; Fiona Eastwood; Mark Fisher; Ian Crabbe; John Jakobsen; Justin Platt (female: 13%; male: 88%).

Nature of business: Merlin Entertainments Ltd (formerly Merlin Entertainments plc) is an entertainment company, running 140 attractions in 24 countries, in four continents. Examples of attractions in the UK include Alton Towers, Legoland and Warwick Castle.

Financial information

Year end	25/12/2021
Turnover	£1,261,000,000
Pre-tax profit	(£94,000,000)

Total employees: 28,000

Main locations: In the UK, there are Merlin attractions in Alton (Staffordshire), Cornwall, Birmingham, Blackpool, Brighton, Surrey, Edinburgh, Norfolk, Loch Lomond, London, Manchester, Scarborough, Warwick, Weymouth, Windsor and York. There are also attractions in the Republic of Ireland, North America, Europe and Asia-Pacific.

Community involvement

The group's CSR strategy mainly focuses on supporting its two charities: The Merlin Magic Wand Children's Charity [Merlin's Magic Wand] (Charity Commission no. 1124081), which provides days out and facilities for children in need; and the Sea Life Trust Ltd (Charity Commission no. 1175859), which focuses on marine conservation.

The group's attractions also provide local community outreach through donations and in-kind support. For example, the Alton Towers Resort accepts applications for free park tickets from charities, community engagement projects and individual fundraisers in Staffordshire and Staffordshire Moorlands. Visit the individual Merlin attractions and brand websites for information on their charitable activities.

Merlin's Magic Wand

The charity provides days out at the group's attractions for children who are seriously ill or disadvantaged or who have disabilities, and their families. The charity also creates 'Merlin's Magic Spaces' for organisations such as hospices and hospitals for children who cannot visit Merlin attractions.

In 2020/21, the charity provided over 30,000 tickets for days out.

Sea Life Trust Ltd

The trust supports conservation projects focusing on oceans and marine life. The trust's areas of focus include: increasing marine protection, reducing plastic litter, campaigning for animal rights and removing lost fishing equipment from oceans.

In-kind support

Several of the group's attractions offer support to charitable causes in their local communities, including complementary tickets. However, most of the attractions' support is given to the group's corporate charities via donated tickets, goods and services.

Employee-led support

Employees support Merlin's Magic Wand by helping with outreach activities and organising fundraising initiatives. Sea Life employees fundraise for the Sea Life Trust.

Applications

The Sea Life Trust only works with several selected conservation partners and therefore does not accept unsolicited funding applications. You can reach the trust by emailing help@sealifetrust.com.

Information on how to apply to Merlin's Magic Wand can be found on the charity's website.

Visit the individual Merlin attractions' websites for further information on their community activities and the procedures for charitable requests and donations.

Community contributions

Total contributions UK	£562,800

Each year the group makes contributions to its two corporate charities. According to the Sea Life Trust's 2020 accounts, the trust received a cash donation of £78,600 from the group and a further £84,000 of gifts in kind. The 2020 accounts for Merlin's Magic Wand Children's Charity show that the group donated £400,200 worth of in-kind gifts and services to the charity during the year. Note: the grant total has been taken from the 2020 accounts of the two corporate charities as these were the latest available at the time of writing (September 2022).

Michelin Tyre plc

Arts, culture and heritage, community services and development, education and training, the environment, formal sciences, health, sports and recreation, technology and engineering

Company registration number: 84559

Correspondent: CSR Team, Campbell Road, Stoke-on-Trent, Staffordshire ST4 4EY (email: michelin.requests@ michelin.com; website: https:// michelindevelopment.co.uk/michelin-respect-communities-programme)

Directors: Philippe Berther; Vincent Gridel; John Howe; Maria Rottger (female: 25%; male: 75%).

Nature of business: Michelin manufactures tyres, tubes, wheels and accessories. The group also produces guides and provides mobility support services.

Financial information

Year end	31/12/2021
Turnover	£459,230,000
Pre-tax profit	£22,060,000

Total employees: 670

Main locations: In the UK, the Michelin group has sites in Stoke-on-Trent and Watford.

Community involvement

Through its Community Involvement Programme, Michelin looks to build relationships with charities, educational establishments and not-for-profit organisations that work to benefit the local communities close to its manufacturing operations in Stoke-on-Trent.

Priority is given to organisations working in Michelin's core focus areas, described below. The following information has been taken from the website.

- **Education:** We are committed to developing creative thinkers for tomorrow's workplace. We foster and support programmes that build reading, literacy and numeracy skills within local schools. We also promote scientific and technical professions and encourage youth development through sport and culture. We believe these programmes nurture creativity and develop important life and work skills.
- **Mobility, safety and environment:** We are committed to support programmes that reduce the impact of our activities on the environment. In addition, we look to support programmes that sustain our natural environment and promote green mobility. We work to educate, raise awareness of and sustain better mobility through road safety initiatives.
- **Community enhancement – health and human:** We are committed to supporting programmes that enrich the

quality of life for individuals and our communities as a whole. Providing support in Health and Human services should be considered and we also believe the Arts and our heritage are a powerful way to expose people to different cultures and celebrate the diversity of all people.

Support can be given in the form of cash donations, in-kind contributions or personnel resources. It is further explained on the company's website that 'support is generally practical in nature and related to specific activities'.

In-kind support

In-kind support is provided via the Community Involvement Programme.

Exclusions

According to the company's website, the Community Involvement Programme does not support requests for or from the following:

- Organisations that do not have tax-exempt status
- Individuals
- Political organisations, candidates or lobby organisations
- Organisations with a limited constituency or membership
- Travel costs for groups or individuals
- Advertising
- Organisations outside the United Kingdom
- Activities that are not in line with Michelin's corporate values and image

Applications

All applications to the Community Involvement Programme must be supported by a completed application form, which is available to download from the company's website. Forms should be returned by email to michelin.requests@michelin.com, along with any supporting evidence. Applicants should allow 30 days for their request to be processed and responded to. Applications are acknowledged in writing.

Community contributions

We were unable to determine a figure for the company's total charitable contributions for 2021.

Microsoft Ltd

Community services and development, education and training, emergency response/relief, the environment, general charitable purposes, human rights, research, social justice, STEM, work outside the UK

Company registration number: 1624297

Correspondent: CSR Team, Microsoft Campus, Thames Valley Park, Reading, Berkshire RG6 1WG (tel: 0344 800 2400; email: ukprteam@microsoft.com; website: www.microsoft.com/en-us/corporate-responsibility)

Directors: Clare Barclay; Keith Dolliver; Benjamin Orndorff (female: 33%; male: 67%).

Nature of business: Microsoft Ltd is a subsidiary of the Microsoft Corporation group, based in Redmond, Washington State, USA. It markets and supports systems, devices and applications software for business, professional and home use.

Financial information

Year end	30/06/2021
Turnover	£4,861,627,000
Pre-tax profit	£220,520,000

UK employees: 3,969

Main locations: The group's UK head office is in Reading and it also has offices in Cambridge, Edinburgh, London and Manchester.

Community involvement

The group provides in-kind technological support, cash donations and matched funding. Its CSR programme focuses on young people and education. The group's Artificial Intelligence (AI) for Good programmes offer technological support and cash grants for individuals, non-profits and organisations around the world.

Education

The group has several initiatives to promote STEM education, working in partnership with schools, businesses and organisations to provide resources for teachers and schools. For example, the Microsoft Showcase Schools Programme has helped to transform education in UK schools with technology.

In 2022, the group helped provide 6 million people with computer science educational programmes through its partnerships with organisations such as Code.org, the Computer Science Teacher Association (CSTA) and CS for All. The group also distributed 26 grants in 24 countries across the globe to train over 24,000 individuals in cybersecurity and helping them to prepare for a role in the field.

Young people

The group works in partnership with the charity UK Youth on its Generation Code programme, which teaches young people aged 11 to 19 how to code and gives them the opportunity to enter a national competition. The Generation Code Accelerator Programme upskills youth workers in the UK through training, mentoring and grant opportunities, so they can become 'digital changemakers' in their local communities.

Humanitarian support

Globally, the group provides technological support, in-kind and cash donations to assist with humanitarian efforts.

In 2022, following the invasion of Ukraine, the group donated £224 million in financial and technological assistance to Ukrainian organisations aiming to connect displaced refugees. This included 173 emergency support missions, amassing over 23,000 hours of support.

As a response to the COVID-19 pandemic, the group raised and donated £361 million in financial, technology and resource donations for organisations combatting the impact of the virus, including research collaborations.

Artificial Intelligence (AI) for Good programmes

According to its website, AI for Good is Microsoft's initiative designed to 'empower researchers, non-profits and organisations with advanced technologies to help unlock solutions to the biggest challenges facing society today'.

AI for Good offers three worldwide open grants programmes:

- **AI for Accessibility** – providing grants to individuals and organisations working to empower people with disabilities through AI solutions that positively impact employment, daily life, and communication and connection. The programme provides access to advanced Microsoft Azure cloud computing resources.
- **AI for Humanitarian Action** – providing grants for non-profits and humanitarian organisations working on projects that develop AI solutions to address challenges in four key areas: disaster response, refugees and displaced people, human rights and the needs of women and children. In 2022, 12 missions were carried out as part of the AI for Humanitarian Action grants programme.
- **AI for Earth** – providing grants to support projects that use AI to change the way people and organisations monitor, model and manage the Earth's natural systems.

AI for Good also has programmes for cultural heritage and health which support specific individuals, non-profits, research and academic collaborations through partnership, investment in AI technology and select cash grants.

In-kind support

Product donations and discounts

Microsoft provides discounts and donations to non-profit organisations in over 200 countries worldwide, including the UK.

Office 365 for charities

Eligible UK charities may apply for Office 365 as a donation. A range of subscription plans are available, some of which donate the programme and others offer the programme at a discounted price.

AI for Good Accelerator Programme

In the UK, Microsoft introduced the AI for Good Accelerator Programme in 2019, which according to the Microsoft website, provides free commercial, technical and social impact support to UK-registered charities and 'purpose-driven ventures with a demonstrable social impact', to help them scale their purpose-driven AI initiatives. The four-month programme is run in partnership with Microsoft for Startups and the Social Tech Trust.

Employee-led support

Employees are encouraged to volunteer in their communities. There is also a worldwide corporate giving programme, through which employees donated £222 million, including matched funding to charitable organisations.

During the year, over 29,000 Microsoft employees volunteered over 720,000 hours of their time to charities, over 1,000 of which was in the form of pro bono legal services.

The group also hosts a 'Hack for Good' event, wherein Microsoft employees collaborate to design and create solutions that aim to empower non-profit organisations.

Commercially led support

As part of its response to the invasion of Ukraine, Microsoft Corporation supported Humble Bundle's 'Stand for Ukraine' campaign. More specifically, Xbox partnered with Humble Bundle to provide a bundle of games for players to purchase, with proceeds going to organisations in Ukraine. With the support of Xbox, Humble Bundle raised over £17.5 million through the campaign.

Applications

Software donations

Microsoft provides software donations and discounts through the Charity Digital Exchange. For more information see www.charitydigitalexchange.org/microsoft.

Office 365 options for charities

For more details of Office 365 donations or discounts see: www.microsoft.com/en-gb/microsoft-365/nonprofit/office-365-nonprofit.

AI for Good grants programme

More information on the AI for Good programmes, including eligibility and applications, can be found at: www.microsoft.com/en-us/ai/ai-for-good.

AI for Good Accelerator Programme

Further information on the programme can be found at: www.microsoft.com/en-gb/business/ai-for-good. Alternatively, email ai4good@microsoft.com for enquiries not answered in the FAQ section.

Contact the correspondent for any further information.

Community contributions

We were unable to determine an exact figure for Microsoft's UK charitable contributions. However, according to the 2022 impact report from Microsoft Corporation (the global group), it made donations of products, financial support and volunteering time totalling £2.8 billion during the year to 302,000 non-profit organisations globally.

The figures for GBP have been converted from USD using the exchange rate at the time of writing (November 2022).

The Midcounties Co-operative

Community enterprise and social entrepreneurship, community services and development, education and training, general charitable purposes, social welfare

Company registration number: IP19025R

Correspondent: Community Team, Co-operative House, Warwick Technology Park, Gallows Hill, Warwick, Warwickshire CV34 6DA (tel: 01902 492235; email: CommunityTeam@midcounties.coop; website: www.midcounties.coop/community)

Directors: Helen Wiseman; Heather Richardson; Vivian Woodell; Olivia Birch; Ellie Boyle; Bernadette Connor; Evelyne Godfrey; Vicky Green; Harvey Griffiths; Stephen Hawksworth; Irene Kirkman; Matthew Lane; Paul Mather; Nick Milton; Fiona Ravenscroft; Barbara Rainford (female: 63%; male: 38%).

Nature of business: The Midcounties Co-operative is registered as an Industrial and Provident Society and has more than 500 trading sites operating within the food, travel, healthcare, funeral care, childcare, energy, post offices, telecoms and flexible benefits business sectors.

Financial information

Year end	22/01/2022
Turnover	£676,460,000
Pre-tax profit	(£8,030,000)

UK employees: 7,303

Main locations: The society describes its 'heartlands' as being Oxfordshire, Gloucestershire, Buckinghamshire, Shropshire, Staffordshire, the West Midlands, Wiltshire and Worcestershire. The society also trades in the surrounding counties and its energy, childcare, travel, telecoms and flexible benefits businesses trade UK-wide.

Community involvement

The Midcounties Co-operative provides support through charity partnerships, volunteering and grant funding.

Grants and funding

- Local Community Grants – groups can apply for up to £250 throughout the year. The grants can be used for individual events or as help for ongoing projects, as long as the main centre of the group is based in a community with a Midcounties store. In 2021/22, grants were awarded to 245 groups.
- Your Community Fund – community groups can apply for grants of £500 to support a community project.
- Campaigns Fund – this fund was established to support the society's political activities. Grants are given to campaign groups whose aims reflect the co-operative values of the society and its members.

Further information on eligibility can be found on the society's website.

Partnerships

The society has a charity partner in each of the 20 regional communities it works in. In 2021/22, £89,000 was raised for charity partners.

The society also supports community groups and charities outside its regional communities through 'Keeping it Local' fundraising partners, as voted for by employees. During 2020/21, the society supported the mental health charity Mind, and Seaful, a charity helping people to reconnect with the ocean to improve their mental health.

The society has worked in partnership with the education charity The Outward Bound Trust since 2013, supporting its Green Pioneers programme. The programme aims to raise awareness of sustainability and environmental issues as well as provide young people from a variety of backgrounds the opportunity to reach their full potential.

The society also has a partnership with Go Beyond, a charity that works with children from vulnerable backgrounds. Every time a customer books a holiday through Co-op Holidays, the society automatically makes a donation to Go Beyond.

The society works with local councils to provide families in need with free meals during the summer and Christmas periods.

Employee-led support

Employees volunteer for a range of good causes, including providing advice and practical help to fundraisers and charities. Every Midcounties Co-op employee is entitled to take 22.5 hours each year for volunteering purposes during their working hours. In 2021/22, employees provided a total of 25,600 volunteering hours.

Commercially led support

Food bank fund

The society has partnered with over 70 local food banks and provides donation points in each of its stores. It also works with food waste organisation Too Good To Go, to donate £1 to the fund for each 'magic bag' sold in its stores during the month of January.

Applications

Grant funding

Eligibility criteria and further information on the different grant funds can be found on the society's website.

Volunteering

For information on getting support from volunteers, contact the correspondent via email.

Community contributions

Cash donations UK	£200,000

According to its 2021/22 annual report, the society awarded grants totalling nearly £200,000 through grants and funding. A figure was not provided for the value of employee volunteering time.

Mills and Reeve LLP

Health, social welfare

Company registration number: OC326165

Correspondent: CSR Team, 4th Floor, Monument Place, 24 Monument Street, London EC3R 8AJ (tel: 0344 880 2666; email: enquiry@mills-reeve.com; website: www.mills-reeve.com/about-us/making-a-positive-impact)

Nature of business: Mills and Reeve is among the 50 largest law firms in the UK.

Financial information

Year end	31/05/2021
Turnover	£124,295,000
Pre-tax profit	£52,005,000

UK employees: 1,000+

Main locations: Mills and Reeve has offices in Birmingham, Cambridge, Leeds, London, Manchester and Norwich.

Community involvement

Mills and Reeve's corporate responsibility programme focuses on the following areas:
- Giving cash donations through its corporate charity, the Mills and Reeves Charitable Trust (Charity Commission no. 326271), and

through matching employees' fundraising efforts

- Undertaking pro bono work for community projects, charities and individuals
- Supporting local charities, schools and not-for-profit groups through employee volunteering and fundraising
- Improving the firm's environmental performance and supporting local environmental projects

In-kind support

Mills and Reeve LLP provides pro bono support to charities and not-for-profit groups.

In 2021, to celebrate Black History Month, Mills and Reeve LLP's Reach programme focused on workplace diversity and inclusion, and donated 198 cross-cultural books to schools local to its offices around the UK.

Employee-led support

Employees can take part in workplace giving and fundraise together across the seven offices.

Exclusions

No grants are available to individuals.

Applications

Contact your local office for further information on pro bono support and partnerships. Contact details can be found at www.mills-reeve.com/offices.

Corporate charity

Mills and Reeve Charitable Trust (Charity Commission no. 326271) – see entry on page 258.

Community contributions

Cash donations UK	£133,000

In 2021, Mills and Reeve LLP donated £121,000 to its corporate charity. A further £12,000 was donated by the firm to food banks across the UK.

Moneysupermarket.com Group plc

Community services and development, general charitable purposes, health, social welfare

Company registration number: 6160943

Correspondent: Katherine Bellau, Company Secretary, Moneysupermarket House, St David's Park, Ewloe, Chester CH5 3UZ (tel: 01244 665700; email: katherine.bellau@moneysupermarket.com; website: http://corporate.moneysupermarket.com/company/csr.aspx)

Directors: Robin Freestone; Lesley Jones; Peter Duffy; Scilla Grimble; Sarah Warby; Caroline Britton; Supriya Uchil (female: 71%; male: 29%).

Nature of business:
Moneysupermarket.com is an online British price comparison business specialising in financial services. The group also owns the website travelsupermarket.com and the financial advice platform MoneySavingExpert.com

Financial information

Year end	31/12/2021
Turnover	£316,700,000
Pre-tax profit	£70,200,000

Total employees: 751

Main locations: The group has three main offices in Ewloe (near Chester), London and Manchester.

Community involvement

Moneysupermarket.com and its employees support charities local to its offices in Ewloe, Manchester and London and donate to The MSE Charity (Charity Commission no. 1121320) that offers grants of up to £7,500 to organisations promoting education and financial management.

The Prince's Trust charity partnership

In January 2019 the group entered a three-year partnership with The Prince's Trust. In 2021, the group chose to extend this partnership for another year, donating a further £100,000 to the trust. The partnership through 2021 consisted of various community initiatives led by employees of the group.

.Community

.Community is the programme through which the group channels its charitable activities. In 2021, the group worked in conjunction with charities UK Youth and the Raspberry Pi Foundation to support local schools with in-kind donations during the COVID-19 pandemic. Examples of other activities and support given through .Community can be found on the group's website.

Employee-led support

Employee fundraising:

As part of the group's partnership with The Prince's Trust, employees of the group raised funds for the trust through their participation in community initiatives. These initiatives included:

- The 'Future Steps' initiative, a virtual fitness challenge through which 95 employees raised £14,000.
- The 'Phones for Future' scheme, where employees donated old phones and IT equipment for recycling, raising £3,000.
- The 'Your Palace to Palace' initiative, that saw employees cycle, run and walk various distances to raise an additional £3,000.
- An employee-led festive raffle, that raised another £3,000.

Bytes Catering partnering with Nanny Biscuit

In 2021, the group's Bytes catering team partnered with charity Nanny Biscuit to prepare and distribute meals to vulnerable people across Wales. Between January and October 2021, the team prepared over 26,000 meals for those in need during the COVID-19 pandemic.

Applications

Contact the correspondent for further information.

Corporate charity

The MSE Charity (Charity Commission no. 1121320) – see entry on page 261.

Community contributions

Cash donations UK	£233,000

According to the group's 2021 annual report, total donations to charitable causes during the year amounted to £233,000. Costings for in-kind support were not provided. The group donated £100,000 to its charity partner The Prince's Trust and £33,000 to charities local to its offices. A further £100,000 was donated by MoneySavingExpert, a subsidiary of the group, to The MSE Charity.

Morgan Stanley and Co. International plc

Community services and development, education and training, health, housing and homelessness, medical research

Company registration number: 2068222

Correspondent: Community Affairs Team, 25 Cabot Square, Canary Wharf, London E14 4QA (tel: 020 7425 1302; email: communityaffairslondon@morganstanley.com; website: www.morganstanley.com/about-us/giving-back)

Directors: James Gorman; Alistair Darling; Thomas Glocer; Robert Herz; Erika James; Hironori Kamezawa; Shelley Leibowitz; Stephen Luczo; Jami Micik; Masato Myachi; Dennis Nally; Mary Schapiro; Perry Traquina; Rayford Wilkins (female: 29%; male: 71%).

Nature of business: The group's principal activity is the provision of financial services to corporations, governments and financial institutions.

Financial information

Year end	31/12/2021
Turnover	£7,565,000,000
Pre-tax profit	£1,940,000,000

Main locations: In the UK, Morgan Stanley has offices in London and Glasgow.

Community involvement

Morgan Stanley and Co. International plc supports organisations in regions where it has a presence through the Morgan Stanley International Foundation (Charity Commission no. 1042671). This includes the boroughs of Tower Hamlets and Newham in London, Glasgow, as well as continental Europe, the Middle East and Africa. Grants are made to organisations focusing on children's health and education.

Charity partners

In 2021, employees in London nominated the Teenage Cancer Trust as its main charity partner and raised over $2 million (approximately £1.45 million) for the charity. Glasgow employees nominated the Scottish Association for Mental Health, raising over $200,000 (approximately £145,500). Other charities were also nominated by employees in both locations. London employees nominated The Felix Project, a charity that supports people facing food poverty. In Glasgow, employees nominated CHAS (Children's Hospices Across Scotland).

Morgan Stanley and Co. International plc also has a partnership with Place2Be, supporting the charity to scale up its programmes for teachers to learn about children's mental health.

Morgan Stanley Alliance for Children's Mental Health

In February 2020, the group announced the establishment of the Morgan Stanley Alliance for Children's Mental Health. It partners with charitable organisations around the world to reduce stigma, increase early intervention and help address the challenges of stress, anxiety and depression. The alliance has reached over 11 million students since its inception.

In-kind support

The Strategy Challenge is Morgan Stanley's global pro bono programme. In 2021, the challenge saw London employees provide four charities with 1,500 hours of volunteering and Glasgow employees provided 500 hours of pro bono advice for six charities.

Employee-led support

In 2021, 2,000 hours of volunteering time was given in the UK by the group's employees as part of the Morgan Stanley Strategy Challenge.

Applications

Contact the correspondent for further information on Morgan Stanley's pro bono programme.

Corporate charity

Morgan Stanley International Foundation (Charity Commission no. 1042671) – see entry on page 258.

Community contributions

Cash donations worldwide	£1,198,000

According to the foundation's accounts, the group made donations totalling £1.19 million to the Morgan Stanley International Foundation.

Wm Morrison Supermarkets plc

Community services and development, education and training, emergency response/relief, general charitable purposes, health, housing and homelessness, social welfare

Company registration number: 358949

Correspondent: Neil Davidson, Chair of Corporate Compliance and Responsibility Committee, Hillmore House, Gain Lane, Bradford BD3 7DL (email: cr@morrisonsplc.co.uk; website: www.morrisons-corporate.com/cr)

Directors: David Potts; Joanna Goff; Jonathan Burke (female: 33%; male: 67%).

Nature of business: Wm Morrison Supermarkets operates a chain of retail supermarket stores under the Morrisons brand.

Financial information

Year end	02/02/2021
Turnover	£17,598,000,000
Pre-tax profit	£201,000,000

Total employees: 110,000

Main locations: Morrisons operates stores throughout the UK.

Community involvement

Morrisons supports general charitable purposes through its grant-making corporate charity the Morrisons Foundation (Charity Commission no.1160224). The company also donates surplus food to local community groups and fundraises for charity partners and other national charities.

Partnerships

In 2020/21, Morrisons continued its charity partnership with Young Lives vs Cancer. During the year, employees raised over £3 million for the charity. Fundraising activities included static cycles, marathons, sponsored walks, coffee mornings and book sales.

In addition to its national charity partner, in 2020/21, Morrisons helped to raise funds for other national charities and campaigns, including The Poppy Appeal (£1.2 million), the Marie Curie Great Daffodil Appeal (£750,000), the Trussell Trust (£200,000) and Children in Need (£65,000).

In-kind support

Morrisons stores partner with over 450 local community groups to donate any unsold food that is safe to eat. It also works with the charity FareShare to redistribute edible surplus food and the Manchester charity The Bread and Butter Thing.

Employee-led support

Community Champions

Each Morrisons store has a 'Community Champion' – a colleague who manages engagement between the store and groups and charities in the local area. Community Champions organise activities to help raise funds for local causes and the Morrisons national charity partner.

Employee fundraising

Colleagues from Morrisons stores, sites and head office raise funds through various activities – from individual running challenges to national in-store events such as 'Morrisons to the Moon' and 'Communi-Tea Parties'.

Matched funding

The Morrisons Foundation matches employees' fundraising efforts up to £5,000, twice per year.

Commercially led support

Morrisons donates money from the sales of certain products to charitable causes.

Applications

General enquiries can be submitted in writing to the correspondent.

Local Opportunities

Enquiries regarding local support or in-kind contributions can be directed to your local store's Community Champion.

Corporate charity

The Morrisons Foundation (Charity Commission no. 1160224) – see entry on page 260.

Community contributions

Cash donations UK	£1,000,000

The foundation's 2020/21 annual report states that it received £1 million from the company during the year.

Motorola Solutions UK Ltd

Education and training, STEM

Company registration number: 912182

Correspondent: Motorola Solutions Foundation, Nova South, 160 Victoria Street, London, Hampshire SW1E 5LB (email: foundation@motorolasolutions.com; website: www.motorolasolutions.com)

Directors: Moncef Elaoud; Oscar Henken; Yvonne Lee; Katherine Maher; Fergus Mayne; Sarah Roberts (female: 50%; male: 50%).

Nature of business: Motorola Solutions is a global provider of communication infrastructure, devices, accessories, software and services. Motorola Solutions UK Ltd is a UK-registered subsidiary whose ultimate parent company is Motorola Solutions, which is incorporated in the USA.

Financial information

Year end	31/12/2020
Turnover	£157,600,000
Pre-tax profit	£10,900,000

UK employees: 504

Total employees: 18,000

Main locations: Motorola Solutions has offices worldwide; its UK office is located in Hampshire.

Community involvement

The group channels its charitable activities through its corporate charity, the Motorola Solutions Foundation.

Motorola Solutions Foundation

The group's foundation is an American charity, that makes grants globally in 30 countries. Support is available in the form of cash donations, in-kind support (namely product donations) and employee participation in voluntary and charitable-giving programmes.

The foundation's grants programme has three areas of interest:

- **Technology and engineering** – engaging students in innovative, hands-on activities such as coding, programming, computer science and robotics
- **Public safety education** – providing resources to first responders and the communities they serve, supporting the families of first responders who are deceased, and investing in key policing initiatives (such as providing leadership training for women and supporting mental well-being)
- **Blended programmes** – programmes that combine both technology and engineering education and public safety education

Within each area of focus, the foundation is particularly committed to supporting underrepresented populations.

Employee-led support

According to the Motorola Solutions UK Ltd 2020 annual report, employees from the company volunteered over 2,000 hours of their time to support the Motorola Solutions Foundation.

Applications

Prospective applicants should first see the Motorola Solutions Foundation page

on the group's website for more information about the foundation, its grants programme and application opening/closing dates. Any queries should be directed to foundation@motorolasolutions.com.

Community contributions

We were unable to determine a figure for the company's or group's total community contributions during 2020. The Motorola Solutions UK Ltd 2020 annual report states that the company donates to the foundation; however, no amount was disclosed.

National Express Group plc

Community enterprise and social entrepreneurship, education and training

Company registration number: 2590560

Correspondent: The National Express Foundation, National Express House, Mill Lane, Digbeth, Birmingham B5 6DD (tel: 0845 013 0130; website: www.nationalexpressgroup.com/our-way/community)

Directors: Sir John Armitt; Ignacio Garat; Chris Davies; Jorge Cosmen; Matthew Crummack; Ana De Pro Gonzalo; Carolyn Flowers; Karen Geary; Mike McKeon (female: 33%; male: 67%).

Nature of business: National Express is a British multinational public transport company that operates bus, coach, train and tram services in the UK, the USA, Spain, Morocco and Germany.

Financial information

Year end	31/12/2021
Turnover	£2,170,300,000
Pre-tax profit	£84,900,000

Total employees: 45,448

Main locations: National Express is headquartered in London.

Community involvement

The majority of the group's charitable activities in the UK are carried out through its corporate charity, The National Express Foundation (Charity Commission no. 1148231).

Partnerships

In the UK, the group works in partnership with the Royal British Legion, The Prince's Trust and CHICKS.

In-kind support

The Ride to Refuge scheme

In 2021, the group worked with Women's Aid organisations to create the 'Ride to Refuge' scheme to provide free bus tickets to survivors of domestic abuse in the West Midlands.

Employee-led support

Staff can apply for funding to support any charities or community initiatives they are personally involved with through the Employee Charity Panel, who meet quarterly to allocate funds to those charities they consider will most benefit.

Employees can also use the group's payroll giving scheme to make regular donations to charities of their choice.

Employees in each location can choose a Charity of the Year to direct employee-led support. For example in 2021, the Birmingham Central garage ran a special zombie bus to mark Halloween. The special service, 666, took passengers around a circuit of the city centre, with donations to Birmingham Children's Hospital being made instead of paying for tickets.

Commercially led support

ShareGift

ShareGift is an independent charity share donation scheme administered by the Orr Mackintosh Foundation. Those shareholders who hold only a small number of shares, the value of which makes it uneconomic to sell them, can donate their shares to ShareGift which will sell them and donate the proceeds to a wide range of charities

Exclusions

The group's website states:

> The focus of our charitable support is in areas aligned to our business and our employees. We are therefore unable to support financial requests from individuals outside of the business, political or denominational groups, arts or sports groups, medical and animal welfare organisations or building projects.
>
> We don't support requests for advertising or sponsorship unless they are a part of a project we are already involved with.
>
> Because of the volume of requests we get, we are also unable to offer free travel for charity 'jailbreaks' and other external fundraising events.

Applications

For information on applying to the National Express Foundation, see the group's corporate charity entry. All other forms of funding are awarded by the Employee Charity Panel – contact your local branch to enquire.

Corporate charity

The National Express Foundation (Charity Commission no. 1148231) – see entry on page 262.

Community contributions

Cash donations worldwide	£849,000

We were unable to determine a total for the group's community contributions; however, the group's annual report for 2021 states that in keeping with the

National Express policy for giving, the group donated 1% of its pre-tax profit to charitable organisations. We have taken this figure as the group's total cash contributions worldwide.

We were unable to determine the amount donated to organisations in the UK.

The National Farmers Union Mutual Insurance Society Ltd

Community enterprise and social entrepreneurship, community services and development, education and training, the environment, health, mental health and well-being, rural communities, social welfare

Company registration number: 111982

Correspondent: CSR Team, Tiddington Road, Stratford-upon-Avon, Warwickshire CV37 7BJ (tel: 0808 134 3935; website: www.nfumutual.co.uk)

Directors: Jim McLaren; John Bailie; Steve Bower; Ali Capper; Brian Duffin; Christine Kennedy; Richard Morley; David Roper; Nick Turner; Ross Ainslie; Alan Fairhead; Nick Watson (female: 17%; male: 83%).

Nature of business: Trading as NFU Mutual, the company is a UK-registered mutual insurance composite. It underwrites more than £1 billion in annual premiums in life and general insurance lines for rural communities within the UK.

Financial information

Year end	31/12/2021
Pre-tax profit	£220,000,000

UK employees: 3,884

Main locations: The NFU headquarters is in Warwickshire. It has various offices located throughout the UK.

Community involvement

The group's charitable donations are distributed via its Agency Giving Fund (not a registered charity), the Farm Safety Foundation (Charity Commission no. 1159000) and its corporate charity The NFU Mutual Charitable Trust (Charity Commission no. 1073064).

The group has pledged to support UK charities with £3.25 million during 2022 to help communities continue to rebuild after the COVID-19 pandemic.

The Agency Giving Fund

The Agency Giving Fund was established in 2020 in response to the COVID-19 pandemic to support frontline charities. Agency offices across the UK were invited to nominate a local charity to receive support. In 2022, the fund returned and the group stated it plans to donate £1.92 million through the fund.

Farm Safety Foundation

The foundation was launched by the group in 2014 as an independent registered charity to preserve and protect the physical and mental well-being of the next generation of farmers. In 2021, the group supported the foundation's 'mental health in farming' training sessions for NFU Mutual agents and farmers.

Road safety

In 2021, the group partnered with The British Horse Society, British Cycling and THINK! as part of the government's road safety campaign to try to reduce the risks for all rural road users. The initiative launched in December and included an interactive road safety guide, expert tips and advice and a prize draw to win high-vis safety merchandise.

Employee-led support

Employees take part in volunteering and fundraising initiatives. The group supports these efforts through its Community Champions scheme.

Applications

Contact the correspondent for more information. Details of local agency offices can be found on the group's website. For more information on the NFU Mutual Charitable Trust, see its separate entry.

Corporate charity

The NFU Mutual Charitable Trust (Charity Commission no. 1073064) – see entry on page 263.

Community contributions

Cash donations UK	£3,300,000

Charitable donations during 2021 amounted to £3.3 million, which included donations to the NFU Mutual Charitable Trust of £1 million (which distributes awards at its discretion), £300,000 to the Farm Safety Foundation and £2 million through the Agency Giving Fund.

National Grid plc

Community enterprise and social entrepreneurship, community services and development, education and training, the environment, renewable/ sustainable energy

Company registration number: 4031152

Correspondent: The Responsibility and Sustainability Team, National Grid House, Warwick Technology Park, Gallows Hill, Warwick, Warwickshire CV34 6DA (tel: 01285 841912; website: www.nationalgrid.com/responsibility/ community)

Directors: Paula Rosput Reynolds; John Pettigrew; Andy Agg; Thérèse Esperdy; Liz Hewitt; Lord Ian Livingston; Iain Mackay; Anne Robinson; Earl Shipp; Jonathan Silver; Tony Wood; Martha Wyrsch (female: 42%; male: 58%).

Nature of business: The principal operations of the group are the ownership and operation of regulated electricity and gas infrastructure networks in the UK and the US.

Financial information

Year end	31/03/2022
Turnover	£18,449,000,000
Pre-tax profit	£3,441,000,000

UK employees: 6,475

Total employees: 23,697

Main locations: The group has sites across the UK.

Community involvement

National Grid seeks to deliver positive impact in the communities in which it serves.

The group's CSR strategy involves partnering with charity organisations and encouraging employees to engage in community causes.

Community investment and Grid for Good

The group works with various charity partners in the UK and the US. Through its Grid For Good programme, the group helps to deliver STEM education and opportunities for disadvantaged young people. In 2021/22 the programme engaged with 2,336 young people in the UK. The group also contributes to food bank donations through its partnership with the Trussell Trust and supports Red Cross organisations.

Community Grants programme

This programme is aimed at charities and community organisations in the areas in which National Grid's work is impacting local people through its operations and site activities.

Eligible organisations must have:
- A bank account in the name of the organisation with at least two signatures who are unrelated
- A constitution (if not a registered charity)
- A management committee with a minimum of three people who are unrelated
- Accounts for the most recent financial year or a financial projection if it is a new organisation (the group will only fund organisations that are financially solvent)

Funding of up to £20,000 is available for projects run by non-profit organisations that meet local needs by providing a range of social, economic and environmental benefits. A list of eligible projects and initiatives can be found on the group's website.

In 2021/22 the Community Grant programme awarded £336,000 in grants to 20 beneficiaries.

Warm Home Fund

In 2017, National Grid plc provided £150 million to establish the Warm Homes Fund (WHF) to be administered by Affordable Warmth Solutions CIC, designed to work in partnership with local authorities, registered social landlords and other stakeholders to address the issue facing fuel-poor households. Over the lifetime of the fund, it has installed improved heating systems in over 24,000 homes.

Rising Energy Prices

The group has partnered with various organisations to provide financial support to those struggling with rising energy prices. These partnerships include a £1 million donation to Citizens Advice, £1 million to the Fuel Bank Foundation and increasing accessibility to the group's Warm Home Fund.

In-kind support

National Grid plc employees share their time and expertise including towards projects for young people to improve their STEM skills, careers education and work experience.

The group also runs an employee-led internship programme for young people aged 17 to 25 with special educational needs and disabilities.

Employee-led support

The group's 2021/22 Responsible Business Report states that it partners with charity organisations to encourage and enable its employees to volunteer their time. In 2021/22 National Grid plc employees volunteered 23,416 hours, with 1,167 employees registered as volunteers of the Grid for Good programme.

Exclusions

The website states that the following will not be supported by the Community Grants programme:

- The advancement of religion
- Political parties or causes
- Medical research
- Core running costs
- Individuals
- People taking part in treks or expeditions
- Statutory organisations such as local government, schools, the NHS or local councils, including parish councils irrespective of whether they have charitable status
- Retrospective funding
- Improvements to land or building over which the applicant does not have tenure

Applications

For the Community Grants programme, the group's website states that it 'prefers to receive applications on-line' but if this is not possible or you need assistance, call the Community Helpline on 01285 841912.

All other enquiries should be directed to the correspondent.

Community contributions

Total contributions worldwide   £18,336,700

According to the group's Responsible Business Report 2021/22, the group's combined community contributions worldwide total was £18.3 million.

Nationwide Building Society

Community services and development, education and training, housing and homelessness, money and debt advice, social welfare

Company registration number: FCA 106078

Correspondent: The Community Grants Team, Nationwide House, Pipers Way, Swindon, Wiltshire SN38 2SN (email: nationwidecommunitygrants@ nationwide.co.uk; website: www. nationwide.co.uk/about/why-choose-nationwide/social-investment)

Directors: Kevin Parry; Debbie Crosbie; Chris Rhodes; May Fyfield; Albert Hitchcock; Alan Keir; Debbie Klein; Tamara Rajah; Gilian Riley; Phill Rivett; Gunn Waersted (female: 55%; male: 45%).

Nature of business: The society provides a comprehensive range of personal financial services.

Financial information

Year end	31/03/2022
Turnover	£3,860,000,000
Pre-tax profit	£1,597,000,000

UK employees: 17,686

Main locations: Nationwide's head office is in Swindon and it has branches throughout the UK.

Community involvement

Each year, 1% of Nationwide's pre-tax profits is donated to good causes, including its own social investment work. Through various initiatives and its corporate charity, Nationwide is committed to tackling the housing crisis and educating young people in numeracy and developing money skills.

Community Grants programme

Nationwide Building Society makes funding available for housing-related charities through its Community Grants programme.

Grants of between £10,000 and £50,000 (over a maximum period of two years) will be awarded to charities, community land trusts and housing co-operatives looking to make positive changes in their local areas. In 2021/22, £4 million was awarded to 94 housing projects across the UK.

Types of funding available include:

- Core costs
- Staff and volunteer costs for the project lead partner
- Small-scale capital costs
- Activity costs
- Development and capacity building costs
- Building works and refurbishment costs

Oakfield Community Response Fund

The Oakfield Community Response Fund was established in spring 2020, in partnership with the Wiltshire Community Foundation in order to support charities and community groups in the Swindon area affected by the COVID-19 pandemic. The fund was created for local groups to apply for grants of up to £10,000 and in 2021/22 the fund awarded 22 grants, totalling £95,000.

The Community Foundation Northern Ireland (NICC no. NIC105105)

In 2021/22, as part of its social investment plan, Nationwide Building Society donated £350,000 to The Community Foundation Northern Ireland to fund seven 'tenant voice' projects, with the overall aim of strengthening the voice of tenants in debates on the private rented sector and housing.

Charity appeals

In 2021/22 the society raised £15,000 for the Poverty Hurts Appeal and over £1 million for the Red Cross Afghanistan and Ukraine appeals.

Partnerships

The society has an ongoing corporate charity partnership with Shelter that in 2021, marked its twentieth anniversary. The society funds the charity's helplines that, according to the Nationwide Social Investment Report, supported 7,000 people with urgent housing needs in 2021/22.

The society also has a partnership with St Mungo's, a charity that supports people facing homelessness. In 2021, the society donated £50,000 to support the digitalisation of the charity's Recovery College.

Nationwide Building Society is also a supporter of Macmillan Cancer Support's World's Biggest Coffee Morning.

COVID-19 response

As a response to the COVID-19 pandemic, Nationwide Building Society lifted restrictions on any community grants made during the pandemic, to help alleviate charities and community groups affected by the virus.

Employee-led support

Volunteering

Staff are encouraged to volunteer their time with the group's charity partner, St Mungo's, to provide it with the tools it needs to deliver a compassionate response to rough-sleepers locally. The society offers two days of paid leave a year to employees wanting to volunteer.

In 2021/22 over 10,338 hours were volunteered by the society's employees, 55% of which were through the society's two-day volunteering commitment.

Every Penny Helps

Through Nationwide Building Society's 'Every Penny Helps' scheme, employees can donate the last few pence of their wages to charities of their choice. In 2021/22 the scheme raised £30,000 for charities such as Alzheimer's UK, St Mungo's and Macmillan Cancer Support.

Payroll giving

In 2021/22, employees chose to donate to charity directly from their salaries through a 'Give As You Earn' scheme, raising £134,000.

Matched funding

The society operates a matched funding scheme, whereby any fundraising will be matched up to £100 per employee per year. The total funds raised through this method in 2021/22 was £40,000.

Macmillan Cancer Support World's Biggest Coffee Morning

In 2021/22, Nationwide Building Society employees collectively raised £65,000 to help people with a cancer diagnosis.

Employee and member giving

The total for combined donations from the society's employee and member giving in 2021/22 was £4 million.

Exclusions

The Community Grants programme does not support:

▶ Individuals/individual sponsorship
▶ Activities generating private profit
▶ Major/large-scale capital costs (for example, vehicles, land or property)
▶ Retrospective costs
▶ Organisations that promote religious or party-political activities

Applications

For the Community Grants programme, prospective applicants must first complete a short eligibility quiz, which is available on the society's website. Following this, eligible applicants will be able to make an application online.

For further details on applying to The Nationwide Foundation, see the corporate charity entry.

Corporate charity

The Nationwide Foundation (Charity Commission no. 1065552) – see entry on page 262.

Community contributions

Cash donations UK	£7,070,000

According to its 2021/22 accounts, Nationwide Building Society invested £7.07 million into a range of local initiatives as well as its own social investment strategy. Since 2007, the society has donated 1% of its pre-tax profits into its social investment plan, with at least 0.25% going to the Nationwide Foundation each year.

The Nationwide Foundation received donations totalling £2.16 million from the building society.

NatWest Group plc

Arts, culture and heritage, community enterprise and social entrepreneurship, community services and development, education and training, emergency response/relief, general charitable purposes, health, social justice, social welfare, sports and recreation

Company registration number: SC045551

Correspondent: Sustainable Banking Committee, 36 St Andrew Square, Edinburgh EH2 2YB (website: www. natwestgroup.com/our-purpose.html)

Directors: Howard Davies; Alison Rose; Katie Murray; Mark Seligman; Frank Danegard; Patrick Flynn; Morten Friis; Robert Gillespie; Yasmin Jetha; Mike Rogers; Lena Wilson; Jan Cargill (female: 42%; male: 58%).

Nature of business: NatWest Group is a UK-based banking and financial services group. It was formerly called Royal Bank of Scotland Group plc and changed its name in July 2020.

Financial information

Year end	31/12/2021
Turnover	£10,512,000,000
Pre-tax profit	£4,032,000,000

Total employees: 62,900

Main locations: NatWest Group operates in the UK, Europe, the Middle East, the Americas and Asia. Its principal UK offices are in Belfast, Birmingham, Bristol, Edinburgh, London and Manchester.

Community involvement

NatWest Group supports a wide range of charitable purposes through the delivery of strategic programmes, cash and in-kind donations and through employee fundraising and volunteering.

CareerSense programme

In 2021, NatWest Group plc launched its CareerSense programme. Designed to provide education and improve employability for 13 to 24-year olds, especially those from minority ethnic groups, the programme reached 8,200 pupils in the UK during the year.

Learning with NatWest

In November 2021, NatWest Group plc launched its 'Learning with NatWest' academy. The programme supports families and communities by providing free resources and learning on climate, employability, entrepreneurship and enterprise, future skills and financial capability.

NatWest Social and Community Capital (Charity Commission no. 1079626)

The group's charity, NatWest Social and Community Capital provides loans to social enterprises, charities, not-for-profit organisations and social businesses, particularly for those unable to access mainstream finance. To apply for a loan, organisations must be based in the UK, be an established third sector organisation with social or environmental aims, and not eligible for mainstream funding from banks. In 2021, the group donated £158,000 to the charity.

The Circle Fund

In February 2021, NatWest Group plc partnered with the charity SafeLives to create The Circle Fund. The fund is a three-year partnership and supports SafeLives to provide small grants to those who have faced economic abuse.

VaccinAid

In 2021, the group made a £260,000 donation to UNICEF's VaccinAid Appeal, that aimed to provide vaccines for two billion people worldwide.

Employee-led support

Do Good, Feel Good

Through the group's Do Good, Feel Good programme, employees are encouraged to fundraise and volunteer for charities of their choice. In 2021, NatWest Group plc employees raised £3.54 million and donated 43,003 hours to charitable causes.

Volunteering

The group's CareerSense programme is run by employees of the group who register as programme ambassadors. Following its launch in 2021, 597 employees were registered as CareerSense ambassadors.

The group also made a pledge in 2021 to plant 100,000 trees to help fight climate change, with employees encouraged to volunteer to plant trees in their local communities.

Commercially led support

Charity Partnership with Cancer Research UK

In 2021, NatWest Group plc established a partnership with Cancer Research UK (CRUK) to create the 'Maximise Your Giving' pilot, launched in October 2021. Customers who have made a payment to CRUK will receive a prompt on their mobile banking app pointing them to the relevant web pages that provide information about maximising charity giving. One of the options is to link through to the CRUK website where the customer can then complete a Gift Aid declaration allowing CRUK to claim the Gift Aid on their donations.

Applications

General enquiries should be submitted in writing to the correspondent.

RBS Social and Community Capital

To apply for a loan from the group's corporate charity visit www.business.rbs.co.uk/business/social-community-capital or contact by email: rbsscc@rbs.co.uk.

Community contributions

 Cash donations UK £7,270,000

According to the group's Economic Social Governance 2021 supplement, the group donated £7.27 million in community investment during the year. We were unable to determine how much of this amount was donated in the UK.

NCC Group plc

General charitable purposes

Company registration number: 4627044

Correspondent: The CSR Team, XYZ Building, 2 Hardman Boulevard, Spinningfields, Manchester M3 3AQ (tel: 0161 209 5200; email: contact form on the website; website: www.nccgroupplc.com/who-we-are/our-sustainability)

Directors: Chris Stone; Mike Madison; Tim Kowalski; Chris Batterham; Mike Ettling; Jenifer Duvalier; Julie Chakraverty; Lynn Fordham (female: 38%; male: 63%).

Nature of business: NCC Group is a global cyber security business operating across multiple sectors, geographies and technologies.

Financial information

Year end	31/05/2021
Turnover	£270,500,000
Pre-tax profit	£14,800,000

Total employees: 1,879

Main locations: The group's head office is in Manchester. It has several offices throughout the UK and operations in North America, Europe, Australia, Japan and Singapore.

Community involvement

NCC Group has a partnership with the Small Charities Coalition. The group offers ad hoc advice and cyber resilience training to small charities. According to NCC Group's 2021 annual report, this service has reached over 28,000 beneficiaries since its inception in 2019.

Employee-led support

The group offers up to £500 of matched funding for any employee-led fundraising per financial year. The group also has established a 'giving back day' whereby employees are encouraged to take a day of paid leave to support local charitable causes in the community.

Commercially led support

According to the 2021 annual report, the group sponsors initiatives in future cyber skills programmes that aim to improve cyber resilience and digital literacy.

Applications

Contact the correspondent for more information.

Community contributions

We were unable to determine a figure for the group's charitable contributions.

Newbury Building Society

Arts, culture and heritage, education and training, the environment, sports and recreation

Company registration number: 206077

Correspondent: CSR Team, 17 Bartholomew Street, Newbury, Berkshire RG14 5LY (tel: 01635 555700; email: marketing@newbury.co.uk; website: www.newbury.co.uk/about-us/community-and-charity)

Directors: Peter Brickley; Chris Brown; Nicola Bruce; Fiona Phillips; Roland Gardner; Lee Bambridge; Phillipa Cardno; Darren Garner; William Roberts; Alistair Welham; Piers Williamson (female: 36%; male: 64%).

Nature of business: Newbury Building Society is a building society based in Newbury, Berkshire.

Financial information

Year end	31/10/2021
Turnover	£19,523,000
Pre-tax profit	£7,635,000

UK employees: 171

Main locations: The society has branches in Abingdon, Alton, Andover, Basingstoke, Didcot, Hungerford, Newbury, Thatcham, Winchester and Wokingham.

Community involvement

Newbury Building Society supports the communities in which it operates through fundraising, sponsorship, donations and volunteering. Each branch of the society chooses local community organisations to support.

Charity Partnership scheme

Through this scheme, the society has established partnerships with a range of community organisations, voted for by employees and members. Charity partners benefit from fundraising activities as well as employee volunteering. Currently (September 2022), the society has nine charity partners: Alton Foodbank, Alzheimer's Society, The Countess of Brecknock Hospice, Friends of PICU, Helen and Douglas House, Newbury and District Cancer Care Trust, Prior's Court School, St Michael's Hospice and Sue Ryder.

Community Support scheme

Each year the society supports local groups, organisations and teams through donations and sponsorships. Awards typically range from £100 to £500. Applications are considered from several different categories including:

- Promote and encourage sporting activities
- Promote and encourage activities in the arts
- Support education and development
- Benefit the environment

In 2021/22, beneficiaries included All Yours, Be Free Young Carers, SeeAbility and Whitchurch Children's Festival.

Sponsorship

The society supports the communities in which it operates through sponsorship. In 2020/21, Newbury Building Society sponsored a poetry writing competition for Thatcham Town Council and was also the main sponsor of Julian House Basingstoke's 'Big Sleep Out', a fundraising event that raised money and awareness for those facing homelessness in Basingstoke.

Employee-led support

Employees are given two days' paid leave to volunteer for local community organisations and charities and each branch of the society chooses which community organisations to support, receiving matched funding from the society.

Employees from across the society participate in various charitable initiatives. In 2020/21, employees took part in an initiative by the Samaritans to help fund its services in the community. Employees in Wokingham, Thatcham and Newbury, raised £2,000 in 2021 for their chosen charities.

Commercially led support

The society sponsors local groups and teams through its Community Support Scheme.

Newbury Building Society makes annual donations to its charity partners through the society's charity account. The society offers charity accounts whereby an account holder can select one of the nine charity partners and the society will donate 0.3% of the interest on the account. In 2021, £23,828 was donated through charity accounts.

Applications

Application forms for sponsorship and donations can be downloaded from the society's website. A leaflet with further information on the schemes is also available to view. Applications are considered twice a year and should be submitted by May or November.

Community contributions

Cash donations UK	£63,000

In 2020/21, the society's charitable donations totalled £63,000. Within this, £11,300 was donated to 22 local community organisations as part of the Community Support Scheme.

Newcastle Building Society

Community enterprise and social entrepreneurship, community services and development, education and training, emergency response/relief, general charitable purposes, health, housing and homelessness, money and debt advice, social welfare

Company registration number: FCA 156058

Correspondent: CSR Team, Newcastle Building Society, Portland House, New Bridge Street, Newcastle upon Tyne, Tyne and Wear NE1 8AL (tel: 0191 244 2000; email: contact form on the website; website: www.newcastle.co.uk)

Directors: Andrew Haigh; Stuart Miller; David Samper; James Ramsbotham; Mick Thompson; Adam Bennet; Anne Shiels; Bryce Glover; Karen Ingham; Stuart Lynn; Michelle Faull (female: 27%; male: 73%).

Nature of business: Newcastle Building Society is a building society based in the North East.

Financial information

Year end	31/12/2021
Turnover	£67,200,000
Pre-tax profit	£25,500,000

UK employees: 600

Main locations: The society has branches across the North East and Cumbria. The society's head office is in Newcastle.

Community involvement

Newcastle Building Society supports its local communities through donations, employee fundraising and volunteering. According to the 2021 annual report, the society's charitable contributions in 2021 reached 21,774 people.

Newcastle Building Society Community Fund (not a registered charity)

Administered by Community Foundation Tyne and Wear and Northumberland (Charity Commission no. 700510), the fund awards grants to charities and community groups local to the society's branches. The fund's income comes from the society's contributions and is also supported by employee fundraising. Customers can nominate projects and charities, local to the branches, that would benefit from financial assistance.

In 2021, the Community Fund focused on making grants to organisations helping to provide workplace and employability skills, tackling debt, fighting food poverty and supporting hospices and cancer care services. The annual report states the following amounts awarded for each of these objectives:
- Workplace and employability skills – £100,000 to 27 charities
- Tackling debt – £20,000 to seven charities
- Fighting food poverty – £46,500 to 17 projects
- Hospices and cancer care services – £24,000 to eight charities

Partnerships

Newcastle Building Society has worked with the Sir Bobby Robson Foundation for several years. The foundation funds projects within the Newcastle upon Tyne Hospitals NHS Foundation Trust. To date, the society has donated over £3 million to the charity, with £50,000 donated in 2021. Money is raised through the society's Community Saver accounts.

The society has a four-year partnership with The Prince's Trust, supporting its 'Team' programme. The 12-week programme aims to help unemployed 16- to 25-year-olds to build their skills, confidence and experience to help them towards gaining employment. The programme is funded by Newcastle Building Society's Community Fund.

The society is also actively involved in Age UK's Dementia Friends initiative.

In partnership with Nursem, Newcastle Building Society donated a month's supply of Nursem's sanitizing hand cream to 7,500 nurses and clinicians across Northumbria Healthcare NHS Foundation Trust.

Newcastle United Foundation

The society announced in 2021 a partnership with the Newcastle United Foundation, pledging £1.1 million over the course of a six-year partnership. The society already sponsors the foundation's employability and training hub that helps to provide people in the community with workplace skills and opportunities.

Employee-led support

Employees volunteer and fundraise for local causes and the charity partners. During 2021, employees spent over 2,875 hours volunteering in their communities. Fundraising activities and the society's Give As You Earn scheme raised £14,772 for the Newcastle Building Society Community Fund during the year.

Exclusions

The society's website states that it cannot fund the following:
- Contributions to general appeals or circulars
- Religious or political activity which is not for wider public benefit
- Public bodies to carry out their statutory obligations
- Activities which solely support animal welfare
- Activities which have already taken place
- Grant making by other organisations
- Privately owned and profit-distributing companies or limited partnerships
- Commercial/profit making ventures

Applications

Community Fund

Charities or groups must be nominated by a current customer of the society. Nominations can be made online using an online form.

The website states that organisations must meet the following criteria in order to be nominated:
- Recognised community groups/ initiatives within the North East or branch area for out of area branches
- Any funding provided must 'make a difference' and be the reason why the initiative would be able to start
- Project must be at a stage where it can start within 3 months
- The funding must be used for a specific project – not just a donation

Check the website for current information on available grants.

Community contributions

Cash donations UK	£750,000

Newcastle Building Society's 2021 annual report states that the combined contributions from grant, matched funding and donations to charity partnerships totalled £750,000. The Newcastle Building Society Community Fund awarded total grants of £185,000.

Next Retail Ltd

Community services and development, health, sports and recreation

Company registration number: 4521150

Correspondent: Joanne Poynor, Head of Sustainable Development, NEXT plc, Desford Road, Enderby, Leicester, Leicestershire LE19 4AT (tel: 0333 777 4577; email: contact form on the website; website: www.nextplc.co.uk/corporate-responsibility/community)

Directors: Michael Roney; Lord Wolfson of Aspley Guise; Amanda James; Richard Papp; Jane Shields; Jonathan Bewes; Dame Dianne Thompson; Tristia Harrison; Tom Hall; Soumen Das (female: 40%; male: 60%).

Nature of business: The principal activities of the group are high-street retailing, home shopping, customer services management and financial services.

Financial information

Year end	25/01/2022
Turnover	£4,376,500,000
Pre-tax profit	£823,000,000

Total employees: 43,040

Main locations: Next has around 500 stores throughout the UK and Ireland. It also has eight UK warehouses, seven UK distribution centres and two international hubs.

Community involvement

Next Retail Ltd supports a wide range of charities and organisations through strategic partnerships, events and cash and product donations. According to the 2022 corporate sustainability report, in 2021/22, the company's contributions reached almost 325 registered charities. Support is also given through commercial sponsorship and grants to individual requests.

Each area of business is allocated a donation fund and employees in the area can decide which community organisations and causes to support.

The company's giving policy targets the following areas:

- Health and the alleviation of pain and suffering
- Environmental protection and improvement
- Education, skills and amateur sport

Partnerships

While the company holds various strategic partnerships with charities across the UK, certain partnerships are highlighted by the company's reporting.

Long-term strategic partnerships are held or have been established with charities such as Changing Inside and Out (CIAO), Doncaster Refurbish, The Terrence Higgins Trust and Parkinson's UK.

In-kind support

Next Retail Ltd donates unsellable or damaged furniture and home accessories to charities and social enterprises for reuse. Since 2008, the company has worked in partnership with Doncaster Refurnish, a social enterprise located close to its main warehouses. In 2021/22, 308 tonnes of furniture was diverted to the charity.

Employee-led support

Employees have raised funds for a range of charities through various activities. The company also operates a payroll giving scheme through which employees can donate to any UK-registered charity. In 2021/22, employees donated £82,000 to charities through the scheme.

Commercially led support

Next Retail Ltd offers commercial sponsorship to a small number of organisations. Local sporting teams are also supported, especially those with which an employee has a direct involvement.

Money is raised for charities across England, Scotland and Wales through the sale of reusable carrier bags in-store. In 2021/22, money raised from bag sales totalled £781,000.

Through its partnership with Parkinson's UK, the company has designed and sold a range of t-shirts and tote bags promoting messages of diversity, inclusion and community. The funds raised from the purchase of these items go to the charity.

Applications

Contact the correspondent for more information via post or by using the contact form on the company's website.

Community contributions

Cash donations UK	£1,187,000
Total contributions UK	£2,900,000

According to the Next Retail Ltd corporate responsibility report for 2022, the company made £2.9 million of community contributions, including in-kind product donations and sponsorships. The total financial contribution and its beneficiaries break down as follows:

Registered charities	£1.13 million
Commercial support and sponsorship	£60,000
Individual requests, local and national groups and organisations	£1,000

Further financial support was raised through the following activities:

Gifts in kind – product donations	£1.48 million
Charity link sales	£211,000
Employee fundraising/charity events	£22,000

Nisa Retail Ltd

General charitable purposes

Company registration number: 980790

Correspondent: CSR Team, Waldo Way, Normanby Enterprise Park, Scunthorpe, North Lincolnshire DN15 9GE (tel: 01724 282028 or 0845 6044999; email: consumer.services@nisaretail.com or use the contact form on the website; website: www.nisalocally.co.uk/community)

Directors: Michael Fletcher; John McNeil (male: 100%).

Nature of business: Nisa is a groceries wholesaler and wholly owned subsidiary of The Co-operative Group.

Financial information

Year end	06/01/2022
Turnover	£1,388,151,000
Pre-tax profit	£7,532,000

Main locations: Nisa has stores throughout the UK.

Community involvement

Nisa seeks to make a positive contribution to the communities in which it operates. The group provides support through its charity Making a Difference Locally Ltd (Charity Commission no. 1123800) which gives grants to local charities and good causes.

Commercially led support

For every Nisa Heritage own product and Co-op own labelled product sold in Nisa retailers' stores, a donation of 0.6% will be made to Making a Difference Locally Ltd.

Applications

Contact the correspondent for more information. To find your nearest Nisa retailer visit: www.nisaretail.com.

For more information on the Make A Difference Locally Charity visit: www.nisalocally.co.uk/community

Corporate charity

Making a Difference Locally Ltd (Charity Commission no. 1123800) – see entry on page 253.

Community contributions

The annual report and accounts for 2021/22 did not provide a figure for charitable contributions.

Nominet UK

Community enterprise and social entrepreneurship, community services and development, education and training

Company registration number: 3203859

Correspondent: Tech for Good Team, Minerva House, Edmund Halley Road, Oxford OX4 4DQ (tel: 01865 332211; email: nominet@nominet.uk; website: www.nominet.uk/tech-for-good)

Directors: Andy Green; Paul Fletcher; Sally Tilleray; Eva Lindquist; Stephen Page; Phil Buckingham; Anne Taylor; Simon Blackler; Ashley La Bolle (female: 44%; male: 56%).

Nature of business: Nominet UK is the .uk domain name registry in the UK.

Financial information

Year end	31/03/2021
Turnover	£49,846,000
Pre-tax profit	£5,162,000

Total employees: 264

Main locations: In the UK, Nominet's head office is in Oxfordshire. It also has an office in Washington, D.C., in the USA.

Community involvement

Through its public benefit programme, Nominet aims to improve the lives of one million young people through technology. It is achieving this goal by awarding direct grants, establishing partnerships and delivering programmes. Focus is given to the areas of online safety, digital skills for the future, access to the internet and digital services targeting mental health. Public benefit work is carried out under three pillars: connected, inclusive and secure. According to the 2021 Social Impact report, the company's public benefit programmes reached 1.8 million young people in 2021.

The Connected programme

The Connected programme aims to ensure that young people have access to the internet and critical digital services. Nominet is working in partnership with the Samaritans supporting the development of two new digital products. These include a self-help tool as well as a system that will allow volunteers to respond to significant volumes of additional contacts. The company has provided support to the charity through technological expertise and with a cash donation of £175,000.

The company has also partnered with the Learning Foundation to create 'Digital Access for All', a task force that develops solutions addressing the issue of digital exclusion.

In 2019 Nominet launched its flagship programme, the Nominet #RESET Mental Health Programme which makes grants to support digital mental health services. The funding will help to increase the digital capacity of UK mental health charities and provide young people with access to better quality and more personal support. Grants will also be awarded to support broader digital initiatives that boost collaboration, pathways and the quality of services across the mental health sector. Through the programme, the company has partnered with the following charities: Barnardo's, Chasing the Stigma, The Anna Freud National Centre for Children and Families, The Mix, Nightline Association, Place2Be, Stem 4 and YoungMinds.

The Inclusive programme

The Inclusive programme supports young people by providing them with the necessary digital skills as well as tackling digital exclusion for young people with disabilities.

Nominet works with youth marketing agency, Livity to deliver the Nominet Digital Neighbourhoods programme. The programme offers young people free training in digital skills before partnering them with SME's for work experience. In addition, the company in partnership with Livity, has created 'THIS IS HOW', a podcast and learning and skills platform for digital careers.

The company also works with Micro:bit Educational Foundation to develop a free education platform to help teachers to deliver creative digital projects and computing lessons.

Nominet is a founding partner of The Prince's Trust's new initiative to transform its online services for young people.

The Secure programme

The Secure programme aims to support organisations that provide advice and support to young people about online safety.

In 2019 the company launched its 'Nominet Tech Innovation Fund: Countering Online Harm', which awards grants to support research, initiatives and programmes that prevent and respond to issues that put young people at risk online. Nominet also works in partnership with the National Crime Agency's Child Exploitation Online Protection Command and the Internet Watch Foundation to enable them to develop tech solutions that counter online harm.

Nominet has also established a partnership with the Scouts to revamp its 'Digital Citizen Badge' that will educate young people on issues such as internet safety and digital resilience.

The Social Tech Trust (Charity Commission no. 1125735)

The Social Tech Trust was established in 2008 as the corporate charity of Nominet UK. In 2018, the charity became fully independent; however, it still receives support from the company in the form of in-kind gifts.

In-kind support

Nominet provides free office space, use of computers and phones as well as financial management services to The Social Tech Trust and Nightline Association.

Employee-led support

Employees take part in fundraising activities for charitable causes.

Applications

Contact the correspondent for further information.

Corporate charity

Social Tech Trust (Charity Commission no. 1125735) – see entry on page 276.

Community contributions

Cash donations UK	£3,442,000
Total contributions worldwide	£3,700,000

The company's 2020/21 annual report states that it invested £3.7 million into public benefit initiatives during the year. This figure includes grants totalling £3.4 million that were donated to public benefit programmes. A breakdown of the company's investment in public benefit initiatives was found in the Nominet Social Impact report for 2021 and is as follows:

Public Benefit Programme	Investment
Internet Safety for All	£967,000
Digital Skills and Careers	£931,000
Essential Digital Services	£568,000
Digital Access and Inclusion	£561,000
Countering Online Harm	£415,000
Total	**£3,442,000**

Norse Group Ltd

Education and training, the environment, health

Company registration number: 5694657

Correspondent: CSR Team, 280 Fifers Land, Norwich, Norfolk, NR6 6EQ (tel: 01603 894100; email: info@ncsgrp.co.uk; website: https://norsegroup.co.uk/corporate-social-responsibility)

Directors: Andy Wood; Andrew Proctor; Justin Galliford; Zoe Repman; Lord Gary Porter; Simon Hardwick; Brian McCarthy (female: 14%; male: 86%).

Nature of business: Norse Group is a holding company which brings together Facilities Management provider Norse Commercial Services, property consultancy NPS Group and care provider NorseCare.

Financial information

Year end	31/03/2021
Turnover	£354,318,000
Pre-tax profit	£1,988,000

Main locations: Norse Group has offices across England and Wales, and its head office is located in Norwich.

Community involvement

The group supports charities and community groups in the areas in which it operates. Support is provided through cash and donations and volunteering. According to its website, the group's CSR strategy focuses on several key areas including supporting older people, well-being and health, local regeneration, employment and youth opportunity, skills and employee development, and environmental management.

Community Fund (not a registered charity)

The Norse Group Community Fund awards grants totalling around £30,000 each year to community groups and charities which are nominated by group employees. In order to be eligible, the nominating employee must be actively involved in the organisation. Grants are usually in the region of £750. The fund also sponsors talented individuals who are often the children or grandchildren of group employees.

In-kind support

The group works with Norfolk ProHelp, a network of professional firms that offer pro bono services to community organisations in need of support. As part of the partnership, Norse Group Ltd companies offer their expertise in several areas including business planning and HR. For more information visit the website: www.norfolkprohelp.com.

The group has also worked with Theatre Royal in Norwich as a sponsor, providing subsidised theatre tickets for students from disadvantaged backgrounds.

Norse Group Ltd also partnered with Polish non-governmental organisation Norfolk Polonia CIC and Norfolk Fire and Rescue Service to provide essential resources to help the Ukraine Humanitarian Aid Effort. This includes logistics support at well as the donation of vans, fuel and generators.

Employee-led support

As well as group-wide initiatives, staff also deliver projects in their communities in response to local need.

Group employees are entitled to take up to eight hours a year paid time off work to volunteer for a good cause.

In 2022, Norse Group Ltd employees volunteered with Norfolk Polonia CIC and Norfolk Fire and Rescue Service to aid Ukrainian humanitarian aid efforts.

Applications

Contact the correspondent for more information.

Community contributions

The group's 2020/21 annual report did not provide a figure for its total community contribution.

Northumbrian Water Ltd

Community services and development, the environment

Company registration number: 4760441

Correspondent: See 'Applications', Northumbria House, Abbey Road, Durham, DH1 5FJ (website: www.nwg. co.uk/responsibility)

Directors: Andrew Hunter; Heidi Mottram; Alan Bryce; Dominic Chan; H. L. Kam; Duncan Macrae; Jacquie McGlade; Bridget Rosewell; Richard Sexton; Peter Vicary-Smith (female: 30%; male: 70%).

Nature of business: Northumbrian Water provides water and sewerage services in the North East and water services in the South East under the brand name Essex and Suffolk water.

Financial information

Year end	31/03/2022
Turnover	£716,700,000
Pre-tax profit	£41,000,000

Total employees: 3,128

Main locations: The group supplies water to the North East, Essex and Suffolk. Its head office is in Durham.

Community involvement

Northumbrian Water contributes at least 1% of its annual pre-tax profits to benefit local communities. Support is provided to environmental projects through its Branch Out grants programme and to local communities through its four community funds.

Branch Out

The Branch Out grant fund helps to deliver projects that benefit the natural environment and local communities within Northumbrian Water's operating area. Grants of up to £25,000 are available to organisations, community groups, or individuals from the public, private, voluntary and education sectors. Examples of the types of projects funded include:

- Water in the natural environment – projects that protect drinking water sources, enhance water quality or provide other benefits to wetland habitats

- Wildlife – by linking up habitats, creating new areas for wildlife to use or finding ways to reconnect people with the natural world around them
- Community – encouraging local communities to enjoy the benefits of being outside and helping them to become more aware of the importance of the natural world, or providing opportunities for Northumbrian Water employees to volunteer to assist with projects in their operating area
- Climate change – help build capacity in the natural environment to deal with the effects of climate change
- Sewerage and drainage – protecting vulnerable areas from diffuse pollution or helping build capacity in the natural environment to help deal with storm events
- Science – scientific research that would benefit Northumbrian Water

Partnerships

The group has partnerships with Healthworks, StepChange and WaterAid.

Community funds

The group has four community funds with the following community foundations:

- Tyne and Wear and Northumberland Community Foundation
- County Durham Community Foundation
- Tees Valley Community Foundation
- Essex Community Foundation

Education

The group provides educational resources and site visits for schools.

Employee-led support

In 2021/22, employees supported 235 organisations through the volunteering scheme, Just an Hour. According to the group website, the scheme allows employees to give a minimum of 15 hours every year to support causes of their choice.

Exclusions

No donations are given to individuals, exclusive religious projects, organisations outside the group's service area, or to cover wages.

Applications

Branch Out grants – in the first instance, consult the group's website at: www.nwg.co.uk/responsibility/ environment/branch-out-funds/branch-out.

Community funds – applications should be made to the relevant community foundation.

Educational visits – to organise a visit, complete the online form available at: www.nwg.co.uk/responsibility/working-with-schools/teachers/site-tours.

Community contributions

Cash donations UK		£241,000

The group's 2021/22 Our Contribution Report states that direct financial contribution to environmental, community and charitable NGOs totalled £241,000.

Norton Rose Fulbright LLP

General charitable purposes, social justice

Company registration number: OC328697

Correspondent: The CSR Team, 3 More London Riverside, London SE1 2AQ (website: www.nortonrosefulbright.com/en/about/corporate-responsibility)

Directors: Gerry Pecht; Rob Otty; Jeff Cody; Alison Deitz; Charles Hurdon; Andrew Robinson; Peter Scott (female: 14%; male: 86%).

Nature of business: Norton Rose Fulbright LLP is a global law firm with over 50 offices in Africa, Asia, Australia, Canada, Europe, Latin America, the Middle East and the USA.

Financial information

Year end	30/04/2021
Turnover	£518,720,000
Pre-tax profit	£161,396,000

Total employees: 8,191

Main locations: The firm has over 50 offices worldwide. In the UK, there are offices in London and Newcastle.

Community involvement

Norton Rose Fulbright's community efforts focus on pro bono, volunteering and grant support to charities local to its offices.

The majority of charitable giving is through the firm's corporate charity, The Norton Rose Fulbright Charitable Foundation (Charity Commission no. 1102142). The foundation supports a wide range of general charitable purposes, including education, medical and social welfare.

Norton Rose Fulbright's UK charity partner include Show Racism the Red Card and The South London Refugee Association.

NHS Charities Together

In 2021, the firm held a dress-up day to raise funds for charities linked to the National Health Service (NHS), called NHS Charities Together. Money raised went towards helping NHS staff and volunteers caring for patients with COVID-19 in the UK. This included staff travel and parking fees, delivery of well-being and overnight packs for those on long shifts, and meals and contributions. Money raised also provided respite, rehabilitation and mental health assistance to NHS staff and their families following the COVID-19 pandemic.

In-kind support

The firm encourages employees to work pro bono for charities and local organisations. Lawyers regularly attend evening drop-in clinics organised by law centres in the London boroughs of Tower Hamlets and Croydon. Beyond legal pro bono work, the finance and marketing teams also provide pro bono support. Many offices offer leave for colleagues to spend on approved volunteer initiatives.

In 2021, the firm's UK IT team repurposed previous generation laptops to distribute to schools close to its London and Newcastle offices. It awarded over 150 laptops to disadvantaged pupils within target schools and launched a fundraising appeal to buy more IT equipment for schools.

Employee-led support

Volunteering

Employees volunteer their legal and non-legal skills to charities and schools local to their office. Each month a team from the London office staffs the Liberty Public Advice Line to answer questions from callers on human rights and civil liberties. The London office also has a partnership with Smart Works, a charity that helps women start their careers or get back into work after a prolonged break. Employees donate interview clothing each month and volunteer to act as interview coaches.

Fundraising

Employees also support fundraising activities for the London Legal Support Trust, which aids local law centres.

Applications

For further information on pro bono support or potential partnerships, contact your local office.

Corporate charity

The Norton Rose Fulbright Charitable Foundation (Charity Commission no. 1102142) – see entry on page 263.

Community contributions

We were unable to determine a figure for the firm's charitable contributions.

Nottingham Building Society

Employment advice, housing and homelessness, money and debt advice

Correspondent: Corporate Responsibility Team, Nottingham House, 3 Fulforth Street, Nottingham, Nottinghamshire NG1 3DL (tel: 0344 481 4444; website: www.thenottingham.com)

Directors: John Edwards; Andrew Neden; Simon Baum; Simon Linares; Kavita Patel; Kerry Spooner; David Marlow; Daniel Mundy; Charles Roe (female: 22%; male: 78%).

Nature of business: Nottingham Building Society is a mutual society that provides mortgages, savings, estate agency services, home insurance and financial planning.

Financial information

Year end	31/12/2021
Turnover	£49,000,000
Pre-tax profit	£74,000,000

Total employees: 700

Main locations: The society has offices across Cambridgeshire, Derbyshire, Hertfordshire, Leicestershire, Lincolnshire, Northamptonshire, Nottinghamshire and South Yorkshire. Its head office is in Nottingham.

Community involvement

The society's support for communities is focused on the key themes of tackling homelessness and promoting financial education and employability.

Partner charities

The society has a long-term partnership with Framework, a small homelessness charity in the East Midlands. It also has partnerships with the National Literacy Trust and Nottingham City Council's StoryParks project.

Samuel Fox Foundation

In 2021, the society launched the Samuel Fox Foundation, which focuses on building skills and employability in local communities. The foundation particularly focuses on supporting young people to fulfil their potential and inspire their futures.

Employee-led support

Employees are given two days' paid leave a year to volunteer. According to the society's 2021 annual report, employees volunteered over 1,000 hours for the society's Career Academy to provide an employability programme for young people.

Commercially led support

The society sponsors Nottingham Panthers ice hockey team and Leicester Tigers rugby club.

Applications

Contact the correspondent for further information.

Community contributions

Cash donations UK		£200,000

The 2021 annual report states that charitable donations during the year totalled £200,000.

Ocado Group plc

Community enterprise and social entrepreneurship, education and training, the environment, health

Company registration number: 7098618

Correspondent: Corporate Responsibility Team, Buildings 1 and 2, Trident Place, Hatfield Business Park, Mosquito Way, Hatfield, Hertfordshire AL10 9UL (tel: 01707 227800; website: https://supportingcommunities.org/funding-news-1/2021/11/17/ocado-foundation-for-good)

Directors: Rick Haythornthwaite; Jörn Rausing; Emma Lloyd; Andrew Harrison; Julie Southern; John Martin; Michael Sherman; Nadia Shouraboura (female: 38%; male: 63%).

Nature of business: Ocado is an online grocery retailer.

Financial information

Year end	01/12/2021
Turnover	£2,500,000,000
Pre-tax profit	(£176,900,000)

Total employees: 18,618

Main locations: Ocado's headquarters is in Hatfield, Herefordshire.

Community involvement

Ocado focuses much of its community involvement on the four key areas of education, the environment, entrepreneurship and eating well. Support is given through cash donations and in-kind and employee-led support.

The Ocado Foundation (not a registered charity)

The foundation was established in 2015 to support employees with their personal fundraising and to be the vehicle for all group fundraising. Donations are made to multiple small, local projects and charities where the impact will be the greatest. The foundation matches employee fundraising and funding in lieu of volunteering hours. During the year, the foundation awarded £16,500 in grants to registered charities.

In-kind support

In 2021, the group donated 280 laptops to those in need.

Employee-led support

Ocado employees have volunteered more than 1,287 hours to a variety of good causes and also take part in various fundraising initiatives on behalf of the foundation.

Applications

Contact the correspondent for further information.

Community contributions

| Total contributions UK | £135,400 |

According to the group's 2021 annual report, it donated £135,400 to support education and communities.

Octopus Capital Ltd

The environment, mental health and well-being

Company registration number: 3981143

Correspondent: The Octopus Giving Team, 6th Floor, 33 Holborn, London EC1N 2HT (email: giving@octopusgroup.com; website: https://octopusgroup.com/about/octopus-giving)

Directors: John Browett; Ruth Handcock; Christopher Hulatt; Stuart Quickenden; Simon Rogerson (female: 20%; male: 80%).

Nature of business: Octopus Capital Ltd is a group of eight businesses including: Octopus Investments, Octopus Energy, Octopus Ventures, Octopus Real Estate, Octopus Wealth; Octopus Moneycoach, Octopus Renewables and Seccl.

Financial information

Year end	30/04/2021
Turnover	£2,263,108,000
Pre-tax profit	(£22,797,000)

Main locations: Octopus Capital Ltd is headquartered in London.

Community involvement

The group supports charities through grants, employee volunteering and matched funding. All these activities are co-ordinated through the group's corporate charity, Octopus Giving (Charity Commission no. 1161273).

Octopus Giving

Octopus Giving makes grants to the group's charity partners. The group's current partners are Thames 21 and GoodGym. Previous partners have included The Choir With No Name, Downright Excellent, FoodCycle and MyBnk. In 2020/21, grants to charity partners totalled £71,300. A further £39,100 was donated in matched funding and smaller charity donations.

In-kind support

The group is corporate sponsor of The Funding Network (TFN), a network which connects potential donors with charitable causes and social entrepreneurship projects through crowdfunding events.

Employee-led support

In 2020/21, employees volunteered for a total of 2,150 hours. Each business has a Giving Champion who encourages employees to volunteer for partners and

local charities. Charities receive £20 for every hour an Octopus employee volunteers with them.

Applications

The group's website states: 'If you would like more information about Octopus Giving or are interested in working with us, please email us on giving@octopusgroup.com.'

Community contributions

| Cash donations UK | £300,000 |

In 2020/21, Octopus Capital Ltd made a £300,000 donation to its corporate charity through its subsidiary Octopus Investments Ltd.

OneSavings Bank plc

Community services and development, education and training, health, housing and homelessness, sports, work outside the UK

Company registration number: 7312896

Correspondent: CSR Team, Reliance House, Sun Pier, Chatham, Kent ME4 4ET (tel: 01634 848944; email: mail@osb.co.uk; website: www.osb.co.uk/corporate-responsibility/focused-on-our-community)

Directors: David Weymouth; Andy Golding; April Talintyre; Noël Harwerth; Graham Allatt; Mary McNamara; Rajan Kapoor; Sarah Hedger; Simon Walker (female: 44%; male: 56%).

Nature of business: OneSavings Bank (OSB) is a specialist mortgage lender focused on underserved sub-sectors of the mortgage market. In October 2019, the group combined with Charter Court Financial Services Group plc (CCFS). CCFS focuses on providing buy-to-let and specialist residential mortgages. Together, the combined group is made up of numerous brands including Kent Reliance, Precise Mortgages and OSB India.

Financial information

Year end	31/12/2021
Turnover	£629,000,000
Pre-tax profit	£464,600,000

Total employees: 1,782

Main locations: OneSavings Bank has a network of branches in the South East, as well as operations in India under the brand OSB India. In 2019, the group combined with Charter Court Financial Services Group plc, meaning it now has operations in West Midlands.

Community involvement
Partnerships
In 2021, the group chose CALM as the first group charity partner. CALM is a charity that raises awareness of mental health issues to encourage people to talk

about mental health, create social change and seek help when needed.

The group has partnerships with several UK organisations. The following information is taken from the group's website:

The Haven, Wolverhampton – supports women and dependent children who are vulnerable to domestic violence, homelessness and abuse, providing them with practical and emotional support.

The Shooting Star Hospice, Fareham/ Fleet – the hospice supports families living in London and Surrey who are dealing with life-limiting conditions, providing care for the families and offering a bespoke service to suit their needs.

Demelza Hospice Care for Children (supported by Kent Reliance through our Children's Savings Accounts), Kent – Demelza provides clinical care, therapies, specialised activities and practical support across Kent, South East London and East Sussex.

The Happy Pants Ranch, Kent – the ranch is a safe haven for over 100 unwanted and abandoned animals, but the Ranch rescued and re-homed well over 200 animals.

Wolverhampton Rugby Club – the Group has a long-standing relationship with Wolverhampton Rugby, a community-based, grassroots club serving both male and female teams from the age of six upwards. Our partnership has meant people of all ages are able to come together, share talents, learn new skills and in turn, strengthen community bonds.

XL@Football Academy – our newest partnership which was established in 2021, is a female football academy with the mission to develop young female footballers and provide a pathway into the professional game, delivering the same level of training, coaching and support as male teams receive.

Employee-led support

Employees are entitled to one paid 'Day to Make a Difference' each year to volunteer for any registered charity or community group. Often employees use this day to support their branch's local charity partner; for example, employees from InterBay Asset Finance volunteered to help Shooting Star Children's Hospices move items from its old warehouse to a new hospice facility. For any additional fundraising activities, the group will provide matched funding (the maximum amount is unspecified). In 2021, 72 volunteering days were logged across the group.

Commercially led support

Each year, the group's brand Kent Reliance raises funds for the Demelza Hospice Care for Children by offering customers a dedicated Demelza Children's Account.

The group sponsors the Wolverhampton Rugby Club. The sponsorship pays for the running of the club, enabling it to remain a hub of the local community.

Applications

National and local charity partners are nominated by employees. Contact the correspondent for further information on the group's CSR activities.

Community contributions

Cash donations worldwide	£394,800

According to its 2021 annual report, the group donated £394,800 through group donations, fund-matching, employee fundraising, Pennies from Heaven and good causes fund applications.

Ovo Energy Ltd

Community services and development, education and training, energy, the environment, rural communities, social welfare, work outside the UK

Company registration number: 6890795

Correspondent: The Ovo Charitable Foundation, 1 Rivergate, Temple Quay, Bristol BS1 6ED (website: www. ovoenergy.com)

Directors: Vincent Casey; Raman Bhatia (male: 100%).

Nature of business: Ovo Energy is an energy supplier based in Bristol.

Financial information

Year end	31/12/2020
Turnover	£932,000,000
Pre-tax profit	(£292,000,000)

UK employees: 1,031

Total employees: 2,479

Main locations: The company's headquarters is in Bristol and it also has an office in London.

Community involvement

Support is provided through the company's corporate charity The Ovo Charitable Foundation (Charity Commission no. 1155954).

Ovo Gives Back

Each year the foundation supports four employee-nominated charities through year-round volunteering and grants of up to £20,000. A further £20,000 is set aside to match any extra money raised by employees. In 2021, Ovo Gives Back supported The Wild Trust. Employees volunteered with the trust to enhance and protect the natural environment in their local communities.

Employee-led support

Employees volunteer with charities chosen for the foundation's Ovo Gives Back initiative.

Commercially led support

Ovo Energy gives all customers on a pay monthly tariff the opportunity to donate to The Ovo Charitable Foundation.

Applications

The recipients of the Ovo Gives Back grants are nominated and voted for by Ovo employees.

Corporate charity

The Ovo Charitable Foundation (Charity Commission no. 1155954) – see entry on page 264.

Community contributions

Cash donations worldwide	£648,000

In 2020, the company donated £648,000 to charitable causes.

Parabola Real Estate Holdings Ltd

Arts, culture and heritage, community services and development, health, medical research, music, rural communities, work outside the UK

Company registration number: 10084921

Correspondent: The Parabola Foundation, Broadgate Tower, 20 Primrose Street, London EC2A 2EW (tel: 0131 603 8300; email: info@ parabola.com; website: www.parabola. com/philanthropy)

Directors: Peter Millican; Tony Hordon; Kirsty MacGregor (female: 33%; male: 67%).

Nature of business: Parabola is a privately owned development and investment group with built accommodation throughout the UK. Parabola Real Estate Holdings Ltd is the holding company of the group.

Financial information

Year end	31/03/2021

Main locations: The group has offices in Edinburgh, Newcastle and London.

Community involvement

All of the group's community involvement is directed through its corporate charity, the Parabola Foundation (Charity Commission no. 1156008).

Applications

For further details on applying to the Parabola Foundation, see the corporate charity entry.

Corporate charity

Parabola Foundation (Charity Commission no. 1156008) – see entry on page 265.

Community contributions

Cash donations UK	£862,900

In 2020/21, the Parabola group donated £862,900 to its corporate charity, the Parabola Foundation. This information has been taken from the Parabola Foundation's 2020/21 annual report.

Paradigm Housing Group

🔍 General charitable purposes

Company registration number: IP28844R

Correspondent: The CSR Team, Paradigm Housing Group, 1 Glory Park Avenue, Wooburn Green, Buckinghamshire HP10 0DF (tel: 0300 303 1010; email: enquiries@ paradigmhousing.co.uk; website: www. paradigmhousing.co.uk)

Directors: Matthew Bailes; Hannah Manyewu; Justin McCarthy; Nicola Ewen; Martyn Jones; Sarah Nickson; Patrick Dawson; Ewan Wallace (female: 38%; male: 63%).

Nature of business: Paradigm is a housing provider in the South East and London, managing over 15,000 homes across 30 local authorities.

Financial information

Year end	31/03/2022
Turnover	£116,840,000
Pre-tax profit	(£11,210,000)

Total employees: 474

Main locations: The group operates in 30 local authorities across the South East and London. A map is available on the group's website.

Community involvement

The group awards grants to a range of voluntary organisations through its grant-making programme. According to its 2021/22 ESG report, the group allocated funds for a grants programme that supports customers and communities in the areas where Paradigm Housing Group. The report states:

It does this by making grants to charitable or community organisations to provide services or carry out activities which help to sustain or improve financial resilience or better social and health outcomes. This included emergency COVID grants to support Foodbanks and groups providing support for people suffering from domestic abuse. The grant programme delegates to the Customer Directorate a budget of £5,000 for emergency grants to customers where there are exceptional cases of financial hardship.

Grants were given for a range of needs including domestic abuse, employment, financial inclusion, food banks, isolation, learning difficulties, mental health and so on.

Applications

Contact the correspondent for further information. At the time of writing (November 2022), the group's website stated the following:

Paradigm has reviewed the work it supports through its grants programme.

We have decided to prioritise the allocation of grants to activities which directly support our customers to manage the cost-of-living crisis. This means that, for now, we will only be making further grants which provide targeted assistance either directly by us or through established partner organisations.

We regret that this means that we are no longer considering applications for new grants.

Community contributions

Cash donations UK	£252,800

According to the group's 2021/22 annual report, its charity donations during the year were £252,800.

Paragon Banking Group plc

🔍 Community services and development, education and training, general charitable purposes, health, housing and homelessness, money and debt advice, social welfare

Company registration number: 2336032

Correspondent: CSR Team, 51 Homer Road, Solihull B91 3QJ (tel: 0345 849 4000; website: www. paragonbankinggroup.co.uk/about-us/ corporate-responsibility/support-community)

Directors: Fiona Clutterbuck; Nigel Terrington; Richard Woodman; Barbara Ridpath; Hugo Tudor; Graeme Yorston; Alison Morris; Tanvi Davda; Robert East; Peter Hill (female: 40%; male: 60%).

Nature of business: Paragon is a specialist banking group that provides mortgages and commercial and personal loans.

Financial information

Year end	30/09/2021
Turnover	£324,900,000
Pre-tax profit	£213,700,000

Total employees: 1,365

Main locations: The group is headquartered in Solihull and has an office in London.

Community involvement

The group supports local communities through volunteering, cash donations, fundraising and partnerships.

Charity of the Year

Each year employees select a charity for a fundraising focus. In 2021, employees raised over £42,500 for the Alzheimer's Society. For 2022, employees have chosen to fundraise for the mental health charity, Mind.

Volunteer scheme partners

Through its employee volunteer programme, the group has partnered with a wide range of organisations including Ready for Work, an initiative helping disadvantaged people back into employment and SIFA Fireside, a specialist centre in Birmingham which supports people experiencing homelessness.

Local schools

The group works with a number of schools in Solihull to assist with career days and help students with CV writing and interviews.

Employee-led support

The group's community volunteer scheme allows employees to volunteer for one day each year for specific initiatives that help with education and tackle poverty. According to the group's website, the scheme focuses on projects that:

- educate school pupils to avoid them getting into poverty
- support individuals currently experiencing poverty
- help individuals to get out of poverty and back into work

In 2020/21, employees used 49 volunteering days.

The group supports the employee-led Paragon Charity Committee. Employees vote yearly on which charities will benefit from the group's fundraising activities which are organised by the committee. In 2021, employees chose to support the Alzheimer's Society

Commercially led support

Paragon sponsors local events. Previously it has sponsored Fun in the Park, an annual fun day in Tudor Grange Park, Solihull, which supports local charities.

Applications

The beneficiaries of the charity committee's fundraising are voted for by employees. Contact the correspondent for further information.

Community contributions

Total contributions UK	£39,600

In 2020/21, the group contributed £39,600 to charitable organisations.

Peel L&P Holdings (UK) Ltd

Arts, culture and heritage, community services and development, education and training, the environment, general charitable purposes, health, medical research, social welfare

Company registration number: 6497115

Correspondent: CSR Team, Venus Building, 1 Old Park Lane, TraffordCity, Manchester M41 7HA (tel: 0161 629 8200; email: Sustainability@peellandp.co.uk; website: https://peellandp.co.uk/our-charities)

Directors: Steven Underwood; John Schofield; John Whittaker (male: 100%).

Nature of business: Peel L&P Holdings (UK) Ltd is a regeneration business that uses natural assets to deliver long-term transformational projects including airports, hotels, waterways, media hubs, leisure facilities, retail, farms/estates and workspaces. It is part of The Peel Group.

Financial information

Year end	31/03/2021
Turnover	£88,430,000
Pre-tax profit	(£37,660,000)

Total employees: 293

Main locations: Peel L&P Holdings (UK) Ltd is based in Manchester. It has operations throughout the UK, with many of its projects located in northern England.

Community involvement

Peel L&P Holdings (UK) Ltd supports a range of charitable causes and organisations, predominantly those located in North West England. In line with the wider Peel Group Charity Strategy, Peel L&P Holdings (UK) Ltd works across charitable programmes in healthcare and medical research, culture and the environment, as well as engaging in social and sustainable activity for the public good. Support is given through grants, in-kind donations and volunteering.

The Peel Group Foundation (registered in the Isle of Man)
Launched in 2022, the foundation was established to provide financial and non-financial support in alignment with The Peel Group's business activities by giving back to the communities in which it operates. The foundation aims to work within five key sectors: healthcare and medical research, culture and heritage, welfare, the environment, education and support for young people. It will also support social and sustainable activity for the public benefit.

Protos Community Benefit Fund
In 2016, the Protos Community Benefit Fund was established after the group developed the Protos site in Manchester. The fund is managed independently by a Benefit Fund Panel and a Community Forum. Funds are available for local community causes every year and open to bids for funding from organisations and causes in local parishes.

In-kind support
The company provides in-kind support to organisations such as the provision of land and resources.

Employee-led support
Employees take part in volunteering and fundraising activities. Examples include cycle challenges and the Liverpool Waters Dragon Boat Race. In 2021/22 over 5,600 hours of volunteer work were spent on community projects.

Commercially led support
The company is a sponsor of Bolton Lads and Girls Club, a youth club and charity that offers universal open access, seven days and nights a week, 51 weeks a year as well as a range of mental health services.

Applications
The Peel Group Foundation
Details of how to apply for funding can be found on the foundation's website: https://peelgroupfoundation.org

Protos Community Benefit Fund
Application forms can be downloaded from the Protos website and should be emailed to the Community Forum's secretary, Keith Butterick: k.butterick@hud.ac.uk. To discuss the application process, contact a local fund member using the contact details provided at: www.protos.co.uk/how-to-apply.

Community contributions

Cash donations UK	£500,000
Total contributions worldwide	£700,000

According to its 2021/22 sustainability and ESG report, Peel L&P Holdings (UK) Ltd provided over £500,000 in cash donations and over £200,000 in-kind donations.

Pennon Group plc

Community services and development, education and training, the environment

Company registration number: 2366640

Correspondent: Sustainability Committee, Peninsula House, Rydon Lane, Exeter, Devon EX2 7HR (tel: 01392 446677; website: www.pennon-group.co.uk/sustainability)

Directors: Gill Rider; Susan Davy; Paul Boote; Neil Cooper; Jon Butterworth; Iain Evans; Claire Ighodaro (female: 43%; male: 57%).

Nature of business: Pennon Group is a British water utility company that owns South West Water.

Financial information

Year end	31/03/2022
Turnover	£792,300,000
Pre-tax profit	£127,700,000

Total employees: 2,636

Main locations: Support is given throughout the South West.

Community involvement

Pennon Group plc and its subsidiaries support communities and charities in the areas in which they operate. Support is provided through charitable donations, partnerships, educational initiatives and so on.

Community funds
In 2020, the group launched two funds:
- Water-Saving Community Fund, which empowers customers to champion and drive initiatives to save water locally
- Neighbourhood Fund, which is supporting communities with much-needed help

Partnerships
The group works in partnership with a number of charities including Air Ambulances, Keep Britain Tidy, the RNLI, Surf Life Saving GB and the Wildlife Trusts.

Charitable donations
The group's website states that its major charitable donations in 2020/21 were awarded to:
- Age UK Cornwall and Isles of Scilly
- Age UK Devon
- Cornwall Air Ambulance Trust
- Cornwall Wildlife Trust
- Devon Air Ambulance Trust
- Devon and Cornwall Food Action
- Devon Wildlife Trust
- Environment Plymouth
- Keep Britain Tidy
- Kerdroya
- My Coast
- RNLI
- South West Coast Path
- South West Tourism Awards
- Surf Life Saving GB
- Theatre Royal Plymouth Young Company Hubs
- Westcountry Rivers Trust

South West Water, a subsidiary of Pennon Group plc, also continued to fund the Beach-Care programme, with Keep Britain Tidy, which organises and co-ordinates voluntary, community-based beach cleans across the South West.

In-kind support
Community programmes
South West Water continued its support of education by providing talks,

resources, work experience placements and by giving lectures at regional universities.

Employee-led support

Employees help to raise funds for the group's preferred charities. South West Water has an active volunteering scheme.

Commercially led support

The group has a sponsorship programme. Previous sponsorships include Beach Schools South West, Cornwall Wildlife Trust, Devon Wildlife Trust, Devon Youth Games Trust, Environment Plymouth, South West Coast Path and Surf Live Saving GB.

Applications

Contact the correspondent for further information.

Community contributions

Cash donations UK	£91,000

According to its annual report, Pennon Group plc contributed £600,000 to communities during 2021/22, which included cash donations totalling £91,000.

Pentland Group Ltd

Arts, culture and heritage, community services and development, general charitable purposes, health, religion, social justice, social welfare, sports and recreation

Company registration number: 793577

Correspondent: CSR Team, 8 Manchester Square, London W1U 3PH (tel: 020 8346 2600; email: corporate. responsibility@pentland.com; website: https://pentlandbrands.com)

Directors: John Morgan; Alison Mosheim; Barry Mosheim; Andrew Rubin; Angela Rubin; Carolyn Rubin; Robert Rubin; Andrew Long (female: 38%; male: 63%).

Nature of business: The main activities of the subsidiary companies are footwear, clothing and sports, consumer products and international trading.

Financial information

Year end	31/12/2020
Turnover	£6,595,700,000
Pre-tax profit	£858,200,000

Total employees: 50,000

Main locations: Pentland's head office is based in London.

Community involvement

The Pentland Group supports charities within its area of operation through financial donations, in-kind support and employee-led support. The group is a family-owned business founded by the Rubin Family, who are also the founders

and trustees of The Rubin Foundation Charitable Trust (Charity Commission no. 327062). The group's subsidiary, JD Sports, has a corporate charity, the JD Foundation (Charity Commission no. 1167090) through which it funnels its charitable giving. The foundation gives to mental health, children and young people, homelessness and youth charities.

Partnerships

Pentland brands partner with charities in the communities in which they operate. The three main goals are inspiring young people to be more active, empowering disadvantaged communities and reducing environmental impact.

In the UK partnerships include SportInspired, a charity that tackles childhood obesity in disadvantaged communities in the UK through sports programmes and Panathlon, which provides sporting opportunities for thousands of young people in the UK with disabilities. The group's website provides full details of the current charity partners.

In 2022, the group began a partnership with The People to launch the Pentland Collective, a free mentoring programme for young people from ethnic minority backgrounds.

The Rubin Foundation Charitable Trust (Charity Commission no. 327062)

This trust is closely connected with the Pentland Group; however, it is not the group's corporate charity. The trust's income comes, in part, from donations from the group.

The trust tends to support a select number of charities on an annual basis and there is a preference for supporting Jewish organisations and causes.

In 2020/21 the trust awarded grants to organisations totalling £790,600.

In-kind support

Pentland Group Ltd donates its brands' products through other charitable organisations. It has a 20-year partnership with In Kind Direct, a network of charitable organisations in the UK and abroad established to distribute donated products. In 2022, donations through In Kind Direct supported 993 charitable organisations.

Employee-led support

Employees are given paid volunteering leave.

Commercially led support

The JD Foundation is predominantly funded by proceeds from the carrier bag charges from JD Sports.

Applications

Contact the correspondent for further information about in-kind donations.

The Rubin Foundation Charitable Trust (Charity Commission no. 327062)

The trust has previously stated that 'grants are only given to people related to our businesses, such as charities known to members of the Rubin family and those associated with Pentland Group Ltd'. Unsolicited applications are unlikely to succeed.

JD Foundation (Charity Commission no. 1167090)

See the foundation's entry in the corporate charity section.

Corporate charity

JD Foundation (Charity Commission no. 1167090) – see entry on page 248.

Community contributions

Every year, Pentland Brands, a subsidiary of Pentland Group Ltd, gives at least 1% of its net profit after tax to charitable causes through product donations and financial contributions. A figure was not provided.

Persimmon plc

Arts, culture and heritage, community services and development, education and training, general charitable purposes, health, housing and homelessness, social welfare, sports and recreation

Company registration number: 1818486

Correspondent: CSR Team, Persimmon plc, Persimmon House, Fulford, York, North Yorkshire YO19 4FE (tel: 01904 642199; email: sustainability@ persimmonhomes.com; website: www. persimmonhomes.com/corporate)

Directors: Roger Devlin; Dean Finch; Nigel Mills; Simon Litherland; Joanna Place; Annemarie Durbin; Shirine Khoury-Haq; Andrew Wyllie; Jason Windsor (female: 33%; male: 67%).

Nature of business: Persimmon Homes is a residential home builder and property developer.

Financial information

Year end	31/12/2021
Turnover	£3,610,500,000
Pre-tax profit	£966,800,000

Main locations: Persimmon has offices throughout the UK, details of which can be found on its website.

Community involvement

Until recently, the company carried out all of its charitable giving through The Persimmon Charitable Foundation (Charity Commission no. 1163608).

The Persimmon Charitable Foundation's 2021 annual report states the following:

> The directors of Persimmon plc have notified the trustees of the Persimmon Foundation that, from 1 October 2022,

Persimmon plc will fund the Community Champions campaign directly, instead of donating the relevant funds to the Persimmon Foundation. Persimmon plc anticipates that this change will enable Persimmon operating businesses to make a smaller number of larger donations to local groups and charities, and better engage with the local communities where the Persimmon Group operates. Following this change, Persimmon plc anticipates that at least the same value of donations will be made under the campaign as was previously donated to the Persimmon Foundation in respect of the campaign.

The Community Champions campaign supports grassroots groups and charities working to improve the quality of life or environment for local people, particularly in the communities where the Persimmon Group operates. Each month, each of Persimmon plc's businesses and head office makes donations of around £2,000 to local causes to match the charities fundraising efforts. During 2021, the Community Champions programme donated £745,000 to 770 local groups.

In 2021, Persimmon plc began a partnership with Volunteer It Yourself (VIY), an organisation that works with young people aged 14 to 24 to learn trade and employability skills while providing them with work experience on local community projects.

Applications
Contact the correspondent for further information.

Corporate charity
The Persimmon Charitable Foundation (Charity Commission no. 1163608) – see entry on page 266.

Community contributions
We were unable to determine a figure for the company's 2021 charitable contributions.

Personal Group Holdings plc

Community services and development, general charitable purposes

Company registration number: 3194991

Correspondent: Sarah Mace, Trustee, PACT, John Ormond House, 899 Silbury Boulevard, Milton Keynes, Buckinghamshire MK9 3XL (tel: 0800 542 5930; email: crm@personalgroup. com; website: www.personalgroup.com)

Directors: Deborah Frost; Mike Dugdale; Bob Head; Andy Lothian; Sarah Mace; Ciaran Astin; Martin Bennett (female: 29%; male: 71%).

Nature of business: Personal Group is a provider of employee benefits and financial services.

Financial information

Year end	31/12/2021
Turnover	£74,510,000
Pre-tax profit	£4,340,000

UK employees: 233

Main locations: The group has sites throughout the UK.

Community involvement
The group supports charities through its corporate charity, the Personal Assurance Charitable Trust [PACT] (Charity Commission no. 1023274), to which it has pledged an annual donation of a minimum of £100,000.

Partnerships
The group has a partnership with the Memusi Foundation, a charity that works to provide children in Kenya with access to high quality education. The group provides financial support as well as assistance on projects from volunteers.

Employee-led support
According to our previous research, employees are able to donate £100 from PACT to a charity of their choice. The trust will also match any fundraising outside work with a donation of up to £250.

Applications
Grants are awarded to charities recommended by staff and policyholders.

Corporate charity
Personal Assurance Charitable Trust (Charity Commission no. 1023274) – see entry on page 266.

Community contributions

Cash donations UK	£100,000

In 2021, Personal Group Holdings plc made charitable donations totalling £100,000.

Pets at Home plc

Animal welfare

Company registration number: 1822577

Correspondent: Corporate Social Responsibility Committee, Epsom Avenue, Stanley Green Trading Estate, Handforth, Cheshire SK9 3RN (tel: 0800 328 4204; email: info@ supportadoptionforpets.co.uk; website: https://investors.petsathome.com/responsibility)

Directors: Ian Burke; Dennis Millard; Sharon Flood; Stanislas Laurent; Zarin Patel; Susan Dawson; Lyssa McGowan; Michael Iddon (female: 50%; male: 50%).

Nature of business: Pets at Home is a retailer of services and equipment for pets.

Financial information

Year end	26/03/2022
Turnover	£1,317,800,000
Pre-tax profit	£148,700,000

Total employees: 10,262

Main locations: There are 430 Pets at Home stores in the UK.

Community involvement
Pets at Home's CSR is focused on supporting animal charities. The company makes donations to its corporate charity The Pets at Home Foundation (Charity Commission no. 1104152) and its VIP lifelines loyalty scheme. The majority of charitable activity is conducted by the foundation.

The Pets at Home Foundation
During the year, the foundation raised £4.9 million and extended its funding to charities that support people through pets. The foundation's total for grant-giving activity was £2.9 million.

Employee-led support
Through the group's 'Pledge for a Better World' days, Pets at Home Group plc employees donated time to support local communities. In 2022, 1,682 employees volunteered 9,683 hours of their time to support local charitable causes.

Commercially led support
VIP Lifelines
The group runs a VIP (Very Important Pets) loyalty scheme. Every time a member makes a purchase they receive points which can be converted into VIP Lifelines for a charity of their choice to purchase food and accessories from local stores. This year £2.9 million worth of lifelines were donated.

Applications
To apply for a grant from the Pets at Home Foundation, visit the foundation's grants application web page: www.petsathomefoundation.co.uk/grant-programme. For any further enquiries, contact the correspondent.

Corporate charity
The Pets at Home Foundation (Charity Commission no. 1104152) – see entry on page 267.

Community contributions

Cash donations UK	£2,980,000

We were unable to determine an exact figure for the group's charitable contributions. However, its 2021/22 annual report states that the group raised and donated £7.5 million for charitable causes during the year. This includes £4.9 million raised for the Pets at Home Foundation and £2.9 million raised through the VIP Lifelines scheme. Note that this total may include donations from customers. The Pets at

Home Foundation's annual report for 2022 states that it received £2.98 million from the group, and we have taken this amount as the group's figure for UK cash donations.

Pfizer Ltd

Community services and development, education and training, emergency response/relief, general charitable purposes, health, medical research, STEM

Company registration number: 526209

Correspondent: Social Investment Team, Ramsgate Road, Sandwich, Kent CT13 9NJ (tel: 01304 616161; website: www.pfizer.co.uk/social-investment)

Directors: Denise Harnett; David Highton; Edwin Pearson; Berkeley Phillips; Susan Rienow; Roger Smith; Julian Thompson (female: 29%; male: 71%).

Nature of business: The principal activities of the company are the discovery, development, manufacture, marketing and sale of pharmaceutical and animal health products.

Financial information

Year end	30/11/2021
Turnover	£2,122,498,000
Pre-tax profit	£113,888,000

UK employees: 1,212

Main locations: The company's head office in the UK is in Walton Oaks, Surrey. It also has operations in Cambridge, Havant, Hurley and Sandwich.

Community involvement

In the UK, Pfizer is committed to improving the health and well-being of communities across the country. According to its website, the company makes both financial and in-kind donations in support of causes that seek to:

- Improve the quality and availability of healthcare, educate people about healthcare practices that empower them to improve their health and serve the most at risk of health problems
- Advance the research and knowledge in medicine, healthcare and allied sciences and science education

Its website states that the company supports academic, community and cultural organisations that are 'committed to meeting the needs and priorities of their communities'.

STEM education

The company is a lead supporter of the 'Community Lab' initiative, run in partnership with Canterbury Christ Church University and Discovery Park. The programme provides schools in Sandwich and the surrounding areas with access to an industry-standard laboratory. Currently, sessions focus on delivering the practical and analytical skills required for BTEC/A-level organic chemistry.

The company also sponsors students in academia and further education. In 2022, the company sponsored 22 PhD students, had 44 active apprenticeships and 92 undergraduate placements.

In-kind support

The company's 'Lab in a Box' initiative enables schools in Sandwich and Kent (and the surrounding areas) to borrow specialist equipment over a two-week period at no cost. A team of STEM Ambassadors run teacher training sessions to demonstrate how to use the equipment, in order to conduct their own experiments.

The company donates various medicines and vaccinations, according to need. For example, Pfizer donated antibiotics and sterile injectable medicines during the 2010 cholera outbreak in Haiti. The company also makes regular donations from its US and European distribution centres to NGOs pre-preparing 'relief kits' to help respond to natural disasters. Since 2013, Pfizer has donated over 1.6 million treatments.

Employee-led support

Each year, Pfizer staff are entitled to up to five days of paid volunteering leave. Employees can choose to lend their skills to the company's STEM programmes, or volunteer with a UK-registered charity.

The company also provides matched funding to staff engaging in fundraising efforts. This is capped at £150 per colleague, per year.

Commercially led support

Sponsorship

Pfizer sponsored the 'Superbugs: The Fight for Our Lives' exhibition at the Science Museum.

Cause-related marketing

The company offers one of its vaccines (Prevenar 13) at the 'lowest prevailing price', to ensure that the countries and governments that need it can access the vaccine. All profits are then donated to selected humanitarian groups reaching and supporting vulnerable people during humanitarian crises.

Applications

Contact the correspondent for more information.

Community contributions

We were unable to determine a figure for the company's total community contributions for 2022.

Phoenix Group Holdings

Education and training, general charitable purposes

Company registration number: 11606773

Correspondent: Yvonne Gray, Head of Sustainability, Juxon House, 100 St Paul's Churchyard, London EC4M 8BU (tel: 020 3567 9100; email: sustainability@thephoenixgroup.com; website: www.thephoenixgroup.com)

Directors: Alastair Barbour; Andy Briggs; Karen Green; Belinda Richards; Hiroyuki Iioka; John Pollock; Katie Murray; Kory Sorenson; Maggie Semple; Stephanie Bruce; Nicholas Scott; Ralesh Thakrar (female: 54%; male: 46%).

Nature of business: The group is a closed life assurance fund consolidator that specialises in the management and acquisition of closed life and pension funds.

Financial information

Year end	31/12/2021
Turnover	£7,455,000,000
Pre-tax profit	£430,000,000

Total employees: 7,885

Main locations: The group has offices in London and Birmingham.

Community involvement

The group aims to contribute to the communities local to its operations, by providing 'donations, skills, time and resources to various causes'. The group is particularly interested in improving educational opportunities and life chances for individuals within said communities.

Partnerships

The group's charity partner of the year in 2021 was Samaritans. The total raised for the charity during the year was £330,000, with £180,000 donated by the group and the remainder raised by employees. The group also has established charity partnerships in Ireland and the rest of Europe. In 2021 for example, Phoenix Group Holdings partnered with European charity ALONE.

The group also supports local communities through educational partnerships and in 2021 launched a second formal school partnership with Ferryhill Primary School in Edinburgh, joining the existing four-year long partnership with Ark Kings Academy in Birmingham.

The Vision for Literacy Business Pledge

Phoenix Group Holdings is a supporter of the Vision for Literacy Business pledge, a campaign that aims to close the digital literacy gap and boost social mobility. As part of the pledge, the group supports various educational institutions in the communities in which it operates.

COVID-19 disaster relief

The group's sustainability report states that in 2021, donations totalling £140,000 were made to charities supporting COVID-19 disaster relief.

In-kind support

In 2021, the group donated learning materials to a STEM community education programme in partnership with London Air Ambulance.

Employee-led support

Employees can apply for matched funding for causes that are meaningful to them, provided that the cause meets the group's charity criteria and is not deemed political or religious. The group operates two matched funding programmes, one relating to onsite fundraising activities that staff are involved in and the other for any fundraising efforts undertaken outside business hours. Staff are encouraged to lend their skills to a one-off opportunity, either as part of the group's pre-arranged voluntary opportunities or by sourcing their own opportunities (again, provided that it meets the group's charity criteria).

Collectively, staff donated over 2,650 hours in 2021 supporting a wide range of beneficiaries such as hospitals, schools, local parks and environmental initiatives. The group's colleague volunteering programme is also used to support schools, by offering weekly reading programmes and providing revision sessions at the group's Wythall site. According to the group's 2021 sustainability report, the total contributions raised by UK employees in 2021 was £389,000.

Exclusions

The group does not support political or religious causes.

Applications

Contact the correspondent for more information.

Community contributions

Cash donations UK	£619,000
Cash donations overseas	£14,000

According to the group's 2021 Sustainability Report, donations from the group to charities in the UK totalled £619,000. The group also donated £14,000 (EUR 16,000) to charities in Europe. The total for cash donations overseas has been converted from EUR to GBP using the exchange rate at the time of writing (September 2022).

Playtech plc

Education and training, mental health and well-being, social welfare

Company registration number: 008505V

Correspondent: CSR Team, Ground Floor, St George's Court, Upper Church Street, Douglas, Isle of Man IM1 1EE (email: contact form on the website; website: www.playtech.com/sustainable-success)

Directors: Brian Mattingley; Mor Weizer; Andrew Smith; Ian Penrose; Anna Massion; John Krumins; Linda Marston-Weston (female: 29%; male: 71%).

Nature of business: Playtech is a gambling software development company.

Financial information

Year end	31/12/2021
Turnover	£1,055,205,000
Pre-tax profit	£529,616,000

Total employees: 6,600

Main locations: The group has offices in London and Northern Ireland. It has a total of 19 offices across the world.

Community involvement

Many of Playtech's key markets have established charity committees, to oversee and direct local community investment activities.

The causes typically supported by the group are:
- Health and well-being
- The environment
- Poverty alleviation
- Homelessness
- Education
- Humanitarian causes

According to the group's 2021 annual report, Playtech pledged in 2019, £5 million over five years into research and programmes undertaken by charities and social enterprise groups that promote 'healthy online living'. The group is particularly interested in research into the treatment of gambling addictions.

COVID Resilience and Recovery Fund

In 2021, the group began accepting its first round of applications for funding from a £3 million fund allocated for charities that provide mental health services during the COVID-19 pandemic. During the year, 43 applications were approved worldwide, including from the UK.

Community investment

The group's annual report also states that £381,000 (EUR 436,000) was donated to 'community investment causes'. This figure includes company donations, employee volunteering and in-kind gifts and services.

Employee-led support

Staff are encouraged to lend their skills in support of 'social and environmental challenges', by taking one volunteering day per year.

The group also provides matched funding to staff engaging in fundraising efforts.

Applications

Contact the correspondent for further information.

Community contributions

Cash donations worldwide	£5,252,000

Playtech's 2021 accounts state that the group made charitable donations totalling £5.25 million (EUR 6 million), 'primarily to charities that fund research into, and for the treatment of, problem gambling but also to a variety of charities operating in countries in which the company's subsidiaries are based'. This total also represents the £3 million COVID-19 Resilience and Recovery Fund created by the group in 2021.

Premier Foods plc

The environment, health

Company registration number: 5160050

Correspondent: The Sustainability Team, Premier House, Centrium Business Park, Griffiths Way, St Albans, Hertfordshire AL1 2RE (website: http://premierfoods.co.uk/responsibility/Supporting-our-communities)

Directors: Simon Rose; Simon Bentley; Colin Day; Roisin Donnelly; Tim Elliot; Richard Hodgson; Tania Howarth; Helen Jones; Yuichiro; Duncan Leggett; Lorna Tilbian; Alexander Whitehouse (female: 40%; male: 60%).

Nature of business: Premier Foods is a food manufacturer. The group owns many well-known brands including Mr Kipling, Ambrosia, Bird's Custard, Angel Delight and Homepride.

Financial information

Year end	22/04/2022
Turnover	£647,700,000
Pre-tax profit	£102,600,000

Main locations: The group's head office is in St Albans. It has sites in Devon, Andover, Kent, Barnsley, Wirral, Stoke, Tamworth, Worksop, Leicestershire, Staffordshire, High Wycombe, Manchester and Southampton.

Community involvement

According to its website, the group aims to 'be a force for good and volunteer our time and expertise to those local causes linked to the issues of food poverty, skills development, employability and local environmental quality'.

In-kind support
In 2021/22 the group donated 616,722 meals to charities including FareShare.

Applications
Contact the correspondent or local site for further information.

Community contributions

Total contributions UK	£901,500

According to the group's 2021/22 annual report, charitable contributions totalled £901,500. This figure includes all direct and leveraged contributions including financial and in-kind donations and the cost of volunteering.

Pret A Manger (Europe) Ltd

🔍 Housing and homelessness

Company registration number: 1854213

Correspondent: Giovanna Pasini, Pret Foundation Manager, 75B Verde, 10 Bressenden Place, London SW1E 5DH (email: Giovanna.Pasini@pret.com; website: www.pret.co.uk/en-GB/sustainability)

Directors: Panayioti Christou; Clare Clough; Gustavo Peixoto; Andrea Wareham (female: 50%; male: 50%).

Nature of business: Pret A Manger (Pret) is an international sandwich shop chain based in the UK.

Financial information

Year end	30/12/2021
Turnover	£372,262,000
Pre-tax profit	£160,562,000

Main locations: The company's head office is in London and it has shops all over the country.

Community involvement
Pret's charitable activity is predominantly channelled through its corporate charity, the Pret Foundation (Charity Commission no. 1050195).

Rising Stars
This programme is administered by the foundation and aims to support those with no fixed address, or those with criminal records, to secure employment. Since its inception, over 500 people have been offered jobs at local Pret shops. The foundation has since launched its 'Shooting Stars' scheme, which selects eight participants of the Rising Stars scheme to take part in an eight-month programme of workshops where they can master the skills to 'climb the career ladder'.

The Pret House
The foundation opened the Pret House at West London Mission St Luke's to provide accommodation to participants of its Rising Stars programme.

Community support
Outside its foundation, the company directly supports (and participates in) various community action programmes, such as Leeds by Example, The Glasgow Cup Movement, Refill and The Cup Recycling Scheme.

In-kind support
The company donates food and other items specifically requested by small charities through the Pret Foundation.

Commercially led support
The company donates 10p from every soup sold in the UK in support of community causes. Money is also donated from Pret's annual Christmas sandwich campaign.

Applications
Contact the correspondent for further information.

Corporate charity
The Pret Foundation (Charity Commission no. 1050195) – see entry on page 268.

Community contributions

Total contributions worldwide	£390,000

According to the company's 2020/21 annual report, Pret made 'payments of a charitable nature' totalling £390,000.

Pricewaterhouse-Coopers LLP

🔍 Community enterprise and social entrepreneurship, community services and development, general charitable purposes

Company registration number: OC303525

Correspondent: David Adair, Head of Community Engagement, 1 Embankment Place, London WC2N 6RH (tel: 020 7212 7140; website: www.pwc.co.uk/who-we-are/our-purpose/empowered-people-communities.html)

Directors: Kevin Ellis; Marco Amitrano; Quentin Cole; Ian Elliot; Ben Higgin; Laura Hinton; Hemione Hudson; Warwick Hunt; Sam Samaratunga; Carl Sizer; Lucy Stapleton; Alison Statham; Paul Terrington; Marissa Thomas (female: 38%; male: 62%).

Nature of business:
PricewaterhouseCoopers (PwC) is a multinational professional services network providing assurance, tax and advisory services.

Financial information

Year end	30/06/2021
Turnover	£4,447,000,000
Pre-tax profit	£1,249,000,000

UK employees: 24,207

Main locations: PricewaterhouseCoopers LLP has offices throughout the UK.

Community involvement
The group engages in a wide range of community causes, through its corporate charity, The PwC Foundation (Charity Commission no. 1144124), and also directly through its social mobility initiatives and by working closely with social enterprise groups.

Social enterprise support
Employees volunteer for various social enterprises through the Social Entrepreneurs Club, which provides mentoring, training and developmental support to 250 social enterprises across the UK.

PwC also operates a social enterprise hub in London, The Fire Station. The hub houses a group of inspiring organisations working together to advance social and environmental change, such as Blossoms Healthcare, Social Enterprise UK and School for Social Entrepreneurs.

Social mobility work
PwC works in partnership with schools across the country, particularly those in deprived areas, to help young people to develop workplace skills and increase employability.

The group also provides paid work experience places and apprenticeships to technology/data science graduates.

Charity of the Year
PwC LLP staff nominate and vote for charities for The PwC Foundation to work with. In 2021, the charities voted for were Hospice UK and Crisis. These charities join the group's long-term partners: Beyond Food and Well-being for Women.

Employee-led support
Staff are encouraged to take part in fundraising activities for the group's charity partners, as well as skills-based volunteering for social enterprises.

One Firm One Day/One Firm Every Day
The group runs an employee-led volunteering scheme called 'One Firm One Day' where staff are encouraged to volunteer and fundraise for causes in local communities. While the focus of the day each year changes, themes are always concurrent with the group's community engagement strategy and in the past have focused on social enterprise, social mobility and mental health and well-being.

In 2021, in light of the COVID-19 pandemic, PwC altered the scheme to 'One Firm Every Day', giving employees more flexibility and time to contribute to the causes for which they choose to volunteer.

Exclusions

The group does not support:

- Political organisations or lobbying groups
- Activist organisations
- Religious bodies (unless for identifiable, broadly based, community support activities)

Applications

Contact the correspondent for more information.

Corporate charity

The PwC Foundation (Charity Commission no. 1144124) – see entry on page 268.

Community contributions

Total contributions UK	£4,800,000

According to its 2020/21 'Non-financial Performance Scorecard', the group's total community contribution was valued at £4.8 million, including in-kind product and service donations. This total includes a donation of £3.63 million to the PwC Foundation, as reported in its 2021 annual report.

Principality Building Society

Community services and development

Company registration number: FCA 155998

Correspondent: Communities Team, PO Box 89, Principality Buildings, Queen Street, Cardiff CF10 1UA (email: community@principality.co.uk; website: www.principality.co.uk/about-us/our-community)

Directors: Nigel Annet; Sally Jones-Evans; Claire Hafner; Derek Howell; David Rigney; Debra Evans-Williams; Jonathan Baum; Julie-Anne Haines; Tom Denman; Michael Jones; Iain Mansfield (female: 36%; male: 64%).

Nature of business: The provision of housing finance and a range of insurance and financial services.

Financial information

Year end	31/12/2021
Turnover	£129,200,000
Pre-tax profit	£64,000,000

Total employees: 860

Main locations: The company has branches throughout Wales.

Community involvement

Principality supports its charity partners and community projects in areas in which the building society has branches.

Partnerships

From 2019 to 2022, the society's two charity partners were Teenage Cancer Trust Cymru and the Alzheimer's Society Cymru. At the conclusion of the three-year partnership with the two charities, the society (with the help of staff and customers) raised over £367,000, with £58,000 of this total being raised in 2021.

The society's charity partners for 2022–2025 are children hospices Ty Hafan and Hope House: Ty Gobaith.

Financial education

Principality Building Society also supports financial education for children and young people. The society provides free digital learning resources for children and young people to learn about managing money. The 2021 annual report states that these programmes reached 24,000 people during the year.

The society partnered with Young Enterprise in 2021 to launch the Fiver Challenge and the Fiver from Home Challenge, giving students aged 5 to 11 a chance to research, plan and create a business with £5.

With the London Institute of Banking and Finance, a £35,000 financial education fund (enabling over 25 secondary schools to access GCSE equivalent qualifications) was set up and this has helped more than 500 schoolchildren.

In-kind support

Principality is committed to delivering financial education in schools. The society works in partnership with Young Money and the London Institute of Banking and Finance to provide 'impactful qualifications and sustainable help'. Through the partnership, Principality Building Society has provided £15,000 worth of numeracy education workshops for children and young people.

The society also donates old IT equipment and resources to charity.

Employee-led support

Staff have engaged in a wide range of fundraising activities in support of the building society's charity partners, including zip wire challenges, touch rugby, golf, half marathons and Trek 26 challenges. The society offers matched funding of up to £150,000 a year for employee fundraising.

The Colleague Network

Beyond donating to its official charity partners, employees can nominate

charitable causes for company giving through the society's colleague network. In 2021, £4,000 was donated to colleague network causes.

Commercially led support

The society provides sponsorship in the fields of support sport, arts and culture.

Through its partnership with the Welsh Rugby Union, Wales' iconic home ground was renamed the 'Principality Stadium'. The building society also sponsors the National Eisteddfod festival and the Royal Welsh Show.

Exclusions

According to the society's website, support is not given to:

- Political or religious causes
- Projects run on behalf of charities by companies for profit
- Causes outside the areas where the society has branches
- Development or running costs for projects
- Individuals

Applications

For support with community projects, prospective applicants should fill out the 'Community Request Form' featured on the website. For more information about sponsorship opportunities, contact: community@principality.co.uk.

Community contributions

Cash donations UK	£300,000

According to the society's 2021 annual report, the building society made donations to charities totalling £200,000.

Principality also invested £100,000 partnering with secondary schools in western Wales and Cardiff.

Procter & Gamble UK

General charitable purposes, health

Company registration number: 83758

Correspondent: CSR Team, The Heights, Brooklands, Weybridge, Surrey KT13 0XP (tel: 01932 896000; website: www.uk.pg.com)

Directors: Anthony Appleton; Andrew Ewen; Radu Maftei (male: 100%).

Nature of business: Procter & Gamble (P&G) UK, operating in the UK and the Republic of Ireland, is a wholly owned subsidiary of The Procter & Gamble Company, incorporated in the USA. The principal activities of the company and its subsidiaries are the manufacture and marketing of innovative consumer products, with associated research and development services. We were unable to find full financial information for the company, as it only has investment subsidiaries registered in the UK.

Financial information

Year end	30/06/2022

Main locations: In the UK and the Republic of Ireland, P&G has sites in Surrey, Greater London, Reading, Manchester, Skelmersdale, Harrogate, Newcastle upon Tyne, Newbridge and Dublin.

Community involvement

P&G supports local communities in the areas the company has a presence. Each of the group's sites across Europe has a dedicated community programme through which it supports local charities with donations.

UK brand partnerships

Many of P&G Ltd's brands have established their own charity partnerships and campaigns, these include:

- Fairy's partnership with Make-A-Wish UK, which marked its 15-year anniversary in 2021. As of November 2022, the partnership had raised over £1.5 million for the charity
- Fairy Non-Bio's partnership with Great Ormond Street Hospital, which has raised over £360,000 since 2017
- Gillette's official partnership with Movember, which has raised over £1.65 million since 2012
- Pampers' long-standing partnership with Bliss, which provides support and product donations for parents of babies born premature or sick
- Pampers also partnered with ASDA to donate nappies to babies in need, with one pack donated for every pack purchased during the campaign

Safe Drinking Water Programme

The Children's Safe Drinking Water Programme helps to provide clean drinking water to children and their families in South America, Asia and Africa. The programme distributes an easy-to-use water purification packet invented by P&G scientists that can clean ten litres of water in just 30 minutes.

Disaster relief

Globally P&G's disaster relief programmes provide daily essential products to victims of natural disasters as well as cash support. In 2021, the group donated £4.3 million to the Global Vaccine Alliance in response to the COVID-19 pandemic.

In-kind support

The group has a longstanding partnership with In Kind Direct, a charity that distributes donated consumer products from manufactures and retailers to UK charities working at home and abroad. Since 2001, the group has donated a total of £50 million in estimated retail value of products, supporting over 7,500 charitable organisations.

Employee-led support

Employees take part in volunteering and fundraising activates in their local communities through the group's 'Community Impact' programme.

In 2021, UK and Ireland employees were offered the opportunity to 'donate' the value of their Christmas hamper (a seasonal benefit employees receive) to homeless charities in the UK and Ireland. As a result, over £12,000 was donated to Focus Ireland and £25,000 was donated to Crisis UK.

Regional Employee-led Community Support

In 2021, several of the group's sites partnered with local charities and community organisations, with employees helping to raise funds and volunteer their time.

At the group's Cobalt site, employees raised £25,000 for both St Oswald's Hospice and Family Gateway, while also donating 160 meals to residents of well-being centres and extra care schemes through a partnership with Age UK North Tyneside and Everyday Care. The Cobalt site also donated Easter eggs to St Oswald's, Family Gateway and The Bay Foodbank.

Employees from the group's Reading Innovation Centre volunteered their time in partnership with community organisations to regenerate a disused piece of land for the community. The site also supported three local charities: Launchpad, a charity for people facing homelessness; Thames Hospice, which provides support for people suffering from life-limiting illness; and No5, which offers counselling to children and young people.

The group's Brookland site continued its support for Young Enterprise, empowering young people across the UK by providing them real business experience. In 2021, the Brookland site sponsored the North Surrey Showcase's Sustainability and Innovation Awards.

Finance and Accounting Support for Charities

In 2021, employees from the group's North Europe finance and accounting team supported charities with their financial services. The charities supported were the Albert Kennedy Trust, Macmillan Cancer Support, Show Racism the Red Card and Women's Aid.

Applications

Contact the correspondent for more information.

Community contributions

We were unable to determine a figure for P&G UK's total community contributions.

Provident Financial plc

Community services and development, money and debt advice

Company registration number: 668987

Correspondent: Rob Lawson, Corporate Responsibility Manager, No. 1 Godwin Street, Bradford BD1 2SU (tel: 01274 351135; email: corporateresponsibility@ providentfinancial.com; website: www. providentfinancial.com)

Directors: Patrick Snowball; Malcolm Le May; Neeraj Kapur; Andrea Blance; Elizabeth Chambers; Paul Hewitt; Angela Knight; Graham Lindsay; Margot James (female: 50%; male: 50%).

Nature of business: Provident Financial is a sub-prime lender specialising in credit cards, home collected credit, online loans and consumer car finance.

Financial information

Year end	31/12/2021
Turnover	£534,600,000
Pre-tax profit	£142,200,000

Total employees: 2,048

Main locations: The group's headquarters is in Bradford.

Community involvement

The group's community investment activities are carried out through its Social Impact Programme. The group has a particular focus on educational programmes and projects for children and young people. In 2021, the group partnered with the following educational causes to deliver its programmes:

- Ahead Partnership
- Innovations for Learning
- Outward Bound Trust
- National Literacy Trust
- National Numeracy
- Leading Children
- School-Home Trust
- Social Mobility Business Partnership

In 2021, the group's national numeracy challenge recorded 57,124 participants.

Community Foundation partnerships

Provident works in partnership with seven community foundations in the UK to distribute its Social Impact funds. Applications to the funds are shortlisted by the community foundations against a criteria list set by the group. The shortlisted applications are then presented to a panel of Provident employees who then decide how the grants should be distributed. In 2021, 51 grants were distributed through community foundations to community organisations.

Participating community foundations include:

- Community Foundation Wales
- Essex Community Foundation
- Foundation Scotland
- Hampshire and Isle of Wight Community Foundation
- Kent Community Foundation
- Leeds Community Foundation
- London Community Foundation

Support for the money advice sector

The group has partnerships with several money advice organisations that provide free advice to those who are having difficulty paying their debts. These include Advice UK, Christians Against Poverty, IncomeMax, the Institute of Money Advisers, the Money Advice Liaison Group, Money Advice Scotland, the Money Advice Trust, The Money Charity and StepChange.

Employee-led support

Volunteering

Employees are offered one paid day each year to volunteer for a charity of their choice. Employees can also get involved through company-led opportunities such as joining the community foundation grant panels, delivering literacy and numeracy programmes, residential trips for underprivileged children and so on. In 2021, 425 hours were spent volunteering by employees.

Matched funding

The group operates a matched funding scheme to support employee fundraising efforts. The group will match up to £500 per person each year. In 2021, £9,900 was awarded to supplement fundraising efforts through the scheme.

Applications

Applications for grants can be made through the community foundations' websites:

- Community Foundation Wales – https://communityfoundationwales. org.uk/grants-overview
- Essex Community Foundation – www.essexcommunityfoundation.org. uk
- Foundation Scotland – www. foundationscotland.org.uk
- Hampshire and Isle of Wright Community Foundation – www. hiwcf.com
- Kent Community Foundation – https://kentcf.org.uk
- Leeds Community Foundation – www.leedscf.org.uk/open-grants
- London Community Foundation – https://londoncf.org.uk

Community contributions

Cash donations UK	£1,230,700
Total contributions worldwide	£1,242,800

The Provident Financial plc 2021 Social Impact Report provided the following breakdown for the group's community contributions during the year.

Cash donations	£1,231,000
Management costs	£126,000
Value of volunteered time	£12,000

We have not included the value of management costs in our figure for total community contributions.

PRS for Music Ltd

Arts, culture and heritage

Company registration number: 3444246

Correspondent: CSR Team, Goldings House, 2 Hays Lane, London SE1 2HB (tel: 020 7580 5544; website: www. prsformusic.com)

Directors: Stephen Davidson; Dru Masters; Julian Nott; Philip Pope; Jackie Alway; Simon Platz; Antony Bebawi; Erica Ingham; Tom Toumazis; Gill Mansfield; Andrea Martin (female: 36%; male: 64%).

Nature of business: PRS for Music is a British music copyright collective made up of two collection societies: the Mechanical-Copyright Protection Society and the Performing Right Society. It undertakes collective rights management for musical works on behalf of its 140,000 members. It represents songwriter, composer and music publisher members' performing and mechanical rights, and collects royalties on their behalf whenever their music is played or performed publicly or reproduced as a physical product.

Financial information

Year end	31/12/2021
Turnover	£107,550,000
Pre-tax profit	£3,090,000

UK employees: 475

Main locations: The company has offices in London and Dublin.

Community involvement

According to the company's website, PRS is committed to funding various events and grassroots organisations that provide developmental opportunities for music creators across the UK and beyond.

PRS's community involvement is channelled through its corporate charity, the Performing Right Society Foundation (Charity Commission no. 1080837), to which it makes cash donations. The company also supports its members, ex-members and their dependants who are in need through the PRS Members' Fund (Charity Commission no. 1181735). Current PRS members are encouraged to donate a proportion of their royalties to the fund. According to the company's website, the company will:

continue to provide PRS Foundation with at least £1 million annually from 2024, as well as continue to subsidise their operational costs and support them in every way possible to raise funding from other sources, so they can continue their important work.

In-kind support

The company provides subsidised use of its premises and a range of associated services to the Performing Right Society Foundation and the PRS Members' Fund.

Applications

More information about the Performing Right Society Foundation and the PRS Members' Fund can be found on the company's website.

Corporate charity

The Performing Right Society Foundation (Charity Commission no. 1080837) – see entry on page 265.

Community contributions

We were unable to determine a figure for the company's charitable contributions for the year.

Prudential plc

Education and training

Company registration number: 1397169

Correspondent: CSR Team, 1 Angel Court, London EC2R 7AG (tel: 020 7220 7588; email: community@prudential.co. uk; website: www.pru.co.uk/about/ prudential-in-the-community)

Directors: Shriti Vadera; Mark FitzPatrick; James Turner; Philip Remnant; Jeremy Anderson; Arijit Basu; Chua Sock Koong; David Law; Ming Lu; George Sartorel; Tom Watjen; Jeanette Wong; Amy Yip (female: 31%; male: 69%).

Nature of business: Prudential provides retail financial services and insurance products in Europe, the USA, Asia and Africa.

Financial information

Year end	31/12/2021
Turnover	£23,226,853,000
Pre-tax profit	£2,030,810,000

Total employees: 23,000

Main locations: Prudential's main offices are in London, Reading, Edinburgh and Stirling. It also has offices in Dublin, Poland and Mumbai.

Community involvement

Globally, Prudential's Community Investment Strategy focuses on social inclusion, education and life skills, disaster preparedness and employee engagement. The group pursues partnerships with charities that align with this strategy as well as providing support through cash donations, in-kind gifts and employee volunteering. In the UK, community investment is focused on the following areas, as stated on the group's website:

- Ensuring young people are work-ready and providing early career opportunities
- Empowering people, so that they can make the most out of work and life
- Helping older people by being part of their communities and enhancing later life

Each of the group's businesses manages its own community investment programmes, guided by the group-wide Community Investment Policy. Prudential also provides support in Asia and Africa through its corporate charity, the Prudence Foundation, and in the US through the Jackson Charitable Foundation.

In the past, Prudential has worked with Age UK, financially supporting the 'Later Life Links' programme and Save the Children's Emergency Fund.

Disaster readiness and relief

The group has a central disaster relief fund to be used to support local communities in response to disasters.

In-kind support

Our previous research suggests that in-kind support is offered to organisations on a local basis. This includes office space, meeting rooms, computers and office furniture.

Employee-led support

Employee volunteering

The Chair's Challenge is the group's flagship international volunteering programme through which employees can sign up to take part in projects. Projects focus on one or more of the group's community priorities and support both large, well-established charities and innovative, smaller projects. In 2021, employees volunteered over 26,000 hours to charitable causes. Prudential donates £150 to its charity partners for every employee who registers for the programme.

Payroll giving

The group operates a payroll giving scheme to allow employees to make donations to local charities.

Exclusions

The group's website states it cannot support the following:

- Political parties or religious organisations
- Sponsorship requests for individuals, including its own employees
- Requests to buy sports equipment for employees who take part in local sports competitions on behalf of the organisation

- Requests for charitable contributions outside its payroll giving policy

Applications

Contact the correspondent for further information.

Community contributions

| Cash donations worldwide | £5,170,000 |

According to the group's 2021 annual report, £5.17 million was spent supporting community activities during the year.

The financial information has been converted from USD using the exchange rate at the time of writing (September 2022).

Quilter plc

Community services and development, education and training, emergency relief, emergency response/relief, money and debt advice, sports, work outside the UK

Company registration number: 6404270

Correspondent: Responsible Business Team, Senator House, 85 Queen Victoria Street, London EC4V 4AB (email: responsiblebusiness@quilter.com; website: www.quilter.com)

Directors: Ruth Markland; Paul Feeney; Mark Satchel; Neeta Atkar; Tim Breedon; Glyn Barker; Tazim Essani; Moira Kilcoyne; Paul Matthews; George Reid; Chris Samuel (female: 30%; male: 70%).

Nature of business: Quilter plc is a financial services group that offers advice, investments and wealth management in the UK and internationally.

Financial information

Year end	31/12/2021
Turnover	£1,053,000,000
Pre-tax profit	£138,000,000

Total employees: 4,000

Main locations: The group's main office locations are in London, Southampton and the Isle of Man.

Community involvement

The group's charitable activities are channelled through its corporate charity, The Quilter Foundation (Charity Commission no. 1175555).

Employee-led support

According to its 2021 annual report, The Quilter Foundation received £100,000 of income from group employee fundraising activities during the year.

Commercially led support

The group sponsors England rugby teams and, as part of this commitment, is the title partner of Quilter Kids First.

This programme is aimed at upskilling coaches in schools and clubs and encouraging children to play rugby.

Applications

For further information see the group's corporate charity entry.

Corporate charity

The Quilter Foundation (Charity Commission no. 1175555) – see entry on page 269.

Community contributions

We were unable to determine a figure for the group's charitable contributions for the year.

Rathbone Brothers plc

Arts, culture and heritage, community enterprise and social entrepreneurship, community services and development, education and training, health

Company registration number: 1000403

Correspondent: CSR Team, 8 Finsbury Circus, London EC2M 7AZ (tel: 020 7399 0000; website: www.rathbones.com/charities)

Directors: Clive Bannister; Paul Stockton; Terri Duhon; Sarah Gentleman; Jennifer Mathias; Ian Cummings; (female: 50%; male: 50%).

Nature of business: The group is an independent provider of investment and wealth management services for private investors, charities and trustees. It operates in the UK and Jersey.

Financial information

Year end	31/12/2021
Turnover	£4,359,000,000
Pre-tax profit	£95,000,000

Total employees: 1,500

Main locations: Rathbone has 15 offices throughout the UK and Jersey. Office locations can be found on the group's website.

Community involvement

Rathbone supports the communities in which it operates through donations, employee volunteering and educational programmes. The group also provides support through its corporate charity the Rathbones Group Foundation (Charity Commission no. 1150432).

The Rathbone Financial Awareness programme

This programme, aimed at 16- to 25-year-olds, forms a significant part of the group's youth development initiatives. The group's investment managers deliver presentations in the group's offices and in schools around the UK. The aim of the programme is to encourage young people to take control of their finances from a young age.

The Rathbones Folio Mentorships programme

This programme gives young writers from state schools the opportunity to be mentored by published authors, one to one, for a year. Rathbone also supports a digital reading programme in schools, in association with The Pigeonhole (a digital book club) and Harper Collins Publishers.

Local communities

Regional offices are encouraged to get involved with local charity projects.

Employee-led support

Employees are entitled to take two and a half days' paid leave each year to volunteer. Employees also take part in fundraising activities and can donate to charities through a payroll giving scheme, which the group then matches. In 2021, employees donated £214,400 through the Give As You Earn scheme. The group matched donations of up to £200 per month. In 2021, it donated £178,000 to causes chosen by employees through this method.

Applications

Contact the correspondent for more information.

Corporate charity

The Rathbones Group Foundation (Charity Commission no. 1150432) – see entry on page 269.

Community contributions

Cash donations UK	£418,000

According to the 2021 accounts, the group made donations totalling £418,000, equivalent to 0.4% of the group's pre-tax profits to charitable causes.

Reach plc

Community services and development, health, housing and homelessness, medical research

Company registration number: 82548

Correspondent: CSR Team, One Canada Square, Canary Wharf, London E14 5AP (tel: 020 7293 3000; website: www. reachplc.com)

Directors: Jim Mullen; Simon Fuller; Nick Prettejohn; Helen Stevenson; David Kelly; Steve Hatch; Olivia Streatfeild; Anne Bulford; Priya Guha; Barry Panayi; Wais Shaifta (female: 36%; male: 64%).

Nature of business: Formerly known as Trinity Mirror plc, Reach is a UK-based newspaper, magazine and digital publisher. It is one of the UK's largest newspaper groups, publishing 240 regional papers in addition to national papers such as the Daily Mirror, Sunday Mirror and Daily Record.

Financial information

Year end	29/12/2021
Turnover	£615,800,000
Pre-tax profit	£143,500,000

Total employees: 4,573

Main locations: The group operates across the UK.

Community involvement

Reach supports its local communities by providing publicity for charities and fundraising campaigns as well as raising awareness of local issues. Previous research indicates that the group also makes cash donations to charities that are connected to the newspaper and advertising industry, or the communities in which the group operates.

Campaigns and fundraising

Reach's regional and national titles are involved with a range of campaigns. For example, in 2021, Reach supported BristolLive 'Benefit Bristol' campaign, which aimed to help families in Bristol that were hit by rising energy costs and the removal of the £20-a-week uplift of Universal Credit.

Awards ceremonies

The group runs several award events, both nationally and at a regional level. In 2021, Reach hosted the North East Charity Awards, which aimed to celebrate the works of local charities and social enterprises, together with the businesses and individuals that support them.

Employee-led support

Our previous research indicates that employees at Reach's regional and national titles take part in volunteering activities.

Applications

Our previous research indicates that enquiries regarding donations should be addressed to the editor or manager of the newspaper/print site based in your community.

Community contributions

Cash donations UK	£50,000

According to its 2021 annual report, Reach donated £30,000 to Manchester based youth charity NGage and £20,000 to the Anthony Walker Foundation.

Reckitt Benckiser Group plc

Education and training, health

Company registration number: 527217

Correspondent: Sustainability Team, 103–105 Bath Road, Slough, Berkshire SL1 3UH (tel: 01753 217800; email: sustainability@rb.com; website: www. reckitt.com)

Directors: Laxman Narasimhan; Nicandro Durante; Jeff Carr; Chris Sinclair; Andrew Bonfield; Elane Stock; Mary Harris; Mehmood Khan; Margherita Valle; Olivier Bohuon; Alan Stewart (female: 33%; male: 67%).

Nature of business: The principal activities of the group are the manufacture and sale of household and healthcare products.

Financial information

Year end	31/12/2021
Turnover	£13,200,000,000
Pre-tax profit	£2,654,000,000

Total employees: 40,000+

Main locations: In the UK, the group is headquartered in London.

Community involvement

Reckitt Benckiser supports health education and disease prevention campaigns and initiatives in the UK and overseas. The group's social impact strategy focuses on three areas: sexual health and rights; maternal and child health; and water and sanitation. Support is provided through financial donations, product donations and volunteering.

Partnerships

The group establishes partnerships with organisations and projects that align with its focus areas. In 2021, Reckitt began a new strategic partnership with the British Red Cross and their Disaster Relief Alliance (DRA). Reckitt pledged to provide product donations to assist in emergency preparedness, a £250,000 grant and time through employee volunteering.

Fight for Access Fund

In March 2020, the group launched the Fight for Access Fund, to improve access to health, hygiene and nutrition for all. The group has committed to an annual investment equivalent to 1% of its adjusted operating profit. The fund will be used to ensure high-quality products are produced, education and information are provided in the right areas, and the availability of the group's products is enhanced.

In-kind support

The group donates products (such as soaps and bleach) and educational material on health safety and hygiene.

Employee-led support

Employee volunteering

The Give Time Programme allows employees to take two days' paid leave each year to volunteer in their local community. In 2021, employees spent 279 hours volunteering.

The group also operates a payroll giving scheme.

Applications

Contact the correspondent for further information.

Community contributions

▨ Total contributions worldwide   £38,200,000

According to the group's 2021 annual report, its total value of cash contributed, employee time in working hours and in-kind product donations amounted to £38.2 million during the year. We were unable to determine how much was given in the UK.

Redrow Group plc

🔍 Arts, culture and heritage, community services and development, education and training, health, sports and recreation

Company registration number: 2877315

Correspondent: CSR Team, Redrow House, St David's Park, Ewloe, Flintshire CH5 3RX (tel: 01244 520044; email: groupservices@redrow.co.uk; website: www.redrowplc.co.uk)

Directors: Richard Akers; Matthew Pratt; Barbara Richmond; Nick Hewson; Nicky Dulieu; Oliver Tan; Graham Cope (female: 29%; male: 71%).

Nature of business: Redrow is one of the largest British housebuilders with a network of 15 operational divisions across the UK.

Financial information

Year end	28/06/2021
Turnover	£1,939,000,000
Pre-tax profit	£314,000,000

UK employees: 2,208

Main locations: Redrow has a network of 15 operational divisions across the UK. It is based in Ewloe, Flintshire.

Community involvement

The majority of the group's giving focuses on the improvement of local communities. Each year, company divisions choose a local charity to support whose purpose aligns with the group's priorities.

Redrow Foundation (Charity Commission no. 1113073)

The group is the founder of the Redrow Foundation (Charity Commission no. 1113073). The foundation is a national charity that makes grants for the relief of poverty and sickness in the UK. The trustees prefer to support organisations that provide accommodation and related assistance to children, older people and those who are sick or infirm. We were unable to view the foundation's accounts or determine how much was awarded in 2020/21.

Wildlife

Redrow has established a partnership with The Wildlife Trusts to develop a group-wide wildlife strategy for all of its sites. The partnership will ensure that Redrow protects, maintains and increases natural habitats in the areas in which it builds.

The group also has an ongoing partnership with the Bumblebee Conservation Trust and works with them to create bumblebee-friendly housing developments.

Employee-led support

The 2020/21 annual report states that 'the company and its employees are actively involved in fundraising activities for our selective charities'.

Applications

For further information contact the correspondent or see the group's corporate charity entry.

Corporate charity

The Steve Morgan Foundation (Charity Commission no. 1087056) – see entry on page 258.

Community contributions

▨ Cash donations UK   £100,000

According to its 2020/21 annual report, the group awarded £100,000 to local charities during the year.

RELX plc

🔍 Education and training, social welfare

Company registration number: 2746616

Correspondent: Marcia Balisciano, Head of Corporate Responsibility, 1–3 Strand, London WC2N 5JR (email: corporate.responsibility@relx.com; website: www.relx.com/corporate-responsibility/being-a-responsible-business/community)

Directors: Adam Westley; Nicolas Luff; Henry Udow (male: 100%).

Nature of business: RELX is a global provider of information and analytics for professional business customers in four major industries: scientific, technical and medical, risk and business analytics, and legal.

Financial information

Year end	31/12/2021
Turnover	£7,244,000,000
Pre-tax profit	£1,797,000,000

Main locations: RELX's head office is in London.

Community involvement

RELX contributes to local and global communities through its RE Cares programme by making cash and in-kind donations to charities and by supporting employee-led initiatives.

RELX Cares

This global programme is supported by a network of staff members – known as RELX Cares Champions – from across the business who organise and promote community engagement. The 2021 Corporate Responsibility Report explains that through the programme, the group prioritises 'education for disadvantaged young people that advances one or more of our unique contributions as a business'.

Each September, a dedicated RELX Cares Month takes place, through which thousands of employees contribute time to volunteering and fundraising activities. The group's volunteering policy, 'Two Days' is also enacted through the programme.

Central donations programme

The group's central donations programme is closely tied to RELX Cares priority of promoting the education of disadvantaged young people. RELX Cares Champions vote on all applications, using decision criteria such as value to the beneficiary and opportunities for staff engagement.

In 2021, RELX Cares Champions donated $280,00 (£259,300 as of September 2022) to 24 charities supporting over 20,700 young people.

Partnerships

In 2019, employees nominated Hope and Homes for Children (HHC) as the group's global fundraising partner. RELX aims to fundraise $135,000 by the end of 2022 (£124,900 as of September 2022).

The group also has a longstanding partnership of more than 20 years with Book Aid International.

In-kind support

Staff are able to take up to two days' paid leave for volunteering purposes (with their line manager's approval).

Gifts in kind

RELX has a product donations policy which is available to download from the website (www.relx.com/corporateresponsibility/policies/Pages/Home.aspx). Product donations are given to registered charities in the form of hardcopy products (e.g. books and educational materials), non-hardcopy products (e.g. free access to journals and investigative solutions) and unwanted IT equipment and office furnishings. It would appear that the majority of product donations are typically given to charities the group has a partnership with.

Employee-led support

Employees are encouraged to volunteer and fundraise for charities.

Applications

RELX's central donations programme, RELX Cares, is employee-led, with donations received by charities nominated by staff.

Aside from the group's central CSR programme, many of the group's subsidiaries have developed their own CSR initiatives.

Contact the correspondent for further information.

Community contributions

Total contributions worldwide	£10,400,000

The Corporate Responsibility Report 2021 states that the group gave a total of £10.4 million in cash and in-kind donations worldwide. In-kind donations included products, services and time.

Renishaw plc

Community services and development, education and training, health, sports and recreation

Company registration number: 1106260

Correspondent: Renishaw Charities Committee, New Mills, Wotton-under-Edge, Gloucestershire GL12 8JR (email: charities.committee@renishaw.com; website: www.renishaw.com/en)

Directors: Sir David McMurty; John Deer; Will Lee; Allen Roberts; Sir David Grant; Catherine Glickman; Juliette Stacey; Stephen Wilson (female: 25%; male: 75%).

Nature of business: Renishaw is a scientific technology company with expertise in measurement, motion control, spectroscopy and precision machining.

Financial information

Year end	30/06/2021
Turnover	£565,560,000
Pre-tax profit	£139,440,000

UK employees: 3,000

Total employees: 5,000

Main locations: The group has 77 offices in 36 countries. In the UK, the group has offices in Gloucestershire, Vale of Glamorgan, Yorkshire and Staffordshire.

Community involvement

Renishaw plc's charitable work is focused through its charities committee and work in promoting STEM subjects to younger people.

Renishaw Charities Committee

The committee is made up of employee representatives who meet regularly to distribute funds made available by the group to support charitable and voluntary organisations local to the group's key UK locations. The committee focuses on projects relating to the following areas:

- Children and young people
- People with disabilities
- Health and fitness
- Lifelong learning
- Community and social development
- Sport and leisure

A separate fund is administered by the committee to aid the victims of global disasters.

STEM outreach

Renishaw plc has been involved in several initiatives to encourage more young people to keep studying STEM (science, technology, engineering and maths) subjects as they get older. It engages with around 22,000 students each year with various outreach programmes in South Wales, Gloucestershire and Bristol.

Employee-led support

Employees take part in fundraising and volunteering.

Exclusions

According to the group's website, it will not do the following:

- Provide prizes for raffles or draws
- Provide funding for projects outside the geographical limitations
- Support charities or organisations seeking funds to redistribute to other charities
- Support political organisations and campaigns
- Purchase tables at charity fundraising events, boxes at sporting events, etc.
- Support national/international organisations (except as stated above)

It will also not support projects that are wholly or partly considered to be personal development (e.g. sports sponsorship or educational/charitable expeditions), or if the applicant is seeking sponsorship to cover the costs of participating in an event.

Applications

Applications should be made online through the 'Charities Committee' section of the website. The committee usually meets in January, March, May, July, September and November to discuss applications.

Community contributions

Cash donations worldwide	£239,000

In 2020/21 the group made donations totalling £239,000 to over 170 organisations through its charity committee.

Rentokil Initial plc

Community services and development, emergency appeals/aid, general charitable purposes

Company registration number: 5393279

Correspondent: The Rentokil Initial Cares Committee, Compass House, Manor Royal, Crawley, West Sussex RH10 9PY (tel: 020 7592 2700; website: https://rbreport.rentokil-initial.com/communities)

Directors: Richard Solomons; Andy Ransom; John Pettigrew; Stuart Ingall-Tombs; Julie Southern; Cathy Turner; Linda Yueh; Sarosh Mistry (female: 38%; male: 63%).

Nature of business: Rentokil is an international company providing services to businesses, including: workwear; plants and landscaping; hygiene services; medical services; pest control; package delivery; catering; electronic security; and cleaning.

Financial information

Year end	31/12/2021
Turnover	£2,956,600,000
Pre-tax profit	£325,100,000

Total employees: 43,000

Main locations: Rentokil has branches throughout the UK. There is a list of branches on the company's website.

Community involvement

Rentokil Initial Cares

The Rentokil Initial Cares programme uses the value of unclaimed shares and dividends to support partner charities. The programme has three focus areas, details of which have been taken from the company's website:

Global and community partnership, providing long-term support for specific charities including Better Futures, Malaria No More UK, Cool Earth UK as well as a number of individual projects.

Local community support and investment at a country or regional level (mostly small amounts but more significant amounts are likely to combine financial and business support with volunteering and value in-kind donations.

Response to national disasters, supporting affected communities where colleagues live.

Community education

Since 2013, over 27,000 people have participated in community education events, mainly in India, Indonesia and Malaysia, through the company's community health and hygiene programme, Better Futures.

Rainforest protection

The company also supports charities that protect biodiversity and rainforests, and promote public health in Asia. It has a partnership with UK climate change charity, Cool Earth.

In-kind support
In response to the COVID-19 pandemic, the company donated £2.5 million worth of PPE to hospitals in India.

Employee-led support
Employees have raised funds for Malaria No More UK by taking part in events such as bike rides, mountain climbs and bake sales. For example, in 2021, 2,000 employees took part in the Race to Kigali, which raised over £200,000.

Applications
Contact your local Rentokil Initial Cares committee. The company's website states:

The Rentokil Initial Cares (RIC) supports local communities in all regions. Each region has an ambassador who coordinates the fund to match colleagues' efforts locally and to commit financial support to those local charities which protect people and enhance lives in line with the Company's purpose.

Community activity is coordinated, monitored and reported (with an approval process for additional funds) through the RIC committee, has clear rules and policies, and results are communicated across the company.

Community contributions
| Cash donations worldwide | £361,000 |

According to the 2021 annual report, £361,000 was donated to charitable organisations. This figure includes matched donations.

Richer Sounds plc

Animal welfare, arts, culture and heritage, citizenship, education and training, health, housing and homelessness, human rights, music, social welfare

Company registration number: 1402643

Correspondent: CSR Team, Richer House, Hankey Place, London SE1 4BB (tel: 0161 474 6811; email: tracyg@richersounds.com; website: www.richersounds.com)

Directors: Julian Richer; David Robinson; Julie Abraham (female: 33%; male: 67%).

Nature of business: Richer Sounds is a video and audio equipment retailer.

Financial information
Year end	01/05/2021
Turnover	£178,140,000
Pre-tax profit	£9,890,000

Total employees: 484

Main locations: The company has stores throughout the UK.

Community involvement
The company has established a number of charitable organisations through which it provides support. These are:
- Acts 435 – a charity that provides financial support to individuals in need.
- ASB Help – a charity that provides advice and support to those who have been affected by anti-social behaviour.
- The Fairness Foundation – is a foundation that supports a range of social and economic issues including democracy, housing, education, etc.
- The Richer Sounds Foundation, which levies a 15% donation from the company's profits.
- Richer Unsigned (not a registered charity) – a not-for-profit organisation designed to help and support musicians and artists by promoting undiscovered music.

Applications
For further information contact the correspondent or see the company's corporate charity entries.

Corporate charity
The Fairness Foundation (Charity Commission no. 1044174) – see entry on page 239.

Community contributions
| Cash donations UK | £1,560,000 |

The company's 2020/21 annual report and accounts state that it made charitable donations of £1.56 million to the Fairness Foundation. Some of this amount was distributed through the foundation to the company's other trusts; for example, the 2020/21 annual report for ASB Help states that it received £55,000 from the Fairness Foundation during the period. We have therefore taken the figure of £1.56 million as the total charitable contribution for Richer Sounds Ltd.

Rightmove plc

Health, STEM

Company registration number: 6426485

Correspondent: CSR Team, 2 Caldecotte Lake Business Park, Caldecotte Lake Drive, Caldecotte, Milton Keynes MK7 8LE (website: https://plc.rightmove.co.uk/responsibility/social/community)

Directors: Carolyn Pollard; Peter Brooks; Jacqueline De Rojas; Alison Dolan; Andrew Findlay; Andrew Fisher; Rakhi Parekh; Laura Tilbian; Amit Tiwari (female: 44%; male: 56%).

Nature of business: Rightmove is a UK property portal.

Financial information
Year end	31/12/2021
Turnover	£304,886,000
Pre-tax profit	£225,649,000

Main locations: Rightmove plc has offices in London and Milton Keynes.

Community involvement
Rightmove plc supports the communities in which it operates through donations, sponsorship and matched funding. According to its website, the group's two pillars of giving are:
- Helping people to be happy in their home – including well-being and mental health
- Increasing opportunity, equality and inclusion in education, particularly STEM careers.

In 2021 the group made donations to CALM, Harry's Rainbow and The Trussell Trust.

Partnerships
In 2021 the group partnered with Generating Genius to provide a scholarship which will allow a student from a disadvantaged background to study a STEM subject at university.

Employee-led support
A number of employees are STEM ambassadors, giving their time to mentor and support individuals who want to pursue STEM careers.

Payroll giving
Employees are able to give directly to any charity from their monthly salary through the Charities Trust.

Employee fundraising
Employee fundraising is supported by the group through its uncapped matched funding programme.

Commercially led support
The group sponsors the local volleyball and ice hockey teams in Milton Keynes.

Applications
Contact the correspondent for further information.

Community contributions
| Cash donations UK | £153,000 |

In 2021 Rightmove plc's charitable donations, including matched funding and sponsorship, totalled £153,000.

Rolls-Royce plc

Arts, culture and heritage, education and training, the environment, STEM

Company registration number: 1003142

Correspondent: The Corporate Sustainability Team, 65 Buckingham Gate, London SW1E 6AT (tel: 020 7222 9020; website: www.rolls-royce.com)

Directors: Anita Frew; Warren East; Panos Kakoullis; Paul Adams; George Culmer; Lord Jitesh Gadhia; Beverly Goulet; Lee Hsien Yang; Nick Luff; Mike Manley; Wendy Mars; Sir Kevin Smith; Dame Angela Strank; Tufan Erginbilic; Pamela Coles (female: 33%; male: 67%).

Nature of business: Rolls-Royce is a global company providing power (gas turbines and reciprocating engines) on land, sea and air.

Financial information

Year end	31/12/2021
Turnover	£11,218,000,000
Pre-tax profit	(£294,000,000)

UK employees: 19,700

Total employees: 44,000

Main locations: The group has sites in Washington, Rotherham, Hucknall, Derby, Birmingham, Bristol and Inchinnan.

Community involvement

Charitable support is focused on communities local to the group's operations with a focus on the environment, education, arts and culture.

STEM programmes and community outreach

The group works closely with schools and universities to encourage interest and diversity in STEM subjects. Projects supported in 2021 include:

- Tackling the digital divide for young people in education in the UK and Germany
- Unnati programmes supporting STEM education and skills training for girls and women facing economic challenge in India
- Habitat for Humanity's Women Build programme to provide homes for financially disadvantaged families in the US

The Diana Award

In 2021, Rolls-Royce plc partnered with The Diana Award, to deliver an anti-bullying ambassador training day to 120 students in 12 secondary schools close to the group's Derby site.

Employee-led support

In 2021, 26,427 hours of employee time was committed to community and STEM projects.

Commercially led support
Sponsorship

Rolls-Royce sponsors the UK Female Undergraduate of the Year awards with the winner receiving a paid summer internship.

Rolls Royce Science Prize

Established in 2004, the Rolls-Royce Science Prize is part of the group's commitment to promote science and engineering in schools.

Exclusions

According to its website, Rolls-Royce does not 'make corporate contributions or donations to political parties or to any organisations, think-tanks, academic institutions or charities closely associated to a political party or cause'.

Applications

Contact your local site or contact the group's sustainability team at www.rolls-royce.com/contact-us/corporate-sustainability-team.aspx.

Community contributions

Cash donations worldwide	£1,790,000
Total contributions worldwide	£6,100,000

The 2021 annual report states that the group invested £6.1 million in supporting local communities during the year, including £2.73 million in global community contributions for STEM education and sponsorship, of which £1.79 million was cash donations.

Rothschild & Co.

Education and training, social welfare

Correspondent: Community Investment Team, New Court, St Swithin's Lane, London EC4N 8AL (email: community.investment@rothschild.com; website: www.rothschildandco.com/en/corporate-sustainability/randco4generations)

Directors: David de Rothschild; Éric de Rothschild; Lucie Maurel-Aubert; Adam Keswick; Daniel Daeniker; Gilles Denoyel; Sir Peter Estlin; Sylvain Héfès; Suet-Fern Lee; Arielle Mallard de Rothschild; Jenifer Moses; Caroline Piwnila; Sipko Schat; Lord Mark Sedwill; Véronique Weill (female: 40%; male: 60%).

Nature of business: Rothschild & Co. is a global financial advisory group, with offices in more than 40 countries worldwide.

Financial information

Year end	31/12/2021
Turnover	£2,550,892,500
Pre-tax profit	£986,251,000

Total employees: 3,816

Main locations: In the UK, Rothschild & Co. has offices in Birmingham, the City of London, Leeds and Manchester.

Community involvement

In 2021, the group established the R&Co4Generations philanthropic fund. The fund is managed under the umbrella of the King Baudouin Foundation (KBF), a public utility foundation registered in Belgium. Rothschild & Co entities contribute to the fund either directly or via KBF's global network of subsidiaries and partner foundations.

R&Co4Generations has three main aims:
- To develop skills and talents in young people
- To cultivate entrepreneurial mindsets
- To promote innovation in response to inequalities and combatting climate change

The group supports the fund in various ways, including grant funding, fundraising campaigns, pro bono advisory support and volunteering campaigns. In 2021, the fund supported 50 charities in over 20 countries, with the average partnership lasting two years.

In-kind support

The group provides pro bono advisory support to charities through its R&Co4Generations programme.

Employee-led support

Employees are encouraged to take at least two days' paid leave to volunteer each year. In 2021, 26% of employees volunteered for the R&Co4Generations programme.

Applications

Contact the correspondent for further information.

Community contributions

We were unable to determine a figure for the group's charitable contributions. Financial information has been converted from EUR using the exchange rate at the time of writing (November 2022).

Rotork plc

General charitable purposes

Company registration number: 578327

Correspondent: Corporate Responsibility Committee, Brassmill Lane, Bath, Somerset BA1 3JQ (tel: 01225 733200; website: www.rotork.com)

Directors: Kiet Huynh; Martin Lamb; Jonathan Davis; Janice Stipp; Peter Dilnot; Ann-ChristinAndersen; Tim Cobbold; Karin Meurk-Harvey (female: 38%; male: 63%).

Nature of business: The group's activities include design and manufacture of actuators and flow control equipment.

Financial information

Year end	31/12/2021
Turnover	£569,160,000
Pre-tax profit	£105,710,000

UK employees: 860

Total employees: 3,296

Main locations: The group has sites in Chadderton, Lutterworth, Bath and Leeds.

Community involvement

Rotork plc partners with international charities whose aims align with the group's strategic purpose, while also making donations to local causes and charitable organisations in the communities where the group has a presence.

Partnerships

In 2021, the group's charity partners were Renewable World, Pump Aid and We Forest. The group also makes donations to individual charities outside of partnership. In the UK, the group donated £5,000 to the Royal United Hospital and £2,000 to the Children's Literature Festival.

Employee-led support

Employees are encouraged to volunteer and donate to causes local to the group's area of operations. Payroll giving is also available for employees wanting to donate to the Rotork Benevolent Support foundation.

Applications

Contact your local Rotork site for further information.

Community contributions

Total contributions worldwide	£135,000

The group's 2021 annual report states: 'Rotork plc contributes 0.1% of profits to partnered international charities and a further 0.1% profits to local causes around the world.' The report also states that the group's total charitable contributions totalled £135,000 during the year.

The Rotork plc Social Impact report also states that the group channelled an additional £80,000 in funds from individuals, Rotork charity committees and donations from the group to the Rotork Benevolent Support Foundation (Charity Commission no. 1189463). We have not included this figure in the group's total contributions as the foundation's annual return reports that funds come principally from employee fundraising or payroll giving.

The Royal London Mutual Insurance Society Ltd

Arts, culture and heritage, community enterprise and social entrepreneurship, education and training, the environment, general charitable purposes, health, medical research, sports and recreation

Company registration number: 99064

Correspondent: CSR Team, 55 Gracechurch Street, London EC3V 0RL (tel: 0345 602 1885; website: www.royallondon.com)

Directors: Kevin Parry; Barry O'Dwyer; Daniel Cazeaux; Kal Atwal; Sally Bridgeland; Ian Dilks; Tim Tookey; Ruth Davidson; Shirley Garrood; Jane Guyett; Mark Rennison (female: 45%; male: 55%).

Nature of business: Principal activities of the group's businesses are provision of pensions, life assurance, savings and investment products, protection insurance and investment management services. The group comprises The Royal London Mutual Insurance Society Ltd and its subsidiaries.

Financial information

Year end	31/12/2021
Turnover	£10,804,000,000
Pre-tax profit	£192,000,000

Main locations: The group has offices in Bath, Dublin, Edinburgh, Glasgow, London, Reading and Wilmslow.

Community involvement

Each year, the group commits over £1 million to social impact initiatives aimed at tackling financial vulnerability. Support is given via charity partners, employee initiatives and more.

Partnerships

In 2021, the group launched a flagship partnership with national charity Turn2us, through which it is providing funding and support for guidance, online tools and financial relief to people in crisis.

In 2021, local partnerships included The Food Chain in London, which provides food for the most vulnerable people living with HIV, The Booth Centre in Alderley Park, which supports people affected by homelessness and Held in Our Hearts in Edinburgh, which supports families after the loss of a baby.

Employee-led support

The group's volunteering programme gives employees two days' paid leave to volunteer.

Through the group's digital community platform KindLink, employees can fundraise for, or donate to, charity

partners and causes they care about. The group matches a proportion of staff fundraising.

Commercially led support

The group sponsors cricket-related initiatives, including one-day international and domestic cricket.

Applications

Contact the correspondent for more information.

Community contributions

Cash donations UK	£1,070,000

The group's 2021 annual report states that grants and donations totalled £1.07 million.

Royal Mail plc

Education and training, humanitarian aid

Company registration number: 8680755

Correspondent: The ESG Team, 185 Farringdon Road, London EC1A 1AA (tel: 0345 774 0740)

Directors: Mark Amsden; Michael Findlay; Baroness Sarah Hogg; Jourik Hooghe; Michael Jevons; Lynne Peacock; Martin Seidenberg; Maria Silva; Simon Thompson; Shashi Verma; Keith Williams (female: 27%; male: 73%).

Nature of business: Royal Mail plc is the ultimate parent company of the Royal Mail Group, which operates through two core divisions: UK Parcels, International and Letters (UKPIL) and GLS (operating in continental Europe and Ireland). The group's main activities include letter and parcel services, and the design and manufacture of UK stamps and philatelic products.

Financial information

Year end	27/03/2022
Turnover	£12,712,000,000
Pre-tax profit	£662,000,000

UK employees: 143,000

Total employees: 162,000

Main locations: The group's headquarters is in London.

Community involvement

The group gives both in-kind and financial support to charities across the UK. According to its Corporate Social Responsibility Report 2020/21 the group's community investment strategy is structured into three key areas:

- **Leverage our national scale:** in response to a reported rise in domestic abuse the group launched Online Safe Spaces (OSS) with the charity Hestia. The service provides support, advice and contact numbers for those experiencing or at risk of domestic abuse.

- **Use our local presence:** the group has supported the charity Missing People since 2004 by posting alerts to postmen and women. It also supported the charity's Home for Christmas Campaign.
- **Unlock potential through education:** Royal Mail supports World Book Day and the National Literacy Trust's Vision for Literacy pledge, which aims to close the national literacy gap and boost social mobility.

Charity of the Year

The group's Charity of the Year programme was paused in 2020/21 due to the COVID-19 pandemic. According to the group's 2021/22 ESG Report, it will be appointing a new charity partner in 2022/23.

The Rowland Hill Fund (Charity Commission no. 207479)

The Rowland Hill Fund provides support to current and former Royal Mail employees who fall on hard times. Royal Mail makes an annual contribution of £50,000 to the fund, plus an additional £60,000 a year in in-kind donations.

Post Office Orphans Benevolent Institution (not a registered charity)

Each year, the Post Office Orphans Benevolent Institution provides grants to children of Royal Mail employees facing hardship. In 2018/19 it distributed grants totalling £302,000. Grants come from the returns generated by investing a fund created by donations from former employees. The fund is used to provide university bursaries and awards for children with special vocational talent. It also assists families where hardship is impacting upon their children.

GLS activities

GLS is the group's European parcel delivery service. It supports numerous charitable projects by organising both regional and nationwide initiatives. These include free parcel shipping for aid organisations and the sponsorship of foundations for people with disabilities.

In-kind support

Articles for the Blind

The group's Articles for the Blind service delivers items free of charge to blind and partially-sighted people across the UK. Charities working with blind and partially sighted people can also use this scheme.

Disaster relief

The group has supported the Disasters Emergency Committee (DEC) with a dedicated PO Box for over 30 years, providing the UK public with a way to respond to national appeals for overseas disasters.

Support for Ukraine

The group has supported vehicles travelling to Poland as part of the Ukrainian Embassy's aid effort carrying food donated by British Army suppliers.

Employee-led support

The group encourages employees to support causes important to them through a range of fundraising and volunteering initiatives.

Matched giving

Money raised for charities and good causes is matched up to £200 per employee per year.

Payroll giving

Employees have the opportunity to make donations directly from their pay to charities of their choice through Payroll Giving. In 2020/21 employees donated over £2 million.

Volunteering

The group offers grants to support Royal Mail employees to support fundraising and volunteer projects.

Applications

Contact the correspondent for further information. It appears that local organisations can also apply directly to their regional office for support.

Community contributions

Cash donations UK	£161,000
Total contributions UK	£3,500,000

According to its 2021/22 ESG data report, Royal Mail plc gave a total of £3.5 million in community contributions. This included £161,000 given as cash donations. A further £2.1 million was donated by Royal Mail employees; however, we have not included this figure in the total.

RSA Insurance Group Ltd

Community services and development, education and training, the environment, general charitable purposes, health, mental health and well-being

Company registration number: 2339826

Correspondent: CSR Team, 20 Fenchurch Street, London EC3M 3AU (tel: 01403 232323; website: www. rsagroup.com)

Directors: Mark Hodges; Alastair Barbour; Sally Bridgeland; Charles Brindamour; Clare Bousfield; Claude Dussault; Robert Leary; Andy Parsons; Ken Norgrove; Charlotte Jones (female: 30%; male: 70%).

Nature of business: The group's principal activity is the transaction of personal and commercial general insurance business.

Financial information

Year end	31/12/2021
Turnover	£3,449,000,000
Pre-tax profit	(£228,000,000)

UK employees: 4,929

Total employees: 6,168

Main locations: RSA works throughout the UK and has main offices in Liverpool, Horsham and London.

Community involvement

RSA Insurance Group Ltd's community contributions are in line with its 'Confident Futures' strategy. Launched in 2019, the strategy aims to integrate responsible business practices into the group's everyday operations. The group's corporate responsibility has a particular focus on supporting projects concerning education of risk management, as well as environmental organisations.

Partnerships

During the year, the group partnered with the Royal Society for the Prevention of Accidents (RoSPA), to deliver educational programmes targeted at over 65s to reduce the risk of falls in the home. This programme is part of a wider behaviour change programme that the group delivers for schools, workplaces and in the home.

The RSA Climate and Risk Education Grant Programme

In 2021, RSA turned to alternative means of charitable contribution as the COVID-19 pandemic made in-person volunteering more difficult. For example, the group launched the RSA Climate and Risk Education Grant Programme, which utilised funds from the UK Dividend Forfeiture Scheme to donate to organisations tackling climate change and reducing carbon emissions, or supporting risk education and behaviour change. In total, the group contributed £295,000 funds to 43 causes.

In-kind support

In 2021, the value of the group's in-kind donations and volunteered time came to £600,000. The group makes in-kind donations through its delivery of educational programmes.

Employee-led support

In 2021, the group achieved the Charities Aid Foundation Silver Payroll Giving Mark for its Give As You Earn scheme. 262 employees signed up to this benefit in which the group offered matched donations of up to £10 per month, with participants making an average donation of £28 per month. RSA donated a further £39,400 in matched funding.

Exclusions

The group is unable to help any organisation which supports one specific religious faith, political parties, sports (unless with compelling community justification), arts (unless supporting disadvantaged groups) or individual sponsorships.

Applications

Contact the correspondent for further information.

The group's Community and Charity Policy Statement states the following:

RSA supports the following priority focus areas which all have a clear link to our business, namely:

- Education and Employability;
- Enterprise and Entrepreneurship; and
- Charities of importance to our people

We also support charities addressing safety and environmental issues in our communities. These focus areas act as a guide but regional variations are acceptable as long as a direct link to the business exists.

Community contributions

Cash donations UK	£870,000
Total contributions UK	£1,470,000

According to the RSA Insurance Group Ltd annual report for 2021, the group's community contributions totalled £1.47 million. Within this total, charitable donations amounted to £870,000. We have taken the remaining £600,000 to represent the value of in-kind donations and volunteered time.

RSM UK Holdings Ltd

Community services and development, education and training, the environment, general charitable purposes, social welfare

Company registration number: 5924823

Correspondent: Joy Welch, Corporate Responsibility Manager, 6th Floor, 25 Farringdon Street, London EC4A 4AB (email: info@rsmukfoundation.com; website: www.rsmuk.com/who-we-are/cr#Charity)

Directors: Patricia O'Flynn; Robert Donaldson; Howard Freedman; Robert Hamlin; Simon Hart; Victoria Kirkhope; Kevin O'Connor; David Punt; Zoe Rudling; Vijaykumar Thakrar; Andrew Westbrook (female: 27%; male: 73%).

Nature of business: RSM is a multinational network of accounting firms.

Financial information

Year end	31/03/2021
Turnover	£85,322,000

Main locations: The group has 32 offices across the UK.

Community involvement

The group's charitable giving is channelled through its corporate charity, the RSM UK Foundation (Charity Commission no. 1179349).

RSM UK Foundation

The foundation supports its national partner charities with long-term funding. These national partner charities include Anthony Nolan, the Duke of Edinburgh's Award, EDGA (formerly the European Disabled Golf Association), Leadership Through Sport and Business and Trees for Cities.

In addition to the national partner charities the foundation also supports local charities with a focus on the environment, community development, social welfare and education.

Employee-led support

The foundation matches employees' fundraising efforts up to £250 per individual. The group also offers a payroll giving scheme.

The group also supports one-off campaigns for compelling causes. In 2022 the group fundraised for UNICEF UK's humanitarian campaign in Ukraine. With employees' donations match-funded by the foundation, over £250,000 was raised to support children in Ukraine.

Applications

See the RSM Foundation's website for further information.

Corporate charity

RSM UK Foundation (Charity Commission no. 1179349) – see entry on page 270.

Community contributions

Total contributions UK	£519,600

In 2020/21 the RSM UK Foundation received a donation of £519,600 from RSM UK Group LLP.

RWS Holdings plc

Community enterprise and social entrepreneurship, community services and development, general charitable purposes

Company registration number: 3002645

Correspondent: The ESG Team, Europa House, Chiltern Park, Chiltern Hill, Chalfont St Peter, Buckinghamshire SL9 9FG (email: online contact form; website: www.rws.com/about/corporate-sustainability)

Directors: Christopher Lewey; Lara Boro; Andrew Brode; David Clayton; Roderick Day; Ian El-Mokadem; Frances Hogan; Julie Southern; Gordon Stuart (female: 33%; male: 67%).

Nature of business: RWS plc is a provider of technology-enabled language, content and intellectual property services.

Financial information

Year end	30/09/2021
Turnover	£694,500,000
Pre-tax profit	£55,000,000

Main locations: The group has offices throughout the world. Its UK offices are in Alnwick, Bloxham, Chalfont St Peter, London, Maidenhead, Nottingham, Sheffield and Wakefield.

Community involvement

The group's charitable giving is focused on its corporate charity, The RWS Foundation (Charity Commission no. 1127138).

In 2020/21 the foundation supported Street Business School (Uganda), Food for the Hungry (Kenya), Brighter Children (worldwide) and St Wilfrid's Centre (UK).

In-kind support

Employees volunteer with Urban Synergy, a charity which helps young people reach their potential through mentoring programmes and seminars.

Applications

For further information contact the correspondent or see the group's corporate charity entry.

Corporate charity

The RWS Foundation (Charity Commission no. 1127138) – see entry on page 271.

Community contributions

Total contributions UK	£271,200

In 2020/21 charitable contributions totalled £271,200.

S&U plc

Christianity, health

Company registration number: 342025

Correspondent: CSR Team, S&U plc, 2 Stratford Court, Cranmore Boulevard, Solihull, West Midlands B90 4LE (tel: 0121 705 7777; email: info@suplc.co.uk; website: www.suplc.co.uk)

Directors: Anthony Coombs; Graham Coombs; Jack Coombs; Chris Redford; Thomas Graham Wheeler; Demetrios Markou; Graham Pedersen; Jeremy Maxwell; Tarek Khlat (male: 100%).

Nature of business: S&U is a specialist finance provider in the UK.

Financial information

Year end	31/01/2022
Turnover	£87,889,000
Pre-tax profit	£47,018,000

UK employees: 200

Main locations: S&U's head office is in Birmingham and it has various locations throughout the UK.

Community involvement

S&U supports charities in its local community through sponsorship, fundraising and through The Keith Coombs Trust (Charity Commission no. 1149791). Support is focused on children with disabilities.

In recent years, the company has supported The National Institute for Conductive Education, Red Boots, Cure Leukaemia for Kids and other charities.

The company also provides scholarships for aspiring and talented young choreographers and designers through the Birmingham Royal Ballet's Ballet Now programme.

On the 10th January each year, Keith Coombs Trust pays for a day of care at the Marie Curie hospice in the West Midlands as a celebration of Keith Coombs' birthday.

In 2022, Keith Coombs Trust also supported The Emily Jordan Foundation, helping to equip people with learning disabilities with skills to facilitate their entry into the workplace.

The company also made contributions to the Christian faith in 2022, providing support for the 'Leap of Faith' project that assists the wider UK church's adoption of a more digital future.

Employee-led support

Employees are encouraged to participate in fundraising activities to raise money for charities. Past examples include a rowing challenge for Marie Curie Cancer Care and sponsorship of kayak rides, cake days and cycle rides.

Commercially led support

Fostering Young Talent at Barnt Green Cricket Club

S&U sponsors the Junior Cricket programme at Barnt Green Cricket Club in Worcestershire, helping to provide coaching and training to children between the ages of 9 and 16.

Applications

Contact the correspondent for further information.

Corporate charity

The Keith Coombs Trust (Charity Commission no. 1149791) – see entry on page 234.

Community contributions

Cash donations UK	£102,000

According to its 2021/22 annual report, the company gave £102,000 in charitable contributions through the Keith Coombs Trust. An additional £100,000 donation has also been announced as a celebration of the trust's tenth anniversary.

Safestore Holdings plc

Community services and development, general charitable purposes

Company registration number: 4726380

Correspondent: The CSR Team, Brittanic House, Stirling Way, Borehamwood, Hertfordshire WD6 2BT (email: customerservice@safestore.co.uk; website: www.safestore.co.uk/corporate/sustainability/overview)

Directors: Helen Bramall; Jane Bentall; Marie-Laure Duhot; David Hearn; Andrew Jones; Ian Krieger; Delphine Mousseau; Gert Van De Weerdhof; Frederico Vecchioli (female: 44%; male: 56%).

Nature of business: The group provides self-storage facilities.

Financial information

Year end	31/10/2021
Turnover	£186,800,000
Pre-tax profit	£94,000,000

Main locations: The group has 130 stores in the UK as well as stores in France, Belgium, the Netherlands and Spain.

Community involvement

The group's main contribution to the communities it works in is the provision of free/discounted storage space to support local charities and community groups.

Safestore Holdings plc also takes part in a number of events each year in order to raise money or awareness for charitable causes. In 2020/21 the group donated cardboard boxes to various charities including City Hearts and The Suit Works.

Charitable fund

The group has a charitable fund with Quartet Community Foundation which supports projects in Bristol, Bath and North East Somerset, North Somerset and South Gloucestershire.

Applications

Contact your local store for further information.

Community contributions

Total contributions UK	£636,900

In 2020/21 the group donated storage space worth £636,900.

Saga plc

Community services and development, education and training, general charitable purposes, health

Company registration number: 8804263

Correspondent: Charity Team, Enbrook Park, Sandgate, Folkestone, Kent CT20 3SE (email: charity4saga@saga.co.uk; website: www.saga.co.uk/saga-charities)

Directors: Sir Roger De Haan; Euan Sutherland; James Quin; Orna NiChionna; Eva Eisenschimmel; Julie Hopes; Gareth Hoskin (female: 43%; male: 57%).

Nature of business: The company provides travel, financial, insurance, health and lifestyle products and services for people aged 50 and over.

Financial information

Year end	31/01/2022
Turnover	£377,200,000
Pre-tax profit	£23,500,000

Total employees: 3,776

Main locations: Saga works throughout the UK and has headquarters in Kent.

Community involvement

This company supports charities that are local to its office sites through cash and in-kind donations, as well as through sponsorship.

Partnerships

During the year, Saga plc made cash donations to its various charity partners, including Leukaemia Care, The Marine Conservation Society and The Plunkett Foundation. A full list of the company's charitable partners can be found on its charity web page: www.saga.co.uk/saga-charities

In-kind support

Saga plc runs an office furniture giveaway scheme, donating unused furniture to local charitable causes. In 2021, the value of furniture donated totalled £184,000.

The company also allowed its office in Thanet to be used as a vaccination centre during the COVID-19 pandemic to aid vaccination efforts.

Employee-led support

Matched funding and fundraising

Matched funding is available through employee payroll giving and fundraising activities. In 2021/22, the total funds raised by customers and employees, including matched funding was £38,000.

Workplace Lottery

Saga plc also runs a workplace lottery for employees to participate in, with proceeds being donated to charity. In 2021/22 this scheme raised £20,600.

Volunteering

According to the 2021/22 annual report, Saga plc offers 12 days of leave for uniformed volunteers. In 2021/22, the company's employees volunteered 3,283 hours of their time to support local charities.

Commercially led support

According to the charity support web page, Saga plc is unable to provide continuous sponsorship; however, the company does engage in sponsorship of the following annual events:

- Creative Folkestone, including the flagship event, the Folkestone Triennial, which is the largest exhibition of newly commissioned art in the UK
- The Folkestone 10k, a popular running event for which Saga plc has agreed to be the mainline sponsor for 2021–23
- Hythe Town FC, where the company has supplied the home kits for the youth teams that will be used until 2023

Applications

The company's charity web page states: 'If you are a Folkestone based charity or good cause and in need of volunteers, office equipment or financial support, please email charity4saga@saga.co.uk as we may be able to help.'

Community contributions

Cash donations UK	£206,000
Total contributions UK	£390,000

The Saga plc 2021/22 annual report states that the company made cash donations totalling £206,000 to its charity partners in 2021. The company also raised £184,000 through its office furniture giveaway scheme.

The Sage Group plc

Community services and development, education and training, social welfare

Company registration number: 2231246

Correspondent: Sage Foundation, C23 5 and 6 Cobalt Park Way, Cobalt Business Park, Newcastle upon Tyne, Tyne and Wear NE28 9EJ (tel: 0191 294 3000; website: www.sage.com/company/sage-foundation)

Directors: Steve Hare; Jonathan Howell; Sangeeta Anand; John Bates; Jonathan Bewes; Annette Court; Drummond Hall; Derek Harding; Andrew Duff (female: 22%; male: 78%).

Nature of business: Sage is a global technology company, providing automated business solutions for accounting and HR.

Financial information

Year end	30/09/2021
Turnover	£1,846,000,000
Pre-tax profit	£347,000,000

Total employees: 11,700

Main locations: The group is based in Newcastle and operates worldwide. It has UK offices in London, Manchester and Winnersh.

Community involvement

The group makes contributions to community and charitable organisations worldwide through its foundation, which is not a registered charity. Its focus areas are education, employment and entrepreneurship. In the UK, there may be some preference for organisations in the North East, where the head office is based.

Sage Foundation

The Sage Foundation was established in 2015 to help the group support charities and the community. The foundation supports local non-profits with funding and volunteer partnerships. Its Grants for Change scheme offers support to organisations that support young people, women and military veterans. However, the foundation accepts proposals for its Grants for Change programme by invitation only.

The foundation is also involved in a range of development programmes that provide support and funding to non-profits. Examples include:

Pathways Back to Work – a programme designed to help people enter the workplace or return to work.

FIRST LEGO League – a programme that challenges young people aged four to 16, to build robots using LEGO bricks and components. The aim of the programme is to develop STEM skills in young people.

In 2021, to celebrate the foundation's five-year anniversary, the group launched a series of programmes, offering over 1,000 free financial literacy training spaces for non-profits, volunteer programmes to support local communities and investments supporting non-profits with an environmental focus.

In-kind support

NPO Success

The Sage Foundation provides donated licenses to eligible charities, social enterprises and non-profit organisations through its software donation programme.

Employee-led support

Volunteering

The group's employees are entitled to five days' paid leave per year to volunteer for charitable causes. In 2021,

employees spent 22,000 working days, with volunteering valued at £3.2 million.

Fundraising

In 2019, the group achieved its 'Million Dollar Challenge', a fundraising initiative designed to mobilise Sage's colleagues, customers and partners to raise a total $1 million for their chosen causes and a range of activities. The target is now to raise $5 million by 2030.

Applications

Eligibility forms for 'NPO Success' product discounts can be found on the group's website. For all other enquiries contact the correspondent.

Community contributions

We were unable to determine a figure for the group's total community contributions. The group's 2020/21 annual report states that it awarded 178 grants to its charity partners and 419 non-profit organisations benefitted from donated or discounted Sage Business Cloud software; however, the value of these donations was not quantified.

J Sainsbury plc

Community services and development, general charitable purposes, health, housing and homelessness, social welfare, sports and recreation

Company registration number: 185647

Correspondent: Corporate Responsibility and Sustainability Committee, 33 Holborn, London EC1N 2HT (tel: 020 7695 6000; website: https://about.sainsburys.co.uk/making-a-difference/our-values)

Directors: Joanna Bertram; Brain Cassin; Jo Harlow; Adrian Hennah; Tanuj Kapilashrami; Kevin O'Byrne; Simon Roberts; Keith Weed; Martin Scicluna (female: 33%; male: 67%).

Nature of business: Sainsbury's is the second largest chain of supermarkets in the UK. Banking and financial services products are offered through the wholly owned subsidiary, Sainsbury's Bank, and the group has several joint ventures, including property development.

Financial information

Year end	05/03/2022
Turnover	£29,895,000,000
Pre-tax profit	£854,000,000

Total employees: 171,000+

Main locations: The group headquarters is in London. There are Sainsbury's stores throughout the UK.

Community involvement

As part of the group's sustainability strategy 'Plan for Better', it supports a number of causes and charities through partnerships, fundraising, donations and volunteering.

Charity partners

In 2021, the group launched a partnership with Neighbourly through which Sainsbury's stores are matched with a donation partner. Neighbourly ensures that any surplus food from the stores is directed to people in need. Charity partners co-ordinate daily collections of food from their Sainsbury's stores. Donation partners support a wide range of local causes including homeless centres, schools, breakfast clubs, community centres, community fridges, community cafes, night shelters, refuges, churches and hospices.

The group has had a longstanding partnership with The Royal British Legion, supporting its Poppy Appeal for over 25 years. In 2021/22, the partnership raised £2.3 million through the Poppy Appeal collections in-store and the sales of products.

The group has also worked in partnership with The Woodland Trust since 2004 and in 2021, planted over 398,300 native trees.

Other partnerships include Comic Relief, Macmillan Cancer Support and The Irish Cancer Charity.

Sainsbury Family Charitable Trusts

The Sainsbury Family Charitable Trusts is the operating office of a group of 17 grant-making charities affiliated with the Sainsbury family. Each trust is operated independently with separate boards of trustees each led by a member of the family.

Helping everyone eat better Community Grant scheme

In 2021, the company launched the Helping everyone eat better Community Grant scheme, designed to support some of the most vulnerable people and communities throughout the UK. The scheme allows each Sainsburys and Argos store to nominate a partner organisation, NGO, registered charity or community group that supports food poverty to receive a grant of up to £500. The scheme is managed by Neighbourly.

In-kind support

Food donations programme

Launched in 1998, the group's food donations programme enables stores to partner with local organisations, to which they donate surplus food. Donation points are available in most stores for customers to provide donations.

As part of the programme, the group partners with a number of organisations including The Felix Project, The Trussell Trust and FareShare. The programme has been further developed through a partnership with Neighbourly. In 2021, the group donated over 2,560,000 meals, which is equivalent to around £4.89 million in savings to charities and community groups

In-kind donations

Recently, the group donated over 2,000 laptops for children as part of the Computers for Kids initiative. Additionally, it donated 470,000 items of clothing with a retail value of around £5.2 million across a number of charities including Comic Relief and Newlife.

Employee-led support

Employee fundraising

Sainsbury's employees fundraise for various partner charities and causes.

Payroll giving

Our previous research suggests employees contribute through payroll giving.

Commercially led support

The group supports Comic Relief and Children in Need by matching customer donations £1 for £1 in The Big Night In Appeal. In 2021/22, the total donation exceeded £4 million and was split between the two charities.

Applications

Contact the correspondent for further information.

Sainsbury Family Charitable Trusts

The trusts vary in their approach to grant-making and applications. Some have their own application forms, whereas others do not accept unsolicited proposals. More details are available from the Sainsbury Family Charitable Trusts website: www.sfct.org.uk.

Community contributions

The group's 2021/22 Plan for Better report stated that total charitable investment was £38.4 million; however, this figure includes commercial initiatives, customer fundraising and colleague fundraising.

The group's 2021/22 annual report states that it donated £2 million to support the crisis in Ukraine. It also matched customer and employee donations with an additional £500,000. Also, £1.7 million was donated to FareShare during the financial period. The group also donated over 2,560,000 meals, which is equivalent to around £4.89 million in savings to charities and community groups.

We were unable to determine a figure for the group's total charitable contributions for the year.

Samworth Brothers (Holdings) Ltd

Education and training, sports and recreation

Company registration number: 409738

Correspondent: CSR Team, Chetwode, 1 Samworth Way, Leicester Road, Melton Mowbray, Leicestershire LE13 1GA (email: sportsopportunityfund@ samworthbrothers.co.uk; website: www. samworthbrothers.co.uk/responsibilities/ community)

Directors: Celia Pronto; Hugo Mahoney; William Kendall; Aileen Richards; Hannu Ryopponen; Mark Samworth (female: 33%; male: 67%).

Nature of business: Samworth Brothers is a British food manufacturer and owner of brands such as Ginsters, Soreen and West Cornwall Pasty Co.

Financial information

Year end	02/01/2021
Turnover	£1,052,249,000
Pre-tax profit	£31,626,000

UK employees: 9,659

Main locations: The group's headquarters is in Melton Mowbray, Leicestershire. It has operations in Leicestershire and Cornwall.

Community involvement

Support is provided to youth sport projects in areas in which Samworth Brothers businesses are located. The group also has a corporate charity, The Samworth Foundation (Charity Commission no. 265647). The foundation awards grants to organisations that address the root causes of sexual exploitation and the environment.

Sports Opportunity Fund (not a registered charity)

The fund has two grant funds:
- A small grant fund that provides grants of up to £1,000 for projects nominated by Samworth Brothers employees
- A large grants fund for larger projects. Multi-year funding is considered and does not require an employee nomination

Projects should be located in areas in which Samworth Brothers businesses play an important role in the community. Projects should help young people develop life skills, confidence and self-esteem through sport. The larger grant awards look for evidence that the project will improve access to sport for young people in particularly hard-to-reach and disadvantaged groups.

Beneficiaries have included: Cothele Gig Club, Leicester Electric Cricket Club,

Leicester and Rutland Youth Sailing Association, Saffron Young People's Project and Warriors Basketball Club.

In-kind support

The group donates surplus food to redistribution organisations, such as the FareShare charity and The Company Shop, a social enterprise. In 2021 the group donated 30,000 lunch bags for healthcare workers and volunteers in Leicestershire vaccination centres.

Employee-led support

Charity Challenge

Every two years the group holds a triathlon-style event called the Samworth Brothers Charity Challenge. Over £1.9 million has been raised since the competition was launched in 2007.

Community volunteering

According to its website, each of the group's businesses have links with organisations in its local community. Employees volunteer their time supporting projects including:

- Helping young people improve their literacy, numeracy and employability skills
- Supporting communities through practical group projects
- Supporting homeless people breaking the 'no home, no job' cycle
- Helping young people coming out of care progress onto the next steps in life

Employability

Employees attend career fairs in schools to encourage young people to consider careers in the food and drink industry. Through partnerships with local schools, employees also mentor college and secondary school pupils on interview techniques and CV writing. Some employees act as STEM ambassadors in schools to demonstrate the importance of STEM skills in the industry.

Exclusions

All applications to the fund need to fulfil the geographic criteria and also demonstrate their relevance to the project criteria.

Applications

Further information and application forms for the Sports Opportunity Fund can be requested from the correspondent.

Corporate charity

The Samworth Foundation (Charity Commission no. 265647) – see entry on page 271.

Community contributions

Cash donations UK	£1,710,000

In 2020/21 cash donations totalled £1.71 million.

Santander UK plc

Community enterprise and social entrepreneurship, community services and development, education and training, health, money and debt advice, social welfare

Company registration number: 2294747

Correspondent: CSR Team, 2 Triton Square, Regent's Place, London NW1 3AN (email: community@ santander.co.uk; website: www. santandersustainability.co.uk)

Directors: Madhukar Dayal; Antonio Dos Santos Simoes; Annemarie Durbin; Lisa Fretwell; Edward Giera; Christopher Jones; Mark Lewis; Dirk Marzluf; Baroness Nicola Morgan; Michael Regnier; William Vereker; Pamela Walkden (female: 33%; male: 67%).

Nature of business: Santander UK provides personal and corporate financial products and services and forms part of the Banco Santander group, which operates internationally with headquarters in Spain.

Financial information

Year end	31/12/2021
Turnover	£4,544,000,000
Pre-tax profit	£1,858,000,000

UK employees: 17,967

Main locations: Santander UK operates throughout the UK and its head office is in London. It is owned by Santander Group, which is based in Spain.

Community involvement

Santander has an extensive programme of support for charitable causes, mainly focusing on education, employment, enterprise and communities. The group's CSR strategy is especially focused on encouraging digital inclusion and financial inclusion and literacy for people of all ages.

The group provides support for these causes through the Santander UK Foundation Ltd (Charity Commission no. 803655), charity partnerships and educational initiatives, such as the Santander Universities programme. Santander employees volunteer with local charities and educational initiatives and they fundraise for nominated charity partners, as well as donating to other charities through the group's matched funding scheme.

Santander Universities

Santander Universities is the group's global programme which aims to remove barriers to higher education by supporting students across three key areas: education, entrepreneurship and employability. Santander partners with universities in the UK to deliver tailored packages of financial and in-kind

support to students. Money that has been donated by the group helps provide scholarships, bursaries, travel grants, paid internships, support for special projects and academic and non-academic awards. In 2021, the programme made donations of £9.2 million, providing over 10,200 scholarships and awards.

Partnerships

Santander provides support to a charity partner, which is chosen by employees. The group's current charity partner (as of October 2022) is Macmillan Cancer Support. The partnership aims to improve financial inclusion and support for people who have cancer. Previous charity partners include the Alzheimer's Society and Age UK.

The group also has a partnership with National Parks UK. Santander is a founding partner of the 'Net Zero With Nature' initiative, which defines the role that the National Parks will play in the UK's fight against climate change and the biodiversity crisis. Santander will fund a new project involving the restoration of 220 hectares of damaged peatland in the Cairngorms National Park in Scotland.

Educational initiatives

Santander runs a number of initiatives designed to provide knowledge into financial education, particularly for young people. These include:

The Numbers Game – the group's flagship programme which is delivered in partnership with Twinkl, the world's biggest online education hub. The programme educates children and young people on maths and financial skills.

In-kind support

The Santander Universities programme offers practical in-kind support to students through its events, awards and educational programmes.

Employee-led support

Employee volunteering and fundraising

Employees regularly volunteer and fundraise for the group's charity partners. In 2021 employees raised over £692,700 for the Alzheimer's Society.

Wise sessions

Employees volunteer for the group's in-school mentoring programme, Wise Workshops. In these sessions, Santander volunteers teach students about topics such as responsible money management, career planning and staying safe online.

Matched funding

Employees also support local charities through the group's matched funding scheme.

In 2021, the Santander Foundation donated a total of £450,200 through its employee Matched Donation Scheme to support employees' fundraising activities for local charities of their choice.

Commercially led support

Santander Breakthrough
Launched in 2011, the Santander Breakthrough programme supports entrepreneurial companies in the UK and is aimed at fast-growing small and medium-sized enterprises. The group provides support with business expertise, recruitment, international opportunities, networking and finance. In 2021, the group invested over £67,200 in the programme.

Sponsorship
The group is the lead sponsor of My Money Week, Young Enterprise's flagship initiative. Each year Young Enterprise delivers My Money Week resources and activities to schools across the UK giving students an introduction to finance.

Exclusions
The group does not accept requests for sponsorship.

Applications
Contact the correspondent for more information or see the corporate charity's entry.

Corporate charity
Santander UK Foundation Ltd (Charity Commission no. 803655) – see entry on page 272.

Community contributions

Total contributions UK	£1,280,000

According to the group's 2021 Environmental, Social and Governance (ESG) Supplement report, its UK community investment totalled £12.8 million.

Saputo Dairy UK

Community enterprise and social entrepreneurship, community services and development, education and training, the environment, general charitable purposes, health, social welfare

Company registration number: 3162897

Correspondent: CSR Team, 5 The Heights, Brooklands, Weybridge, Surrey KT13 0NY (tel: 01372 472200; website: www.uk.saputo.com)

Directors: Tom Atherton; Adam Braithwaite; Maxime Therrien (female: 33%; male: 67%).

Nature of business: Dairy Crest produces branded dairy products in the UK and Europe. Dairy Crest Group was bought by the Canadian company Saputo in 2019. The group's trading name is now Saputo Dairy UK.

Financial information

Year end	31/03/2021
Pre-tax profit	£25,300,000

Main locations: The group has UK offices or operations in Weybridge in Surrey (head office), Cornwall, Frome, Kent, Kirkby and Nuneaton.

Community involvement
The group's community investment is focused on promoting physical activity and proper nutrition. According to its website, the group is committed to investing 1% of its annual pre-tax profits into its local communities through financial contributions, product donations and volunteering. Each site is allocated an annual budget to support its local community.

Charity partners
The group is a long-term supporter of The Prince's Countryside Fund, which exists to protect, improve and promote the British countryside and the businesses which work within it. Saputo and its employees raise £50,000 for the charity annually and help to raise awareness of the priorities and successes of the charity.

Summer camps
The group runs a series of summer camps for underprivileged children, helping them to avoid inactivity.

Employee-led support
Employees are encouraged to take one paid volunteering day each year.

Applications
According to our previous research, applicants should apply in writing to their local site, referenced 'Local Community Committee'.

Community contributions

Cash donations UK	£200,000

We were unable to determine a figure for the group's total charitable contributions for 2020/21.

Schroders plc

Community services and development, education and training, general charitable purposes, health, mental health and well-being, social welfare, work outside the UK

Company registration number: 3909886

Correspondent: Corporate Responsibility Team, 1 London Wall Place, London EC2Y 5AU (tel: 020 7658 6000; email: use the contact form on the group's website; website: www.schroders.com/en/about-us/corporate-responsibility)

Directors: Peter Harrison; Richard Keers; Ian King; Sir Damon Buffini; Rhian Davies; Claire Fitzalan Howard; Rakhi Goss-Custard; Leonie Schroder; Deborah Waterhouse; Matthew Westerman; Dame Elizabeth Corley (female: 55%; male: 45%).

Nature of business: Schroders is an international asset management provider. The group's work is divided into wealth management and asset management.

Financial information

Year end	31/12/2021
Turnover	£2,959,500,000
Pre-tax profit	£764,100,000

Total employees: 5,650

Main locations: The group's offices in the UK are located in London, Chester, Edinburgh, Manchester and Oxford. The group operates from 38 locations across Europe, the Americas, Asia, the Middle East and Africa.

Community involvement
The group provides support through charity partnerships, cash donations, gifts in kind and matched funding. It also has a strong focus on employee-led giving, including payroll giving and volunteering.

Schroders Giving partnerships
The group partners with charities across the globe focusing on the topics of inclusion, disability, social mobility and mental health. The group's 2021 accounts state that its 'priorities are providing opportunities for students from low-income backgrounds and supporting those with a disability, mental health challenges or those at risk of going to prison'. The partnerships offer opportunities for employees to take part in volunteering and fundraising activities.

In the UK, the group has a partnership with the Social Business Trust, which works with social enterprises to address social challenges, such as educational disadvantage, employability and the care of older people.

Education and employment
The group works with its charity partners to offer workshops, mentoring and work placements for emerging talents who are disadvantaged. In 2021, the group ran work placements with three UK charities Amos Bursary, Snowdon Trust and the Social Mobility Foundation.

Charity competition
In 2019, the group launched a global competition in which staff can nominate a charity to receive support. The winners are voted for by colleagues and Schroders' board members. In 2021, the competition winners included Goodwill Caravan (receiving £65,000), Home from Home (receiving £40,000), The Talent

Tap (receiving £30,000) and Max Foundation (receiving £15,000).

In-kind support
According to its 2021 annual report, the group provides gifts in kind and organises frequent charitable collections.

Employee-led support
Payroll giving
Payroll giving schemes operate in several of the group's offices. In the UK, 24% of employees chose to give in this way during 2021, raising £1.3 million. The group matched payroll giving contributions.

Volunteering
The group offers its employees up to 15 hours of volunteering leave a year. In the UK, it also supports employees who volunteer outside office hours by donating £20 per hour towards their charity (with an annual cap). In 2021, employees around the world contributed over 4,000 hours of volunteer work, inside and outside office hours. Many employees volunteer with the group's charity partners.

Applications
Contact the correspondent for further information.

Community contributions
Cash donations UK	£4,200,000
Cash donations worldwide	£4,900,000

In 2021, the group donated £4.9 million to charitable causes worldwide, of which £4.2 million was given in the UK. The total figure includes the group's commitment to match employee payroll giving during the year (£1.3 million).

Scott Bader Company Ltd

Arts, culture and heritage, community enterprise and social entrepreneurship, community services and development, education and training, emergency response/relief, the environment, general charitable purposes, health, social welfare, work outside the UK

Company registration number: 189141

Correspondent: Hayley Sutherland, Commonwealth Secretary, Wollaston Hall, Wollaston, Wellingborough, Northamptonshire NN29 7RL (tel: 01933 663100; email: use the contact form on the website; website: www.scottbader. com/humanity/scott-bader-commonwealth/how-to-access-funds)

Directors: Paul Smith; Kevin Matthews; Dianne Walker; Debbie Baker; David Rossouw; James McTaggart; Sam Boustred; Julie Thorburn; Jean-Marc Ferran (female: 33%; male: 67%).

Nature of business: The company is an internationally operating manufacturer

and distributor of chemicals and related products. The annual report and accounts for 2021 state: 'Scott Bader Company Ltd is wholly owned as a financial and social investment by The Scott Bader Commonwealth Ltd, a company Ltd by guarantee and a registered charity. [...] Every employee of Scott Bader may become a member of The Commonwealth and, by this means, become a trustee holding, in common with other members, the shares of Scott Bader Company Ltd.'

Financial information
Year end	31/12/2021
Turnover	£270,040,000
Pre-tax profit	£8,600,000

UK employees: 298

Total employees: 703

Main locations: The company's headquarters is located in Wellingborough, Northamptonshire. The group has manufacturing sites and offices manufacturing sites in Europe, the Middle East, South Africa, Canada and India.

Community involvement
The company's charitable giving is mainly channelled through its charity and parent company, Scott Bader Commonwealth Ltd (Charity Commission no. 206391), which makes grants to charities worldwide. Companies within the group also make donations to local charities based near their office/site.

The company's website states the following:

Every year, a minimum of 5% of Scott Bader's operating profit is given to the Commonwealth to be donated to charitable activities and projects around the world.

In-kind support
The company offers its facilities as in-kind support for local charitable organisations.

Employee-led support
The company provides matched funding (up to £1,000 per employee) for employee fundraising initiatives, which are managed by the Commonwealth charity.

Employees are also encouraged to volunteer for local organisations and group employees are entitled to one day of paid leave for volunteering each year.

Commercially led support
The company sponsors and organises local community events. In the past this has included:
- Trips to the local funfair for a group of young people with disabilities
- Five-a-side football matches

- An annual Christmas tea party for 100 elderly residents from Wollaston and the surrounding villages

Exclusions
According to its website, the company will not fund requests solely in support of: animals, individuals in need, travel and adventure schemes, art projects, sports clubs, medical research and equipment, general appeals, and the construction renovation or maintenance of buildings in the UK.

Applications
General enquiries regarding the company's giving can be sent using the contact form on its website.

Corporate charity
The Scott Bader Commonwealth Ltd (Charity Commission no. 206391) – see entry on page 272.

Community contributions
Cash donations worldwide	£567,600

In 2021, the company donated £552,000 to Scott Bader Commonwealth Ltd and a further £15,600 was donated directly to other charities.

Scottish Midland Co-operative Society Ltd

Arts, culture and heritage, community services and development, education and training, the environment, general charitable purposes, health, housing and homelessness, mental health and well-being, social welfare, sports and recreation

Company registration number: SP2059RS

Correspondent: Community and Membership Team, Hillwood House, 2 Harvest Drive, Newbridge, Edinburgh EH28 8QJ (tel: 0131 335 4433; email: membership@scotmid.co.uk; website: https://scotmid.coop/community-and-charity)

Directors: Harry Cairney; Shelia Downie; Iain Gilchrist; Jim Watson; Kaye Harmon; Richard McCready; David Paterson; Michael Ross; Andy Simm; Eddie Thorn (female: 18%; male: 82%).

Nature of business: The Scottish Midland Co-operative Society, trading as Scotmid Co-operative, is an independent retail consumers' co-operative.

Financial information
Year end	25/01/2020
Turnover	£385,000,000
Pre-tax profit	£5,700,000

UK employees: 3,880

Main locations: Scotmid's headquarters is in Edinburgh and the group has stores throughout Scotland, Northern England and Northern Ireland.

Community involvement

The group supports local charities and groups by making cash donations and supporting employee-led initiatives.

Community Grants

Charities can apply for grants of up to £500 through the group's Community Grant programme. The group focuses on projects that fall into one of the following categories:

- Children and young people
- Social inclusion and education
- Active lifestyles
- The environment
- Health and well-being
- Older people
- Fairtrade
- Arts and culture

Charity of the Year

The group picks a charity partner each year to support through various fundraising initiatives. The group aims to raise £300,000 each year for its charity partner. The group's partner for 2022/23 is Guide Dogs.

Defibrillators

Scotmid has worked with the Scottish Ambulance Service since 2011 to install public access defibrillators in Scottish communities, particularly remote communities and areas of high footfall.

Clothes recycling

The group has 54 Salvation Army clothes banks at Scotmid and Lakes and Dales Co-operative stores all over Scotland and the north of England. When people donate clothes, the money raised is split between the Salvation Army and Scotmid and Lakes and Dales stores for investment in its communities.

The group raises enough money through this initiative to be able to deliver a separate grant fund which exclusively benefits local community projects that have an environmental focus.
Beneficiaries have included: Mearns and Coastal Healthy Living Network and Keswick in Bloom (£1,000 each); Edinburgh Young Carers (£800).

Employee-led support

Employees take part in various fundraising initiatives on behalf of the group's Charity of the Year.

Commercially led support

Community Connect

Through the Community Connect initiative, members of the society can vote for 'Good Cause Groups' using a community connect card each time they shop. The three groups with the most votes can receive awards of up to £15,000, depending on how many votes they receive. Charities in the local community centred around Scotmid or Semichem stores are able to apply to become Good Cause Groups.

Fairtrade

Scotmid supports ethical trading by: supporting Fairtrade groups throughout Scotland; giving advice and providing resources to schools to help them gain Fairtrade status; giving Fairtrade talks to community groups; and supporting Fairtrade events with in-kind donations.

Scotmid is also the main sponsor of the Edinburgh Fair Trade Steering Group's events and the Lord Provost's Fairtrade Awards each year.

Exclusions

Community Connect

The programme does not consider applications which involve:

- Promoting political activities or causes
- Promoting religious beliefs
- Salaries or other running costs
- Making grants to other people or organisations
- Projects that have already happened or will be finished before the awards are made
- Sponsored events
- Individual or team sponsorship or bursaries
- Overseas projects
- Projects that public authorities are responsible for
- Applications from charities that are currently or have been Scotmid's Charity of the Year covering a three-year period
- A group which has received funding (actual or in-kind) of more than £1,500 in the last three years from Scotmid

Community Grants

The Community Grants programme cannot support the following:

- Groups other than community, self-help and voluntary groups
- Groups which use their surplus for the benefit of an individual or business
- Overseas charities or overseas activities
- Projects that do not benefit a community served by one of the stores
- Core activities of statutory services
- Religious worship
- Party political activity
- Individual sponsorship (individuals acting for the benefit of the local community can apply)
- Travel and accommodation costs
- Ongoing running costs (applications must be for one-off investments, purchases or events)

Applications

Community Connect

Local groups and charities can apply to become a 'Good Cause Group' if they:

- Benefit the local community centred around Scotmid or Semichem stores
- Have the greatest possible benefit to their community
- Have a project or initiative that will cost in the region of £15,000 to complete and is scheduled to be completed within 24 months of the award date

Community Connect has two award cycles every year. Groups are chosen each April and September. If you would like to be sent a reminder when applications open, email the correspondent with your contact details.

The full terms and conditions for groups thinking of applying can be found here: www.scotmid.coop/community-connect-terms-and-conditions.

Community grants

Groups or individuals in need of a community grant can apply via an online form available at: www.scotmid.coop/community-and-charity/supporting-local-communities/community-grant-form.

Alternatively, application forms can be downloaded and returned to: Membership Team, Corporate Communications, Scotmid, Hillwood House, 2 Harvest Drive, Newbridge, EH28 8QJ, or emailed to membership@scotmid.com.

Applications are welcome from groups including: local community, self-help or voluntary groups and charities (including local branches of national charities) or individuals acting for the benefit of the local community.

Charity partners

Openings for Charity of the Year applications are advertised on the group's website. Applications involve a proposal of no more than six pages of A4 which should be sent to: membership@scotmid.co.uk. For further information contact the correspondent.

Clothes Bank grant

To apply, email the correspondent with 200–300 words about your project and what help is required. The group ask that you include your contact details.

Community contributions

▥ Total contributions UK		£635,000

According to its 2021/22 annual report, the group's charitable contributions totalled £635,000, of which £150,000 was donated to 24 good causes through its Community Connect initiative. Note that the figure stated includes funds raised through carrier bag sales.

ScottishPower UK plc

Arts, culture and heritage, citizenship, community services and development, education and training, energy, the environment, health, money and debt advice, social welfare, STEM

Company registration number: SC117120

Correspondent: The CSR Team, 320 St Vincent Street, Glasgow G2 5AD (email: crfeedback@scottishpower.com; website: www.scottishpower.com/pages/corporate_social_responsibility.aspx)

Directors: Marion Venman; Nicola Connelly; Donald Wright (female: 33%; male: 67%).

Nature of business: ScottishPower is an energy company involved in the generation, transmission and distribution of electricity, principally in the UK. ScottishPower has three business divisions: Networks; Renewables; and Retail. ScottishPower has been part of the Iberdrola Group since April 2007.

Financial information

Year end	31/12/2021
Turnover	£5,349,700,000
Pre-tax profit	£550,600,000

UK employees: 5,600

Main locations: The group has sites in Cheshire, Merseyside, North Wales, North Shropshire and Scotland.

Community involvement

The majority of the group's support is given through its long-term partnership with Cancer Research and its corporate charity, the ScottishPower Foundation (OSCR no. SC043862). ScottishPower also partners with organisations to deliver community programmes, and it provides support to communities neighbouring its windfarms through community benefit funds.

Cancer Research UK

ScottishPower UK plc has had a partnership with Cancer Research since 2012 and has raised over £35 million for the charity.

Community benefit funds

During the development and operation of its onshore windfarms, ScottishPower Renewables creates community benefit funds that support the neighbouring communities. In 2019, benefit funds were provided to communities in Argyll and Bute, South Ayrshire and Dumfries and Galloway.

National Skills Academy for Power

The National Skills Academy for Power (NSAP) brings together employers, skills organisations and stakeholders in order to improve skills in the energy sector. ScottishPower UK plc is represented on the board and also contributes to the Think Power online resource, the most comprehensive source of information on careers in the UK power industry.

The Institution of Engineering and Technology (IET) Power Academy

The IET Power Academy is a partnership between industry and education institutions which seeks to improve skills in the power-engineering sector, through a combination of financial support and work placements for students. ScottishPower UK plc is a partner and also a member of the executive.

PowerWise

PowerWise is a safety education programme teaching primary schoolchildren aged 4 to 11 the potential dangers of electricity in the home and outdoor environment.

In-kind support

ScottishPower employees can take one day of paid leave for volunteering each year. In 2021 this was increased to two days to support COP26. In 2021, 1,050 members of staff took part in volunteering activities organised by ScottishPower and contributed over 4,800 hours during paid company time.

Employee-led support

STEM Ambassadors

ScottishPower has STEM Ambassadors who are dedicated employee volunteers who encourage young people in local schools to study STEM subjects.

Matched funding

Employee fundraising efforts are matched up to a maximum of £200 per application. Employees take part in a wide range of fundraising activities for the group's charity partner.

Payroll giving

The group operates the Give As You Earn scheme in the UK.

Applications

For more information on the group's CSR activities contact the correspondent. For local requests, contact the relevant regional office.

For more information on the ScottishPower Renewables community benefit funds, contact the Community Liaison team at communitybenefit@scottishpower.com.

Full information on the Green Economy Fund can be found here: www.spenergynetworks.co.uk/pages/green_economy_fund.aspx. Questions regarding the fund should be directed to greeneconomyfund@spenergynetworks.co.uk.

Corporate charity

ScottishPower Foundation (OSCR no. SC043862) – see entry on page 273.

Community contributions

Total contributions UK	£23,200,000

According to the group's annual report and accounts for 2021, the group contributed £23.2 million during the year through cash donations, in-kind support and time and management costs associated with running community programmes.

SDC Builders Ltd

Community services and development, general charitable purposes

Company registration number: 1251716

Correspondent: The Community Fund Team, Limegrove House, Caxton Road, Bedford MK4 1OQQ (tel: 01234 363155; email: contact form on the website; website: www.sdc.co.uk/about-sdc/community-fund)

Directors: Andrew Mitchell; Carl Bennett; Daniel Changer; Adam Knaggs; Martin Lowndes; Andrew Mitchell; Andrew Shiner; Francis Shiner; Gary Wykes (male: 100%).

Nature of business: SDC Builders provides construction services across a diverse range of sectors including commercial, manufacturing, automotive, healthcare and education. The company operates under the umbrella of an Employee Benefit Trust. This means instead of being owned by shareholders, the company is governed by a board of trustees, who are responsible for safeguarding SDC's long-term prosperity and sharing any profits among members of staff and the wider community.

Financial information

Year end	30/09/2021
Turnover	£179,120,000
Pre-tax profit	£2,140,000

Main locations: The company is based in Bedford and it also has an office in Oxfordshire.

Community involvement

The company provides financial and in-kind support to causes local to its offices through its Community Fund.

Community Fund

According to its website, the fund was created in 2016 to 'provide a mechanism for supporting the wider community'. Funded by an annual donation from the Employee Benefit Trust, charities and community groups can apply for grants and/or the time and experience of SDC's staff. Since its inception, the fund has donated over £100,000 to local causes. Recent examples include:

▶ The refurbishment of numerous Scout huts across East Anglia and the Midlands

◗ New gardening tools for volunteers at the Higgins Museum in Bradford
◗ Helping to establish a new community café in Oxford

Applications

Applications should be made using the online form on the company's website. The team considers applications at bi-monthly meetings.

Community contributions

The company's 2020/21 accounts did not provide a figure for charitable contributions.

SEGRO plc

Community enterprise and social entrepreneurship, education and training, health, social welfare

Company registration number: 167591

Correspondent: Central Charity Committee, 1 New Burlington Place, London W1S 2HR (tel: 020 7451 9100; email: SEGRO.Charity.UK@SEGRO.com; website: www.segro.com/csr/community/overview)

Directors: Andy Harrison; David Sleath; Mary Barnard; Sue Clayton; Soumen Das; Carol Fairweather; Simon Fraser; Andrew Gulliford; Martin Moore; Linda Yueh (female: 40%; male: 60%).

Nature of business: Industrial and commercial property development, construction and investment, supply of utility services and the provision of services associated with such activities.

Financial information

Year end	31/12/2021
Turnover	£546,000,000
Pre-tax profit	£356,000,000

Total employees: 372

Main locations: In the UK, the group has offices in London and Slough. The group also has several locations across Europe.

Community involvement

SEGRO supports various causes directly through its Central Charity Committee and through its two funds administered by several Community Foundations. The group is particularly interested in education and improving employment.

Charity partners

The group's charity partners are selected based on their capabilities to improve the lives of young and disadvantaged people. Currently, its UK charity partners are Pathways to Property, City Harvest and LandAid. The partnership with LandAid helps homeless young people in temporary accommodation to find employment. The partnership with City Harvest provides warehouse and logistics space to food banks. The

partnership with Pathways to Property helps to create diversity within the real estate sector.

Centenary Fund

In 2020, the group announced the launch of its Centenary Fund. The group will distribute £10 million to causes such as supporting young and disadvantaged people into employment, creating community spaces to support training, and improving health and well-being.

The fund is being administered by six community foundations on SEGRO's behalf. Eligible regions include:
◗ London (see the website for specific boroughs)
◗ Thames Valley (Slough, Reading and Bracknell)
◗ Midlands and surrounding areas (North West Leicestershire, Coventry, Hertfordshire and Northamptonshire)

Employee-led support

SEGRO's company-wide 'Day of Giving' gives staff the opportunity to volunteer for a cause of their choice. Outside this initiative, staff engage in a wide range of fundraising efforts such as skydives, swims, walks and 'sleep-outs'. In 2021, 234 employees took part, undertaking a wide range of activities including packaging food parcels, painting hospital gardens, collecting rubbish, planting trees, and riverside and environmental clearances.

Applications

The group's charitable work and donations are managed by its Central Charity Committee. A charitable donation request form can be downloaded from the website and returned to the committee by post or email.

For the Centenary and Community Funds, contact the relevant community foundation.

Community contributions

Total contributions worldwide	£1,300,000

The group's 2021 accounts state that SEGRO's total contributions to charity during the year totalled £1.3 million. This figure includes direct donations, in-kind support, as well as employee volunteering.

Serco Group plc

Community services and development, community transport, health, social justice, social welfare

Company registration number: 2048608

Correspondent: The ESG Team, Serco House, 16 Bartley Wood Business Park, Bartley Way, Hook, Hampshire RG27 9UY (website: www.serco.com/esg)

Directors: David Eveleigh; Ann Bashforth; Nigel Crossley; Krupali Desai; Ian El-Mokadem; Timothy Lodge; Dame Susan Owen; Lynne Peacock; John Rishton; Rupert Soames (female: 40%; male: 60%).

Nature of business: Serco plc is a government services contractor.

Financial information

Year end	31/12/2021
Turnover	£4,424,600,000
Pre-tax profit	£192,200,000

Main locations: In the UK, the group has offices in Hampshire, Solihull and London. It operates globally with offices throughout Asia, Europe, the Middle East and North America.

Community involvement

The group mainly supports charities through its corporate charity, the Serco Foundation (Charity Commission no. 1150338). The foundation supports a wide range of initiatives in countries in which Serco Group plc has a presence including Asia-Pacific, Europe, North America and the Middle East. According to its website these initiatives include:
◗ new and innovative approaches to the delivery of public services
◗ programmes and charities supporting vulnerable citizens
◗ academic research for public benefit
◗ programmes that foster skills development in the public sector

Applications

See the foundation's entry for further information.

Corporate charity

The Serco Foundation (Charity Commission no. 1150338) – see entry on page 273.

Community contributions

We were unable to determine a figure for the group's charitable contributions.

Severn Trent plc

Community services and development; environment; health; money and debt advice; social welfare; water, sanitation and hygiene (WASH)

Company registration number: 2366619

Correspondent: The CSR Team, Seven Trent Centre, 2 St John's Street, Coventry CV1 2LZ (email: use the online CSR contact form; website: www.stwater.co.uk)

Directors: Tom Delay; Kevin Beeston; James Bowling; John Coghlan; Olivia Garfield; Christine Hodgson; Sharmila Nebhrajani; Dominique Reiniche; Philip Remnant; Gillian Sheldon (female: 44%; male: 56%).

Nature of business: The group's principal activities are the supply of water and sewerage services, waste management and the provision of environmental services in the UK and internationally.

Financial information

Year end	31/03/2021
Turnover	£1,693,800,000
Pre-tax profit	£267,200,000

Total employees: 7,000

Main locations: Within the UK, the group operates in the Midlands and mid-Wales.

Community involvement

Over the next five years, the group is committing to donating 1% of its annual profits (over £10 million) to local projects through the Severn Trent Community Fund.

Severn Trent Community Fund (not a registered charity)

Non-profit organisations (with a governing document) can apply for a grant of between £2,000 and £250,000 from the fund. The website states that the fund looks to support projects that:

- Help people to lead a healthier life and gain new skills
- Help to create better places to live in and use
- Help to look after the natural environment, give people greater access to that environment to help to look after water

The group is particularly interested in projects that have a connection to water, although this is not essential. If applying for a grant of over £75,000, projects must incorporate all three themes.

Projects must be located in the Severn Trent region and must benefit the communities in which Severn Trent customers reside.

The fund is administered by a panel, made up of Severn Trent customers, who help to identify local community needs.

The Severn Trent Water Charitable Trust Fund (Charity Commission no. 1108278)

The group makes an annual donation of £3.5 million to its corporate charity. The fund aims to support people experiencing poverty and debt, by making grants to individuals who cannot meet the cost of water charges in the Severn Trent area.

Partnerships

Severn Trent has a long-term partnership with WaterAid. The group's fundraising and volunteering have helped bring water and good sanitation to communities across the world.

The group also supports Children in Need and Comic Relief, by volunteering at the two charities' national call centres and by engaging in fundraising activities.

Employee-led support

The group's Community Champions programme encourages staff to volunteer in their local communities. All staff are permitted to take two days' paid voluntary leave per year.

Applications

Applications to the Severn Trent Community Fund can be made online on the Severn Trent website. Prospective applicants are advised to consult the eligibility criteria before applying.

All other enquiries should be directed to the group's designated 'CSR enquiries' form on its website.

Community contributions

Cash donations UK	£6,920,000

Of the total amount donated, £1.5 million was awarded to 93 projects through the Severn Trent Community Fund.

The group also donated £1 million to The Severn Trent Water Charitable Trust Fund.

Shaftesbury plc

Arts, culture and heritage, community services and development, education and training, emergency response/ relief, the environment, health, social welfare

Company registration number: 1999238

Correspondent: Andrew Price, Chair of the Community Investment Committee, 22 Ganton Street, Carnaby, London W1f 7FD (tel: 020 7333 8118; email: shaftesbury@shaftesbury.co.uk; website: www.shaftesbury.co.uk/en/sustainability/community.html)

Directors: Brian Bickell; Simon Quayle; Tom Welton; Chris Ward; Jonathan Nicholls; Richard Akers; Ruth Anderson; Helen Coles; Jennelle Tilling (female: 33%; male: 67%).

Nature of business: Shaftesbury is a property investor and developer. It owns portfolio properties in London's West End (Carnaby, Charlotte Street, Chinatown, Covent Garden, Soho).

Financial information

Year end	30/09/2021
Turnover	£112,700,000
Pre-tax profit	(£194,900,000)

Total employees: 47

Main locations: The group operates in the West End of London.

Community involvement

The group works with charities, educational organisations and other non-profit, community groups within its 'villages' (i.e. its areas of operation). Support comes in the form of financial donations and in-kind donations, particularly space and advice.

Community Investment Committee

Shaftesbury makes grants and other awards through its Community Investment Committee, which is made up of employees from all over the country. Investment is focused on delivering change and tackling challenges in the West End of London and in areas in which the group has a presence. Causes typically supported are:

- Education
- Health
- Emergency relief
- Arts and culture
- Social welfare
- Other

In-kind support

The group allows individuals and organisations to use its various spaces for charitable purposes. It currently provides space for Choose Love, a refugee charity, and My Runway Group, a youth empowerment organisation.

Employee-led support

Staff are able to take up to 74 hours volunteering leave per year.

Applications

Enquiries should be sent by email.

Community contributions

Total contributions UK	£1,200,000

According to the group's 2021 annual report, Shaftesbury values its total community contributions at £1.2 million. The report features the following breakdown:

Money	42%
In-kind contributions	41%
Time	10%
Management costs	7%

Shawbrook Group plc

Community services and development, general charitable purposes, health

Company registration number: 7240248

Correspondent: The CSR Team, Lutea House, Warley Hill Business Park, The Drive, Great Warley, Brentwood, Essex CM13 3BE (email: companysecretary@shawbrook.co.uk; website: www.shawbrook.co.uk)

Directors: John Callender; Marcelino Castrillo; Dylan Minto; Lindsey McMurray; Cedric Dubourdieu; Paul Lawrence; Andrew Didham; Michele Turmore; Lan Tu; Janet Connor (female: 20%; male: 80%).

Nature of business: Shawbrook is a specialist UK lending and savings bank founded in 2011 to serve the needs of SMEs, trusts and charities in the UK with a range of lending and saving products.

Financial information

Year end	31/12/2021
Turnover	£475,200,000
Pre-tax profit	£197,200,000

Total employees: 1,000+

Main locations: The bank has operations in Brentwood, Redhill, Glasgow, London, Kent, Manchester, Birmingham and Leeds.

Community involvement

Shawbrook supports local causes within the communities in which it operates. It identifies its own causes, while also supporting employee-nominated charities. The bank's chair engages with chosen charities and subsequently makes direct donations.

Shawbrook also supports its Corporate National Charity Partner, which is voted for by its staff. At the time of writing (September 2022), the bank's latest charity partner was Mental Health UK. Shawbrook made an initial donation of £10,000 to the charity and will focus on raising crucial funds for the charity over the course of this partnership.

Employee-led support

Shawbrook provides matched funding to staff engaging in various fundraising efforts.

The bank also encourages staff to undertake voluntary work through its 'Making a Difference Days' initiative, through which every employee is entitled to one day's paid volunteering leave per year.

Applications

Contact the correspondent for more information.

Community contributions

Cash donations UK	£46,000

According to the bank's 2021 annual report, Shawbrook made charitable donations totalling £10,000. A further £36,000 was awarded in matched funding to 43 charities, including Mind and Rainbow Trust.

Shell (UK Ltd)

🔍 Arts, culture and heritage, community enterprise and social entrepreneurship, community services and development, education and training, the environment, STEM

Company registration number: 140141

Correspondent: Head of Shell UK Social Investment, Shell Centre, York Road, London SE1 7NA (tel: 020 7934 1234; website: www.shell.co.uk/sustainability.html)

Directors: Richard Jory; Monika Khullar; Simon Roddy; Madeline Whitaker; David Bunch; Liz Andrew; Jo Coleman; Colin Crooks (female: 50%; male: 50%).

Nature of business: Shell is a global group of energy and petrochemicals companies. Its activities in the UK correspond to those of the group and include exploration, production and sale of oil and natural gas and marketing of petroleum products. Shell activities also include: generating electricity (including wind power); providing oil products for industrial uses; producing petrochemicals used for plastics, coatings and detergents; and developing technology for hydrogen vehicles.

Financial information

Year end	31/12/2021
Turnover	£26,200,000,000
Pre-tax profit	£153,000,000

Total employees: 86,000

Main locations: Shell operates throughout the UK and globally. The group has operations or offices in Aberdeen, Fife, London, Manchester, Norfolk, Peterhead and Warwickshire.

Community involvement

Shell supports communities close to its sites and operations in the UK and promotes STEM education. Across the world, the group helps to deliver energy and transport initiatives in low-income communities.

Grants for community groups

The group makes grants of up to £1,000 to community groups within its areas of operation, namely its sites in Aberdeen city, Mossmorran in Fife, St Fergus near Peterhead and Bacton on the Norfolk coast.

Eligible organisations must be active within the above areas, or the prospective project or event must benefit communities in the above areas.

Shell Foundation (Charity Commission no. 1080999)

The group's corporate charity aims to 'create and scale business solutions to enhance access to energy and affordable transport' in low-income communities affected most by these issues.

The Shell Centenary Scholarship Fund (Charity Commission no. 1071178)

The group's other corporate charity is committed to providing funding to postgraduate students in the UK and in the Netherlands, mainly those studying STEM. The fund is also active in Africa, focused on helping to deliver leadership initiatives.

STEM education

Shell provides opportunities and the resources needed for young people engaging in STEM. The group's initiatives include:

- Tomorrow's Engineers: this programme provides students with hands-on engineering experiences. Since its inception, the programme has reached circa 60 secondary schools across Scotland.
- Girls in Energy: this course provides girls and young women with the information and inspiration required to pursue careers in the energy industry. It is a one-year course, targeted at those aged between 14 and 16.
- Bright Ideas Challenge: this is a cross-curricular school's competition encouraging young people to devise innovative solutions that could provide power in cities in the future. Winners of the competition were awarded over £45,000 in cash prizes.

A full list of STEM initiatives run by the group can be found on the website.

Employee-led support

Shell employees are encouraged to undertake voluntary work, using their skills to support social and environmental projects.

Shell provides Employee Action Grants to its staff and retired staff, who volunteer for a minimum of 20 hours a year with a UK charity or community group.

Commercially led support

Shell's longest-running sponsorship commitment in the UK is the Fife Art show. Winning pieces at the show are purchased by Shell and donated to NHS Fife, to go on display at various healthcare centres in the area.

Applications

Application forms for grants for community groups can be downloaded on Shell's website.

Enquiries for the Shell Foundation should be sent to: info@shellfoundation.org. Enquiries for the Shell Centenary Scholarship Fund should be directed to: si-tscsf@shell.com.

Community contributions

Total contributions worldwide	£82,740,000

In the group's 2021 Sustainability Report, Shell values its 'voluntary' social investment at £82,740,000 (USD 94 million).

Note: the group's financial information has been converted from USD using the exchange rate at the time of writing (October 2022).

Shoe Zone Ltd

🔍 Community services and development, general charitable purposes

Company registration number: 148038

Correspondent: The CSR Team, Haramead Business Centre, Humberstone Road, Leicester, Leicestershire LE1 2LH (tel: 0116 222 3000; email: investorrelations@shoezone. com; website: www.shoezone.com/ OurCharities)

Directors: Anthony Smith; Charles Smith; Clare Howes; Steve Orr; Catherine Bowen; Terry Boot (female: 33%; male: 67%).

Nature of business: The company is a footwear retailer in the UK and Ireland. It is a wholly owned subsidiary of Shoe Zone Group Ltd.

Financial information

Year end	05/10/2021
Turnover	£119,100,000
Pre-tax profit	£9,500,000

Total employees: 2,854

Main locations: The company's head office is based in Leicester and it has stores throughout the UK.

Community involvement

According to its website, Shoe Zone supports charities and causes local to Leicestershire where the company's Head Office and Distribution Centre is based.

The company has supported Children in Need for several years, by undertaking fundraising activities throughout its stores. According to the company website, Shoe Zone has raised £754,000 for Children in Need between 2013 and 2022. Shoe Zone also fundraises for Comic Relief and in 2022 raised £27,900 for the charity.

Charitable support is also provided to charities through the company's corporate charity The Shoe Zone Trust (Charity Commission no. 1112972). Shoe Zone is committed to contributing 2% of profits to the trust each year.

Employee-led support

Employees undertake voluntary work in support of local charities. For example, employees helped to redecorate the coffee bar at the Leicester MENCAP Society Centre and helped out at the Herrick Playground and the hall at the Helen Webb House.

Commercially led support

The proceeds from Shoe Zone's carrier bag sales are donated to its corporate charity, The Shoe Zone Trust.

Applications

Contact the correspondent for more information.

Corporate charity

The Shoe Zone Trust (Charity Commission no. 1112972) – see entry on page 274.

Community contributions

Cash donations UK	£270,000

According to the company's 2020/21 accounts, Shoe Zone donated over £270,000 to charitable causes.

Shoosmiths LLP

🔍 Animal welfare, community services and development, general charitable purposes, health, legal advice

Company registration number: OC374987

Correspondent: Nicola Ellen, Head of Corporate Responsibility, 100 Avebury Boulevard, Milton Keynes MK9 1FH (tel: 07921 067993; email: nicola.ellen@ shoosmiths.co.uk; website: www. shoosmiths.co.uk/our-responsibility/ corporate-responsibility)

Directors: Gauis Powell; Alison Matthews; Simon Boss; Peter Duff; Ben Bennett; Chris Stanton; Kristen Hewson; Richard Follis; Stephen Porter; Stuart Little; Louise Hadland; Monica Burch (female: 33%; male: 67%).

Nature of business: Shoosmiths LLP is a national law firm.

Financial information

Year end	30/04/2021
Turnover	£167,895,000
Pre-tax profit	£55,400,000

UK employees: 1,650

Main locations: The firm has offices in Belfast, Birmingham, Edinburgh, Leeds, London, Manchester, Milton Keynes, Northampton, Nottingham, Solent and the Thames Valley.

Community involvement

Shoosmiths supports a wide range of charities and causes near its offices. From the firm's previous beneficiaries, causes typically supported by Shoosmiths are:

- Legal education
- Health
- Social welfare
- Animal welfare

Charity partners

Shoosmiths offices select annual charity partners, to support by way of grants and fundraising. The following information is taken from the Shoosmiths website (the asterisk indicates a repeated partnership):

Our 2021/2022 charity partners are:

Belfast: Aware NI* – the depression charity for Northern Ireland and the only charity working exclusively for people with depression and bipolar disorder.

Birmingham: NSPCC – believes every childhood is worth fighting for and works to prevent abuse, help rebuild children's lives and supports families.

Edinburgh: MCR Pathways – mentoring programme and charity that provides disadvantaged children with a mentor.

Leeds: Leeds Mind – helps people build on their strengths, overcome obstacles, and become more in control of their lives.

London: The Change Foundation and specifically its Street Elite Programme* – this programme engages with young people on the edges of gangs and crime across London helping them from NEET (not in education, employment or training) into work, apprenticeships, training or education opportunities.

Manchester: Business in the Community – the oldest and largest business-led membership organisation dedicated to responsible business. Shoosmiths has been a corporate member of BITC since 2000 and we will be working together to tackle barriers to employment and social mobility in the Manchester area.

Milton Keynes: The Henry Allen Trust – provides advice, support, fun and laughter to families facing childhood cancer.

Northampton: Northamptonshire Mind* – offers support to anyone who faces mental health challenges including self-improvement courses, one to one support, social groups, support into employment and mental health navigators.

Nottingham: Improving Lives* – works in partnership with many services to support Nottingham City adult residents with complex health and social needs to manage the challenges they face more effectively.

Sheffield: Roundabout – South Yorkshire's local youth housing charity provides shelter, support and life-skills to young people aged 16–24 who are homeless or at risk of homelessness.

Solent: Acts of Kindness – helps people facing an immediate crisis, is on hand to help people improve their lives and loves community projects where it can really make a difference.

Thames Valley: No5* – provides listening and counselling support to 11- 25 year olds living, working or studying in Reading.

In-kind support

The firm provides pro bono legal advice in all areas of law that are practiced across the business. According to Shoosmiths 2020/21 ESG report, it delivered 2,107 hours of pro bono work during the year.

Employee-led support

Shoosmiths employees are entitled to one day of paid volunteering leave per year. The firm's website states:

We are keen to hear from charities and other community organisations who our staff could volunteer for during the week, near to one of our 13 national locations.

According to Shoosmiths 2020/21 ESG report, employees volunteered 459 hours to charitable causes.

Applications

Contact the correspondent for more information.

Community contributions

We were unable to determine a figure for the firm's charitable contributions for the year.

Siemens plc

Arts, culture and heritage, community services and development, education and training, the environment, social welfare, STEM

Company registration number: 727817

Correspondent: Corporate Citizenship Manager, Pinehurst 2, Pinehurst Road, Farnborough, Hampshire GU14 7BF (tel: 01276 696000; email: info.cc.uk@siemens.com; website: www.siemens.com/global/en.html)

Directors: Sharon Kahanov; Carl Ennis; James Murnieks (female: 33%; male: 67%).

Nature of business: Siemen's principal activities in the UK cover manufacture and sale of products in the areas of: electricity generation and distribution; transportation systems; industrial and building automation; metallurgical engineering; and healthcare equipment and services. The company also provides IT and other business infrastructure services. The company is a subsidiary of the Siemens Group AG.

Financial information

Year end	30/09/2021
Turnover	£6,230,000,000
Pre-tax profit	£291,000,000

UK employees: 8,600

Total employees: 303,000

Main locations: The company has offices worldwide. In the UK, its head office is in Frimley, Surrey, but it also has offices in several locations across England, Scotland and Wales – a full list can be found online at: www.siemens.co.uk/en/about_us/index/uk-locations-text.htm.

Community involvement

Through its Corporate Citizenship initiative, Siemens provides support to the community with a focus on the following areas: access to technology, access to education and sustaining communities. In the UK, Siemens invests in education programmes and establishes strategic partnerships with charities and local organisations. Employees also take part in fundraising and volunteering activities.

Education programmes

The Curiosity Project is Siemens UK-wide engagement programme that aims to inspire young people and bring science, technology, engineering and maths (STEM) subjects to life. The project consists of a series of bite-sized DIY science videos on YouTube and education programmes for schools that provide free, curriculum-linked resources. Through the programme Siemens works with organisations such as Greenpower, Edinburgh Science and the Prince's Teaching Institute.

Partnerships and sponsorships

Globally, Siemens works with several charitable organisations supporting local communities, arts and culture, education and science, and sports. Siemens supports local charities in the UK through fundraising events and initiatives. It has previously had partnerships with the Charities Aid Foundation, Mind and Teach First. Siemens also has a long-standing partnership with The Wildlife Trusts through which it supports the charity with volunteering, donations and environmental education.

Employee-led support

Volunteering and fundraising

Employees are offered two days' paid leave to volunteer each year. Employees also take part in fundraising activities for the charity partners and charities of their choice. Siemens will match any money raised.

Employee donation programme

In 2018, Siemens implemented 'Cents4Sense', a global donation programme. Once a year, employee shareholders can donate one dividend of their Siemens shares to societal projects worldwide. Every donation made is matched by Siemens. According to the 2021 sustainability report, £573,800 (€655,000) has been raised through this programme from 2018 to 2021.

Payroll giving

Siemens operates a payroll giving scheme.

Applications

Contact the correspondent for further information.

Community contributions

| Total contributions worldwide | £39,650,000 |

The 2021 Sustainability Information Report states that Siemens plc donated a total of £39.65 million to community investment during the year. The financial information has been converted from USD to EUR using the exchange rate at the time of writing (October 2022).

SIG plc

Community enterprise and social entrepreneurship, community services and development, education and training

Company registration number: 998314

Correspondent: CSR Team, Adsetts House, 16 Europa View, Sheffield S9 1XH (tel: 0114 285 6300; email: info@sigplc.co.uk; website: www.sigplc.com/sustainability/sustainability/our-communities)

Directors: Steve Francis; Andrew Allner; Ian Ashton; Alan Lovell; Kath Durant; Bruno Deschamps; Shatish Dasani; Gillian Kent; Gillian Kent; Simon King; Christian Rochat (female: 22%; male: 78%).

Nature of business: The principal activity of the group is the supply of specialist products to construction and related markets in the UK, the Republic of Ireland and mainland Europe. The main products distributed are insulation, roofing, commercial interiors and specialist construction products.

Financial information

Year end	31/12/2021
Turnover	£2,291,000,000
Pre-tax profit	£19,300,000

Total employees: 6,800

Main locations: The group has branches across the UK. There are also branches in Belgium, France, Germany, Ireland, Luxembourg, Poland and the Netherlands.

Community involvement

According to its Charitable Activities Policy, the group will support charities and community projects that enhance engagement in the communities in which it operates. Focus is given to projects that help to manage the sustainability of the local environment, educate young people and support disadvantaged groups. The group will also support charities that are important to its employees.

Partnerships

In the UK, SIG plc supports and fundraises for Cancer Research UK and the Rainy Day Trust, which is a charity that helps people who work in the construction industry who are in particular need of assistance.

Employee-led support

Volunteering and fundraising

Employees are encouraged to volunteer in teams for charitable or community activities. They also take part in fundraising activities to raise money for both local and national charities. SIG operates a matched funding scheme to support employees' fundraising efforts by matching donations of up to £500.

Payroll giving

In the UK, the group operates a payroll giving scheme through which employees can donate to any UK-registered charity.

Commercially led support

SIG provides sponsorship to local and professional sports teams.

Exclusions

SIG will not support the following:

- Political parties
- Books, research papers or articles in professional journals
- Faith-related causes, organisations or activities
- Anything that conflicts with its ethics policy

Applications

Contact the correspondent for further information. Activities may also be organised by local divisions of the group.

Community contributions

The group's 2021 accounts did not include a figure for its charitable contributions.

Signature Aviation plc

🔍 Community services and development, education and training, emergency response/relief, general charitable purposes

Company registration number: 53688

Correspondent: CSR Team, Terminal 1 Percival Way, London Luton Airport, Luton, Bedfordshire LU2 9PA (email: contact form on the website; website: www.signatureaviation.com)

Director: Michael Friisdahl; Tony Lefebvre; Amy Alexy; Derek DeCross; Rick Elieson; Maria Garton; Anurag Gupta; Geoff Heck; Paul Hirt; Marty Kretchman (female: 20%; male: 80%).

Nature of business: Signature Aviation plc is a multinational aviation services group that provides full-service support for business and general aviation travel.

Financial information

Year end	31/12/2021
Turnover	£2,285,000,000
Pre-tax profit	£238,000,000

Total employees: 8,000

Main locations: The group is headquartered in London and has operations in more than 370 locations across five continents.

Community involvement

Signature Aviation's Charitable Giving Programme includes a matched giving and discretionary giving programme, details of which have been taken from the group's website:

- The matched giving programme will match funds raised for a charity/not-for-profit organisation by four or more Signature employees.
- The discretionary programme will award funds to: charities or communities with significant needs that are closely associated with the areas in which we operate; charities or relief exercises that are responding to disaster or other events that impact employees or that are in regions in which we operate; charities whose operations are associated with aviation or that are linked to employees, customers or suppliers.

Partnerships

The group works in partnership with international and national charitable organisations associated with the wider aviation community, including Women in Aviation International (founders of Girls in Aviation Day), Veterans Airlift Command and the Angel Flight network.

Employee-led support

Employees are encouraged to fundraise and volunteer for local community and charitable groups. Donations are matched by the group under its matched-giving programme.

Applications

We were unable to find information relating to applications following the group's change of name. According to Signature Aviation's website, it will allocate funds annually to its matched-giving and discretionary programmes.

Community contributions

The group did not provide a figure for its charitable contributions for the year.

Simmons & Simmons LLP

🔍 Arts, culture and heritage, community services and development, education and training, the environment, human rights, social justice, social welfare

Company registration number: OC352713

Correspondent: CSR Team, CityPoint, One Ropemaker Street, London EC2Y 9SS (tel: 020 7628 2020; email: responsible.business@simmons-simmons.com; website: www.simmons-simmons.com)

Nature of business: Simmons & Simmons LLP is a limited liability partnership providing legal services and international tax advice.

Financial information

Year end	30/04/2021
Turnover	£427,510,000
Pre-tax profit	£161,440,000

Total employees: 1900

Main locations: The firm has 25 offices worldwide; its UK offices are located in London, Bristol and Cambridge.

Community involvement

Simmons & Simmons provides support primarily through its pro bono programme. Support is also given to charitable organisations and individuals through the firm's corporate charity, the Simmons and Simmons Charitable Foundation (Charity Commission no. 1129643).

Young Talent Programme

The Young Talent Programme was designed to raise the aspirations of students from disadvantaged backgrounds. In partnership with Frederick Bremer School in Walthamstow, London, the programme gives students access to opportunities within the legal profession and an insight into the world of work. Each year, a group of Year 10 students are selected to participate in the seven-year programme, which includes activities such as work experience, skills sessions, presentation work and a paid internship.

The Big Issue Foundation

The firm works in partnership with the Big Issue Foundation and supports its Vendor Development Programme. Employees deliver training and provide work experience to Big Issue vendors to enhance their job prospects.

In-kind support

Pro bono

Simmons & Simmons provides pro bono legal advice to individuals, local charities, international NGOs and social and environmental enterprises. Previous examples of the firm's pro bono work include:

Social Finance – advice provided by the firm enabled a not-for-profit organisation to develop a national End of Life Care Integrator. The firm also helped the organisation to set up the world's first social investment-backed programme in health and work, which has resulted in transformational change in the employment rates of people with health conditions and disabilities.

Access to Justice Programme – the programme launched in 2015 and is run and supervised by the firm's senior pro bono lawyer. The scheme delivers end-to-end casework for welfare benefit appeals at the First Tier Tribunal, specialising in the area of disability benefits. The firm takes cases directly from South West London Law Centre and other front-line disability services.

The firm also provides free administrative services to its charitable foundation.

Employee-led support

Employees are encouraged to take part in pro bono activities via the firm's charitable foundation. For example, volunteers from the firm attend a weekly surgery offering free legal advice to members of the local community who would not otherwise have been able to afford it.

Commercially led support

In the past, the firm has supported organisations through sponsorship. For example, in 2021 the firm became the lead sponsor of women's rugby at Railway Union RFC in Dublin.

Previous organisations supported include Donmar Warehouse, English National Ballet and the Frieze London Art Show.

Applications

Contact the correspondent for further information.

Corporate charity

The Simmons and Simmons Charitable Foundation (Charity Commission no. 1129643) – see entry on page 274.

Community contributions

Cash donations UK	£146,700

No figure was given for the firm's total charitable contributions for 2020/21. However, during the period, £146,700 was donated by the group to its charitable foundation. We have taken this as the figure for cash donations.

Simplyhealth Group Ltd

🔍 Health, housing and homelessness

Company registration number: 5445654

Correspondent: CSR Team, Hambleden House, Waterloo Court, Andover, Hampshire SP10 1LQ (tel: 0300 100 1030; email: Corporate.Giving@ simplyhealth.co.uk; website: www. simplyhealth.co.uk/about-us/charitable-giving)

Directors: Gil Baldwin; Mike Hall; Sneh Khemka; Jenny Knott; Tracy Dunley-Owen; Richard Gillies; Duane Lawrence; Martin Stead; Nicholas Potter (female: 22%; male: 78%).

Nature of business: Simplyhealth provides health cash, dental, accident and personal health plans for individuals and businesses in the UK.

Financial information

Year end	31/12/2021
Turnover	£198,200,000
Pre-tax profit	(£14,700,000)

Total employees: 1,001

Main locations: Simplyhealth has offices in Andover and Winchester.

Community involvement

Simplyhealth supports communities across the UK by improving access to healthcare. It does this through charitable giving and employee volunteering. The company donates 10% of its pre-tax profits each year to healthcare charities or community projects.

Partnerships

The company has charity partnerships with a number of charitable organisations including, Sported, a charity that helps keep community youth sports clubs open; Dentaid, a charity that works to increase access to dental care for vulnerable people; The Lady Garden Foundation, which raises awareness and funding for gynaecological health and The Mental Health Foundation.

Since 2016 the company has worked in partnership with TeethTeam, a school-based tooth-brushing programme that teaches children about the importance of good oral health. The project aims to improve the dental health of children across the country. In 2019, 4,240 children participated in the programme and Simplyhealth's support paid for 32,452 toothbrushes and 16,632 tubes of toothpaste.

The company also has a partnership with healthcare charity, Nuffield Health

Charitable giving

The company supports local and national healthcare charities with cash donations. For example, support has been given to local homeless charity, Trinity Winchester. The support will enable the charity to provide free dental treatment via 12 monthly surgeries and visits from Dentaid mobile dental units. The company has also supported Brainwave, a charity supporting children with disabilities. The company's donation funded a senior physiotherapist which will enable more children with disabilities across the UK to gain greater independence.

Full criteria and information on how to apply for funding can be found on the company's website.

Support for Ukraine

The company has pledged to donate £150,000 to the Disasters Emergency Committee Ukraine Humanitarian Appeal by matching donations made by its customers, colleagues, friends and family. The company also offered £1,000 to any colleague who opened their home to refugees.

Employee-led support

Employees are offered three days' leave each year to volunteer for local causes.

The company operates a payroll giving scheme through which employees can donate to charity.

Commercially led support

The company has a partnership with England Rugby (RFU) and is the lead partner of the RFU's safety awareness campaign, RugbySafe.

Applications

Full details of how to apply for funding can be found on the company's website.

Community contributions

Cash donations UK	£626,000

We were unable to determine a figure for the company's total charitable contributions. However, over £626,000 was awarded to health and sport-related charities.

Skipton Building Society

🔍 Social welfare

Company registration number: 153706

Correspondent: CSR team, The Bailey, Skipton, North Yorkshire BD23 1DN (tel: 0345 850 1722; email: a web chat feature is available on the society's website; website: www.skipton.co.uk/ about-us/community-and-charitable-giving)

Directors: Gwyn Burr; Mark Lund; Ian Cornelius; Andrew Bottomley; Richard Coates; Denis Hall; Heather Jackson; Philip Moore; Bobby Ndawula; Helen Stevenson (female: 30%; male: 70%).

Nature of business: Skipton Building Society is the fourth largest in the UK. The society has several subsidiary companies, including Connells Group, one of the largest estate agency networks in the UK. In 2010 it merged with Chesham Building Society, based in Buckinghamshire. All branches now operate under the 'Skipton' name.

Financial information

Year end	31/12/2021
Turnover	£1,384,300,000
Pre-tax profit	£271,800,000

UK employees: 15,038

Main locations: The society's head office is in Skipton, North Yorkshire.

Community involvement

The society provides support to its communities through charity partnerships and donations to its corporate charity, the Skipton Building Society Charitable Foundation (Charity Commission no. 1079538).

Charity partnership programme

Through its charity partnership programme, the society chooses a charity to support with fundraising and other activities. The society has a partnership with Mental Health UK and supports Clic, the charity's online community that helps to connect people and organisations to provide mental health advice, information and support. From 2017 to 2019, the society was in partnership with the Alzheimer's Society and Alzheimer Scotland through which £250,000 was raised by employees and customers.

Community giving

In 2019 the society launched an annual 'Community Giving' initiative. Mortgage brokers and employees of intermediary firms are invited to nominate a housing or homelessness cause, to receive one of 40 £1,000 donations. In 2021, £40,000 was donated to 40 charities and community groups.

Employee-led support

Volunteering

Employees are offered three days' paid leave each year to volunteer for a charity of their choice. They can also take an extra day to support the society's charity partner.

Matched funding and payroll giving

The society matches employee fundraising efforts up to £500 for individuals and £1,000 for a team. Employees can also donate to charity through a payroll giving scheme. In 2021, the society contributed to employees' fundraising efforts by donating an additional £15,000 to 33 charities.

Commercially led support

The building society provides sponsorships to local charities and groups. Examples of sponsorships include Citizens Advice Skipton, Skipton BID and Young Enterprise.

Applications

Each branch has its own community fund. Contact your local branch to find out more. Details of local branches can be found on the society's website.

Corporate charity

Skipton Building Society Charitable Foundation (Charity Commission no. 1079538) – see entry on page 274.

Community contributions

Cash donations UK	£500,000

According to the 2021 accounts, the society donated £500,000 to charity, primarily to the Skipton Building Society Charitable Foundation.

Sky Ltd

Arts, culture and heritage, community services and development, the environment, sports and recreation

Company registration number: 2247735

Correspondent: Bigger Picture Team, Grant Way, Isleworth, Middlesex

TW7 5QD (tel: 0333 100 0333; website: www.skygroup.sky/corporate/bigger-picture)

Directors: Thomas Reid; Simon Robson (male: 100%).

Nature of business: Sky is a Europe-wide entertainment company. In the UK and the Republic of Ireland, Sky provides paid television, broadband and streaming services. BSkyB launched its digital television services in the UK on 1 October 1998.

Financial information

Year end	31/12/2021
Turnover	£309,000,000
Pre-tax profit	£227,000,000

Total employees: 34,335

Main locations: Sky has offices across the UK and Europe.

Community involvement

Sky's community involvement is channelled through its CSR programme, the Bigger Picture. Sky wishes to use its scale and reach to make a positive impact in the world, with a particular focus on opportunities for young people and protecting the environment.

Sky Academy and the MAMA Youth Project

The MAMA Youth Project provides media and television industry training for young people from under-represented groups and those with limited educational or employment opportunities. Sky has worked with the charity since 2011 and every year provides financial support to put 24 trainees through the programme, as well as work experience placements with Sky and several of its production company partners.

Sky Academy Studios offers schoolchildren in the UK and Italy the chance to experience what a career in the media could be like. Children aged 8 to 16 are invited to the studios to create their own news reports, trailers and vlogs, helping them to develop new skills and confidence.

Sky Ocean Rescue

The Sky Ocean Rescue campaign was launched in partnership with WWF (World Wide Fund for Nature) in 2017, to raise awareness of plastic pollution and highlight easy ways people can take action. Since its inception, the campaign has reached nearly 48 million people across Europe. According to the group's website, Sky Ocean Ventures is investing £25 million over five years into innovations that help to reduce the global flow of plastic into the oceans.

Sky has been working with WWF and Swansea University to pilot the UK's largest seagrass replanting project, aiming to plant over one million seeds to

create the UK's first restored seagrass meadow. According to the group's 2021 impact report, the project is now expanding to other parts of the UK.

Equality and inclusion

Sky Ltd committed over £1 million to a partnership with Sir Lewis Hamilton's charitable foundation, Mission 44, aiming to keep children in school, transforming their lives for the better. The group donated over £1 million to local charities working on inclusion in Italy, Germany, the UK and Ireland.

Sky also has a £3 million partnership with Kick It Out, to end discrimination in football.

Time to Care

In 2021, Sky Ltd launched its Time to Care campaign to tackle loneliness among older people. Through the campaign, the group launched a befriending line to talk to older sky customers and in 2021, 22,700 connections were made using the line.

In-kind support

According to its 2021 impact report, the group over 480 tickets for cultural events were provided to children from disadvantaged families.

Employee-led support

Employee volunteering

In 2019 the group launched Sky Cares, a volunteering programme that enables employees to give their time to local communities during work hours. The programme has four main focus areas: loneliness, homelessness, young people and the environment. The group has 58 charity partnerships across Europe, all of which benefit from employee volunteering. These partnerships include Age UK, the Conservation Volunteers, NSPCC and many more. In 2021, employees volunteered 32,642 hours through the Sky Cares Programme.

Commercially led support

Over the past 20 years, Sky has contributed more than £10 billion to British and Irish sports organisations and has previously partnered with British Cycling.

Sky mentors and sponsors promising young athletes through its Sports Sponsorship Programme. Since 2011, the group has supported over 24 young athletes.

Sky Cares is a sponsor of the Badu Sports Mentoring Programme, supporting a group of young people aged between 14 and 18 to fulfil their full potential. In 2021 the group supported the Badu Mentoring Group with virtual mentoring session.

Applications

Contact the correspondent for further information.

Community contributions

According to its 2021 Bigger Picture impact report, the group's investment for societal impact totalled £27.8 million; however, no further breakdown was given. We were unable to determine a figure for the group's community contributions.

Slaughter and May (Trust Ltd)

🔍 Education and training

Company registration number: 335458

Correspondent: The CSR Team, One Bunhill Row, London EC1Y 8YY (tel: 020 7600 1200; email: use the contact form on the firm's website; website: www.slaughterandmay.com)

Directors: Caroline Phillips; Sally Wokes; Robert Byk; Deborah Finkler; Jill Hoseason; Claire Jeffs; John Nevin; Guy O'Keefe; Richard Smith; Isabel Taylor; David Watkins (female: 55%; male: 45%).

Nature of business: Slaughter and May is a multinational law firm.

Financial information

Year end	30/04/2021

Main locations: The firm's UK office is located in Islington, London. It works in over 130 countries globally.

Community involvement

The firm supports general charitable purposes with a focus on education, employability and young people. Support is provided through cash donations, pro bono legal advice, matched funding, employee volunteering and fundraising. Much of the firm's community outreach is concentrated in the London Borough of Islington, where its UK office is based.

The firm's charitable donations are made through its corporate charity The Slaughter and May Charitable Trust (Charity Commission no. 1082765).

Partnerships

At a local level, the firm works with St Luke's Community Centre in Islington to deliver projects for the local community, such as 'Firm Futures', where employees volunteer as business mentors for local unemployed people wanting to set up their own businesses.

The firm also works in partnership with Macquarie to deliver the Community Resourcing (CoRe) programme, which supports charities in Islington. Teams of employee volunteers are matched with local charities and provide strategic support over a six-month period.

In 2021, the firm commenced partnerships with three local not-for-profit organisations as part of its community programme. They include Beam, which supports homeless people, to build their network and crowdfund their way into long-term employment; Talk for Health, a social enterprise that teaches people an evidence-based method for therapeutic talking; and Bags of Taste, which works with people in food poverty, helping them to achieve an improved and healthier diet on a low budget.

Education and employability

Working together with national charity partners and local schools, the firm delivers a wide range of programmes aimed at promoting educational attainment and literacy. Recent highlights of the firm's education initiatives include:

- **Tutoring** – The firm works in partnership with educational charity The Access Project, and the Central Foundation Boys' School to help students achieve places at top universities. Since its launch in 2012, five times more students are now going to the most selective universities
- **Mentoring** – Volunteers help students make decisions about university progression and write their personal statements for their university applications
- **Literacy** – The firm funds the National Literacy Trust's annual literacy survey and provides reading support at local primary schools
- **Work experience** – The firm's Excellerators Programme is designed for year 12 students, offering a week-long placement across legal and business services teams to give an insight into the variety of roles. Following a week at the firm, students then go on to the Insight Week provided by the Social Mobility Business Partnership, a social mobility scheme set up with ITV
- **Reading Support** – In 2020, the firm introduced a reading support scheme for children ages five to seven, using the online platform TutorMate.The scheme pairs young, struggling pupils from a local primary school with reading support volunteers who commit to a 30-minute reading session a week

In-kind support

Pro bono

The firm provides pro bono support and last year collaborated on projects involving education, access to justice and community citizenship. It also provides an annual series of legal workshops for charities and produces a free legal toolkit for charities. Islington Law Centre is also supported with financial donations and pro bono support.

Employee-led support

Employee fundraising

The firm has a payroll giving scheme and provides matched funding for employees who fundraise in their own time for charities and schools through its Funds for Fundraisers scheme.

Employee volunteering

The firm's employees volunteer through a range of initiatives with its charity partners, such as helping with the Job Club at St Luke's Community Centre in Islington, or offering support with reading for children at local primary schools.

Applications

The firm's website states that it is 'unable to accept unsolicited funding applications from schools, charities or individuals'.

Corporate charity

The Slaughter and May Charitable Trust (Charity Commission no. 1082765) – see entry on page 275.

Community contributions

No figure was given for the group's overall charitable contribution during the year.

Smith & Nephew plc

🔍 Education and training, health, medical research

Company registration number: 324357

Correspondent: Local CSR Team, Croxley Park, Building 5, Hatters Lane, Watford, Hertfordshire WD18 8YE (email: sustainability@smith-nephew.com; website: www.smith-nephew.com)

Directors: Roberto Quarta; Anne-Francoise Nesmes; Deepak Nath; Helen Barraclough; Erik Engstrom; Robin Freestone; Jo Hallas; John Ma; Katarzyna; Mazur Hofsaess; Rick Medlock; Marc Owen; Angie Risley; Bob White (female: 38%; male: 62%).

Nature of business: Smith & Nephew is a global medical technology business established in 1856.

Financial information

Year end	31/12/2021
Turnover	£4,721,550,800
Pre-tax profit	£530,857,400

Total employees: 18,976

Main locations: In the UK, Smith & Nephew has sites in Hull and Watford.

Community involvement

Smith & Nephew plc's charitable activity prioritises organisations with a focus on human services or the promotion of healthcare access. The company makes in-kind product and cash donations to support educational programmes for young people, with a particular focus on STEM programmes.

The company also makes contributions in the form of grants for education and sponsorships.

In-kind support

Product donations

The company donates products to charitable or not-for-profit organisations, medical institutions, accredited educational programmes, medical foundations or professional societies as governed by its Global Policy and Procedure.

Employee-led support

Employee volunteering and fundraising

Employees are encouraged to volunteer for charities local to the communities in which the company operates. Equally, different employee charity teams nominate charities to support for the year. In 2021, the charity team in Hull nominated the Children's Heart Foundation, East Riding Foodbank, Mires Beck Nursery and Mind as targets for charitable donation. Each charity received £5,000 from Smith & Nephew plc.

The company also offers employees eight hours of paid leave for volunteering. In 2021, due to the COVID-19 pandemic, the company made an additional 240 hours available for employees with a professional background in healthcare, in order to support frontline workers.

During the year, employees volunteered 9,675 hours of their time to support charitable causes; 698 of these hours were volunteered through the company's COVID Global Volunteer Policy for Registered Healthcare Professionals.

Matched funding

The company matches employees' eligible charitable donations up to $500 (or the equivalent in the local currency) per employee on an annual basis.

Applications

Contact your local site for further information.

Community contributions

| Cash donations worldwide | £17,280,000 |
| Total contributions worldwide | £18,710,000 |

According to the 2021 corporate sustainability report, 'philanthropic activities' totalled £1.42 million. This consisted of £55,900 in cash, product donations of £1.3 million and £65,800 from matching employee donations. A further £17.3 million was awarded in grants for education and sponsorships. We were unable to determine how much was given in the UK.

The above financial information has been converted from USD using the exchange rate at the time of writing (September 2022).

DS Smith Holdings plc

🔍 Education and training, the environment

Company registration number: 1377658

Correspondent: CSR Team, 7th Floor, 350 Euston Road, Regent's Place, London NW1 3AX (tel: 020 7756 1800; website: www.dssmith.com/ sustainability/building-strong-foundations/looking-after-people-and-our-communities/responsible-neighbour/ charitable-foundation)

Directors: Geoff Drabble; Miles Roberts; Adrian Marsh; Celia Baxter; Alan Johnson; Alina Kessel; David Robbie; Louise Smalley; Rupert Soames; Iain Simm (female: 33%; male: 67%).

Nature of business: DS Smith is a provider of sustainable packaging solutions, paper products and recycling services worldwide.

Financial information

Year end	30/04/2021
Turnover	£5,980,000,000
Pre-tax profit	£231,000,000

Total employees: 29,309

Main locations: The group has headquarters in London and operations in 37 countries around the world.

Community involvement

Most of the group's charitable activities in the UK are co-ordinated through its corporate charity, The DS Smith Charitable Foundation (Charity Commission no. 1142817) which supports charities engaged in conservation of the environment and training or education.

Individual businesses within the group also run their own initiatives and there are also group-wide partnerships.

Commercially led support

DS Smith sponsors Keep Britain Tidy's Green Flag scheme which recognises and rewards well-managed parks and green spaces. As part of the sponsorship DS Smith has pledged to volunteer and fundraise, supporting the development of green spaces and the Green Flag Award for both communities and businesses in the UK across all its sites.

Applications

See the group's corporate charity entry for further information.

Corporate charity

The DS Smith Charitable Foundation (Charity Commission no. 1142817) – see entry on page 275.

Community contributions

We were unable to determine a figure for the group's charitable contributions.

Smiths Group plc

🔍 Education and training, the environment, health, social welfare

Company registration number: 137013

Correspondent: Corporate Responsibility Team, 4th Floor, 11–12 St James's Square, London SW1Y 4LB (tel: 020 7004 1600; website: www.smiths.com)

Directors: Sir George Buckley; Pam Cheng; Paul Keel; Dame Ann Dowling; Clare Scherrer; Tanya Fratto; Karin Hoeing; Mark Seligman; Richard Howes; Noel Tata; Bill Seeger (female: 45%; male: 55%).

Nature of business: The group has five divisions which are involved in the following markets: medical; industrial; energy; aerospace; communication; engineered components; and threat and contraband detection. Its customers include governments, hospitals, petrochemical companies, equipment manufacturers and service providers in other sectors.

Financial information

Year end	31/07/2022
Turnover	£2,566,000,000
Pre-tax profit	£103,000,000

Total employees: 21,950

Main locations: The group has operations in over 50 countries. The group's UK operations are based in London.

Community involvement

In 2021, Smiths group plc's charitable giving was principally channelled through employee-led activity. However, the group did donate to the British Red Cross's Ukraine Appeal and £20,000 to charities nominated by its employees.

Employee-led support

Beyond Boundaries

In 2019, Smiths Interconnect launched a pilot of Smiths Beyond Boundaries, a programme which gives employees a paid day to volunteer with their local communities.

In 2022, as part of the Beyond Boundaries programme, employees volunteered in their local communities in various ways:

- Volunteering at schools, care homes and other community organisations
- Organising collections and providing support for food banks and community pantries
- The maintenance of green spaces and community gardens

- Educational sessions in schools on environmental matters

Other employee-led support

Teams from Smiths Detection in Hemel Hempstead volunteer their time to deliver STEM activities and educational sessions to local schools. The senior leadership team volunteered at five different charities in 2022 as part of the Smiths Group plc leadership summit.

The group also operates a STEM ambassador scheme, whereby employees lead STEM projects. In 2022 the project was 'Tomorrow's Technology Today'. As part of the programme, employees helped to deliver a 12-week assessed project for a local all-girls school.

In 2022, the group also ran a pilot of a site-led community engagement scheme in which employees voted for organisations to receive company donations. The programme was followed by a £20,000 donation by the group and a day of paid leave for employees to volunteer.

Applications

Contact the correspondent for further information.

Community contributions

We were unable to determine a figure for the group's total community contributions for 2022. Smiths Group plc annual report for 2022 states that the group donated an unspecified amount to the British Red Cross Ukraine Appeal and that £20,000 was donated as part of a pilot site-led community engagement scheme.

Societe Generale International Ltd

Arts, culture and heritage, education and training, health, sports and recreation

Company registration number: 5407520

Correspondent: The CSR Team, One Bank Street, Canary Wharf, London E14 4SG (email: online contact form; website: www.societegenerale.co.uk/en/our-commitments/corporate-social-responsibility)

Directors: Marcia Cantor-Grable; Michael Collins; Alexandre Fleury; Keith McArdle; Phillipe Robeyns; Stephen Swift (female: 17%; male: 83%).

Nature of business: The group specialises in corporate and investment banking, private banking services, asset management, prime brokerage and vehicle and equipment finance.

Financial information

Year end	31/12/2021
Turnover	£1,070,134,000
Pre-tax profit	£137,141,000

Total employees: 318

Main locations: In the UK, the group's headquarters is in London. It has several other locations across the UK, and in Jersey, Guernsey and Gibraltar.

Community involvement

Societie Generale supports a wide range of charities and causes through its corporate charity, partnerships, work placements and scholarships for young musicians. The group has a particular interest in education, employability, health, music, art and sport.

Societe Generale UK Foundation (Charity Commission no. 1039013)

Through its corporate charity, the group funds a number of key strategic projects, particularly in the fields of education, employability and climate change, as well as providing matched funding to employees engaging in various fundraising and volunteering efforts.

Partnerships

At the time of writing (November 2022), the group's charity partner is Shelter, a charity that supports people facing homelessness. Through a three-year partnership, the group is supporting the charity's employability scheme, Getting Real Work Opportunities (GROW). The programme offers 12-month paid work placements for people who have experienced homelessness.

The group's previous charity partners include Young Lives vs Cancer, Mind, NSPCC and Friends of the Elderly, among others.

The Young Influencers Programme

As part of the group's commitment to improving the accessibility of the banking sector, Societé Générale International Ltd has established its 'Young Influencers Programme'. The programme consists of a six-month series of interactive workshops delivered by the group's employees who volunteer for the programme. In 2021, 75 16- to 18-year-olds were enrolled on the programme, with a specific focus on women and students from disadvantaged backgrounds. On completion of the programme, students are encouraged to apply for a paid work placement the following summer.

Music

According to the group's website, the group supports young musicians by awarding scholarships to students to help with their professional development. The group also supports leading music schools by lending instruments.

Employee-led support

Staff are entitled to one day's paid volunteering leave per year. Employees can undertake their own personal volunteering, or take part in the range of education and employability programmes organised by the group such as business planning workshops, adult literacy lessons and primary tutoring.

Employees also give their time to volunteer for the group's Young Influencers Programme.

Commercially led support

For over a decade, Societé Générale has been a worldwide partner of the Rugby World Cup. The group is also a corporate member of the Royal Albert Hall and the Glyndebourne Opera Festival.

The group is the first sponsor of the Victoria and Albert Museum to have supported two of the gallery's flagship exhibitions in successive years.

Applications

To apply for funding for scholarships awarded by the group, visit: https://fondation.societegenerale.com/en/foundation. For any further enquiries, contact the correspondent.

Corporate charity

Societe Generale UK Foundation (Charity Commission no. 1196579) – see entry on page 276.

Community contributions

We were unable to determine a figure for the group's community contributions during 2021.

Sodexo Ltd

Health, nutrition and diet

Company registration number: 842846

Correspondent: The CSR Team, 1 Southampton Row, London WC1B 5HA (tel: 020 7404 0110; website: https://uk.sodexo.com/social-impact)

Directors: Stuart Carter; Sean Haley; Sarah Perry; Angelo Piccirillo; Jean Renton; Marc Rolland (female: 33%; male: 67%).

Nature of business: The group provides a wide range of food services, soft services and technical services to both private and public sector organisations in the UK and Ireland.

Financial information

Year end	31/08/2021
Turnover	£1,363,917,000
Pre-tax profit	£46,022,000

Total employees: 40,189

Main locations: In the UK, the group has several locations with its head office in London. The group also operates globally.

Community involvement

Sodexo Ltd makes grants to charities directly (although its grant-making policy is not specified) as well as making awards through its corporate charity, the Stop Hunger Foundation (Charity Commission no. 1110266).

Sodexo's main focus is food and nutrition.

Employee-led support

Employees are entitled to take paid leave from work to undertake voluntary work. According to the group's 2021/22 social impact web page, staff spent around 2,000 hours volunteering for charities such as FareShare and the Trussell Trust.

Applications

For further information contact the correspondent or see the company's corporate charity entry.

Corporate charity

Sodexo Stop Hunger Foundation (Charity Commission no. 1110266) – see entry on page 277.

Community contributions

Cash donations UK	£256,500
Total contributions UK	£557,300

The group's 2020/21 accounts state that donations to UK charities totalled £256,500. According to the 2020/21 Stop Hunger Foundation's accounts, the group donated a further £143,800 to its corporate charity. The group also donated employee time, valued at £157,000.

Sony Europe B.V.

General charitable purposes, STEM

Company registration number: FC035527

Correspondent: CSR Committee, Sony UK Technology Centre, Pencoed, Bridgend CF35 5HZ (email: CSRPCD@ eu.sony.com; website: www.sonypencoed. co.uk/community)

Directors: Hideyuki Furumi; Atsuki Matsuzawa; Ricky Londema (male: 100%).

Nature of business: The company is the distributor of Sony branded products.

Financial information

Year end	31/03/2021
Turnover	£3,146,129,337
Pre-tax profit	£13,002,669

Main locations: Support is primarily given to organisations and schools within a 30-mile radius of the Sony UK Technology Centre in Bridgend.

Community involvement

Educational visits and programmes

Sony Europe B.V. hosts regular visits from schools, colleges and universities. The Sony UK Technology Environmental Centre is also used by schoolchildren for environmental field trips.

The company supports several of the programmes run by The Engineering Education Scheme Wales (EESW), which encourages young people to choose a career in one of the STEM subjects. The company also supports the schools programme of the charity Ospreys in the Community, by providing pupils with the opportunity to learn about local engineering prospects and see the latest technology as it is built.

The Sony Technology Community Fund (not a registered charity)

The company has established a community fund that supports local organisations with product donations to aid fundraising.

In-kind support

The company supports local organisations through the donation of Sony products, which can be used for fundraising or raffles.

Applications

In-kind support – to be eligible for in-kind support organisations should be located within 30 miles of the company's UK Technology Centre in Bridgend. Application forms can be requested from the website: www.sonypencoed.co.uk/ community-support. The CSR Committee meets approximately every four weeks to discuss donations.

Educational visits – enquiries about educational visits to the Sony UK Technology Park can be made using an online form on the company's website: www.sonypencoed.co.uk/contact/ educational-visits.

Community contributions

We were unable to determine a figure for the company's community contributions for 2020/21.

The Southern Co-operative Ltd

Community services and development

Company registration number: IP01591R

Correspondent: Community Engagement Team, 1000 Lakeside, Western Road, Portsmouth, Hampshire PO6 3FE (tel: 023 9222 2500; email: community@southerncoops.co.uk; website: https://southern.coop/how-we-do-it/community)

Directors: Mark Ralf; Neil Blanchard; Elizabeth Rogers; Beverly Wyatt; Joanne Gray; Helen Jackson; John Lay; Jessica Danyluk; Anthony Scott; Olusoji John (female: 55%; male: 45%).

Nature of business: The Southern Co-operative (TSC) is an independent consumer co-operative society. It operates more than 300 food, funeral and Starbucks coffee stores across the south of England.

Financial information

Year end	30/01/2022
Turnover	£494,090,000
Pre-tax profit	£3,289,999

UK employees: 4,000

Main locations: TSC has various stores and funeral homes across the south of England, including west and south Outer London. There is also a store in Gwent, Wales.

Community involvement

The Southern Co-operative Ltd's (TSC) Love your Neighbour programme provides funding, in-kind donations and partnership opportunities.

Love Your Neighbourhood

This programme is funded by the carrier bag charge and focuses on four community themes: to create greener, safer, healthier and more inclusive communities. The programme features the following:

- In-kind product donations
- Local fundraising (giving out cash donations of between £50 to £1,000)
- Local partnerships
- Employee volunteering
- Food bank collection points
- Community defibrillators

Support is focused on local charitable or not-for-profit organisations in areas where the co-operative operates.

In 2021/22, the company donated £30,000 across 64 food banks.

Safer Neighbourhood Fund

The fund provides support to UK charities delivering innovative programmes in local communities to reduce crime, support people who have previously offended and those at risk of offending.

Greener neighbourhoods

The company has a partnership with the Hampshire and Isle of Wight Wildlife Trust's Wilder Portsmouth programme, which is helping people take action to create and enhance wild spaces across Portsmouth.

It also has a partnership with Dorset Wildlife Trust supporting its Natural Choices programme which helps people across the county experience the health and well-being benefits of regular contact with nature through a programme of events and activities.

The company supports Neighbourly's Seeds of the Change programme and donated £26,000 in 2021/22 to help small charities and local causes create green spaces for local communities.

In-kind support
The company provides gifts in kind for community/fundraising events such as prizes, hampers or refreshments.

Employee-led support
As part of TSC's community involvement, colleagues and members are encouraged to volunteer their time for local good causes or environmental projects. Employees and customers actively fundraise for the society's local charity partners.

Applications
Details of how to apply for support can be found on the community section of the company's website.

Community contributions

Total contributions UK		£323,300

According to its 2021/22 annual review, TSC made charity and community contributions totalling £321,500 and donated time valued at £1,800. A further £281,000 was donated through the carrier bag charge; however, we have not included this amount in the grant total.

Southern Water Services Ltd

General charitable purposes, health

Company registration number: 2366670

Correspondent: Community Engagement Team, Southern House, PO Box 41, Yeoman Road, Worthing, West Sussex BN13 3NZ (tel: 0330 303 0277; email: community@southernwater.co.uk; website: www.southernwater.co.uk/community)

Directors: Keith Lough; Ian McAulay; Sebastiaan Boelen; Paul Sheffield; Rosemary Boot; Mike Putnam; Dame Gillian Guy; Kevin McCullough; Malcolm Cooper; Mark Mathieson; Will Price; Steve Fraser; Richard Manning (female: 15%; male: 85%).

Nature of business: Southern Water provides water supply and wastewater services in the South East.

Financial information

Year end	31/03/2022
Turnover	£823,500,000
Pre-tax profit	(£847,600,000)

Total employees: 2,216

Main locations: The company provides services in the South East.

Community involvement
Southern Water Services Ltd provides support through its community grants scheme and community action group. The company also delivers educational talks and visits to local schools and community groups.

Partnerships
Southern Water Services Ltd is a partner of We Are UK Water, a conglomerate of British water providers that deliver educational events to children and young people in the UK. Through this, the company is also partnered with World Water Day and World Toilet Day, delivering online sessions.

Community grant scheme
In 2021/22, the company's community grants scheme received 200 applications for financial support. 80 projects were approved and the scheme distributed grants totalling £304,000.

In-kind support
In 2021/22, the company delivered 2,500 hours of its educational talks and visits to schools, reaching 56 schools virtually and 17 schools with in-person visits. The company also delivered talks to six community groups.

Employee-led support
Employees engage in volunteering and fundraising activities. In 2021/22 a total of 1,438 volunteer hours were completed by employees. The company's employees also form a part of its community action group, nominating a cause to receive company donations annually.

Commercially led support
Southern Water Services Ltd is a supporter of the Brighton Festival.

Applications
Volunteering – to request volunteering support from Southern Water employees, organisations should email the company at volunteer@southernwater.co.uk.

Regional support – at the time of writing (October 2020) the company's website stated: 'We will continue to support our regional charities with a second wave of funding later in the year. If you're interested in hearing more about this funding when it opens, email community@southernwater.co.uk.'

Community contributions

Cash donations UK		£324,000

In 2021/22 the company's community grants scheme donated £304,000 to community projects and causes. The company's community action group, made up of employees, customers and young people, nominated Mountbatten Hospice as the recipient of a £20,000 company donation.

SPAR (UK) Ltd

Emergency response/relief, food, general charitable purposes, health

Company registration number: 634226

Correspondent: CSR Team, Mezzanine Floor, Hygeia Building, 66–68 College Road, Harrow, Middlesex HA1 1BE (tel: 020 8426 3700; email: contact form on the website; website: www.spar.co.uk)

Directors: Suzanne Dover; Claire Hoste; Lee Johnson; Christopher Lewis; Ian Taylor (female: 40%; male: 60%).

Nature of business: SPAR (UK) Ltd is a voluntary, independently owned trading company operating convenience and grocery stores under the SPAR banner throughout the UK. The company's 2020/21 annual report states: 'SPAR (UK) Ltd is the Central Office of the SPAR retail organisation owned 100% by SPAR Food Distributors Ltd whose shareholders are five regional distribution companies. The companies are: A F Blakemore and Son Ltd; Appleby Westward Group Ltd; C J Lang and Son Ltd; Henderson Wholesale Ltd; and James Hall and Company (Holdings) Ltd.'

Financial information

Year end	30/04/2021
Turnover	£188,296,000
Pre-tax profit	£495,100

UK employees: 81

Main locations: The company operates across the UK.

Community involvement
SPAR provides support to its national charity partner through employee fundraising as well as through donations gained from the income received from the sale of certain SPAR products. The company also provides more general charitable support through its corporate charity, the SPAR Charitable Fund (Charity Commission no. 236252), which supports employees in need and makes grants to charities and emergency appeals.

Partnerships
The majority of SPAR (UK) Ltd's charitable activities are carried out in partnership with national charities. Since 2017, SPAR has partnered with the health charity Marie Curie. SPAR provides support to its partner through employee fundraising as well as through donations from the income received from the sale of certain SPAR products.

In-kind support
James Hall and Company, the SPAR wholesaler for the north of England, has a partnership with Too Good To Go which allows customers to purchase 'magic bags' of surplus stock in order to

prevent food waste. This wholesaler also works with over 70 food banks across the north of England to provide donations of surplus stock.

James Hall and Co's SPAR-branded food donation bins have helped raise nearly £20,000 in food donations for food banks across northern England during the year.

Food donation bins are provided in many SPAR stores across the UK.

Employee-led support

Employees regularly organise fundraising activities to raise money for SPAR's partner charity.

Commercially led support

Each year, the company supports Marie Curie's 'Blooming Great Tea Party' fundraising initiative, by donating income received from the sale of certain ranges of cakes, teas and coffees to charity.

The company has also announced it will sponsor the Willington Cricket Club for the 2023 season.

Applications

For general enquiries, use the contact form available on the company's website.

Contact your local store manager for enquiries regarding local initiatives. Contact details can be found online using the store locator.

For enquiries about the SPAR Charitable Fund, email michelle.geraghty@spar.co.uk.

Corporate charity

SPAR Charitable Fund (Charity Commission no. 236252) – see entry on page 277.

Community contributions

Cash donations UK	£100,000

According to the SPAR UK Ltd community web page, the company's communities cashback scheme awarded a total of £100,000 to charities across the UK during 2021/22. The company also makes donations to its corporate charity, the SPAR Charitable Fund (Charity Commission no. 236252); however, no total could be determined for donations made by the company to the fund.

Spirax-Sarco Engineering plc

Community enterprise and social entrepreneurship, community services and development, education and training, emergency response/relief, health, work outside the UK

Company registration number: 596337

Correspondent: Sustainability Committee, Charlton House, Cirencester Road, Charlton Kings, Cheltenham, Gloucestershire GL53 8ER (tel: 01242 521361; email: info@ spiraxsarcoengineering.com; website: www.spiraxsarcoengineering.com)

Directors: Jamie Pike; Nicholas Anderson; Nimesh Patel; Angela Archon; Peter France; Caroline Johnstone; Richard Gillingwater; Andy Robson; Jane Kingston; Olivia Qui; Kevin Thompson (female: 36%; male: 64%).

Nature of business: Spirax-Sarco Engineering plc is a British manufacturer of steam management systems and peristaltic pumps and associated fluid path technologies. The group is made up of three businesses: steam specialties (Spirax-Sarco and Gestra); electric thermal solutions (Chromalox and Thermocoax); and fluid path technologies (Watson-Marlow).

Financial information

Year end	31/12/2021
Turnover	£1,344,500,000
Pre-tax profit	£333,900,000

UK employees: 2,225

Total employees: 8,202

Main locations: In the UK, the group is based in Cheltenham and has operations across the country. It also has operations in over 60 countries worldwide.

Community involvement

The group supports local communities through 'financial donations to registered charities; educational provision; in-kind donations of products, services or the use of company facilities; and company-supported employee volunteering.' Much of the group's charitable support is channelled through the Spirax-Sarco Group Charitable Fund (not a registered charity).

Spirax-Sarco Group Charitable Fund

In 2021, the group's charitable fund donated £345,100 to charitable causes. Grants included a £35,000 donation to UNICEF's VaccinAid, £10,000 to Acorn's Children Hospice and £2,000 to Gloucestershire Young Carers.

Spirax-Sarco Engineering Group Education Fund

The Spirax-Sarco Engineering Group Education Fund was established in 2021 with the aim to address inequality in access to education. The group made an initial donation of £1 million and aims to provide £5 million by 2030, additional to its regular charitable activity. The fund is accessible to companies within the group to distribute in local communities where educational inequality is present.

Operating Companies' donations

In 2021, companies within the group contributed £336,000 in cash and in-kind donations for local causes. Of this total, £100,000 was given in in-kind donations.

In-kind support

The group provides in-kind donations such as products and office equipment. In 2021, operating companies donated the equivalent of £100,000 in in-kind donations.

Employee-led support

In 2021, employees donated £47,000 and contributed over 11,000 hours to fundraising and community engagement activities. Group employees are entitled to three days' paid volunteering leave each year.

Exclusions

According to its Charitable Donations Policy, the group will not provide funding for any of the following:

- Commercial organisations
- Political parties, organisations, or political events
- Religious organisations where the donation is used to promote a particular faith or belief (note: donations to religious organisations could be acceptable if the organisation is undertaking charitable work, such as disaster relief, where receipt of aid is not conditional upon religious affiliation)
- Organisations that discriminate in the allocation of their support according to race, sexual orientation, gender, religion, or disability
- Organisations that are involved in human rights abuses, are subject to UN, EU, UK or US Sanctions, or violate the Group Sanctions, Embargoes & Restrictions Policy
- Organisations whose activities contribute to environmental damage
- Organisations that cause harm to animals
- Individuals or private pursuits
- Research projects such as books, research papers or articles in professional journals
- Activities that contravene the Group Anti-Bribery and Corruption Policy, the Group Human Rights Policy or the Group Management Code
- Activities prohibited by law or regulation or that are deemed offensive or inappropriate
- Activities that encourage a relationship of dependence

Applications

Enquiries can be submitted using an online form in the 'Contact us' section of the group's website.

Group charitable donations are managed locally and are made at the discretion of each company's general manager. As such, applications for funding should be submitted in writing to your local company. Contact details are available on the group's website.

Community contributions

Cash donations worldwide	£1,671,000

In 2021, the group established the Spirax-Sarco Engineering Group Education Fund with a £1 million donation. The 2021 annual report also states that the group's charitable fund donations totalled £345,100 and donations from companies within the group totalled £336,000. The figure for donations from the companies within the group include £100,000 of in-kind donations.

SSE plc

Community services and development, education and training, the environment, general charitable purposes

Company registration number: SC117119

Correspondent: Craig Mullen, Community Investment Manager, Inveralmond House, 200 Dunkeld Road, Perth, Perthshire PH1 3AQ (tel: 01738 456000; email: sustainability@sse.com; website: www.sserenewables.com/communities)

Directors: Sir John Manzoni; Alistair Phillips-Davies; Gregor Alexander; Martin Pibworth; Tony Cocker; Dame Elish Angiolini; John Bason; Dame Sue Bruce; Debbie Crosby; Peter Lynas; Helen Mahy; Melanie Smith; Dame Angela Strank (female: 46%; male: 54%).

Nature of business: SSE produces, distributes and supplies electricity and gas and provides other energy-related services.

Financial information

Year end	31/03/2022
Turnover	£8,608,200,000
Pre-tax profit	£3,482,200,000

Main locations: The group operates across the UK and Ireland.

Community involvement

The group supports communities within its areas of operation through a range of community investment funds and employee volunteering. The majority of SSE plc's community giving comes from SSE Renewables.

Community investment funds

Through SSE Renewables' community investment programme, financial support is delivered to a diverse range of community projects near its renewable developments in the UK and Ireland. SSE Renewables currently manages 46 local funds, some of which are managed on behalf of its joint venture partners. In 2021/22, these funds awarded £9.8 million in the UK and Ireland to help support over 1,000 projects.

For full details of all of the group's community funds including beneficial areas, eligibility criteria and deadlines see the website.

Sustainable Development Fund

In addition to its community funds, SSE also provides grants to support strategic projects in Dumfries and Galloway, the Highlands, North Lincolnshire, Perth and Kinross, the Scottish Borders and South Lanarkshire.

According to the group's website, the funds support projects that help to achieve the following objectives:

- Creating opportunities – increase opportunities for education and employment.
- Empowering communities – build resilience and protect vulnerable residents.
- Building sustainable places – stimulate meaningful community regeneration.

Further information about eligibility criteria and deadlines is provided on SSE Renewables' website.

Resilient Communities Fund

The Resilient Communities Fund is delivered by Scottish and Southern Electricity Networks. It offers support for communities to prepare for extreme weather events and supports projects that build the resilience of the most vulnerable people in the community. The fund opens once a year to not-for-profit community groups and charities in its electricity distribution network areas in central southern England and the north of Scotland.

Scholarship funds

SSE Renewables has a scholarship programme that is funded by some of its larger windfarms in England, Ireland and Northern Ireland to help students progress towards further education. The Scholarships focus on science, technology, engineering and mathematics (STEM) subjects in a bid to help fulfil employment demands in these fields.

The Scottish Hydro Electric Community Trust (OSCR no. SC027243)

The Scottish Hydro Electric Community Trust is an independent charitable trust, which was established by SSE to provide help to individual customers in the north of Scotland (Dunblane northwards), faced with high charges for an electricity connection.

Employee-led support

Employees take part in volunteering activities.

Exclusions

According to the group's website, grants from the SSE's local community funds cannot be awarded for: political or religious causes; to subsidise the cost of energy consumption; for purposes

'adverse to SSE's interests'; to replace statutory funding; or to individuals. Grants from the Sustainable Development Fund are not awarded for individuals, or groups without a constitution.

For further details on all exclusions for the group's community investment funds, refer to the group's website.

Applications

Community investment funds

Application forms for each of the local community investment funds, as well as the Sustainable Development Fund, are available on the SSE Renewables website (www.sserenewables.com/communities), along with guidance, deadlines and contact details for each fund.

Resilient Communities Fund

To apply to the Resilient Communities Fund, visit www.ssen.co.uk, where applications can be downloaded, along with guidance notes and deadlines.

Scholarship funds

Application forms can be downloaded from the SSE Renewables website (www.sserenewables.com/communities/scholarship-funds).

The Scottish Hydro Electric Community Trust

For more details and to apply, check the trust's website at www.shect.org.

Community contributions

In 2021/22, SSE plc contributed £9.7 million to communities across the UK and Ireland. This contribution includes donations made by SSE's 32 community investment funds and its Resilient Communities Fund, matched funding, as well as the financial value of employee volunteering. Note: the figure for community investment in the Republic of Ireland was converted from Euros using the exchange rate at the time of writing (October 2022).

The total figure was broken down in the 2021/22 sustainability report as follows: Community investment in Great Britain (£8.3 million); Community investment in the Republic of Ireland (£983,800); community investment in Northern Ireland (£450,000).

St James's Place plc

Community services and development, education and training, general charitable purposes, health, mental health and well-being, money and debt advice, social welfare, special educational needs, work outside the UK

Company registration number: 3183415

Correspondent: CSR Team, St James's Place House, 1 Tetbury Road, Cirencester, Gloucestershire GL7 1FP

(tel: 01285 640302; website: www.sjp.co.uk/about-st-james-place/our-responsibilities)

Directors: Andrew Croft; Craig Gentle; Emma Griffin; Rosemary Hilary; Simon Jeffreys; Lesley-Ann Nash; Roger Yates; John Hitchins; Paul Manduca (female: 33%; male: 67%).

Nature of business: St James's Place is a financial services group involved in the provision of wealth management services.

Financial information

Year end	31/12/2021
Turnover	£18,025,899,999
Pre-tax profit	£842,400,000

UK employees: 2,419

Total employees: 2,673

Main locations: The group has offices in Aberdeen, Belfast, Bristol, Cambridge, Cardiff, Cirencester, Edinburgh, Essex, Glasgow, Leeds, Liverpool, London, Manchester, Newbury, Newcastle, Nottingham, Solent, Solihull and Westerham.

Community involvement

The group supports a wide range of charitable causes with a particular focus on social mobility, social inclusion employability and financial education. Support is provided through local community partnerships, cash and in-kind donations and employee volunteering. Support is also given through the group's corporate charity the St James's Place Charitable Foundation (Charity Commission no. 1144606), which makes grants to registered charities under the following themes:

- Children and young people who are disadvantaged or have a disability
- Hospices
- Cancer support
- Mental health

Charity support

The group supports a number of local charities in and around rural Cirencester, close to the group's head office. The group also provides the charity with pro bono support, employee volunteering and in-kind gifts, such as access to meeting rooms. Beneficiaries have included: Barn Theatre, The Churn Project, the Cirencester Opportunity Group, Cirencester Signpost and New Brewery Arts.

Employability and financial education

The group works with local schools and colleges to provide a variety of financial education programmes for students. The group's free programmes are accredited by Young Money and are delivered by employees and group partners. For example, volunteer-led Financial Education Days give students the opportunity to learn about a range of topics related to personal finance and become self-confident in their ability to manage their own money. In 2021, the group supported the delivery of financial education sessions to 12,881 young people.

As part of its focus on employability and financial awareness, the group supports youth development through organisations such as Career Ready, The Duke of Edinburgh's Award (DofE), The Money Charity, National Numeracy Day and Young Enterprise.

Strategic charity partner

In 2018, the group established a five-year Strategic Partnership with the DofE, to support the bridging of education and employment for young people. The group supports the DofE by sharing its skills, resources and networks. All of St James's Place's apprentices undertake the DofE.

In-kind support

The group provides pro bono support to its long-term charity partners through its charity support programmes.

Employee-led support

Each year employees are entitled to take two days' paid leave to support the group's charitable foundation or volunteer for a local community group or charity of their choice. In 2021, employees volunteered a total of 12,395 hours of their time. According to the 2021 annual report, this contribution had a total value of £599,400. In addition to offering employees time to volunteer during working hours, the group also supports volunteering which employees undertake in their own time by awarding grants of £300 to the charities they support. In 2021, 42 of these grants were awarded.

Every year the group arranges several 'community team challenges', whereby groups of employees work together to deliver projects which benefit their local community. In 2021, the group hosted its largest ever volunteering challenge involving over 200 employees over a five-day period, where, alongside the volunteering group SPLASH Community Projects, volunteers transformed an outdoor play area for one of the group's local charity partners, Cirencester Opportunity Group (COG).

The group runs a payroll-giving scheme. In 2021, 85% of employees gave every month through their salary. Funds donated by employees to the St James's Place Charitable Foundation are matched by the group. In 2021, the group donated a total of £6.2 million to its foundation in matched funding.

Applications

Contact the correspondent for further information. Alternatively, general enquiries can be submitted using an online form on the group's website.

Corporate charity

St James's Place Charitable Foundation (Charity Commission no. 1144606) – see entry on page 278.

Community contributions

Cash donations UK	£6,200,000

According to its 2021 annual report, the group's community investment totalled £6.2 million.

St Mary's Football Group Ltd (Southampton Football Club)

Community enterprise and social entrepreneurship, community services and development, education and training, health, social welfare, sports and recreation

Company registration number: 6951765

Correspondent: Greg Baker, Head of Saints Foundation and Community Partnerships, St Mary's Stadium, Britannia Road, Southampton, Hampshire SO14 5FP (tel: 023 8071 8621; email: gbaker@saintsfoundation.co.uk or foundation@saintsfc.co.uk; website: www.southamptonfc.com/saints-foundation)

Directors: Martin Semmens; Rasmus Ankersen; Rolf Bolgi; Henrick Kraft; Dragan Solak; Toby Steele (male: 100%).

Nature of business: St Mary's Football Group Ltd is the ultimate parent company of Southampton Football Club, a professional football club competing in the English Premier League.

Financial information

Year end	30/06/2021
Turnover	£157,250,000
Pre-tax profit	(£22,780,000)

UK employees: 385

Main locations: The club is based in Southampton.

Community involvement

Southampton FC's community involvement is channelled through the Saints Foundation (Charity Commission no. 1090916) which delivers targeted programmes across the following areas:
- Involvement
- Health
- Empowerment

As part of Southampton FC's sustainability strategy, The Halo Effect, the club supports a range of organisations and initiatives.

Mental health

In partnership with the NHS Solent Trust, the club launched the Saints By Your Side mental health campaign.

It also works with a number of organisations to raise awareness of gambling addictions and support including the RecoverMe app and Sportsbet.io.

Environment

The club has pledged to plant 250 trees every time one of its academy players makes their first team debut.

Donation appeal

In 2021 the club donated £10,000 to Southampton City Council's Christmas Toy Appeal in 2021. It also encouraged its fans to get involved with the appeal.

In-kind support

The club provides free office space to the Saints Foundation.

Sport

In 2021, the club launched Grow Your Game, a programme to support the development of grassroots football in Hampshire with more than 700 coaches enrolling since its inception in the summer. It also partnered with Virgin Media to deliver a streamed PE lesson featuring the first team to over 400 schools nationwide.

Applications

Contact the correspondent for further information on the Saints Foundation.

General enquiries to the club can be submitted using the online contact form on its website.

Charity requests

Charity requests, including signed merchandise, can be made by contacting the club via the following email address: charities@saintsfc.co.uk.

Community contributions

Cash donations UK	£20,000
Total contributions UK	£187,000

According to the Saints Foundation's 2020/21 annual report, the club committed donations of £20,000. The club also provided the foundation with in-kind support with an estimated value of £167,000.

St. Modwen Properties plc

Community enterprise and social entrepreneurship, community services and development, education and training, the environment, health, sports and recreation, urban communities

Company registration number: 349201

Correspondent: CSR Committee, Two Devon Way, Longbridge, Birmingham, West Midlands B31 2TS (tel: 0121 222 9400; email: info@stmodwen.co.uk; website: www.stmodwen.co.uk/delivering-responsibly)

Directors: Rachel Kentleton; Peter Krause; Nicholas Porter; Sarwjit Sambhi; Adam Shah (female: 20%; male: 80%).

Nature of business: St Modwen Properties is a residential and commercial property investment and development group specialising in the regeneration of brownfield land and urban environments.

Financial information

Year end	31/12/2021
Turnover	£428,800,000
Pre-tax profit	£184,000,000

Total employees: 654

Main locations: The group has operations across England and South Wales and is headquartered in Birmingham.

Community involvement

The group's CSR activities focus on education and employment initiatives that encourage people to develop skills relating to the property and construction industries. The group also aims to raise awareness of careers in these industries through its CSR activities.

Partnerships

The group has a partnership with LandAid, a charity working to tackle youth homelessness. The group has pledged to donate £30,000 to LandAid, with the funds raised going towards the St Basils Live and Work project which aims to provide apprenticeship opportunities and living accommodation to young people facing homelessness.

Education and employability

According to its website, the group has stated it aims to invest 1% of the group's cash profits every year into education partnerships.

Previously, the group partnered with Ahead Partnership and Ark Kings Academy, a Birmingham secondary school, to deliver the Longbridge Leisure Challenge. The challenge engaged over 100 students in an active consultation on a proposed regeneration project in their town.

According to St Modwen Logistics' website, the group commits to visiting 50 schools located adjacent to its large construction sites at least once a year 'to talk about relevant aspects of construction health and safety education and training'.

The group signed the Armed Forces Covenant in 2019. The group provides members of the armed forces community with training and a recruitment pathway into the house-building and property sectors.

Protection of wildlife

The group is committed to protecting and enhancing biodiversity in the areas where it operates. For example, in Swansea, the group created and manages a purpose-built bat house. It also has a partnership with Staffordshire Wildlife Trust to create a living landscape along a major stretch of the River Trent.

Employee-led support

Employees take part in fundraising and volunteering activities. Events include the annual St Modwen Charity Run to raise money for LandAid.

Commercially led support

The group offers sponsorship opportunities for local sports clubs.

Applications

Contact the correspondent for more information.

Community contributions

We were unable to determine a figure for the group's total contributions in 2020/21.

Stagecoach Group Ltd

Community enterprise and social entrepreneurship, community services and development, education and training, general charitable purposes, health, housing and homelessness, mental health and well-being, rural communities

Company registration number: SC100764

Correspondent: Charity Committee, 10 Dunkeld Road, Perth, Perthshire PH1 5TW (email: charity@stagecoachgroup.com; website: www.stagecoachgroup.com)

Directors: Martin Griffiths; Ross Paterson; Ray O'Toole; Lynne Weedall; Scott Auty; Hamish Mackenzie; Miguel Costa; Florian Hubel (female: 13%; male: 88%).

Nature of business: Stagecoach is an international transport group that operates bus, coach and tram services.

Financial information

Year end	30/04/2022
Turnover	£1,176,500,000
Pre-tax profit	£39,300,000

Total employees: 36,000

Main locations: The group has operations in the UK, mainland Europe and North America.

Community involvement

As part of its sustainability strategy, Stagecoach Group Ltd has committed to donating 0.5% of its pre-tax profits to charitable and community causes each year.

Giving for Good

Support is given to local charities under the following themes:

- Promoting health and well-being
- Supporting young people, skills and employment
- Addressing loneliness and social isolation
- Increasing accessibility and opportunity

The group also has a monthly fund dedicated to providing one-off support to smaller, local charities.

At the time of writing, (October 2022), the group's charity partners were as follows:

- Missing People – a national organisation that offers assistance to people who run away/go missing and their families
- Trussell Trust – supports a nationwide network of food banks
- Roald Dahl's Marvellous Children's Charity – provides specialist nurses and support for children with serious illnesses
- Happy Days – provides respite breaks to children with terminal illnesses, disabilities or experience of abuse children as well as to young carers

Partnerships

In 2020, Stagecoach Group plc completed its three-year partnership with the Diana Award, with which it collaborated on the #BeNiceBus project, an anti-cyber bullying campaign. As part of the project, a bus donated by Stagecoach undertook a three-year educational tour of schools across the UK, delivering interactive sessions about cyber bullying to over 11,000 young people.

In 2020, Stagecoach Group plc launched a partnership with Greggs Foundation to support its work delivering breakfast clubs for young schoolchildren. Stagecoach helps to provide morning meals and refrigeration for food.

The group has worked in partnership with disability charities to improve its services. For example, Stagecoach North Scotland has a long-standing relationship with the RNIB and in 2019, the group signed a charter from RNIB that commits to meeting the needs of passengers with a visual impairment. As part of its commitment, the group participated in RNIB's 'Swap With Me' campaign in 2019, in which drivers took part in a training session to better understand the everyday travel experience of people with sight loss.

In-kind support

Donations

The group supports a variety of initiatives with donations of vehicles. For example, in support of Breast Cancer Awareness month in October 2019, Stagecoach donated buses to the 'Change + Check' breast cancer awareness campaign and the Prevent Breast Cancer initiative in Greater Manchester. The buses were used to advertise the benefits of regular breast checks and examinations.

Free transport

The group offers free transport to a wide range of individuals and organisations, such as the armed forces community, homeless people, health campaigns and local and national charities.

Stagecoach has committed to offering free travel every year for military and ex-military personnel on 11 and 14 November.

Employee-led support

Stagecoach Group Ltd employees take part in fundraising activities which the group supports.

Commercially led support

Stagecoach Group Ltd provides sponsorship to charity events.

Applications

Contact the correspondent for further information.

Community contributions

We were unable to determine a figure for the charitable contributions for 2020/21. However, the group has stated that it is committed to donating 0.5% of its pre-tax profits to charitable and community causes each year.

Standard Chartered plc

Community services and development, education and training, health

Company registration number: 966425

Correspondent: Standard Chartered Foundation, 1 Basinghall Avenue, London EC2V 5DD (tel: 020 7885 8888; email: sc.foundation@sc.com; website: www.sc.com/sustainability)

Directors: José Viñals; Bill Winters; Andy Halford; Shirish Apte; David Conner; Gay Huey Evans; Byron Grote; Christine Hodgson; Jackie Hunt; Robin Lawther; Maria Ramos; Phil Rivett; David Tang; Carlson Tong; Jasmine Whitbread (female: 40%; male: 60%).

Nature of business: Standard Chartered is a multinational banking and financial services company.

Financial information

Year end	31/12/2021
Turnover	£6,040,000,000
Pre-tax profit	£3,347,000,000

Total employees: 81,904

Main locations: The group operates globally in 63 countries. In the UK, the group is headquartered in London.

Community involvement

Standard Chartered works with local partners to deliver programmes that improve people's health and educational opportunities. In 2019, the Standard Chartered Foundation (Charity Commission no. 1184946) was established by the group to be the lead partner in delivering its philanthropic activities. Support is also provided through in-kind donations and employee volunteering.

Futuremakers

Futuremakers is a global fundraising initiative to support programmes helping the next generation to learn, earn and grow. In 2021, the group contributed £12.4 million through fundraising and group donations. The group is inviting disadvantaged young people to take part in community programmes to learn new skills and improve their chances of getting a job or starting their own business. The incentive includes the programmes Goal, which aims to equip adolescent girls with the skills they need to be economically successful, and Youth to Work, which aims to develop opportunities that support young people to become job-ready.

Seeing is Believing

Seeing is Believing is a partnership set up between Standard Chartered and the International Agency for the Prevention of Blindness in 2003. The programme aims to prevent and treat avoidable blindness and provide eye care in countries in Asia, Africa and the Middle East where there is a lack of quality, affordable eye care. The partnership came to an end in 2021.

In-kind support

All employees are offered three days' paid leave to volunteer each year. In 2019, employees volunteered for more than 31,600 days.

Employee-led support

Employees volunteer and fundraise for partner and local charitable organisations. In 2019 employees raised £1.24 million.

Financial education

The group provides financial education programmes which aim to build financial awareness among young people and micro and small businesses. Programmes are delivered on a voluntary basis by Standard Chartered employees.

Applications

The group's website states: 'If you are a non-profit organisation operating in the areas of education, employability or entrepreneurship, and you are interested in working with us, please email us at sc.foundation@sc.com.'

Community contributions

Cash donations worldwide	£28,100,000
Total contributions worldwide	£37,400,000

The 2021 annual report states that total community investment by the group amounted to £37.4 million, of which 57.7% was cash contributions totalling £28.1 million, 23.4% was employee time was valued at £10.13 million, and 5.34% was gifts in kind totalling £2.3 million. As is our practice, management costs and employee donations have been excluded from the total of £37.4 million. It was not specified how much was given in the UK.

The financial information has been converted from USD to GBP using the exchange rate at the time of writing (October 2022).

Stewarts Law LLP

General charitable purposes

Company registration number: OC329883

Correspondent: The Stewarts Foundation, 5 New Street Square, London EC4A 3BF (tel: 020 7822 8000; website: www.stewartslaw.com/about/social-impact)

Nature of business: Stewarts Law LLP (Stewarts) is a litigation-only law firm in the UK.

Financial information

Year end	30/04/2021
Turnover	£75,842,000

Total employees: 400

Main locations: The firm has offices in Leeds and London.

Community involvement

The firm awards grants to charities through its corporate charity, The Stewarts Law Foundation (Charity Commission no. 1136714).

The firm has also supported the Access to Justice Foundation for several years and plans to continue this partnership.

The firm also has a partnership with The Social Mobility Foundation, a charity whose aim is to make a practical improvement in social mobility for young people across the UK. It provides opportunities and networks of support for 16- and 17-year-olds who are unable to obtain them from their schools or families. Students on the foundation's programme spend a week in either the London or Leeds offices, learning about key legal concepts and receiving mentorship from a qualified lawyer.

Charity of the Year

Staff are asked to nominate and vote for the firm's annual charity partner. In the year 2020/21, the firm chose to support two charities which were Shooting Star's Children's Hospices and Forget Me Not Children's Hospices.

In-kind support

Stewarts Law LLP provides pro bono legal advice in areas including debt, pension insurance and human rights issues. The firm estimates that it provides over 10,000 hours of free legal support each year. Examples of organisations or programmes that Stewarts Law LLP supported in 2021 are:

- The Legal Service, through which the firm provides pro bono support for those affected by serious or life-threatening injuries
- The Access to Justice Foundation, the aim of which is to improve access to justice for the most vulnerable in society
- LawWorks, an organisation that supports lawyers to volunteer their professional skills to assist individuals and community groups who cannot afford to pay for legal help and who are unable to access legal aid or other forms of financial assistance
- The National Pro Bono Centre, a charity that acts as a hub for pro bono charities across the legal sector
- Justice, an all-party law reform and human rights organisation that carries out research and analysis to generate, develop and evaluate ideas for law reform
- The firm also accepts pro bono work from Advocates for International Development, a charity that empowers lawyers to use their skills to fight world poverty

Employee-led support

Employees fundraise and volunteer for their chosen charities, as well as for the firm's Charity of the Year. Stewarts Law LLP encourages participation in fundraising events.

Applications

Contact your local office for more information.

Corporate charity

The Stewarts Law Foundation (Charity Commission no. 1136714) – see entry on page 279.

Community contributions

Cash donations UK	£812,400
Total contributions worldwide	£812,400

According to the Stewarts Foundation annual accounts, £812,400 was donated by the firm to the foundation in 2021.

J Stobart and Sons Ltd

General charitable purposes, religion

Company registration number: 783738

Correspondent: CSR Team, Newlands Mill, Hesket Newmarket, Wigton, Cumbria CA7 8HP (tel: 01697 478261; email: info@jstobartandsons.co.uk; website: www.jstobartandsons.co.uk)

Directors: Linda Rigg; Peter Stobart; Richard Stobart; Ronald Stobart (female: 25%; male: 75%).

Nature of business: The manufacture and retail of animal feedstuffs.

Financial information

Year end	31/12/2020
Turnover	£17,170,000
Pre-tax profit	£278,300

UK employees: 17

Main locations: The company is based in Cumbria.

Community involvement

J. Stobart and Sons provides support through its corporate charity, The Stobart Newlands Charitable Trust (Charity Commission no. 328464). The trustees are directors and shareholders of J. Stobart and Sons Ltd, which is the source of almost all of the trust's income. This family trust makes up to 70 grants a year, nearly all on a recurring basis to Christian religious and missionary bodies.

Applications

Contact the correspondent for further information.

Corporate charity

The Stobart Newlands Charitable Trust (Charity Commission no. 328464) – see entry on page 279.

Community contributions

Cash donations UK	£875,000

In 2020, the company made donations of more than £875,000 to its corporate charity, The Stobart Newlands Charitable Trust.

Stoke City Football Club Ltd

🔍 Health, social welfare, sports and recreation

Company registration number: 99885

Correspondent: Adrian Hurst, Head of Community; Stoke City Community Fund; Stoke City Community Trust, bet365 Stadium, Stanley Matthews Way, Stoke-on-Trent ST4 4EG (tel: 01782 592252; website: www.stokecityfc.com/community)

Directors: Paul Wright; Robert Kenyon; Michael Potts; Keith Humphreys; Robert Lee; David Edwards; Michael Moors; Paul Doona; Ian Bailey (male: 100%).

Nature of business: Stoke City FC Ltd is a professional football club competing in the English Premier League.

Financial information

Year end	31/05/2021
Turnover	£40,280,000
Pre-tax profit	(£42,515,000)

Total employees: 234

Main locations: Stoke City FC headquarters is based in Stoke-on-Trent.

Community involvement

Stoke City FC's charity and community work is carried out by Stoke City Community Trust (Charity Commission no. 1104006). The club also provides in-kind support in the form of signed items, tickets and hospitality.

Stoke City Community Trust

This self-funding and financially independent charity was founded in 1989 and first registered in March 2004 under the name Stoke City Football in the Community. The trust's web page explains how it 'engages with people in many varied ways to stimulate an environment in which they can realise their potential and subsequently accomplish more in whatever walk of life they choose for personal and professional development'.

Stoke City Community Trust works in communities within its catchment areas (Stoke-on-Trent, Newcastle-under-Lyme, Staffordshire Moorlands, Stafford, South Staffordshire and parts of north-western Shropshire), using sport, particularly football, to connect with people of all ages, abilities and social backgrounds. Its programmes fall within the following focus areas: sports participation, education and lifelong learning, and health and well-being.

Stoke City Community Fund (not a registered charity)

This fund, which provides grants for small, community-based projects in Staffordshire and South Cheshire, is administered by the Stoke City Community Trust. Grants of between £100 and £1,000 are awarded to local groups, projects, community groups, self-help organisations, youth groups and charities whose work benefits their local communities. As the fund's funding criteria information describes, support can be given with 'anything from equipment to event costs, help towards rent or fixtures, sport or computer equipment'.

Monthly charity draw

The club holds a monthly draw into which individuals and charities can enter to win a charity donation. According to the Stoke City website, each month, the following prizes are available:

▷ A personalised signed shirt from a member of the first-team squad
▷ Ten pairs of tickets to a nominated fixture
▷ A behind-the-scenes ground tour of the bet365 Stadium for up to six people

Exclusions

The funding criteria for the Stoke City Community Fund state that grants cannot be awarded for:

▷ Groups other than community, self-help and voluntary groups
▷ Social enterprises (including CICs, IPS or Credit Unions except for non-core activity)
▷ Grant or loan schemes
▷ Political campaigning
▷ Cadets
▷ Statutory bodies
▷ A private profit making organisation/commercial organisation
▷ Any project that has already started
▷ For the sole benefit of any individual
▷ Specific religious worship
▷ Projects administered by a third party
▷ Projects that could be reasonably expected to secure finance by other means
▷ Non-charitable purposes' (groups do not have to be a charity to apply, however the project funded must have a charitable purpose i.e. benefit the wider community)

Applications

Stoke City Community Fund

An application form with funding criteria is available to download from the club's website (www.stokecityfc.com/community/fund). The Community Fund panel sits once a month and successful applicants are notified within two months of their application being submitted. A helpful list of FAQs included with the fund's downloadable application form informs that groups requiring further clarification regarding the eligibility of their project items can contact the club via email at communityfund@stokecityfc.com. It is also noted that, as the fund has limited funds, successful applicants do not always receive the entire amount applied for.

Monthly charity draw

There is an online application form available via the website (www.stokecityfc.com/community/charity). Applications must be made using the online form at least 24 hours before the last Friday of each month. Due to the volume of applications received, only winners are notified. Unsuccessful applications are not carried forward into future draws; however, unsuccessful applicants may reapply. The website further notes that 'All prizes relating to a fixture are valid for one game only and are subject to availability. Terms and conditions apply.'

Stoke City Community Trust

Enquiries can be directed to the trust by telephone, email or post using the contact information above.

Community contributions

The annual report and accounts for 2020/21 did not declare a figure for charitable donations.

STV Group plc

🔍 Community enterprise and social entrepreneurship, community services and development, education and training, social welfare

Company registration number: SC203873

Correspondent: STV Appeal Team, Pacific Quay, Glasgow G51 1PQ (tel: 0141 300 3000; email: enquiries@stv.tv; website: www.stvplc.tv)

Directors: Paul Reynolds; Simon Pitts; Lindsay Dixon; Simon Miller; Anne Marie Cannon; Ian Steele; David Bergg; Aki Mandhar (female: 38%; male: 63%).

Nature of business: STV Group is a Scottish media company.

Financial information

Year end	31/12/2021
Turnover	£144,500,000
Pre-tax profit	£20,100,000

Total employees: 463

Main locations: STV has locations across Scotland.

Community involvement

The group's main initiative is the STV Children's Appeal, which was launched in 2011 by STV and The Hunter Foundation.

The STV Children's Appeal aims to tackle child poverty in Scotland by providing practical help such as food and clothes, creating opportunities for training and employability, and offering social and emotional support. Since its inception, the appeal has raised over £29 million.

Every year, to commemorate the various fundraising efforts that have taken place, a telefundraiser is broadcast on STV. The group covers all overheads for the charity, as well as donating money raised from recycling old mobile phones directly to the STV Appeal.

Employee-led support

Employee fundraising

STV employees raise funds for the STV Appeal by organising and participating in various activities, including raffles, the 10x challenge, Kiltwalks and quizzes. The group offers matched funding for employee fundraising efforts; however, we were unable to determine the amount given through matched funding during the year.

Applications

The charity does not accept unsolicited applications. It works with specialists in the field of child poverty who advise the STV Children's Appeal on which projects require support.

Community contributions

Cash donations UK	£92,500
Total contributions UK	£846,500

STV Group and The Hunter Foundation fund the operating costs of the STV Appeal to ensure that all funds raised are applied to charitable projects.

According to the STV Appeal's 2021 accounts, the group provided £92,500 in cash donations and £754,000 in the form of in-kind donations.

Superdry plc

Community enterprise and social entrepreneurship, community services and development, education and training, general charitable purposes, social welfare

Company registration number: 7063562

Correspondent: The Sustainability Team, Unit 60, The Runnings, Cheltenham, Gloucestershire GL51 9NW (tel: 01242 578376; email: company. secretary@superdry.com; website: https:// corporate.superdry.com)

Directors: Peter Sjolander; Julian Dunkerton; Shaun Wills; Faisal Galaria; Georgina Harvey; Alastair Miller; Helen Weir; Ruth Daniels (female: 38%; male: 63%).

Nature of business: Supergroup is a UK clothing company and owner of the Superdry label.

Financial information

Year end	25/04/2021
Turnover	£556,100,000
Pre-tax profit	(£36,700,000)

Total employees: 2,822

Main locations: The group's head office is based in Cheltenham, but it has retail operations worldwide.

Community involvement

The group makes direct donations to its charity partner, as well as providing donations to causes supported by its staff through matched funding. The group is also interested in supporting young people in employment and in study, particularly in subjects related to fashion.

Partnerships

Superdry partners with national charities. The group provides financial assistance, as well as organising various fundraising efforts in aid of the chosen charity.

At the time of writing (October 2023), the group's charity partner was Oxfam. The charity is supported by the group's 'Give Back' scheme, whereby customers can return unwanted secondhand garments, to be donated to the charity.

Superdry School Days

The group works with local schools and colleges to provide work experience to students.

In-kind support

In addition to donating materials to university students, the group continues to donate faulty garments to Newlife, a charity for children with disabilities. These garments are de-branded and sold by Newlife, generating £247,000 in sales for the charity in 2021.

The group also donated 300,000 individual pieces of PPE to NHS frontline workers during the COVID-19 pandemic.

Employee-led support

The group provides matched funding to employees engaging in various fundraising activities.

Commercially led support

The group is a sponsor of the Invictus Games in The Hague, providing kits to teams from the UK, Netherlands, the US, Afghanistan and Iraq.

Applications

Contact the correspondent for more information.

Community contributions

Cash donations UK	£6,700
Total contributions worldwide	£253,700

According to its 2020/21 accounts, the group donated £247,000, raised by selling faulty returns, to its charity partner, Newlife. A further £6,700 was donated to Winston's Wish, a bereavement charity based in Wales.

Swansea City Football 2002 Ltd

Community enterprise and social entrepreneurship, education and training, health, sports and recreation

Company registration number: 4305508

Correspondent: Community Trust, The Liberty Stadium, Swansea SA1 2FA (tel: 01792 616607; email: info@ scfccommunitytrust.co.uk; website: www. swanscommercial.co.uk/community-trust)

Directors: Gareth Davies; Romie Chaudhari; Elizabeth Davies; Gareth Davies; Robert Henreich; Huw Jenkins; Jason Levien; Martin Morgan; Samuel Poter; Jacob Silverstein; Julian Winter (female: 18%; male: 82%).

Nature of business: Football club.

Financial information

Year end	31/07/2021
Turnover	£27,550,000
Pre-tax profit	£4,650,000

UK employees: 177

Main locations: The company is based in Swansea.

Community involvement

The club has a registered charity, Swansea City AFC Community Trust (Charity Commission no. 1126933), through which support is given to local communities in South West Wales in the areas of education, sports and health projects aimed at improving the lifestyles of local people and neighbourhoods.

In 2020/21, grants totalling £559,900 were awarded to community organisations, charities and grassroots sports teams across South West Wales.

Exclusions

Groups excluded from applying for grants include:
- Faith and political groups
- Counties outside Swansea, Pembrokeshire, Neath Port Talbot, Carmarthenshire and Ceredigion
- Individuals

Staff costs are not supported.

Applications

As the club delivers its community support through the associated trust, applicants are advised to contact the charity at the contact details given.

Community contributions

We were unable to determine a figure for Swansea City Football Club's charitable contributions for 2020/21.

John Swire & Sons Ltd

Education and training, general charitable purposes

Company registration number: 133143

Correspondent: The Swire Charitable Trust, Swire House, 59 Buckingham Gate, London SW1E 6AJ (tel: 020 7834 7717; email: info@scts.org.uk; website: www.swire.com/en/community/swire_trust.php)

Directors: Martin Cubbon; Baroness Lydia Dunn; Nicholas Fenwick; James Hughes-Hallett; Gordon McCallum; Barnaby Swire; John Swire; Merlin Swire; Samuel Swire; William Wemyss; Sean Pelling (female: 9%; male: 91%).

Nature of business: The principal activities of the group are transport, particularly aviation, shipping, cold storage and road transport, industrial and trading activities and property.

Financial information

Year end	31/12/2021
Turnover	£12,080,000,000
Pre-tax profit	£926,000,000

Total employees: 79,477

Main locations: The group's head office is in London. It also has operations in Hong Kong.

Community involvement

John Swire & Sons Ltd directs its charitable contributions through several charities connected to the group in the UK and Hong Kong.

The Swire Charitable Trust (Charity Commission no. 270726)

The trust is funded by the group and makes donations to charities across all sectors and regions that have been championed by Swire's stakeholders. It has three core funding programmes, in the fields of opportunity, heritage and the environment.

The Swire Educational Trust formally merged with The Swire Charitable Trust in 2015. The trust was established to sponsor graduate and postgraduate places in the UK for scholars across the world, with a particular interest in funding students from the communities in which the group operates.

This work continues today, with many of the trust's scholars attending Oxford, as well as London, Reading and Southampton universities.

Swire family charitable trusts

The following grant-making charities are also linked to the Swire family:

- The Adrian Swire Charitable Trust (Charity Commission no. 800493)
- John Swire 1989 Charitable Trust (Charity Commission no. 802142)
- Swire 2765 (Charity Commission no. 1150225)
- The SCS Trust (Charity Commission no. 1184007)

The Swire Charitable Trust website provides the following information on these charities:

> The donations made by these family trusts are driven by the Trustees and the Swire family. The trusts support the work of a wide range of charities, across all sectors, both in the UK and overseas and are managed by the same staff team as the Swire Charitable Trust. It is rare for donations to be made in response to unsolicited applications.

The Swire Chinese Language Foundation

The foundation was launched with a £25 million commitment from John Swire & Sons Ltd. It aims to 'widen the learning' of Mandarin Chinese in Britain through its 12 centres across the country.

Charitable activity in Hong Kong

The group also supports its Hong Kong-registered charity, The Swire Group Charitable Trust. It provides funding to non-profit organisations operating in Hong Kong and the Chinese mainland, in the fields of education, the arts and marine research.

The group also provides scholarships for Chinese students at several Hong Kong universities.

Applications

For further information on the Swire Charitable Trust, see the corporate charity entry.

Corporate charity

The Swire Charitable Trust (Charity Commission no. 270726) – see entry on page 279.

Community contributions

We were unable to determine a figure for the group's total charitable contributions.

Syncona Investment Management Ltd

Health

Company registration number: 10497864

Correspondent: The Syncona Foundation, 2nd Floor, 8 Bloomsbury Street, London WC1B 3SR (email: contact@synconaltd.com; website: www.synconaltd.com/sustainability)

Directors: Melanie Gee; Virginia Holmes; Rob Hutchinson; Kemal Malik; Gian Reverberi; Cristina Csimma; Julie Cherrington (female: 25%; male: 75%).

Nature of business: Syncona is an investment company focused on healthcare.

Financial information

Year end	23/06/2022
Turnover	£25,391,000
Pre-tax profit	£8,838,000

UK employees: 900

Main locations: The company has locations in London and Guernsey.

Community involvement

The company donates 0.35% of its net asset value to charitable causes. The majority of this donation is awarded to the company's charity, the Syncona Foundation. Separate donations are made to the Institute of Cancer Research, but from 2023 onwards, the company will donate exclusively to its foundation and the foundation will distribute the funds to its charity partners.

Applications

The company channels most of its giving through its corporate charity, which does not consider unsolicited applications.

Corporate charity

The Syncona Foundation (Charity Commission no. 1149202) – see entry on page 280.

Community contributions

| Cash donations UK | £4,200,000 |
| Total contributions worldwide | £4,200,000 |

According to the company's 2021/22 accounts, Syncona Investment Management Ltd made donations totalling £4.2 million. Of this total, £2.8 million was donated to The Syncona Foundation (Charity Commission No. 1149202). The remaining amount went to the Institute of Cancer Research and the company's other charitable activity.

TalkTalk Telecom Group Ltd

Education and training, health, technology

Company registration number: 7105891

Correspondent: The CSR Team, Soapworks, Ordsall Lane, Salford M5 3TT (tel: 020 3417 1000; email: concerns@talktalkplc.com; website: www.talktalkgroup.com/our-responsibilities)

Directors: Sir Charles Dunstone; Phil Eayres; Tristia Harrison; Jonathan Thackray (female: 25%; male: 75%).

Nature of business: TalkTalk provides television, telecommunications, internet access and mobile network services to businesses and consumers in the UK.

Financial information

Year end	31/03/2021
Turnover	£1,348,000,000
Pre-tax profit	£28,000,000

Total employees: 2,001

Main locations: The group operates across the UK.

Community involvement

TalkTalk supports various charities and causes by way of financial and in-kind donations. The group is particularly interested in causes relating to internet safety and health.

Partnerships

The group has a long-term partnership with Ambitious about Autism. In 2021, the group donated to the charity and was the lead partner on the Employ Autism project in the North West. The project connects business with young people with autism and supports the provision of paid work placements.

According to the group's 2021 annual report, the group also works in partnership with the Internet Watch Foundation, which aims to eliminate access to sexual abuse imagery online. Specifically, Talk Talk Telecom Group Ltd provides financial support for the foundation's hotline function, which is a means for those affected by sexual abuse imagery and members of the public to report the abuse.

TalkTalk also partners with local schools and universities to help deliver growth and skills initiatives, as well as several well-being initiatives in Salford.

In 2021, the group also made donations to the Salford Food Share network to help fund emergency food support and donated to support the production of personal protection equipment (PPE) during the COVID-19 pandemic.

Online safety and security

In 2014, the group joined forces with other internet companies to launch Internet Matters, a not-for-profit organisation which 'empowers parents and carers to keep children safe in the digital world'. The group works to bring in new partners to the organisation, as well as providing financial and in-kind support.

In-kind support

The group provides in-kind support to the organisation Internet Matters with free marketing for the organisation.

In 2021, as a response to the closure of schools due to the COVID-19 pandemic, the group donated laptops to Salford City College.

Employee-led support

Employees are encouraged to undertake voluntary work through the group's Give Something Back Day, allowing staff to take paid time off work to do so. Staff also engage in fundraising efforts for the group's charity partner, Ambitious about Autism.

The group has also established employee-led networks that partner with local organisations and promote volunteering opportunities. In 2021, employee networks engaged with the University of Salford to launch a mentorship scheme to minority ethnic students, as well as organising the TalkPride network fundraiser for Salford Pride and partnering with Women in Tech to collaborate with other organisations on International Women's Day.

Commercially led support

The group sponsors Salford City Football Club.

Applications

Contact the correspondent for more information.

Community contributions

Cash donations UK	£100,000

Talk Talk Telecom Group Ltd's annual report for 2021 states that the group's charitable donations during the year totalled £100,000.

Tata Steel Europe Ltd

Animal conservation, education and training, the environment, health, mental health and well-being, sports and recreation, STEM

Company registration number: 5957565

Correspondent: Nia Singleton, Community Liaison Manager, 30 Millbank, London SW1P 4WY (tel: 01639 871111; email: spukcommunity1@tatasteeleurope.com; website: www.tatasteeleurope.com)

Directors: Dr Henrik Adam; Thachat Narendran; Koushik Chatterjee; Om Prakash Bhatt (male: 100%).

Nature of business: Tata Steel Europe is involved in the manufacture and sale of steel products. It is a wholly owned subsidiary of Tata Steel Global Holdings Pte Ltd, registered in Singapore. The ultimate parent company is Tata Steel Ltd, incorporated in India.

Financial information

Year end	31/03/2022
Turnover	£8,876,000,000
Pre-tax profit	£796,000,000

Total employees: 20,400

Main locations: Tata Steel Europe has steelmaking sites in the UK and the Netherlands, and manufacturing plants across Europe. The group operates in 26 countries and has commercial offices in more than 35 countries across Europe. The global group, Tata Steel Ltd, operates in more than 100 countries spread across six continents.

Community involvement

Tata Steel Europe supports the communities in which it operates through its Community Partnership Programme, which awards donations to organisations under the themes of education, the environment and health and well-being. Support is also offered through education programmes, sponsorship and partnerships.

Community Partnership Programme

The group's Community Partnership Programme supports charitable and non-profit organisations in the communities in which it operates. The main theme of the programme is 'Future Generations'. The programme accepts applications for financial and in-kind (products and services) support. All funded projects should support 'Future Generations' and align with one of the following sub-themes:

- Education
- Environment
- Health and well-being

Partnerships

In the UK, the group partners with local sports clubs and organisations that work with young people, schools and community members to improve levels of activity, healthy eating, teamwork and behaviour.

Education programmes

The group proactively supports learning and education with programmes in the UK and Netherlands, particularly in the areas of science and technology. For example, in Wales more than 2,600 schoolchildren benefit from Tata Steel's education and learning initiatives every year. In South Yorkshire, the group partners with the Titans Community Foundation to deliver an annual event which uses sport as a way of encouraging young people to take an interest in maths and science.

The group also engages with young people, particularly girls, through programmes aimed at promoting employment opportunities in the steel and engineering sectors.

Environment

Tata Steel Europe protects and enhances biodiversity at its operating sites. In partnership with the Merseyside Ringing Group, the group invested in three man-made islands at its Shotton Works site to protect the largest colony of Common Tern birds in South Wales.

UK Steel Enterprise

UK Steel Enterprise is a subsidiary of Tata Steel Europe. It aims to help the economic regeneration of communities affected by changes in the steel industry by supporting small and medium sized businesses with finance and business premises. In addition, the company also offers in-kind and financial support to various community initiatives. For more information, see the website at www.ukse.co.uk/community/.

In-kind support

The group offers in-kind donations to charitable and non-profit organisations through its Community Partnership Programme.

Employee-led support

Employees of the group subsidiary, UK Steel Enterprise, often get involved in the local projects that the company supports. For example, they visit schools and universities and work in partnership with local development and enterprise agencies to offer advice.

Commercially led support

Sponsorship

In the UK, Tata Steel Europe continued to sponsor the Kids of Steel triathlon series, which it launched in partnership with the British Triathlon Federation in 2007, with the aim of introducing young people to the sport of triathlon. The group also sponsors the Kids of Steel Run every year, which it launched in Wales in 2014 following the success of the triathlon initiative.

Each year, the group sponsors the annual Tata Steel Chess Tournament in the Netherlands, which brings together the world's leading chess players and passionate amateurs with its grandmaster groups and amateur events.

Exclusions

The website notes that Tata Steel Europe is 'not able to offer support to commercial or profit-making organisations or individuals undertaking fundraising challenges (in particular to cover participation fees, expeditions or trips carried out by individuals in the context of fundraising)'.

Applications

Applications to the Community Partnership Programme can be made through the group's website: www.tatasteeleurope.com/en/sustainability/communities/community-partnership-programme. Applications are assessed by a panel of representatives from Tata Steel and the communities in which it operates.

Openings for corporate sponsorships are made available on the group's website.

Community contributions

We were unable to determine a figure for Tata Steel Europe's total contributions for 2021/22.

Tate & Lyle plc

Community services and development, education, education and training, food, health, mathematics, social welfare, STEM, work outside the UK

Company registration number: 76535

Correspondent: Community Relations Manager, 1 Kingsway, London WC2B 6AT (tel: 020 7257 2100; email: sustainability@tateandlyle.com; website: www.tateandlyle.com)

Directors: Dr Gerald Murphy, Nick Hampton; Dawn Allen; Kwok Wah Cheung; Patricia Corsi; Dr Isabelle Esser; Paul Forman; Lars Frederiksen; Anthony Hampton; Kimberley Nelson; Jane Stanley; Warren Tucker (female: 42%; male: 58%).

Nature of business: The group is a global provider of ingredients and solutions for the food and beverage industry. Its areas of expertise are beverages, dairy, soups, sauces and dressings.

Financial information

Year end	31/03/2022
Turnover	£1,375,000,000
Pre-tax profit	£42,000,000

Total employees: 4,522

Main locations: The group has operations worldwide and its head office is based in London.

Community involvement

The group's community involvement strategy focuses on the following three areas: health, education (particularly STEM) and food poverty. The group's 2021/22 annual report states that particular emphasis is given to supporting children and young people in these areas. Support is typically provided through partnerships, cash donations, scholarships and employee volunteering.

Locally, businesses within the group support community initiatives near to their facilities and offices. At a global level, the group works with a range of partners including, registered charities, educational institutions and non-governmental agencies. The group also partners with local schools and education foundations as part of its work providing educational support and mentorship opportunities.

In 2021/22, the group provided educational programmes to 33,000 children and young people across Latin America, the US and the UK.

STEM-focused grants

Each year, the group awards grants to teachers in order to support STEM-focused educational projects, which allow their students to explore careers in science, technology, engineering and mathematics. In addition to funding the projects, group employees are also encouraged to volunteer their time and expertise to help make the projects a success.

Support for Ukraine

In 2022, the group made donations to the British Red Cross Ukraine Relief Fund, while encouraging employees to give to its charity partners in Łódź, Poland, and Boleráz, Slovakia, where the group has an office and a plant respectively, to provide food, clothes, shelter and medicines for refugees arriving in both regions.

In-kind support

During 2021/22, the group provided 1.2 million meals to people in need.

Employee-led support

Employees from businesses across the group are encouraged to volunteer for projects with partner charities as well as with local community initiatives. In 2022, the group offered matched funding for any employee donations to support its charity partners in Poland and Slovakia, helping to support refugees arriving from Ukraine.

Applications

Queries regarding the group's CSR policies or charitable activities can be submitted using an online form on its website.

Community contributions

Cash donations worldwide	£548,000

In 2021/22, the group's cash community spend and charitable donations totalled £584,000. It was not possible to determine from the group's annual accounts what proportion of this figure was given in the UK. Funds were distributed in the following areas: health (33%); education (38%); hunger (29%).

Taylor Wimpey plc

Community enterprise and social entrepreneurship, community services and development, education and training, general charitable purposes, housing and homelessness, social welfare, sports and recreation

Company registration number: 296805

Correspondent: Charity Committee, Gate House, Turnpike Road, High Wycombe, Buckinghamshire HP12 3NR (tel: 01494 558323; email: See 'Applications'; website: www.taylorwimpey.co.uk/about-us/who-we-are/charity-and-local-support)

Directors: Irene Dorner; Jennie Daly; Chris Carney; Robert Noel; Lord Jitesh Gadhia; Scilla Grimble; Humphrey Singer; Mark Castle; Clodagh Moriarty (female: 44%; male: 56%).

Nature of business: Taylor Wimpey is a housebuilding company that develops residential homes in the UK and Spain.

Financial information

Year end		31/12/2021
Turnover		£4,284,900,000
Pre-tax profit		£679,600,000

UK employees: 5,271

Total employees: 5,358

Main locations: The company has 24 regional businesses across the UK, with a head office in High Wycombe. The company also has operations in Spain.

Community involvement

The company supports local, regional and smaller national charities, particularly those local to its operations, as well as smaller community groups in local areas.

The company's Charity and Community Support Policy outlines the following priorities for its charitable activities:

- Projects which promote aspiration and education in disadvantaged areas
- Intervening and improving homeless situations for seriously economically disadvantaged groups in the UK
- Local projects that have a direct link with our regional businesses and developments

The policy also states that contributions are not limited to financial support alone, but also include employee volunteering time.

Partnerships

Taylor Wimpey has several partnerships with national charities as well as local charity partners across the UK. The company's six national charity partners are: CRASH (the construction and property industry's charity for the homeless), Crisis, End Youth Homelessness, the Foundations Independent Living Trust, St Mungo's and the Youth Adventure Trust.

National charity partners are selected by the company's Charity Committee and donations to these charities are overseen by the committee. Meanwhile, regional charities are selected by the company's regional businesses. Each of these businesses has a discretionary charity budget from which it makes Community Chest grants to support local organisations. Past beneficiaries of these grants have included charities, museums, hospices, sport teams and volunteer groups.

Community development

At sites where the company will be working over a long time period, it may set up Community Development Trusts to support long-term activities or fund community development workers. Through the trusts, the company organises community events and supports the formation of community groups.

In-kind support

Regional divisions in the company often provide in-kind support to schools, such as career workshops, donations of building materials and free visits to the company's construction sites. Regional divisions also distribute a book designed to educate young children on the housebuilding process.

Employee-led support

Volunteering

Taylor Wimpey's volunteering policy allows employees to take up to two days' paid leave per year to volunteer.

Fundraising

A notable example of employee fundraising in 2021 was the annual Taylor Wimpey Challenge, organised in partnership with the Youth Adventure Trust (YAT), a charity which provides adventure camps and day activities for vulnerable young people. The company-wide fundraising event saw 169 staff members take on hiking and biking challenges across the Brecon Beacons. The event raised £103,000, of which £75,000 was donated to the YAT and the rest to a selection of charities local to Taylor Wimpey's regional businesses.

Graduate Challenge

Participants of the company's graduate programme take part in a charity project each year, offering their business experience to help one of the company's charity partners. In 2021, the company's graduates entered The Prince's Trust 'Million Makers' challenge to raise money for vulnerable children and young people. Through two of the challenge's initiatives, the graduates raised £27,000.

The Youth Adventure Trust Housebuilder's Challenge

In 2021, 15 teams from Taylor Wimpey plc entered the Youth Adventure Trust's 'Housebuilder's Challenge' raising over £47,000 for the trust.

Commercially led support

In 2019 and 2020, the company took part in The Festival of the Girl event, a non-profit initiative that aims to inspire and educate girls aged 7–11. In 2020, the company donated £1,000 towards the running of the initiative and employees produced an animation that highlighted career opportunities in the housing industry. In 2019, the company donated £500 and employees ran a stall at the event.

The company's regional businesses often sponsor sports teams and cover the costs of sports kits as part of their commitment to working in partnership with local communities.

Exclusions

Support is generally not given to larger national charities, major events that are able to attract large corporate donors or elicit a national response, or political parties. The company prefers to select causes where employees can be directly involved, rather than simply providing financial assistance. The company's 'Donations Policy' and 'Charity and Community Support Policy' are both available to view on its website.

Applications

Requests for support can be submitted using an electronic form on the company's website at: www. taylorwimpey.co.uk/why-choose-us/charity-and-local-support.

Community contributions

Cash donations worldwide	£945,000

In 2021, the company donated £945,000 to various charities and local community causes, the majority of which were in the UK. This figure does not include funds raised by Taylor Wimpey employees which totalled £161,000 in 2021.

Tesco plc

Community services and development, education and training, emergency appeals/aid, emergency response/relief, the environment, food, general charitable purposes, health, housing and homelessness, medical research, social welfare, sports and recreation, work outside the UK

Company registration number: 445790

Correspondent: Group Corporate Responsibility Committee, Tesco House, Shire Park, Kestrel Way, Welwyn Garden City, Hertfordshire AL7 1GA (tel: 0800 505555; email: cr.enquiries@uk.tesco.com; website: www.tescoplc.com)

Directors: John Allan; Ken Murphy; Imran Nawaz; Melisa Bethell; Bertran Bodson; Thierry Garnier; Stewart Gilliland; Steve Golsby; Byron Grote; Simon Patterson; Alison Platt; Lindsay Pownall; Kate Whitworth (female: 31%; male: 69%).

Nature of business: Tesco plc is a British multinational groceries and general merchandise retailer. The group also provides retail banking and insurance services through its subsidiary, Tesco Bank, mobile services through Tesco Mobile, and petrol station services.

Financial information

Year end		26/02/2022
Turnover		£61,344,000,000
Pre-tax profit		£2,033,000,000

Total employees: 354,744

Main locations: Tesco plc operates in the UK and the Republic of Ireland,

Czech Republic, Hungary, Poland, Slovakia, Thailand and Malaysia. The group's headquarters is in Welwyn Garden City, Hertfordshire.

Community involvement

The group supports causes (including health, children and young people, poverty, social welfare and the environment), through financial donations and in-kind support. The group works with several charity partners on different initiatives. Employee 'Community Champions' support local community projects by providing information and access to fundraising opportunities. Tesco's community grant programmes in the UK, the Republic of Ireland and Central Europe provide funding for local community projects voted for by customers.

Community Champions

Tesco Community Champions are employees who are responsible for engagement with their local community. They are responsible for co-ordinating activities such as local community events and promoting the group's charitable activities. Community Champions work with local charities to organise in-store activities, including bag packing and store collections. Each store has a budget for community donations, which can be used to respond to requests from local charities.

The store collections scheme allows charities to collect money or food at the front of Tesco stores.

Partnerships

In January 2018, Tesco launched a five-year charity partnership with Cancer Research UK, Diabetes UK and British Heart Foundation with the aim of promoting healthier living, as well as supporting the prevention and cure of cancer, diabetes and heart disease.

In 2020, Tesco Ireland extended its partnership with Temple Street Children's Hospital for another year. The partnership began in 2014 and finished in 2021, having raised €7 million (£6.1 million as at October 2022) for the hospital to help it purchase life-saving equipment for the treatment of sick children.

Since 2007, the group has worked with the charity British Red Cross, supporting it through both financial and in-kind donations, bucket collections and employee fundraising. Through this partnership, Tesco is also a member of the Disaster Relief Alliance which aims to provide preventative support before emergencies occur. In 2022, the group appealed for donations to the war in Ukraine, with customers and colleagues raising £4 million for the British Red Cross Ukraine Appeal.

Tesco partners with WWF (World Wide Fund for Nature) with the aim of halving the environmental impact of the average UK shopping basket. To do this, the partnership focuses on helping customers to eat more sustainably, restoring nature in food production and eliminating waste.

Tesco is also a corporate partner of the National Emergencies Trust and plays an active role in the charity's governance.

In-kind support

Tesco is committed to tackling food waste. In the UK and Ireland, the group continued to support FareShare and the Trussell Trust in 2021/22 through its food redistribution programmes. The group also delivers food donation programmes in Central Europe and Asia. In 2021/22, the group donated 52.6 million meals across all of its partnerships and schemes related to food redistribution.

Surplus Food Donation Scheme

Through the 'Community Food Connection' programme, Tesco partners with FareShare and the Irish social enterprise FoodCloud to redistribute surplus food from its stores to charities and community groups. Using the FareShare FoodCloud app, stores alert charities to the amount of surplus food they have at the end of each day. This food can then be collected by the charities free of charge and turned it into meals for those in need. According to the group's website, more than 2 million meals are donated to 4,000 charities and community groups each month.

Food collection programme

Through its food collection programme run in partnership with The Trussell Trust and FareShare, Tesco encourages customers to donate long-life food to charity using its in-store food collection points. Following each food collection, Tesco tops-up its customers' donations by 20%. Customers can also donate using their Tesco club card points.

In addition, across the UK Tesco has community rooms on its premises, which it makes available for various community classes and activities. Contact your local Community Champion for more information.

Employee-led support

Employees take part in fundraising events for Tesco's charity partners. Employees can also use two half-day shifts to volunteer for a local food bank or local group of their choice.

Tesco has partnered with Cancer Research UK's Race for Life since 2002. Over that time, 400,000 employees have taken part in Race for Life events and raised over £55 million for Cancer Research UK.

Commercially led support

Community grants programmes

Tesco supports local community and voluntary projects in the UK, Ireland and Central Europe via three grants programmes – Bags of Help, Tesco Community Fund and You Choose, We Help, respectively. The funds are raised through the sale of 'bags for life'. In 2021/22 the group distributed over £89.2 million and supported more than 49,000 local projects through these programmes.

Bags of Help (UK)

Bags of Help is a grants programme administered by the charity Groundwork UK. Grants are available for community groups and charities (including schools, health bodies, parish/town councils, local authorities and social housing providers) in England, Scotland and Wales. Projects range from improving community buildings and outdoor spaces, to new equipment, training coaches and volunteers, and hosting community events. Customers can vote for the projects they want Tesco to support.

Buy One to Help a Child campaign

In 2021/22, Tesco plc donated to its charity partner FareShare through its 'Buy One to Help a Child' campaign, where the group gave a donation for every piece of fruit and vegetables purchased across its stores and online. This provided FareShare with 3 million meals' worth of food to help charities and community groups.

Exclusions

Individuals and profit-making organisations are not eligible to apply for the Bags of Help grants. According to the Bags of Help website (https://tescobagsofhelp.org.uk), the following projects are also ineligible:

- Work that has already taken place
- Political donations
- Fundraising activities or challenges (e.g. costs for a sky dive etc.)
- Running costs and organisation overheads
- Conferences or seminars
- Activities which collect funds for redistribution to other charities or individuals
- Overseas appeals
- Expeditions or overseas travel
- Promotion of a religious or political cause
- Marketing promotions
- Research projects
- Projects or activities that the state has a legal obligation to provide

Tesco Express stores do not take bookings for charity collections.

Applications

To request support from a local store, charities should contact their local

Community Champion. This includes requests for donations and to arrange a bag packing session. A list of contact details can be downloaded from the website: www.tescoplc.com/sustainability/publications/policies/downloads.

Applications for donations of surplus food from Tesco should be made through FareShare FoodCloud – charities can register their interest here: www.FareShare.org.uk/FareShare-foodcloud.

To request permission to do a store collection, register online through the Taste At Tesco website – www.tasteattesco.com/charity-registration.aspx. To request a December booking, contact your local Community Champion.

For further information on eligibility and applications for the Bags of Help (UK) grant, visit https://tescobagsofhelp.org.uk/home/community-apply-bags-help-grant. Check the website for the current theme of funding. Queries can be sent to tescobagsofhelp@groundwork.org.uk.

To nominate a good cause to be shortlisted for the Tesco Community Fund (Ireland), request a nomination form at your local store.

For any other enquiries, contact the Group Corporate Responsibility Committee at cr.enquiries@uk.tesco.com, or email customer services at customer.service@tesco.co.uk.

Community contributions

We were unable to determine a figure for Tesco plc's corporate giving in 2021/22.

Thales UK Ltd

Community services and development, education and training, the environment, health, humanitarian aid, STEM

Company registration number: 868273

Correspondent: Mike Seabrook, Company Secretary and Director of Ethics, 350 Longwater Avenue, Green Park, Reading, Berkshire RG2 6GF (tel: 0118 943 4500; email: ethics.cr@thalesgroup.com; website: www.thalesgroup.com/en/global/corporate-responsibility/thales-solidarity)

Directors: Michael Seabrook; Alexandra Cresswell; Paul Gosling; Ewen McCrorie; Christopher Shaw; Suzanne Stratton; Lynne Watson (female: 29%; male: 71%).

Nature of business: Thales Group is a global technology business operating in the fields of aerospace, defence, digital security, transport and space, across both civil and military environments. Thales UK Ltd designs, manufactures and exports sonar systems, military air training solutions, electronic warfare systems, missile systems and unmanned air systems. The company's immediate parent company is Thales Holdings UK plc, and the ultimate parent company is Thales SA, incorporated in France.

Financial information

Year end	31/12/2021
Turnover	£948,000,000
Pre-tax profit	£45,970,000

UK employees: 6,500

Main locations: The group has operations in 56 countries and is based in France. In the UK, the group's main locations are Belfast, Bristol, Cheadle Heath, Crawley, Doncaster, Glasgow, Leicester, London, Reading and Templecombe.

Community involvement

In 2019 the group launched the Thales Solidarity programme, a group-wide CSR strategy aimed at providing support and finance to projects in the fields of education and professional inclusion, digital citizenship and environmental protection. This programme supports projects local to the group's operating sites worldwide through the Thales Solidarity Fund (formerly the Thales Foundation). Meanwhile, The Thales Charitable Trust (Charity Commission no. 1000162) supports a range of charities in the UK, particularly those focusing on child health and education.

Thales Solidarity Fund

The group replaced its foundation with the Thales Solidarity Fund – an endowment fund aimed at supporting projects that leverage innovation and technology to serve three focus areas:

▶ Education and professional integration
▶ Digital citizenship
▶ Environmental protection

The fund finances two types of projects. Firstly, community engagement projects and initiatives that are selected by employees via an annual call for projects. Secondly, one- to three-year 'pilot projects', described on the website as projects that aim to 'prototype or scale up an initiative, offers innovative solutions to critical challenges and have a potential for international development'. According to the website, in 2022, the Thales Solidarity Fund supported 29 projects in 22 countries.

Education

In the UK, Thales delivers educational programmes and activities in schools and universities to encourage engagement with STEM subjects. To deliver these programmes, Thales works in partnership with various organisations, such as Teach First and Primary Engineer, a not-for-profit that designs engineering curriculums to encourage children and young people towards STEM careers.

Armed Forces Covenant

In the UK, Thales is a signatory of the Armed Forces Covenant which demonstrates the company's commitment to employing and supporting the armed forces community.

Partnerships

According to Thales UK 2021 annual report, the company nominated Asthma + Lung UK as its charity partner for the year 2022. The company fundraised for the charity and for the British Heart Foundation.

In-kind support

Education

In the UK, Thales offers its own STEM resources to primary and secondary schools, including handbooks, brochures and presentations.

Employee-led support

The Thales Solidarity Fund supports projects proposed by employees. The fund has a network of employee delegates which promote its activities, as well as ambassadors who encourage employees to volunteer for community projects and initiatives. The following information is taken from the group's website:

> The Thales Solidarity programme makes it easy for employees to get involved in a variety of ways through its online engagement platform. The programme aims to meet the needs of partner organisations by connecting them with employees who wish to contribute their knowledge, expertise, time, generosity or simply their energy.

Commercially led support

In the UK, the company sponsors several charity events each year, including the Railway Children charity's annual ball and the Military Mind Corporate Symposium organised by Combat Stress. Also, through its partnership with Primary Engineer, the company sponsors the Primary Engineer Leaders Award, a school-based engineering project run by the charity.

Each year, Thales attends the Big Bang UK Young Scientists and Engineers Fair in Birmingham, as well as smaller Big Bang events across the UK. Here, the company showcases its STEM activities and materials.

Applications

Contact the correspondent for more information on Thales' CSR activities.

For further information on the Thales Solidarity Fund, visit the website or email solidarity@thalesgroup.com.

Corporate charity

The Thales Charitable Trust (Charity Commission no. 1000162) – see entry on page 281.

Community contributions

Cash donations UK	£175,000

According to Thales UK 2021 annual report, it donated £175,000 to charitable organisations during the year.

Thames Water Ltd

Community services and development; education and training; the environment; health; humanitarian aid; money and debt advice; social welfare; water, sanitation and hygiene (WASH); work outside the UK

Company registration number: 2366623

Correspondent: The Community Investment Team, Clearwater Court, Vastern Road, Reading RG1 8DB (email: community.investment@thameswater.co.uk; website: www.thameswater.co.uk)

Directors: Ian Marchant; Alastair Buchanan; Nick Land; Ian Pearson; Jill Shedden; David Waboso; Michael McNicholas; Paul Donovan; John Morea (female: 11%; male: 89%).

Nature of business: Thames Water is responsible for public water supply and wastewater treatment.

Financial information

Year end	31/03/2021
Turnover	£2,176,800,000
Pre-tax profit	(£850,500,000)

Total employees: 7,000

Main locations: The company's head office is in Reading. The Thames Water area covers parts of: London, Surrey, Kent, Surrey, Berkshire, Gloucestershire, Oxfordshire, Buckinghamshire and Wiltshire. A map of the region is available on the website.

Community involvement

Support is mainly provided through funding to charities in the Thames Water area which have a link to water and the environment or water and healthy living.

Charitable support: small grants programme

Charities within the Thames Water supply area can apply for charitable support from the company. The Charities Committee guidelines state the following:

Whilst we are a large organisation, we do not have unlimited funds. The Charities Committee has therefore agreed to support organisations or projects where

there is a good link to our core business of water supply and wastewater treatment which falls under the following criteria:

Water and the environment – Our focus is on enhancing the quality of life within urban areas by improving open spaces, especially natural environments that are adjacent to water – for example rivers or canals. By 'environment' we mean the environment in which people live as well as the natural environment.

Water and healthy living – We support projects that encourage individuals to look after their own health and encourage a healthy lifestyle through the benefits of water

Full eligibility criteria can be found on the company's 'Investing in our communities' web page. In 2021, Thames Water provided support to The Wild Trust through this programme.

Previous beneficiaries have included:

- **The Ahoy Centre, London** – the donation enabled the purchase of additional boatbuilding materials for the water sports-based charity's apprenticeships
- **The KIDS' Adventure Playground, London** – with the grant, the charity KIDS was able to organise educational and fun trips to help children with disabilities in Hackney connect with their local river, discover wildlife and learn more about water pollution
- **Surrey Care Trust, Woking** – the company provided funding for the Surrey Care Trust's Swingbridge boat initiative, which gives young people and vulnerable adults the opportunity to crew boats, take part in conservation projects and enjoy boat trips

Community speakers

The company has several community speakers, who are available to speak to community groups about what the company does and how to be more water efficient.

Charity partnership

The company has a long-term partnership with WaterAid which has seen over £35 million donated to the charity through customer and employee fundraising since 1981. In 2021, Thames Water raised £55,000 for WaterAid.

The company also works in partnership with a range of other charities to deliver projects and programmes, such as Age UK, Citizens Advice, RSPB, Step Change, The Wildlife Trusts and WWF (World Wide Fund for Nature).

Schools

Thames Water has a school education programme, which includes education centres, talks in schools, online resources, mentoring and work experience placements. According to its 2020/21 sustainability report, 6,796

students benefitted from this programme during the year.

Thames Water Trust Fund (Charity Commission no.1126714)

According to the company's website, the Thames Water Trust Fund provides grants for third-sector organisations which offer Thames Water customers long-term support and free debt advice, such as Citizens Advice. It also provides grants for essential household goods, including washing machines, fridges and beds, to customers whose long-term circumstances suggest they will not be able to afford these items.

In-kind support

The company gives employees two volunteering days per year.

Employee-led support

Employees are encouraged to fundraise and volunteer for charitable organisations. The company's matched funding scheme matches employees' fundraising efforts up to a maximum of £2,000 for registered charities. There is also a payroll-giving scheme in place. The company adds an extra 10% to employees' combined donations.

In 2020/21, employees volunteered for 729 hours to support those who were shielding due to the COVID-19 pandemic. In addition, employees and customers also fundraised for the company's long-term charity partner WaterAid, raising £55,000 for the charity during the year.

Exclusions

According to the grant guidelines, the following are not supported:

- Political and sectarian activities
- Organisations with a racial or religious bias
- Individuals fundraising for national charities
- Individuals fundraising for personal challenges (non-charitable)
- Salaries/project management fees, etc
- Overseas charities other than our principal charity, WaterAid
- Projects outside of the Thames Water region

Applications

Application forms for charitable support can be downloaded from the company's website and should be returned by email or post to: Community Investment Team, Thames Water, 2nd Floor East, Clearwater Court, Reading, RG1 8DB. The committee meets quarterly; application deadlines can be found on the website.

Community speaker request forms can also be downloaded from the website.

Community contributions

Cash donations UK	£400,000

According to its 2020/2 sustainability report, Thames Water donated £400,000 to 52 charitable projects through its Community Relief Fund.

the7stars UK Ltd

🔍 Housing and homelessness, social welfare

Company registration number: 5387218

Correspondent: the7stars foundation, Floor 6–9, Bush House, North West Wing, 57 Aldwych, London WC2B 4PJ (tel: 020 7436 7275; email: info@ the7starsfoundation.co.uk; website: https://the7starsfoundation.co.uk)

Directors: Jennifer Biggam; Gareth Jones; Nicholas Maddison; Liam Mullins; Rhiannon Murphy; Helen Rose; Rhys Williams (female: 43%; male: 57%).

Nature of business: the7stars is an independent media agency.

Financial information

Year end	31/03/2022
Turnover	£389,030,000
Pre-tax profit	£5,100,000

UK employees: 235

Main locations: The company's head office is in London.

Community involvement

The company provides support through its corporate charity, the7stars Foundation (Charity Commission no. 1168240), to which it makes cash donations. The foundation supports disadvantaged young people under the age of 16, particularly those in need due to homelessness, addiction and abuse and those who are young carers.

Applications

See the corporate charity entry for more information.

Corporate charity

the7stars Foundation (Charity Commission no. 1168240) – see entry on page 281.

Community contributions

Cash donations UK	£241,800

According to the company's 2021/22, it donated £241,800 to charities in the UK during the financial year.

Timpson Group Ltd

🔍 Community services and development, education and training, social welfare

Company registration number: 2339274

Correspondent: CSR Team, Timpson House, Claverton Road, Wythenshawe, Manchester M23 9TT (website: www. timpson-group.co.uk)

Directors: Sir John Timpson; James Timpson; Stephen Robertson; Paresh Majithia; Sarah Dunning (female: 20%; male: 80%).

Nature of business: Timpson is a retail services provider that specialises in shoe repairs, key cutting and engraving, as well as dry cleaning and photo processing.

Financial information

Year end	25/09/2021
Turnover	£212,200,000
Pre-tax profit	£24,530,000

Total employees: 3,950

Main locations: The group operates stores across the UK.

Community involvement

The group's charitable activities are delivered through the Timpson Foundation (not a registered charity) and the Alex Timpson Trust (Charity Commission no. 1174098). The group also makes charitable donations to a selection of charities each Christmas.

The Timpson Foundation

The Timpson Foundation specialises in the recruitment of marginalised groups within society, particularly ex-offenders. The group's website states that approximately 10% of its workforce is made up of individuals with a criminal conviction. Timpson has also invested in several training academies which are located within prison grounds. The academies offer practical training to better prepare individuals for employment upon release. The group also offers prisoners who are eligible for release on temporary license (ROTL) the opportunity to gain work experience in its stores.

Free Jobs scheme

Through Timpson's Free Jobs scheme, employees are encouraged to provide services such as punching a hole for a belt or stitching a shoe, free-of-charge, but request that customers make an in-store charitable contribution. The scheme has previously helped to raise over £4 million for children's charities. Now, funds raised by the scheme will be used to support the work of the Alex Timpson Trust. In 2020/21 customers donated a total of £190,000 to the charity.

Oak View Academy

Since 2014, the Timpson Foundation has provided financial and mentoring support to Oak View Academy, a small primary school in Winsford. Before becoming an academy, the school was the second worst-performing primary in England. The Timpson Foundation provided a bursary to help the school relaunch. The funding helps to provide a free breakfast club, interactive

educational workshops and Spanish lessons.

Employee-led support

Employees are encouraged to fundraise for local charities and the group matches their efforts up to £250.

Commercially led support

Three guidebooks on attachment written by Sir John Timpson, based on his experience as a foster carer, are available free of charge from any Timpson, Max Spielmann, or Johnsons the Cleaners store.

Applications

Contact the correspondent for further information.

Community contributions

Cash donations UK	£399,000

According to its 2020/21 annual report, the group's charitable contributions totalled £399,000. Of this, £259,000 was contributed to the Timpson Foundation and academies, £75,000 was awarded to the Alex Timpson Trust and £60,000 was given in charitable donations. An additional £190,000 was raised by customers through the group's Free Jobs scheme; however, we have not included this amount in the grant total.

TJX UK

🔍 Community services and development, the environment, health

Company registration number: 3094828

Correspondent: CSR Team, 73 Clarendon Road, Watford, Hertfordshire WD17 1TX (tel: 01923 473000; website: www.tkmaxx.com/uk/en/about-tkmaxx/corporate-responsibility/communities)

Directors: Susan Beaumont; Alicia Kelly; Lisa Schwartz; David Averill; Erica Farrell; John Klinger (female: 33%; male: 67%).

Nature of business: The main activity of TJX UK is the retail of brand-name merchandise through T.K. Maxx and Homesense stores, as well as the TKMaxx.com website. TJX UK's immediate parent company is TJX Europe Ltd and its ultimate parent company and controlling party is The TJX Companies, Inc., incorporated in Delaware, USA.

Financial information

Year end	29/01/2022
Turnover	£3,309,100,000
Pre-tax profit	£14,400,000

Total employees: 27,000

Main locations: There are T.K. Maxx stores nationwide and Homesense stores in England, Scotland and Wales. See the store search facility for details of T.K.

Maxx and Homesense locations (www. tkmaxx.com/store-locator/page/ storelocator).

Community involvement

Globally, TJX's community strategy focuses on helping families and children succeed and thrive in four main impact areas:

- Fulfilling critical basic needs
- Providing education and training
- Supporting research and care for people with life-threatening illnesses
- Empowering women

It does this in three ways:

- Giving through its foundations in the USA, Canada and Europe
- Cause marketing and in-store fundraising
- Employee volunteering, fundraising and giving

In the UK, TJX UK supports its communities by partnering with local and national charities. The company wishes to help vulnerable children and young people achieve their full potential. Support is also provided through The T.K. Maxx and Homesense Foundation (Charity Commission no. 1162073).

Recently, TJX has broadened its global giving priorities to provide more direct support to Black communities. In the UK, the group has supported Access UK, Runnymede and the Stephen Lawrence Charitable Trust.

Partnerships

Cancer Research UK – as the charity's biggest corporate supporter, the company and its customers raise money to support research into cancers that affect young people.

The Prince's Trust – since 2013 the company has supported the trust's Get into Retail programme.

The environment

Through a partnership with Neighbourly, the company is supporting environmental and clean-up initiatives in UK communities.

Commercially led support

Comic Relief

In aid of Comic Relief, TJX UK stores sell specially designed t-shirts and homeware products from which a portion of the profits are donated.

Applications

Contact your local store for more information.

Corporate charity

The T.K. Maxx and Homesense Foundation (Charity Commission no. 1162073) – see entry on page 281.

Community contributions

Cash donations UK		£4,400,000

TJX UK's annual report states that 'company, community fund donations and fundraising activities came to the value of £4.4 million'.

Tottenham Hotspur Ltd

Education and training, health, sports and recreation

Company registration number: 1706358

Correspondent: CSR Team, Lilywhite House, 782 High Road, Tottenham, London N17 0BX (tel: 0344 499 5000; website: www.tottenhamhotspur.com)

Directors: Matthew Collecott; Donna-Maria Cullen; Daniel Levy; Jonathan Turner (female: 25%; male: 75%).

Nature of business: Tottenham Hotspur FC is a professional football club.

Financial information

Year end	30/06/2021
Turnover	£360,410,000
Pre-tax profit	(£80,190,000)

Total employees: 672

Main locations: The club's community activities are mainly delivered in North London, especially in the Haringey and Enfield districts.

Community involvement

The club's charitable activities are mostly directed through its charity, the Tottenham Hotspur Foundation (Charity Commission no. 1113725), which delivers a wide range of health, education, sport and employability programmes across North London.

Partnerships

The club's official charity partner is Noah's Ark Children's Hospice, North London's only 'hospice-at-home' service offering support to children and young people with life-limiting or life-threatening illnesses and their families. The partnership aims to raise awareness of the charity's work and drive the recruitment of volunteers.

In partnership with Kick Racism Out of Football, the club participates in a week of action aimed at eliminating racism from football permanently. It also supports the anti-racism charity Show Racism the Red Card.

Spurs Wishes

The Spurs Wishes initiative was launched in 2011 and exists separately to the club's foundation. It brings together the club's staff, management and players to assist fans with terminal illnesses by giving them memorable experiences.

Tottenham Tribute Trust (Charity Commission no. 1094092)

The Tottenham Tribute Trust was set up in 2002 to help former players and staff of the club who have fallen on difficult times. For more information, see www. tottenhamtt.org

In-kind support

The group makes donations of Tottenham Hotspur memorabilia to local registered charities, particularly those in the Haringey and Enfield districts. Any spare kits or equipment is given to the Tottenham Hotspur Foundation.

Exclusions

The club's website states the following:

Support for significant campaigns and/or the victims of a major national or international disaster are dealt with by the Club centrally and (the club) do not, therefore, accept individual donation requests for such causes

More information on what the club is unable to support can be found on the website.

Applications

Contact the correspondent for further information.

Spurs Wishes

Appeals to Spurs Wishes can be made using an application form on the club's website.

Community contributions

Cash donations worldwide	£156,400

According to the group's annual report and accounts for 2020/21, the group made cash donations totalling £156,400 to international, national and local charities during the year. The accounts also note that the group 'continues to make contributions with a value in excess of £0.5 million per annum' to the Tottenham Hotspur Foundation; however, a figure was not provided. We were therefore unable to determine a figure for the group's total charitable contributions.

Town Centre Securities plc

Community enterprise and social entrepreneurship, community services and development

Company registration number: 623364

Correspondent: CSR Team, Town Centre House, The Merrion Centre, Leeds, West Yorkshire LS2 8LY (tel: 0113 222 1234; email: info@tcs-plc.co.uk; website: https://tcs-plc.co.uk)

Directors: Edward Ziff; Ben Ziff; Michael Ziff; Ian Marcus; Paul Huberman; Jeremy Collins; Stuart MacNeill (male: 100%).

Nature of business: Town Centre Securities plc is a property investment and development company.

Financial information

Year end	30/06/2022
Turnover	£14,520,000
Pre-tax profit	£11,010,000

Total employees: 127

Main locations: The group's head office is in Leeds and it owns properties across the UK.

Community involvement

The group supports a wide range of local charitable causes with a focus on children and young adults.

The group has long-standing relationships with a number of local and national charities across the UK. Its charity partners include the First Give programme in Yorkshire, a charity that encourages students to learn about social issues in their communities and take part in activities such as fundraising. Another recent partner includes Tempus Novo, a Leeds-based charity that helps ex-offenders get back into employment.

The group has worked with the Ahead Partnership social enterprise. In 2019/20 it hosted a competition for local schoolchildren in which they had to create an Easter-themed product/ prototype made of recyclable items or create a marketing/social media campaign to discourage the use of single-use plastic items.

The group also supports young entrepreneurs through the not-for-profit Leeds Enterprise Advisory Programme (LEAP), which runs an enterprise programme for students aged 14 to 19.

Employee-led support

Employees volunteer for charitable causes. In 2021/22, head office staff collectively donated more than 100 hours of their time to work shifts at the Leeds Hospitals Charity Shop.

Applications

Contact the correspondent for further information.

Community contributions

Cash donations UK	£35,000

According to its 2021/22 accounts, the group made charitable donations totalling £35,000.

Toyota Motor Manufacturing (UK) Ltd

Education and training, the environment, health

Company registration number: 2352348

Correspondent: CSR Team, Burnaston, Derby, Derbyshire DE1 9TA (tel: 01332 282121; email: external.affairs@toyotauk.com; website: www.toyotauk.com)

Directors: Akito Takami; Richard Kenworthy (male: 100%).

Nature of business: Toyota Motor Manufacturing (UK) is a car and engine manufacturer.

Financial information

Year end	31/03/2022
Turnover	£2,155,310,000
Pre-tax profit	£90,900

Total employees: 3,000

Main locations: The company has plants in Deeside (North Wales) and Burnaston (Derbyshire).

Community involvement

Toyota supports community groups, charities and schools in the areas surrounding its plants in Deeside and Burnaston. Support is provided through cash and in-kind donations, employee volunteering and fundraising, and educational programmes. According to its website, the company's main charitable areas of focus are social deprivation/inclusion, road safety and health, although the company does also support some environmental causes.

In addition, grants are awarded through the company's corporate charity the Toyota Manufacturing UK Charitable Trust (Charity Commission no. 1124678).

School programme

As part of its school programme, Toyota offers a range of educational programmes for primary, secondary and sixth-form students. These programmes are designed to inspire young people to achieve their full potential and choose STEM subjects and careers. Full details of all the company's current education programmes are provided on its website.

Toyota Fund for Europe

The Toyota Fund for Europe (TFfE) operates at a pan-European level to support a wide range of projects in countries in which Toyota has operations. The fund supports environmental, road safety and education projects. Each local Toyota company operates its own funding to support local projects. Proposals are evaluated by the local Toyota company, following its own selection criteria. Further details about the fund can be found on the company's website.

In-kind support

Local charitable events are regularly supported through the donation of raffle prizes. Occasionally, local organisations, schools and colleges are provided with parts and components to be used as training aids.

Employee-led support

Employee involvement in the community is encouraged and, where suitable, supported financially through the company's corporate charity.

Commercially led support

Sponsorship

Since 1992 the company has been a corporate sponsor of Derby County Football Club.

Public visit programme

Toyota runs a public visit programme that allows members of the public, customers and businesses to visit their local plant and learn about its operations.

Applications

Further information on public visits and education programmes can be found on the company's website. General enquiries should be submitted in writing to the correspondent.

Corporate charity

Toyota Manufacturing UK Charitable Trust (Charity Commission no. 1124678) – see entry on page 282.

Community contributions

Cash donations UK	£512,900
Total contributions UK	£598,700

In 2021/22, the company made charitable contributions totalling £512,900. This was broken down as follows: donations to local charities in Burnaston and Deeside (£460,900); charities supporting health/medicine (£50,300) and environmental charities (£1,700). In addition, in-kind donations totalling £85,800 were provided during the year.

All financial information has been converted from Euros using the exchange rate at the time of writing (October 2022).

Trailfinders Ltd

Community services and development, medical research, social welfare, sports and recreation

Company registration number: 1004502

Correspondent: CSR Team, 48 Earls Court Road, London W8 6FT (email: trailfinders@trailfinders.com; website: www.trailfinders.com)

Directors: Lawrence Comber; Nikki Davies; Lady Fiona Gooley; Sir Michael Gooley; Tristan Gooley; Toby Kelly; Jeremy Latimer; Edwin Lee; Russell McHardy; David Ness; Mathew Raymond; Ross Simpson; Mark West; Simon Wheeler; John O'Dowd; John Sheffer; Simon Woodward (female: 12%; male: 88%).

Nature of business: Trailfinders is a travel company based in the UK and the Republic of Ireland.

Financial information

Year end	28/02/2022
Turnover	£186,970,000
Pre-tax profit	(£35,858,000)

Main locations: The company has travel centres in the UK and the Republic of Ireland.

Community involvement

The majority of Trailfinders' community involvement is directed through its corporate charity, The Mike Gooley Trailfinders Charity (Charity Commission no. 1048993), which makes grants to charities. Occasionally the company makes cash donations directly to charities.

According to its 2021/22 annual report, Trailfinders Ltd made grants to charities supporting medical research, community projects which encourage young people to participate in outdoor activities and armed forces veterans' organisations.

Applications

For further information, contact the correspondent or see the company's corporate charity entry.

Corporate charity

The Mike Gooley Trailfinders Charity (Charity Commission no. 1048993) – see entry on page 244.

Community contributions

Cash donations UK	£5,700,000

The company made charitable donations totalling £5.7 million in 2021/22.

Travis Perkins plc

🔍 Community services and development, general charitable purposes, health

Company registration number: 824821

Correspondent: CSR Team, Lodge Way House, Harlestone Road, Northampton, Northamptonshire NN5 7UG (tel: 01604 752424; email: communications@ travisperkins.co.uk; website: www. travisperkinsplc.co.uk)

Directors: Nick Roberts; Alan Williams; Jasmine Whitbread; Marianne Culver; Pete Redfern; Coline McConville; Heath Drewett; Jora Gill (female: 38%; male: 63%).

Nature of business: Travis Perkins is involved in the marketing and distribution of timber, building and plumbing materials and the hiring of tools to the building trade and industry generally.

Financial information

Year end	31/12/2021
Turnover	£4,586,700,000
Pre-tax profit	£305,600,000

Main locations: The group has operations throughout the UK; its head office is in Northampton.

Community involvement

Charitable activities are generally organised by each of the businesses within the group. Each one has a partnership with a different national charity selected by employees.

Volunteer It Yourself

Volunteer It Yourself (VIY) is a social enterprise which helps young people aged 14 to 24 gain trade skills through the renovation of local community premises. In 2021, the group supported over 545 young people across 35 VIY projects nationwide.

Partnerships

The group has partnerships with Macmillan Cancer Support, Mind, Prostate Cancer UK, Whizz-Kidz, Northampton Saints Rugby, VIY, The Lighthouse Club and Youthbuild UK.

Ukraine

The group's community and charity web page states that the group made a 'substantial' donation to the Disasters Emergency Committee appeal following the invasion of Ukraine, as well as setting up a JustGiving page for employees to donate.

In-kind support

In 2021, 35 Travis Perkins and Toolstation branches donated products and materials, to a total value of £127,000.

Employee-led support

Employee fundraising activities include a colleague lottery, as well as payroll giving and other initiatives. Fundraising and volunteering activities are generally organised by each business individually.

In 2021, employees donated £7,000 to the Disasters Emergency Committee's Ukraine appeal through the group's JustGiving page.

Applications

The group's website states: 'Charity sponsorships and donations are dealt with by our individual businesses.' A list of branch locations can be found at www. travisperkinsplc.co.uk/our-businesses.

Community contributions

Total contributions worldwide	£944,600

The Travis Perkins plc annual report for 2021 provided the following breakdown of charitable contributions. We have excluded payroll giving and group initiatives from the group's total contributions.

Macmillan Cancer Support	£751,600
VIY material contributions	£76,000
Mind	£35,000
Payroll giving and group initiatives	£49,000
Prostate Cancer UK	£30,000
Whizz-Kidz	52,000
Total	£993,600

Tullis Russell Group Ltd

🔍 General charitable purposes

Company registration number: SC150075

Correspondent: CSR Team, Rothersfield, Markinch, Fife KY7 6PB (tel: 01592 753311; website: www.tullisrussell.com)

Directors: Frederick Bowden; Andrew Carmichael; Stephen Dobson; Heunghyun Jung; Geoffrey Miller (male: 100%).

Nature of business: Tullis Russell Group is an employee-owned company producing coating for paper and other products.

Financial information

Year end	31/03/2022
Turnover	£43,939,000
Pre-tax profit	£2,225,000

Total employees: 207

Main locations: Historically the company had a site in Fife but it has since moved operations to Bollington in Cheshire.

Community involvement

The majority of the group's giving is through its corporate charity, the Russell Trust (OSCR no. SC004424), which makes grants to organisations in Fife.

Applications

For further information, contact the correspondent or see the group's corporate charity entry.

Corporate charity

Russell Trust (OSCR no. SC004424) – see entry on page 270.

Community contributions

Total contributions worldwide	£201,000

The group declared cash donations of £201,000 in 2021/22. According to the group's annual report, the Russell Trust received the majority of this donation, although no amount was specified.

Turner and Townsend Ltd

🔍 Education and training

Company registration number: 6468643

Correspondent: Corporate Responsibility Team, Low Hall, Calverley Lane, Horsforth, Leeds LS18 4GH (email: CR@turntown.com; website: www.turnerandtownsend.com/en/about-us/corporate-responsibility/community-value)

Directors: Vincent Clancy; James Dand; Jeremy Lathom-Sharp; Patricia Moore; Murray Rowden; Sean Christie (female: 17%; male: 83%).

Nature of business: Turner and Townsend is a professional services company specialising in project management, cost management and consulting across the property, infrastructure and natural resources sectors.

Financial information

Year end	30/04/2021
Turnover	£664,546,000
Pre-tax profit	£112,658,000

Total employees: 6,233

Main locations: The group operates globally with 100 offices in 45 countries. In the UK, the group works from 16 offices across England, Scotland and Northern Ireland.

Community involvement

Turner and Townsend supports a wide range of charitable purposes with a focus on education and social mobility.

Partnerships

Worldwide, the group has local partnerships with 150 schools, organisations and charities. In the UK, the group has partnered with the National Literary Trust to deliver educational programmes for children and young people.

In-kind support

Through the group's partnership with the National Literary Trust, over 10,000 books have been donated since 2018.

Employee-led support

Group employees are encouraged to volunteer their time to assist with the delivery of the group's programmes. The group offers one day of paid leave each year for employees who wish to volunteer. In 2020/21, employees volunteered a total of 8,415 hours.

Applications

For general queries, contact the correspondent.

Community contributions

According to its 2020/21 corporate responsibility report, during the year the group's donations totalled £515,800. This figure includes employee donations, but it was not possible to determine what proportion of this figure came from the group itself. The value of pro bono and employee volunteering hours was not quantified.

Tyman plc

The environment, formal sciences, housing and homelessness, social welfare

Company registration number: 2806007

Correspondent: The Sustainability Team, 29 Queen Anne's Gate, London SW1H 9BU (tel: 020 7976 8000; website: www.tymanplc.com/sustainability)

Directors: Peter Ho; Jason Ashton; Pamela Bingham; Helen Clatworthy; Jo Hallas; Nicky Hartery; David Randich; Dr Paul Withers (female: 50%; male: 50%).

Nature of business: Tyman plc supplies engineered components to the door and window industry. Its UK and Ireland division is made up of three businesses: ERA, Zoo and Access 360.

Financial information

Year end	31/12/2021
Turnover	£635,700,000
Pre-tax profit	£49,600,000

Main locations: In the UK, Tyman plc has sites in Carlisle, London, the West Midlands, Suffolk and Hertfordshire.

Community involvement

The group supports charities through cash donations, employee volunteering and in-kind contributions. In the past, community programmes have been managed at a local level, with each business focusing on causes important to it. According to the group's 2021 annual report, during 2021 three core themes were identified to be the focus of the group's giving from 2021 onwards. These are:

- Housing projects for disadvantaged people
- STEM education projects
- Environmental protection/restoration projects

Applications

Contact your local Tyman plc site for further information.

Community contributions

Cash donations worldwide	£50,800
Total contributions worldwide	£53,900

In 2021 the group's charitable contributions totalled £53,900. This included cash donations of £50,800, costed employee volunteering of £2,100 and in-kind contributions of £1,000. A further £26,800 was given through employee cash donations.

Ulster Carpet Mills (Holdings) Ltd

Community enterprise and social entrepreneurship, medical research, mental health and well-being, social welfare

Company registration number: NI001207

Correspondent: The Trustees, Castleisland Factory, Craigavon BT62 1EE (tel: 028 3833 4433; email: jwmt@ulstercarpets.com; website: https://johnwilsontrust.com)

Directors: David Acheson; Nicholas Coburn; Lydia Inglis; Jesper Jensen; Mary Montgomery; Caroline Somerville; Edward Wilson; Jeremy Wilson; John Wilson; Richard Wilson (female: 30%; male: 70%).

Nature of business: Ulster Carpet Mills is a luxury carpet manufacturer.

Financial information

Year end	31/03/2021
Turnover	£53,800,179
Pre-tax profit	£1,301,929

Total employees: 583

Main locations: The company operates in the UK and the USA. Its head office is in Craigavon, Northern Ireland.

Community involvement

The company's community activities are primarily channelled through its corporate charity, The John Wilson Memorial Trust (NICC no. 105836).

The John Wilson Memorial Trust

The John Wilson Memorial Trust was set up in memory of the late John Wilson, son of Ulster Carpet Mills' founder, George Walter Wilson.

The trust provides grants to charities in the area of mental health. In addition, the trust offers funding for local small to medium-sized enterprises, as well as bursaries and scholarships to support medical research. The trust primarily supports organisations in the area surrounding the company's head office in Craigavon. Full information about the trust's recent projects can be found on its website.

In the past, the trust has awarded grants to Action Mental Health (AMH MensSana) to support mental health counselling for young people across Northern Ireland. Grants have also been awarded to the East Belfast Independent Advice Centre and Links Counselling Service.

Applications

Visit the trust's website for further information: https://johnwilsontrust.com

Community contributions

A figure for the company's total community contributions was not included in its 2020/21 accounts.

Unilever plc

Community enterprise and social entrepreneurship, community services and development, the environment, health, social welfare

Company registration number: 41424

Correspondent: Sustainable Living Team, Unilever House, Springfield Drive, Leatherhead, Surrey KT22 7GR (tel: 0800 010109; email: online contact form; website: www.unilever.co.uk/sustainable-living)

Directors: Maria Varsellona; Nils Anderson; Dr Judith Hartman; Adrian Hennah; Alan Jope; Andrea Jung; Susan Kilsby; Rong Lu; Strive Masiyiwa; Youngme Moon; Nelson Peltz; Graeme Pitkethly; Hein Schumacher; Feike Sijbesma (female: 43%; male: 57%).

Nature of business: Unilever is one of the world's leading suppliers of fast-moving consumer goods in foods, household and personal care products.

Financial information

Year end	31/12/2021
Turnover	£45,741,656,800
Pre-tax profit	£7,462,543,200

Total employees: 149,000

Main locations: The group has operations worldwide. In the UK, Unilever's head office is in Surrey, and it has various other locations across the country.

Community involvement

Unilever delivers an extensive range of charitable activities, focusing particularly on sustainability.

Unilever's Sustainable Living Plan

The group's Sustainable Living Plan aims to reduce its carbon footprint while increasing positive social impact. The plan is a culmination of various partnerships and initiative around the world, within the group's three areas of interest:

▶ Improving health and well-being
▶ Reducing environmental impact
▶ Enhancing livelihoods (with a particular interest in empowering and creating opportunities for women)

Community investment

The group's community investment strategy is aligned with the Unilever Sustainable Living Plan. In 2021 the group reported that of its total charitable contribution: 67% was invested in community activities; 21% was spent on commercial initiatives designed to deliver positive social and environmental

impact while growing the Unilever brand; and 12% was given in charitable donations.

Applications

Contact the correspondent for more information.

Community contributions

Cash donations worldwide	£43,000,000
Total contributions worldwide	£82,000,000

According to the group's Sustainability Performance data, community contributions were broken down as follows:

Cash	52%
In kind	44%
Employee time	1%
Management	3%

Note: the group's financial information has been converted from EUR using the exchange rate at the time of writing (November 2022).

Unite Group plc

Community services and development, education and training, general charitable purposes, health, social welfare

Company registration number: 3199160

Correspondent: The CSR Team, South Quay House, Temple Back, Bristol BS1 6FL (tel: 0117 302 7000; email: info@unite-students.com; website: www.unite-group.co.uk)

Directors: Richard Huntingford; Richard Smith; Joe Lister; Elizabeth McMeikan; Ross Paterson; Ilaria del Beato; Dame Shirley Pearce; Thomas Jackson; Sir Steve Smith (female: 30%; male: 70%).

Nature of business: Unite Group is a developer and operator of student accommodation across the UK.

Financial information

Year end	31/12/2021
Turnover	£266,900,000
Pre-tax profit	(£343,100,000)

Total employees: 1,797

Main locations: The group has accommodation in university cities across the UK.

Community involvement

The group's charitable contributions are channelled predominantly through its corporate charity, The Unite Foundation (Charity Commission no. 1147344). Unite also supports other charities through partnerships and its Charity of the Year initiative.

The Unite Foundation

Established in 2012, the foundation works with 29 university partners across the UK to provide accommodation scholarships to aspiring students in need.

Each scholar is entitled to free, year-round accommodation for the duration of their degree (three years).

Since the foundation's inception, over 500 students have been supported.

Partnerships

The group has long-term partnerships with Into University, a charity focused on raising the aspirations of young people, and the British Heart Foundation.

Through its partnership with the British Heart Foundation, the group encourages students and employees to donate unwanted goods to the charity.

The group has a property at Nelson House, where it provides a multi-agency homelessness prevention hub for young people, which is run by Bristol Youth MAPs and other agencies, with fully renovated and fitted ground-floor rooms at a significantly reduced rent.

The group also provides office space and funding for a mental health worker for Bristol's Street Intervention Service.

Unite Group plc also has a partnership with Streetwise, an organisation in Bristol that supports people experiencing homelessness.

In-kind support

The group provides management and office space for the Unite Foundation, as well as office space for Bristol's Street Intervention Service and Streetwise.

Employee-led support

The group runs a volunteering scheme, which gives staff the opportunity to undertake voluntary work for a day each year. Since the scheme began, staff have spent over 6,000 hours volunteering. In 2021, 296 hours were volunteered by Unite Group plc employees.

The group also offers a choice between matched funding and a Give As You Earn scheme for employees who wish to fundraise.

Commercially led support

The group has sponsored Bristol Pride since 2017 and Better Bristol, which is part of Bristol 24/7.

Applications

For the Unite Foundation, contact info@unitefoundation.co.uk. For all other enquiries, contact info@unite-students.com.

Community contributions

We were unable to find a total for the group's total community contributions. In the past, the group has made donations to its foundation, The Unite Foundation. However, the foundation's accounts for 2021 report that the group did not make a significant donation during the year. According to the group's community web page, the group will donate 1% of its annual profits to the foundation going forward.

United Utilities Group plc

Community enterprise and social entrepreneurship, community services and development, education and training, the environment, formal sciences, social welfare, technology and engineering

Company registration number: 6559020

Correspondent: Corporate Responsibility Team, Haweswater House, Lingley Mere Business Park, Lingey Green Avenue, Great Sankey, Warrington, Cheshire WA5 3LP (tel: 01925 237000; website: www. unitedutilities.com)

Directors: Sir David Higgins; Steve Mogford; Phil Aspin; Louise Beardmore; Liam Butterworth; Kath Gates; Alison Goligher; Paulette Rowe; Doug Webb (female: 40%; male: 60%).

Nature of business: United Utilities Group is the intermediate holding company of the UK's largest listed water business. The group owns and manages the regulated water and wastewater network in the North West through its subsidiary United Utilities Water (UUW).

Financial information

Year end	31/03/2022
Turnover	£1,862,700,000
Pre-tax profit	£439,000,000

Total employees: 5,728

Main locations: The group has a head office based in Warrington. It has locations and operations across the North West.

Community involvement

The group supports community groups and charities across the North West. Contributions include cash donations, employee volunteering and matched funding. The group also supports its customers who are experiencing financial hardship.

United Utilities Trust Fund (Charity Commission no. 1108296)

The group's corporate charity makes grants to individuals in need who are struggling to meet water and/or sewerage charges in areas operated by United Utilities.

Grants are also awarded to debt relief/ advice organisations.

The CaST Fund

The group allocates funds for the CaST (Catching Systems Thinking) fund that provides funding to community groups across the North West, with a focus on community engagement in nature.

One of the first projects to receive funding is led by the Mersey Rivers Trust and focuses on establishing community participation on the lower catchment area of the River Bollin. It aims to increase the number of people connecting with nature and accessing local blue-green space for health and well-being.

The Rivington Heritage Trust

The trust was established by United Utilities to preserve and care for Rivington Terraced Gardens.

Partnerships

United Utilities has many partnerships with charities and non-profit organisations working within the group's three areas of focus:

- Affordability and vulnerability
- The environment and recreation
- Education and skills

In 2022, the group signed two memoranda of understanding with the RSPB and The Rivers Trust.

STEM

Through the Engineering Masterclass and STEM Ambassador schemes, the group seeks to bridge the engineering skills gap in the North West.

As part of its commitment to STEM education, the group runs apprenticeship programmes and graduate placements at its training centre in Bolton, as well as sending STEM Ambassadors into schools to encourage the younger generation to pursue careers in STEM.

Employee-led support

Employees are entitled to up to three days' volunteering leave per year and additional leave is granted for school governor duties.

The group also supports employee fundraising efforts by providing matched funding of up to £250 per person per year. Staff can also donate to charities and causes of their choice through the group's payroll giving scheme.

Applications

Applications for the United Utilities Trust Fund can be made online at www. uutf.org.uk.

All other enquiries should be directed to the correspondent.

Corporate charity

United Utilities Trust Fund (Charity Commission no. 1108296) – see entry on page 282.

Community contributions

| Total contributions UK | £2,800,000 |

According to the group's annual report for 2022, the group contributed £2.8 million in 'community investment',

of which £300,000 was allocated to the CaST fund.

Unum Ltd

Arts, culture and heritage, community services and development, education and training, health, social welfare

Company registration number: 983768

Correspondent: CSR Team, Milton Court, Dorking, Surrey RH4 3LZ (tel: 01306 887766; email: UnumUKCSR@unum.co.uk; website: www.unum.co.uk)

Directors: Cheryl Black; Sarah Davies; Jonathan Fletcher; Clifton Melvin; Nicholas Poyntz-Wright; Michael Simonds; Mark Till; Stuart Vann (female: 25%; male: 75%).

Nature of business: Unum is an employee benefits provider offering financial protection through the workplace including income protection, life insurance, critical illness and dental cover. The company is a member of the Unum Group.

Financial information

Year end	31/12/2021
Turnover	£534,510,000
Pre-tax profit	£121,848,000

Main locations: The company has offices in Basingstoke, Birmingham, Bristol, Dorking, Glasgow and London.

Community involvement

Unum channels its charitable giving through its corporate giving programme, as well as through the various partnerships it holds with charities. The company is particularly interested in funding initiatives within the fields of education, health and well-being (including disability) and arts and culture.

The Unum Community Fund (not a registered charity)

The company's corporate giving programme awards grants of up to £5,000 for community partnership projects. According to the company's website, eligible projects must help to achieve the following aims:

- Help to build resilient, more equitable and inclusive communities (priority will be given to those organisations working to end racism, discrimination and bias and promoting social justice)
- Develop projects which will have significant, tangible impact in the regions in which Unum's offices are located
- Build long-term relationships between our employees and local communities
- Develop opportunities for our employees to volunteer in the local community and enhance teamwork, communication and project management skills

Partnerships

The charities and other non-profit organisations supported by the company are nominated and voted for by its employees. The only prerequisite is that nominated charities must work within the company's fields of interest (education, health and well-being, and arts and culture).

When nominated, organisations are supported for a two-year period. Previous beneficiaries include the Alzheimer's Society, St Michael's Hospice in North Hampshire and Woodlands School in Leatherhead.

For 2022/23, the company's national charity partner is Rewilding Britain. The local charity for Basingstoke is Naomi House and Jacksplace, while the Dorking office nominated the Queen Elizabeth Foundation for Disabled People (QEF) as its chosen charity.

In-kind support

Unum hosts an annual Food Drive, through which the company and its employees donate food and supplies to two charities, Spotlight UK and The Meeting Room. In 2021, the Food Drive raised £7,000.

Employee-led support

Unum staff are entitled to take two days' paid leave to volunteer each year. In 2021, staff spent 2,894 hours volunteering. Employees also engage in fundraising efforts for the group's charity partners.

Staff can also make donations to charities and causes of their choice through payroll giving.

In 2021, the company established a carbon-offsetting scheme with Ecologi. Through the scheme, employees can offset their carbon emissions by donating to Ecologi, which uses the donation to fund global climate projects and plant trees on behalf of Unum Ltd.

Applications

Applications for the Community Fund can be made online on the company's website. All other enquiries should be directed to the correspondent.

Community contributions

We were unable to determine a figure for the company's total community contributions; however, the Unum Ltd 2021 annual report states that the company raised over £250,000 for local communities and that this figure includes employee-led engagement and corporate donations.

UPP Group Holdings Ltd

🔍 Education and training

Company registration number: 6218832

Correspondent: CSR Team, First Floor, 12 Arthur Street, London EC4R 9AB (tel: 020 7398 7200; email: info@upp-ltd.com; website: www.upp-ltd.com)

Directors: Mark Bamford; Stuart Bousfield; Elaine Hewitt; Paul Milner; Jaime Fernandez-Cuervo Infiesta; Chilei Kao; Robert McClatchey (female: 14%; male: 86%).

Nature of business: The group's principal activity is the development, funding, construction and operation (including facilities management) of student accommodation.

Financial information

Year end	31/08/2021
Turnover	£229,720,000
Pre-tax profit	(£33,690,000)

Total employees: 921

Main locations: The group's head office is in London. It owns and manages property at universities across the UK.

Community involvement

The group's giving is channelled through its corporate charity, the UPP Foundation (Charity Commission no. 1166323). The foundation also provides sector leaders and experts with a public policy platform, to debate the future of higher education. UPP Group Holdings Ltd typically donates 3% of the net cash it generates to the foundation.

Employee-led support

Employees are given the opportunity to take part in volunteering activities. Funds raised for selected charities benefit from matched funding from the UPP Foundation.

Applications

Contact the correspondent for further information. Enquiries for the UPP Foundation should be directed by email to: upp-foundation@upp-ltd.com.

Corporate charity

UPP Foundation (Charity Commission no. 1166323) – see entry on page 283.

Community contributions

Cash donations UK	£270,000

The UPP Foundation's 2020/21 annual report states that it received a donation of £270,000 from UPP Group Holdings Ltd. We have taken this amount as the group's cash donations figure.

The Very Group Ltd

🔍 General charitable purposes, health, technology and engineering

Company registration number: 4730752

Correspondent: CSR Team, Skyways House, Speke Road, Speke, Liverpool, Merseyside L70 1AB (tel: 0844 292 1000; email: csr@theverygroup.com; website: www.theverygroup.com/about-us/charity)

Directors: Aidan Barclay; Howard Barclay; Benjamin Fletcher; Jacqueline Humphries; David Kershaw; Mark McMenemy; Philip Peters; Stuart Winton; Lionel Desclée de Maredsous; Timothy Franklin; Richard Mayfield; Dirk Van den Berghe (female: 8%; male: 92%).

Nature of business: The Very Group is a multi-brand online retailer and financial services provider, formerly known as Shop Direct Ltd.

Financial information

Year end	03/07/2021
Turnover	£2,317,100,000
Pre-tax profit	£81,700,000

UK employees: 4,500

Total employees: 4,500

Main locations: The group's head office is in Liverpool. It also has an office in Dublin and offices in England, in London, Manchester, Derby, Wrexham and Bolton.

Community involvement

Very aims to have a positive impact on the communities in which it operates. It provides support through fundraising, employee-led initiatives and in-kind donations.

Charity partners

In the UK, Very develops partnerships with local charities through which it provides funding and employee-led support.

The group has a partnership with children's reading charity Coram Beanstalk, which recruits, trains and supports volunteers to provide reading support in primary schools. The Very Group Ltd plans to raise £600,000 for the charity to give 40,000 children access to one-to-one reading support. Previous charity partners have included homelessness charities, the Booth Centre in Manchester and the Whitechapel Centre in Liverpool.

Financial literacy

The group delivers financial literacy training across communities in the UK and overseas. According to its website, the group plans to launch a school programme to advance understanding of the role of personal finance for teenagers in the UK.

In-kind support

In partnership with the Roald Dahl Story Company, the group is selling a collection of Roald Dahl pyjamas and bedding for children, 100% of the profits of which will be donated to its charity partner, Coram Beanstalk.

Employee-led support

Employees take part in volunteering and fundraising initiatives. The group supports its employees' fundraising efforts through matched funding and payroll giving.

Commercially led support

In 2020 the group began a scheme with a homelessness charity, Emmaus, which allows customers who are purchasing new items of furniture to donate their unwanted items.

The group has also recently begun a partnership with Re-Fashion to create a customer takeback scheme on clothing. Very Group customers are signposted to Re-Fashion, from which they can then request a bag in which they can send no-longer-worn clothes free of charge. The clothes are then resold online with a percentage of the profits going to support charities and sustainability-linked initiatives.

Exclusions

The group does not support any charities that have religious or political connections.

Applications

Contact the correspondent for further information.

Community contributions

The annual report and accounts for 2020/21 did not provide a figure for charitable donations.

Victrex plc

Community services and development, education and training, formal sciences, professional and applied sciences, technology and engineering

Company registration number: 2793780

Correspondent: Social Responsibility Ambassadors, Victrex Technology Centre, Hillhouse International, Thornton Cleveleys, Lancashire FY5 4QD (tel: 01253 897700; email: admin@victrex.com; website: www.victrexplc.com)

Directors: Jakob Sigurdsson; Martin Court; Jane Toogood; Janet Ashdown; Brendan Connolly; David Thomas; Ros Rivaz; Vivienne Cox; Ian Melling (female: 44%; male: 56%).

Nature of business: Victrex is a leading global manufacturer of high-performance polymers.

Financial information

Year end	30/09/2021
Turnover	£306,300,000
Pre-tax profit	£92,500,000

Total employees: 886

Main locations: The group has operations in the UK and internationally. Its head office is in Thornton Cleveleys, Lancashire.

Community involvement

Victrex plc provides support through charitable donations, employee volunteering and education initiatives.

Partnerships

The group has a partnership with Catalyst Discovery Centre, which teaches school-aged children about chemistry and how polymers are made.

Education

Victrex plc engages in a number of education initiatives in its local communities, particularly in support of STEM. For example, as part of the government's National Apprenticeship Week in 2021, Victrex plc ran six career workshops for young people in the local area.

The group also developed a two-day virtual work experience programme aimed at 14- to 16-year-old students across the UK, with a focus on BAME and female students. In 2020/21, the programme provided 38 young people with a total of over 380 hours of work experience in STEM careers.

Employee-led support

The group's employee-led Community Investment Team manages Victrex's charitable giving. Staff are encouraged to suggest activities and causes to support.

Employees volunteer for local causes and provide support to education initiatives as STEM Ambassadors. In 2020/21, employees spent over 3,500 hours volunteering.

Applications

Contact the correspondent for more information.

Community contributions

Cash donations UK	£88,200

According to Victrex's 2020/21 annual report, the group made charitable donations totalling £88,200.

Virgin Money UK plc

Arts, culture and heritage, community services and development, education and training, general charitable purposes, health, social welfare, sports and recreation

Company registration number: 9595911

Correspondent: Corporate Support Team, Jubilee House, Gosforth, Newcastle upon Tyne, Tyne and Wear NE3 4PL (tel: 0141 248 7070; website: www.virginmoneyukplc.com)

Directors: David Bennett; Paul Coby; Geeta Gopalan; Darren Pope; Tim Wade; David Duffy; Clifford Abrahams; Elena Novokreshchenova; Sara Weller (female: 33%; male: 67%).

Nature of business: Virgin Money UK plc is a holding company that owns Clydesdale Bank plc, which in turn trades as Clydesdale Bank, Yorkshire Bank and Virgin Money in the UK.

Financial information

Year end	30/09/2021
Turnover	£1,489,000,000
Pre-tax profit	£417,000,000

Total employees: 7,415

Main locations: The group's head office is in Newcastle. It also has offices in Glasgow, Leeds and London.

Community involvement

Virgin Money UK, formerly known as CYBG plc, provides support to its local communities through charity partnerships, cash donations and via its corporate charity, the Virgin Money Foundation (Charity Commission no. 1161290).

Partnerships

Each year, Virgin Money partners with one charity which it supports through employee fundraising and for the Virgin Money London Marathon. In 2021 the group's Charity of the Year was Macmillan Cancer Support.

Clydesdale Bank and Yorkshire Bank

Virgin Money's subsidiaries, Clydesdale Bank and Yorkshire Bank, also support charities through sponsorships, partnerships and employee-led initiatives. Recently, the banks have supported Scotland's Charity Air Ambulance, Cycle Yorkshire and Count Me In, a community-based programme designed to help pre-school children learn how to count.

Education

The group works with a variety of organisations to deliver a range of educational programmes related to financial awareness, employability and enterprise. Current initiatives include:

- **Make £5 Grow:** An annual competition for primary schools across the UK, which encourages enterprise and related skills. Pupils aged 9 to 11 are provided with a loan of £5 each to start small business initiatives. Further information can be found at https://make-5-grow.co.uk/.
- **Virgin StartUp:** A support and mentoring programme for young entrepreneurs

In 2020, the group launched the Emerging Stars programme, which supports up-and-coming stars in music and entertainment with mentorship, bursaries and unique opportunities to perform.

In-kind support

The group offers the use of its Virgin Money Lounges free of charge to community groups and charities for events. It also provides in-kind support to the Virgin Money Foundation in the form of the use of facilities and employee time.

Employee-led support

Volunteering

Employees are entitled to two days' paid leave to volunteer on a bank-led activity in their local community. Activities can include beach clean-ups, school presentations, mentoring and more.

Fundraising

Employees organise fundraising initiatives for the group's charity partners.

Commercially led support

Sponsorship

The group is the title sponsor of the Virgin Money London Marathon. Previously, Virgin Money has sponsored two events at the Edinburgh Fringe Festival, the Virgin Money Fringe on the Royal Mile and the Virgin Money Fringe on the Mound.

Applications

Contact the correspondent for further information.

Corporate charity

The Virgin Money Foundation (Charity Commission no. 1161290) – see entry on page 283.

Community contributions

Cash donations UK	£1,000,000
Total contributions UK	£1,400,000

The group's 2020/21 annual report states:

> The Group made donations of £1m in the year (2020: £1m) to the Foundation to enable it to pursue its charitable objectives. The Group has also provided a number of support services to the Foundation on a pro bono basis, including use of facilities and employee time. The

estimated gift in kind for support services provided during the year was £0.4m.

Viridian International Ltd

🔍 The environment, social welfare

Company registration number: 3750310

Correspondent: CSR Team, 15 Station Road, St Ives, Huntingdon, Cambridgeshire PE17 4BH (tel: 01327 878050; email: online contact form; website: www.viridian-nutrition.com/charity.aspx)

Director: Cheryl Thallon (female: 100%).

Nature of business: Viridian International is a producer and distributor of vitamins and health supplements.

Main locations: The company supplies its products in over 20 countries worldwide.

Community involvement

The company supports environmental and children's charities through its charity donation programme.

Viridian Nutrition Charity Donation programme

Through the Viridian Nutrition Charity Donation programme, the company provides cash donations to a wide range of registered charities. Beneficiary charities are nominated on an annual basis by the company's stockists, with the only restriction being that 40% is donated to children's charities and 40% is donated to environmental charities. The remaining 20% is donated to other charitable causes. Since the programme was established, the company has donated over £550,000.

Previous beneficiaries have included Comic Relief, Friends of the Earth, NSPCC, RSPB, Save the Children, Shelter, Terrence Higgins Trust, The Prince's Trust, The Woodland Trust and UNICEF.

Applications

Contact the correspondent for further information.

Community contributions

Information on the company's community contributions was not available.

Vodafone Group plc

🔍 Community enterprise and social entrepreneurship, community services and development, education and training, the environment, health, social welfare, technology, women's rights

Company registration number: 1833679

Correspondent: CSR Team, Vodafone House, The Connection, Newbury, Berkshire RG14 2FN (tel: 01635 33251; email: GroupMedia@vodafone.com; website: www.vodafone.com)

Directors: Nick Read; Margherita Della Valle; Val Gooding; Sir Crispin Davis; Michel Demaré; Dame Clara Furse; Maria Amparo Moraleda Martinez; David Nish; Jean-François van Boxmeer; Debra Kerr; Stephen Carter; Delphine Ernotte Cunci; Simon Segars (female: 46%; male: 54%).

Nature of business: Vodafone is a mobile telecommunications provider operating worldwide.

Financial information

Year end	31/03/2022
Turnover	£39,352,890,000
Pre-tax profit	£3,414,570,000

Total employees: 92,866

Main locations: The group operates in 21 countries worldwide.

Community involvement

The group's charitable activities are channelled primarily through its corporate charity, The Vodafone Foundation (Charity Commission no. 1089625). Globally, the group runs a variety of initiatives focusing on online safety, digital skills and inclusion.

Vodafone foundations

Vodafone has 27 foundations globally that make up a corporate funding network. The foundations invest in programmes that support communities in countries where Vodafone operates. The UK-registered Vodafone Foundation supports a wide range of projects in the areas of health, education and disaster relief. The Vodafone Foundation is funded by an annual contribution from Vodafone Group plc and Vodafone UK.

Online safety

Previously, the group worked in partnership with The Diana Award to deliver the Be Strong Online initiative, a digital skills programme designed to encourage older children to pass on their knowledge to younger peers. The programme consisted of a series of learning modules covering topics such as self-esteem, peer pressure and digital footprints.

In-kind support

The Great British Tech Appeal

In partnership with Barnardo's, Vodafone UK's Great British Tech Appeal asks the public to donate old pre-used smartphones and tablets, which are then redistributed to disadvantaged children and families, along with six months of free data, calls and texts.

Employee-led support

Employees can take part in volunteering and activities with the Vodafone Foundation. For example, in 2019, Vodafone employee volunteers visited Mozambique to provide communications support for the humanitarian relief programme following Cyclone Idai.

Employees also participate in fundraising activities through the Vodafone Foundation. The foundation provides matched funding to support the fundraising efforts.

Applications

Contact the correspondent for further information.

Corporate charity

The Vodafone Foundation (Charity Commission no. 1089625) – see entry on page 284.

Community contributions

Cash donations UK	£14,960,000

No figure was provided for the group's charitable contributions; however, the Vodafone Foundation's 2020/21 accounts note that the group donated £14.96 million to the charity during the year. We have taken this figure as the group's cash donation. Note: the grant total relates to a different year than the rest of the financial information as this was the latest available to view.

The financial information was converted from EUR using the exchange rate at the time of writing (October 2022).

Warburtons Ltd

Agriculture and farming, community enterprise and social entrepreneurship, community services and development, education and training, the environment, health, social welfare

Company registration number: 178711

Correspondent: Nicola Atkinson, Community and Communications Co-ordinator, Back o' th' Bank House, Hereford Street, Bolton, Lancashire BL1 8HJ (tel: 01204 556600; email: nicola.atkinson@warburtons.co.uk; website: www.warburtons.co.uk/corporate/sustainability/community)

Directors: David Light; Jonathan Warburton; William B. Warburton; William R. Warburton; Andrew

Higginson; Mary-Ann Kilby (female: 17%; male: 83%).

Nature of business: Warburtons is a family-owned bakery producer and distributer.

Financial information

Year end	25/09/2021
Turnover	£567,900,000
Pre-tax profit	£23,548,000

Total employees: 4500+

Main locations: The company operates across the UK.

Community involvement

Warburtons provides support through its community investment strategy, Family Matters. Support is given in a variety of ways including through grants, a national school visitors programme, product donations, volunteering, matched funding, fundraising and payroll giving.

In 2022, the company launched The Warburtons Foundation (not a registered charity) to channel its community giving. The foundation aims to support families across the UK who are facing challenges by providing food education, product donations and community initiatives. Upon its launch, the foundation committed to donating 1 million products by the end of 2022.

Financial giving programme

Warburtons' financial giving programme offers support to charitable projects, activities and organisations that provide a direct benefit to families. The support is intended to reach charities and organisations delivering work that aligns with the company's key priorities, taken from the company's website:

- 'Health – supporting families to care for each other and lead healthier lives
- Places – supporting families to flourish in communities that are safer, greener and more inclusive
- Skills – supporting families to gain useful skills for life and work'

Warburtons has three grant programmes for charitable organisations:

- **Community grants** – grants of up to £400 are available to organisations in England, Scotland and Wales to support ongoing activities. Applications for community grants are reviewed quarterly.
- **Development grants** – grants of up to £3,000 are available to registered charities and CICs delivering projects within 15 miles of the company's sites. The grants are intended to support previous community grant holders to pilot new ideas that will benefit families and communities.
- **Project grants** – grants of £1,000 to £10,000 are available to registered charities and CICs delivering projects within 15 miles of a bakery or depot

site. Project grants can be used to scale up existing activities that have been proven to have a positive impact.

Partnerships

Since 2015, Cancer Research UK has been the company's charity partner. Employees regularly participate in various fundraising activities for the charity. In 2020/21, £304,400 was raised through employee fundraising and donations from the company.

Warburtons works in collaboration with several organisations including Business in the Community, WRAP (Waste and Resources Action Programme), WWF (World Wide Fund for Nature), the Food and Drink Federation, Charities Aid Foundation and the British Nutrition Foundation.

Wheat Education Project

The project, launched in partnership with education charity The Country Trust, aims to give disadvantaged children in local communities the opportunity to visit rural areas and gain a better understanding of where their food comes from. During 2020, farm visits were not possible due to the COVID-19 pandemic: as a result, the company provided a 'Farm in a Box', which included a range of resources, to continue providing education in schools. In 2020/21, over 400 of these boxes were sent out.

In-kind support

Product donations

Warburtons bakery sites provide support to local communities through the donation of products. The donations are given to school breakfast clubs, food banks and to support community activities. Warburtons has had a partnership with FareShare since 2019 through which thousands of products are redistributed to families in need across the UK. In 2020/21, the company donated over 1.47 million products to the community, supporting over 680 organisations. Of this number, 615,500 products were donated through the company's FareShare partnership.

Employee-led support

Payroll giving

The company operates a payroll giving scheme and in 2020/21, Warburtons employees donated over £41,600 through the scheme.

Matched funding

The company matches employee fundraising up to £250 per person or up to £375 for funds raised for Cancer Research UK. In 2020/21, the company donated £28,500 to boost employee fundraising efforts.

Skills exchange

The company has a skills exchange programme that enables employees to volunteer with local organisations.

Exclusions

The company's Financial Giving Policy provides a comprehensive list of exclusions that apply to Warburtons' community grant and project grant programmes. The policy is available to download from the company's website.

Applications

Product donations

Applications for product donations can be submitted using an online form at www.warburtons.co.uk/corporate/sustainability/product-donation.

Community Grants

Applications for community grants can be submitted online at www.warburtons.co.uk/corporate/sustainability/community/grant.

Both development grants and project grants are managed through a closed process. As such, unsolicited applications for these programmes are not accepted.

Community contributions

▓	Cash donations UK	£472,200

The company's 2020/21 annual report states that during the year, Warburtons awarded a total of £472,200 through its community and charitable grants programme. A figure for the company's in-kind donations was not provided. As such, we have taken the figure of £472,200 as the company's total for community contributions for the financial year.

Waterstones Booksellers Ltd

🔍 Arts, culture and heritage, education and training

Company registration number: 610095

Correspondent: CSR Team, 203–206 Piccadilly, London W1J 9HD (website: www.waterstones.com)

Directors: James Daunt; Kate Skipper; Emma Hillyard (female: 67%; male: 33%).

Nature of business: Waterstones is a British retailer of books, stationery and other related products. Some stores also sell food and drink products.

Financial information

▓	Year end	24/04/2021
	Turnover	£230,890,000
	Pre-tax profit	£5,780,000

UK employees: 3,000+

Main locations: The company operates stores across the UK. It also has stores in the Republic of Ireland, the Isle of Man, Jersey, the Netherlands and Belgium.

Community involvement

The company supports a range of charitable causes, with a particular focus on literacy and reading, especially among children.

Partnerships

Since 2013, Waterstones has worked closely with BookTrust, a charity that works to raise children's and young people's literacy levels. The company is a founding partner of the charity's Children's Reading Fund, and its stores and booksellers regularly participate in fundraising and awareness-raising initiatives. Since the partnership began, the company has raised over £200,000 to support BookTrust's programmes, including the Letterbox Club to help improve the educational outlook for children in care.

Exclusions

The company's website states that it is unable to consider individual requests for donations or sponsorship.

Applications

Contact the correspondent for further information.

Community contributions

▓	Cash donations UK	£162,000

According to its 2020/21 annual report, the company donated a total of £162,000 to charitable causes during the year.

Wates Group Ltd

🔍 Community enterprise and social entrepreneurship, community services and development, education and training, the environment

Company registration number: 1824828

Correspondent: CSR Team, Wates House, Station Approach, Leatherhead, Surrey KT22 7SW (tel: 01372 861000; website: www.wates.co.uk)

Directors: David Allen; Paul Chandler; Sue Harris; Jeremy Newsum; Joe Oatley; Philip Wainwright; Andrew Wates; Charles Wates; James Wates; Jonathan Wates; Timothy Wates (female: 9%; male: 91%).

Nature of business: The Wates Group is a family-owned construction, property services and development company.

Financial information

▓	Year end	31/12/2021
	Turnover	£1,662,026,000
	Pre-tax profit	£35,902,000

Total employees: 3,810

Main locations: The group has 20 offices throughout the UK and a head office in Surrey.

Community involvement

Wates provides support to its local communities through cash donations, partnerships, educational programmes and its corporate charities, The Wates Family Enterprise Trust (Charity Commission no. 1126007) and The Wates Foundation (Charity Commission no. 247941).

Partnerships

Wates has an ongoing partnership with The Conservation Volunteers to help deliver its Treeathlon campaign. Since 2019, employees have planted more than 15,000 native trees.

The group also has a partnership with The Prince's Trust and Manpower to help employ 16- to 24-year-olds at risk of long-term unemployment.

In 2021, the group established a partnership with The Children's Book Project, providing donation points for books in Southwark, London, Birmingham, Leeds and Manchester. During the year, 24,000 books were donated for the charity.

Employee-led support

Volunteering and fundraising

Employees volunteer in their local communities providing support to schools, sports clubs and community groups. Employees also take part in fundraising activities and their efforts are matched by the Wates Family Enterprise Trust. In 2021, employees raised £90,000 for 53 organisations, and the company matched the donations with £49,000.

Payroll giving

The group operates a Give As You Earn scheme, which allows regular salary deductions to support good causes. The donations are matched by the Wates Family Enterprise Trust.

The Children's Book Project

The collection and organising of book donations for the project is carried out by Wates Group Ltd employees.

The Green Schools Programme

Wates Group Ltd employees volunteer to deliver educational programmes as part of the group's Green Schools scheme. Volunteers are trained to deliver weekly workshops on environmental sustainability, wherein pupils develop ideas for environmental community projects.

Applications

Contact the correspondent for further information.

Corporate charity

The Wates Foundation (Charity Commission no. 247941) – see entry on page 285; Wates Family Enterprise Trust (Charity Commission no. 1126007) – see entry on page 284.

Community contributions

Cash donations worldwide	£841,000

The group's 2021 annual report states that it made charitable donations amounting to £841,000 during the year, £825,000 of which was donated to the Wates Family Enterprise Trust (Charity Commission no. 1126007).

The Watford Association Football Club Ltd

🔍 Education and training, health, sports and recreation

Company registration number: 104194

Correspondent: Rob Smith, Community Director, Watford FC, Vicarage Road Stadium, Watford WD18 0ER (tel: 01923 496258; email: community@watfordfc. com or Rob.smith@watfordfc.com; website: www.watfordfccsetrust.com)

Directors: Scott Duxbury; David Fransen; Stuart Timperley (male: 100%).

Nature of business: Watford FC is a professional football club.

Financial information

Year end	30/06/2021
Turnover	£57,060,000
Pre-tax profit	(£21,730,000)

Main locations: The trust works in Hertfordshire and the London boroughs of Harrow and Hillingdon.

Community involvement

The club delivers most of its charitable activities through its associated registered charity, Watford FC's Community Sports and Education Trust (Charity Commission No. 1102239), which delivers a range of programmes focused on sport, inclusion, health, education and community in Hertfordshire and the London boroughs of Harrow and Hillingdon. The club also supports local charities through in-kind and cash donations.

In-kind support

According to our previous research, the club can arrange for items of merchandise to be signed for fundraising purposes in exchange for a donation to Watford FC's Community Sports and Education Trust.

Commercially led support

The club holds charity football matches and other fundraising activities.

Applications

Contact the correspondent for more information.

Community contributions

The company's accounts for 2020/21 do not provide a figure for the club's community contributions during the year.

Watkin Jones Group plc

🔍 General charitable purposes

Company registration number: 4084303

Correspondent: Watkin Jones Community Fund, 7–9 Swallow Street, London W1B 4DE (tel: 020 3617 4453; email: Communityfund@watkinjones. com; website: www.watkinjones.com)

Directors: Alan Giddins; Richard Simpson; Sarah Sergeant; Simon Laffin; Liz Reilly (female: 40%; male: 60%).

Nature of business: Watkin Jones Group is a construction and property development company.

Financial information

Year end	30/09/2021
Turnover	£430,211,000
Pre-tax profit	£51,121,000

UK employees: 711

Main locations: The group's head office is in London. The group also has offices in Bangor, Cardiff, Cheshire and St Asaph.

Community involvement

The group supports general charitable purposes through cash donations and employee volunteering. In 2021, the group also established food bank collection points across its properties.

Watkin Jones Community Fund (not a registered charity)

Through its community fund, the group awards grants to support projects which benefit local communities. The fund aims to provide financial assistance to a wide range of projects with a particular emphasis on enhancing the physical environment and improving quality of life for local people. Applications are welcomed from all community-based groups and not-for-profit organisations. Grants are typically of up to £1,000 but in exceptional circumstances, the group may consider applications for larger amounts.

Employee-led support

Employees often visit local schools and colleges to discuss careers options and invite students to tour current developments to gain an insight into the construction sector. In 2021, the group established its Giving Back scheme, encouraging employees to volunteer in their local communities. Activities included local litter pick-ups and donations to local charities. A figure could not be determined for employee

time or funds volunteered during the year.

Applications

Application forms are available by emailing Communityfund@watkinjones.com.

Community contributions

We were unable to determine a figure for the group's total community contributions during 2021.

The Weir Group plc

🔍 Arts, culture and heritage, community enterprise and social entrepreneurship, community services and development, education and training, health

Company registration number: SC002934

Correspondent: CSR Team, 1 West Regent Street, Glasgow G2 1RW (email: use the contact form on the group's website; website: www.global.weir)

Directors: Jon Stanton; John Heasley; Barbara Jeremiah; Clare Chapman; Engelbert Haan; Mary Jo Jacobi; Sir Jim McDonald; Stephen Young; Graham Vanhegan; Dame Nicola Brewer; Tracey Kerr Ben Magara; Srinivasan Venkatakrishnan (female: 38%; male: 62%).

Nature of business: The Weir Group provides specialist engineering services and products.

Financial information

Year end	31/12/2021
Turnover	£1,933,600,000
Pre-tax profit	£209,500,000

Total employees: 11,000

Main locations: The group has operations worldwide. In the UK, it has offices and facilities in Glasgow, Rochdale, Strathclyde and Todmorden. The group's head office is in Glasgow.

Community involvement

The group provides support through community partnerships, charitable contributions and employee volunteering. Support is primarily given to projects with a strong focus on education, health and community.

Employee-led support

In 2021, to celebrate 150 years of Weir, the group launched the #MyDayofPurpose campaign, which gave employees the opportunity to take part in community activities of their choosing. In 2021, activities included raising environmental awareness, volunteering for local causes, tree-planting and cycling across the globe.

Applications

Enquiries regarding charitable giving and philanthropy can be made using the relevant contact form on the group's website.

Community contributions

Cash donations UK	£482,700

The 2021 annual report states that during the year, the group donated £482,700 to charitable causes. Charitable support was given for the following causes: community (56%), health (32%) and education (12%).

Wellington Management International Ltd

Arts, culture and heritage, education and training

Company registration number: 4283513

Correspondent: Wellington Management UK Foundation, Cardinal Place, 80 Victoria Street, London SW1E 5JL (tel: 020 7126 6700; email: wmukf@wellington.com; website: www. wellington.com)

Directors: Abogado Nominees Ltd; Susanne Ballauff; Natasha Brook-Walters; Yolanda Courtines; Henry Duffy; Stefan Haselwandter; Amy Kramer; Lucinda Maria; Shanna O'Reilly; Jawan Parker; Mary Shannon; Edward Steinborn; Luke Stellini (female: 58%; male: 42%).

Nature of business: Wellington Management (Wellington) is a global investment management firm. We have taken the financial information for this record from the company registered in the UK. All other information has been taken from the group's (Wellington Management Group LLP) 2021 sustainability report.

Financial information

Year end	31/12/2021
Turnover	£338,530,000
Pre-tax profit	£85,390,000

UK employees: 387

Total employees: 1,922

Main locations: In Europe, Wellington has offices in London, Frankfurt, Luxembourg and Zurich.

Community involvement

Wellington's CSR strategy focuses on supporting the communities in which its employees live and work. The group has two corporate charities, one in the UK and one in the USA. Both make grants to support educational opportunities for disadvantaged young people, including arts-based programmes. In the UK, the group's charitable giving is channelled through the Wellington Management UK Foundation (Charity Commission no. 1167369).

In 2021, The Wellington Management UK Foundation gave £1 million in grants to 24 organisations

In-kind support

Employees are given two days' paid leave each year to volunteer for non-profit organisations.

Employee-led support

The group's Annual Appeal allows employees to fundraise and donate to global and regional non-profit organisations through payroll giving. The group matches 100% of employees' donations. According to the group's 2021 sustainability report, £1.04 million (USD 1.2 million) was raised through this programme during the year.

Applications

See the website or contact the correspondent for up-to-date information.

Corporate charity

Wellington Management UK Foundation (Charity Commission no. 1167369) – see entry on page 285.

Community contributions

The figures in the 2021 annual report were converted from USD to GBP based on the exchange rate at the time of writing (October 2022). We were unable to determine a figure for the company's charitable giving in 2021.

Wesleyan Assurance Society

Education and training, health, social welfare

Company registration number: ZC000145

Correspondent: Wesleyan Foundation, Colmore Circus, Birmingham B4 6AR (website: www.wesleyan.co.uk/cr/caring-about-your-community)

Directors: Nathan Moss; Anne Torry; Andrew Neden; Linda Wilding; Ian McCaig; Philip Moore; Harpreet Sood; Rita Bajaj; Mario Mazzocchi; Gillian Cass (female: 50%; male: 50%).

Nature of business: Wesleyan is a financial services mutual that provides specialist advice and solutions to professionals such as doctors, dentists, teachers and lawyers.

Financial information

Year end	31/12/2021
Turnover	£8,500,000,000
Pre-tax profit	£6,100,000

UK employees: 1,523

Main locations: The society's head office is in Birmingham.

Community involvement

The society provides most of its support through its foundation, which makes grants for education, health, innovation and social development. Wesleyan staff also volunteer and fundraise for its charity partners.

Wesleyan Foundation (not a registered charity)

The foundation was launched in May 2017 and supports projects that promote or develop education, health and social development. Registered charities as well as constituted voluntary and community groups are supported. Organisations should be based within the UK and have an income of under £250,000. Grants are administered by the following community foundations:

- Heart of England Community Foundation (Coventry and Warwickshire)
- Birmingham and Black Country Community Foundation
- Quartet Community Foundation (Bristol)
- Leeds Community Foundation
- Leicester and Rutland
- Nottinghamshire Community Foundation
- Northern Ireland Community Foundation
- Foundation Scotland
- South Yorkshire Community Foundation
- The Community Foundation in Wales

Employee-led support

Employees in 2021 took 105 volunteering days, which equates to 700 hours. Staff also supported students across Birmingham with mentoring through the Social Mobility Foundation and The Girls' Network.

Applications

To apply to the Wesleyan Foundation, visit the relevant community foundation website, where further information on the grant schemes can be found. Any queries should be directed to your local community foundation.

Community contributions

Cash donations UK	£1,045,000

According to the Wesleyan Assurance Society Annual Report and Accounts 2021, almost £1.05 million was donated to charitable causes during the year.

Wessex Water Services Ltd

Community services and development, education and training, the environment, money and debt advice, social welfare

Company registration number: 2366648

Correspondent: CSR Team, Claverton Down Road, Claverton Down, Bath, Somerset BA2 7WW (tel: 01225 526000; email: sustainability@wessexwater.co.uk; website: www.wessexwater.co.uk)

Directors: Collin Skellett; Andy Pymer; John Thompson; Mohammed Saddiq; Ruth Jefferson; Jim McKenna; Kate Mingay; Tim Gardam; Kevin Wall; Dame Fiona Reynolds; Francis Yeoh; Hong Yeoh; Mark Yeoh; Hann Yeoh; Huw Davis; David Barclay (female: 13%; male: 87%).

Nature of business: Wessex Water is a regional water and sewage treatment business serving South West England. The ultimate parent company of Wessex Water Services Ltd is YTL Corporation Berhad (incorporated in Malaysia).

Financial information

Year end	31/03/2021
Turnover	£514,700,000
Pre-tax profit	£833,000,000

UK employees: 2,547

Main locations: The company operates in various locations across the South West, including Avon, Dorset, Gloucestershire, Hampshire, Somerset and Wiltshire.

Community involvement

The company focuses most of its charitable support through its foundation in the region where it operates and contributes to environmental and educational projects. Support is provided through grants, in-kind support, volunteering and fundraising.

Wessex Water Foundation

The Wessex Water Foundation was launched in response to the COVID-19 pandemic. The company's website states:

> The Wessex Water Foundation will provide at least £500,000 of funding every year to local communities. The fund will enable us to continue investing in strengthening communities and local environments.
>
> Part of this will involve continued funding for local groups, supporting debt advice organisations and charities dealing with those affected by poverty, mental and physical health issues, hunger, housing problems and unemployment.

The foundation works in partnership with four of the region's community foundations (see the applications section).

Watermark scheme

The Watermark scheme supports environmental projects based in the Wessex Water region. It is organised by the Conservation Foundation (Charity Commission no. 284656) and applications are reviewed by a panel of experts.

Grants of up to £1,500 are available to schools, parish councils, youth groups and community organisations. A special project receives the Wessex Watermark gold award, worth £2,500, which is awarded every quarter.

The awards are open to research projects identified in local authority biodiversity action plans (BAP) or Wessex Water's own BAP (see below).

BAP Partners Programme

Now in its sixth phase, the BAP Partners Programme funds projects that will conserve and enhance biodiversity in the region where the company operates. Partnerships and grants are made to wildlife conservation organisations. The programme generally funds projects that focus on habitat creation, species or survey work, restoration work or more strategic work to enhance biodiversity or water quality. Small project grants and major grants, which comprise long-term funding over five years, are available. See the website for current information.

In-kind support

The company offers a free education service to schools and colleges in the region in which it operates. This includes visits to primary and secondary schools to deliver a range of services including school assemblies and classroom learning. Schools can also book a visit to one of eight education centres across the region.

Commercially led support

The company works with debt advisers and other community-based organisations to support vulnerable customers to afford their ongoing water bills and repay their debt.

Exclusions

Support is not generally given to private companies, individuals or government organisations.

Applications

Wessex Water Foundation

For more details about the Wessex Water Foundation, contact the relevant community foundation

- Somerset Community Foundation: info@somersetcf.org.uk
- Wiltshire Community Foundation: info@wiltshirecf.org.uk
- Quartet Community Foundation: info@quartetcf.org.uk
- Dorset Community Foundation: admin@dorsetcf.org

Watermark Awards

Applications for the Watermark Awards can be directed to the company by emailing community@wessexwater.co.uk. More information can be found on the website: www.conservationfoundation.co.uk

BAP Partners Programme

Application forms for the BAP Partners Programme are available on the company's website, under the 'Environment' section. For any other enquiries, email BAP@wessexwater.co.uk

Schools

Schools can apply for an education service, site or school visit using the company's online form, available under the 'Community' section of the website. For any other enquiries, email education@wessexwater.co.uk.

Community contributions

Cash donations UK	£578,600

In 2020/21, £578,600 was donated to UK charities, of which £225,300 was donated to local debt advice agencies to help provide debt and financial advice to customers in the company's area of operation who are struggling to pay their water bills.

Western Power Distribution

Arts, culture and heritage, community services and development, education and training, the environment

Company registration number: 9223384

Correspondent: CSR Team, Avonbank, Feeder Road, Bristol BS2 0TB (tel: 0800 096 3080; email: info@westernpower.co.uk; website: www.nationalgrid.co.uk)

Directors: Phil Swift; Ian Williams; Alison Sleightholm; Graham Halladay; Anthony Cardew; Maurice Fletcher (female: 17%; male: 83%).

Nature of business: Western Power Distribution is the trading identity of the following four electricity distribution companies: Western Power Distribution (East Midlands) plc (company no. 2366923); Western Power Distribution (West Midlands) plc (company no. 3600574); Western Power Distribution (South West) plc (company no. 2366894); and Western Power Distribution (South Wales) plc (company no. 2366985).

Financial information

Year end	31/03/2022
Turnover	£599,000,000
Pre-tax profit	£269,300,000

Total employees: 6,500

Main locations: The company operates across the Midlands, the South West and Wales.

Community involvement

Western Power Distribution supports local causes in the areas where it operates. The three main strands of support are education, safety and the environment. Support is provided through cash and in-kind donations, educational programmes, and bursaries, sponsorship and partnerships.

The environment

The group partners with Gloucestershire and Avon Wildlife Trusts and Groundworks Wales. The group's website details recent environmental initiatives it has supported:

- A donation to support a Wildlife Watch group for school years 1–3 in the South West.
- Support for Nottinghamshire Wildlife Trust's 'Keeping It Wild' programme, where a group of city-based children get to meet, learn new skills and experience the great outdoors. The theme of this year's programme was also about plastic pollution and included an excursion which taught the group about the impact of plastic waste on the environment.
- Additional plants and shrubs have also been donated to local councils in Lincolnshire and Derbyshire.

Education and safety

Each year, the group delivers educational safety sessions for schoolchildren. These include school visits and life skills initiatives. The group also supports the British Heart Foundation's initiative to provide CPR kits in Bristol schools, bursaries for underprivileged students in South Wales involved in the Duke of Edinburgh's Award, and a creative writing and arts programme in South Wales.

Fuel poverty

The group also works with four charitable organisations to provide signposting and referral services for vulnerable customers who are at risk of fuel poverty. In 2021/22, these projects supported over 113,000 customers, leading to estimated annual savings of £60 million for these customers.

Employee-led support

Staff members take part in the safety and educational initiatives organised by the group and volunteer to support their local communities.

Exclusions

To qualify for support, organisations must fall within the group's distribution area.

Applications

For further information about the group's community support, contact the company that relates to your distribution area.

Community contributions

Cash donations UK £1,200,000

According to its 2021/22 annual report, during the year the group assisted 128 charitable and non-charitable organisations as part of a commitment of £199,000. In addition, Western Power Distribution also donated £1 million to charities and local authorities through its Community Matters Fund.

Westmorland Ltd

Education and training, the environment, general charitable purposes, social welfare, sports and recreation

Company registration number: 5357857

Correspondent: Community Team, Rheged, Penrith, Cumbria CA11 0DQ (tel: 01539 624511; website: https://westmorlandfamily.com)

Directors: Henry Dimbleby; Sarah Dunning; Laurence King; Jane Lane; Nabil Subuh (female: 40%; male: 60%).

Nature of business: Westmorland operates a range of hospitality services, including motorway service stations, hotels and visitor centres.

Financial information

Year end	30/06/2021
Turnover	£69,390,000
Pre-tax profit	£2,354,000

UK employees: 1,000

Main locations: The company operates services in Cumbria, Gloucestershire and Lanarkshire.

Community involvement

Westmorland supports a wide range of local charities and community groups in the areas where it operates. Support is provided through a community fund, charity partnerships, employee volunteering and in-kind donations.

The Westmorland Family Community Fund (not a registered charity)

According to Cumbria Community Foundation's website (which administers the fund) the fund provides 'grants for groups which support the development of young people and the communities of Tebay, Brough, Shap, Kirby Stephen, and Appleby-in-Westmorland. Some projects in the Penrith area will also be considered.' Grants are usually of £500 upwards.

Partnerships

As part of an ongoing partnership with the Gloucestershire Gateway Trust, the company has agreed to donate a proportion of the annual turnover from its Gloucester services to the trust, which is then distributed to a range of partner charities.

In 2020/21, £319,000 was donated for distribution to community partners such as All Pulling Together, Together in Matson, Fair Shares, The Wildlife Trusts, The Nelson Trust, Play Gloucestershire, The Venture, White City and GL Communities.

Employee-led support

The company offers a volunteer day for all employees.

Applications

The Westmorland Family Community Fund

The Westmorland Family Community Fund is administered by Cumbria Community Foundation. For further information about the fund including details of how to apply, contact Ellen Clements on 01900 825760 or email ellen@cumbriafoundation.org.

Gloucestershire Gateway Trust

The Gloucestershire Gateway Trust website provides a telephone number (01452 699741) and an email address (office@ggtrust.org) for enquiries.

Community contributions

Cash donations UK £525,000

The company's 2020/21 accounts state that charitable donations of £206,000 and £319,000 were made to Cumbria Community Foundation and Gloucestershire Gateway Trust, respectively.

WH Holding Ltd (West Ham United)

Community services and development, education and training, the environment, health, housing and homelessness, social welfare, sports and recreation, work outside the UK

Company registration number: 5993863

Correspondent: Kerry Downes, Head of Community at West Ham United Foundation, London Stadium, Queen Elizabeth Olympic Park, London E20 2ST (tel: 020 7473 7720; email: foundation@westhamunited.co.uk; website: www.whufc.com/club/community/foundation)

Directors: David Sullivan; David Gold; Karren Brady; Andy Mollett; J. Albert Smith; Daniel Harris (female: 17%; male: 83%).

Nature of business: West Ham United is a professional football club competing in the Premier League.

Financial information

Year end	31/05/2021
Turnover	£192,730,000
Pre-tax profit	(£26,920,000)

Total employees: 582
Main locations: The football club is based in East London.

Community involvement

The club's community support is principally channelled through its charity, the West Ham United Foundation (Charity Commission no. 1114458). The foundation delivers a wide range of programmes focusing on health and well-being, education, social welfare, inclusion, and children and young people. The club also provides ongoing support for its charity partners.

West Ham United Foundation

The West Ham United Foundation works with partners to deliver a broad range of community outreach programmes in Newham, East London and Essex, and internationally. Following the club's move to the London Stadium in 2017, the foundation committed to investing around £2.5 million each year until 2027.

In 2018, the foundation launched the Player's Project, an initiative whereby players from the club become ambassadors for local community projects. The Player's Project delivers over 30 programmes in 11 areas of work: equality; the environment; learning; careers; loneliness; poverty; local enterprise; health and well-being; young people; sporting ambition; and community engagement.

Full details of all of the foundation's current programmes are available on the club's website.

Partnerships

The club has two principal charity partners, the Moore Family Foundation and DT38 Foundation.

- **Moore Family Foundation** – Established in memory of West Ham and England player Bobby Moore, the foundation provides life-changing opportunities for Year 6 pupils in Newham, Tower Hamlets, Barking and Dagenham, Thurrock, Brentwood and Basildon. As part of the partnership, the West Ham United Foundation provides literacy and numeracy support for pupils. The foundation also arranges matchday tours of the club's stadium.
- **National Literacy Trust** – In 2020/21, WH Holding Ltd continued its partnership with the National Literacy Trust, raising money and donating books to support its work with some of the most disadvantaged children in the UK. So far, WH Holding Ltd has donated 100,000 books to those who need them most.

- **DT38 Foundation** – The foundation was established in memory of club academy player Dylan Tombides to raise awareness and change the stigma associated with men's health issues with a focus on testicular cancer.

The club's other charity partners include Richard House Children's Hospice, The Bobby Moore Fund for Cancer Research UK, Blesma, Ambition Aspire Achieve and St Francis Hospice.

The club also works with charities such as Crisis and Newham Rise – Change Grow Live to tackle the issues of homelessness and drug and alcohol abuse.

In-kind support

WH Holding Ltd makes in-kind donations every year.

Commercially led support

Players and staff volunteer for local community projects via the foundation's volunteering programme, the Player's Project.

Applications

Contact the correspondent for more information.

Community contributions

Cash donations UK	£787,800

According to WH Holding Ltd's 2020/21 sustainability report, it donated £787,800 to charities.

Charitable donations were broken down as follows:

Cash donation	£580,000
Gifts in kind	£117,000
Management cost	£70,000
Employee time donated	£20,000

Wheatley Housing Group Ltd

Arts, culture and heritage, community services and development, education and training, health, housing and homelessness, mental health and well-being, money and debt advice, social welfare, sports and recreation

Company registration number: SC426094

Correspondent: The Foundation Team, Wheatley House, 25 Cochrane Street, Glasgow G1 1HL (tel: 0800 479 7979; email: foundation@wheatley-group.com; website: www.wheatley-group.com)

Directors: Jo Armstrong; Bernadette Hewitt; Jo Boaden; Bryan Duncan; Maureen Dowde; Lindsey Cartwright; Eric Gibson; Caroline Gardner (female: 38%; male: 63%).

Nature of business: Wheatley Housing is a housing, care and property management group.

Financial information

Year end	31/03/2022
Turnover	£1,233,000,000
Pre-tax profit	£16,000,000

Total employees: 2,632
Main locations: The group operates across Scotland.

Community involvement

The group mainly offers community support through its corporate charity, The Wheatley Foundation Ltd (OSCR no. SC046607), which delivers a wide range of programmes focusing on the issues of employability, education, digital inclusion, poverty, sport and art within Wheatley communities across Scotland. Programmes are delivered directly as well as in collaboration with a wide range of local and national partners. The foundation aims to support Wheatley's tenants, care clients and factored homeowners.

According to the group's website, the foundation's five key areas of interest are as follows:

- Poverty: tackling social exclusion and taking people out of poverty;
- Employability: Wheatley Works is creating job, career, training and apprenticeship opportunities;
- Education: providing access to Higher and Further Education;
- Digital Inclusion increasing and expanding digital and online access and capability;
- Sport and Art: helping people, old and young, to lead more vibrant, active lives.

Recent examples of the foundation's programmes include:

- **My Money:** A £4.2 million service, funded by the Big Lottery Fund and the European Social Fund, providing financial advice and support to disadvantaged people in Glasgow through a team of specialist mentors recruited from the third sector.
- **Wheatley Bursaries:** A programme offering full-time students up to £1,500 a year for two years and part-time students £750 a year.

Full details of all of the foundation's current programmes are available on the group's website.

Community engagement

The group delivers community engagement projects in its residential communities. For example, the following information has been taken directly from the group 2021/22 annual report:

Wheatley's Community Improvement Partnership ("CIP") – a specialist team of seconded police and our own frontline staff – continued to work with our communities to tackle anti-social behaviour and crime

At Wheatley Care, we continued to grow our capacity to deliver personalised care services this year, enabling the people we work for to achieve their desired outcomes through flexible and responsive support delivered by a trained and skilled workforce. In 2021/22, Wheatley Care supported 7,751 people across our services, helping them get the most out of their lives and achieve their own positive outcomes.

In-kind support

The foundation provides a range of in-kind support through its programmes, for example:

- Home Comforts provides tenants in financial difficulty with free, good-quality recycled white goods and furniture
- Click and Connect centres offer free access to computers and tuition to help tenants get online.
- EatWell provides fresh food to Wheatley's most vulnerable customers

Applications

General enquiries can be emailed to the correspondent. Alternatively, a contact form is available on the group's website.

The Wheatley Foundation

The group's website states the following about applications to its foundation: 'The Foundation was set up by Wheatley Group, and is funded by the group and its subsidiaries, to benefit our customers. As a result, we are not open to receiving unsolicited proposals and applications.' Details of the foundation's team members are available on the group's website.

Community contributions

Cash donations UK	£611,000

According to the Wheatley Group 2021/22 annual report, it donated £611,000 to charitable causes during the year.

WHSmith plc

Arts, culture and heritage, community services and development, education and training, the environment, health, literacy, mental health and well-being, urban communities, work outside the UK

Company registration number: 5202036

Correspondent: CSR Team, Greenbridge Road, Swindon, Wiltshire SN3 3LD (tel: 01793 616161; email: corporate. responsibility@whsmith.co.uk; website: www.whsmithplc.co.uk)

Directors: Ian Houghton; Kalvinder Atwal; Annette Court; Carl Cowling; Nicola Dulieu; Simon Emeny; Robert Moorhead; Marion Sears; Henry Staunton; Maurice Thompson (female: 30%; male: 70%).

Nature of business: WHSmith is a convenience, book and stationery retailer

and is made up of two core businesses – travel and high street. WHSmith Travel has stores in airports, hospitals, train stations and motorway services.

Financial information

Year end	31/08/2021
Turnover	£4,010,000,000
Pre-tax profit	£19,000,000

Total employees: 11,235

Main locations: The group has operations throughout the UK, as well as international units in 20 countries across China, the Middle East, Australia, Asia-Pacific, India and Europe. Its main offices are in London and Swindon.

Community involvement

According to its website, WHSmith is committed to making a positive impact wherever its stores operate. The group supports a wide range of local causes, although the promotion of literacy remains the primary focus of its community involvement.

The group raises funds through the carrier bag levy, the sale of charity products as well as employee and customer fundraising. The group also provides in-kind support for projects that support literacy. In addition, through its charity The WHSmith Group Charitable Trust (Charity Commission no. 1013782), the group provides grants to literacy projects.

Charity partners

In 2017, WHSmith began fundraising for three charities, as voted for by employees: Cancer Research UK, Mind and the National Literacy Trust. According to the group's 2020/21 sustainability report, it fundraised £215,000 for those charities during the year.

In-kind support

As part of its long-term commitment to supporting the National Literacy Trust's Young Readers Programme, each year WHSmith hosts school visits to its stores and it donates books to participating schools.

Each year WHSmith supports World Book Day. In 2020/21 WHSmith partnered with the WHSmith Trust to donate £244,000 worth of book vouchers to schools across the UK, helping them to increase their library resources.

Employee-led support

WHSmith actively supports employee volunteering and fundraising efforts. In 2020/21, WHSmith employees and customers raised £104,000 for charitable causes.

According to the group's website, 'The WHSmith Trust matches employee fundraising or the value of time spent volunteering up to £1,000. The trust also

makes grants to employees who are members of a school parent-teacher association or a Board of Governors.'

Commercially led support

WHSmith supports a broad range of charities through the products it sells in stores, such as Christmas cards, cookery books, charity bears, bags and jigsaws.

Community grants

According to the 2020/21 sustainability report, the WHSmith Community Fund distributes the proceeds of the group's carrier bag levy to customer-nominated charities, schools, hospitals, hospices and community organisations in the UK.

Applications

General queries about corporate responsibility should be made by email to corporate.responsibility@whsmith.co.uk or by telephone on 01793 616161.

Corporate charity

The WH Smith Group Charitable Trust (Charity Commission no. 1013782) – see entry on page 276.

Community contributions

Cash donations worldwide	£717,000

The group's 2020/21 sustainability report provides the following helpful breakdown of its community contributions:

Cash donated	£580,000
Gifts in kind	£117,000
Staff time donated	£20,000
Management costs	£70,000

We have taken the figure of £717,000 (excluding management costs) to represent the group's total community contributions. It appears that the group's charitable giving is mainly concentrated in the UK, although we were unable to determine the exact proportion.

Wilkinson Hardware Stores Ltd

Community services and development, education and training, the environment, general charitable purposes, health, mental health and well-being

Company registration number: 8856837

Correspondent: CSR Team, J. K. House, Roebuck Way, Manton Wood, Worksop, Nottinghamshire S80 3EG (tel: 01909 505505; email: charity@wilko.com; website: www.corporate.wilko.com)

Directors: Sonia Fennell; Karen Mackay; Christopher Martin; Timothy Philips; Jerome Saint-Marc; Lisa Wilkinson (female: 50%; male: 50%).

Nature of business: Wilkinson Hardware Stores is a high-street chain which sells homewares and household goods under the name Wilko.

Financial information

Year end	01/02/2021
Turnover	£1,361,000,000
Pre-tax profit	£4,400,000

Total employees: 16,260

Main locations: The group has outlets throughout the UK and is headquartered in Worksop, Nottinghamshire.

Community involvement

The group awards small donations to various local causes in the areas where its stores operate and supports families in need through its partnerships with national charities.

Helping Hands

As part of the group's Helping Hands initiative, every Wilko store is given a small budget to be distributed in the form of cash donations or in-kind support to local groups and community projects. Organisations that can receive support include: local schools, playgroups and nurseries, parent or family groups, disability groups, youth clubs, groups for older people, luncheon clubs, community and tenants' associations and local authorities.

Community Care Plan

Wilkinson Hardware Stores launched the Community Care Plan to help families during the lockdowns by donating cash and products to food banks, the NHS and care homes, schools, animal shelters and other community groups and shelters.

In-kind support

As part of the Helping Hands initiative, the group's various stores donate Wilko gift cards or products to community groups. In-kind support can also include employee volunteer time.

In addition, according to the group's 2020/21 annual report, it donated 92,000 Easter eggs to NHS staff and the local community, 92,000 bottles of water and 10,920 individual nappies to foodbanks, 12,000 tea bags to support Mental Health Awareness week in Nottingham.

Employee-led support

Together for Families programme

In March 2018, the group launched its Together for Families programme, designed to support families in times of need. As part of the programme, Wilko employees and customers raise money to support three partner charities which work to tackle social issues affecting family life, namely, Alzheimer's Society, Save the Children and Teenage Cancer Trust. The funds raised are split equally between the charities, and 10% of donations made to Alzheimer's Society

go to Alzheimer's Scotland. The group aims to have raised £5 million for these charities by the end of the partnership.

Volunteering

Wilko employees are entitled to one day per year to volunteer in their local communities.

Commercially led support

Carrier bag levy

The group donates funds received from its 5 pence carrier bag levy to charities across the UK. Between 2011 and 2020, the group donated over £3 million to 13 charities and good causes in this way. Currently, the money raised is donated to The Prince's Trust, Keep Britain Tidy and Keep Wales Tidy.

Exclusions

The Helping Hands initiative cannot support the following:

- Expeditions
- Political parties
- Private or fee-paying schools
- Branches of national charities
- Profitable organisations
- Third-party private fundraising groups

Applications

Applications for small financial or in-kind donations through the Helping Hands scheme should be directed to your local Wilko store. Application forms can be collected from the store or downloaded from the group's corporate website. Once completed they should be returned to the store.

Any other enquiries can be made in writing to the correspondent at the group's address.

Community contributions

Cash donations UK	£1,380,000

According to Wilkinson Hardware Stores' 2021 annual report, it donated £1.38 million to charitable causes during the year.

Willmott Dixon Holdings Ltd

Community enterprise and social entrepreneurship, community services and development, education and training, general charitable purposes, social welfare

Company registration number: 198032

Correspondent: The Willmott Dixon Foundation, Suite 201 The Spirella Building, Bridge Road, Letchworth Garden City, Hertfordshire SG6 4ET (tel: 01462 671852; website: www. willmottdixon.co.uk/our-approach/social-value-and-sustainable-futures)

Directors: Rick Willmott; Colin Enticknap; Graham Dundas; Wendy

McWilliams; John Waterman; Hugh Raven; Christopher Sheridan; Julie Hirigoyen (female: 25%; male: 75%).

Nature of business: Willmott Dixon specialises in construction, residential development and property support services.

Financial information

Year end	31/12/2021
Turnover	£1,101,470,000
Pre-tax profit	£11,210,000

Total employees: 2,185

Main locations: The group has locations across England.

Community involvement

The group delivers most of its community activities through its corporate charity, The Willmott Dixon Foundation (Charity Commission no. 326530), which supports training projects for young people and the welfare of people with disabilities. Support is provided through cash and in-kind donations, employee fundraising and volunteering.

In 2020 the group launched its Now or Never strategy. The website provides details of how Willmott Dixon will address environmental issues in partnership with other businesses, communities and individuals. In October 2020 it launched a digital work experience programme for young people interested in entering the construction sector.

Employee-led support

Each year, management trainees from across the business are nominated to take part in the Foundation Trainee Challenge. According to the group's website, the challenge aims to 'identify, plan and deliver a project which will leave a lasting legacy in the local community'. While fundraising plays a part in the challenge, the primary aim is to create positive change through the donation of time and skills.

Staff also mentor young people through the foundation and engage in voluntary work of their choice. In 2021, employees donated over 29,000 hours of their time to various community activities.

Applications

Contact the correspondent for more information.

Corporate charity

The Willmott Dixon Foundation (Charity Commission no. 326530) – see entry on page 286.

Community contributions

Total contributions UK	£2,400,000

According to the group's 2021 Performance Review, the group

valued its financial contributions and in-kind donations at £1.4 million. This figure also includes donations made by staff.

A further £1 million was spent on social enterprises.

Wise Music Group Ltd

Education and training, general charitable purposes, health

Company registration number: 884449

Correspondent: The CSR Team, 14–15 Berners Street, London W1T 3LJ (tel: 020 7612 7400; email: music@wisemusic.com; website: www.wisemusic.com)

Directors: Nicholas Kemp; Christopher Butler; John Castaldo; Claude Duvivier; Ian Gilroy; David Holley; David Rockberger; Jonathan Smith; Marcus Wise; Mildred Wise; Robert Wise; Tomas Wise (female: 8%; male: 92%).

Nature of business: Wise Music Group is engaged in the publishing, wholesaling and retailing of printed music and books and is a publisher of standard and classical music copyright.

Financial information

Year end	31/12/2021
Turnover	£7,414,590,000
Pre-tax profit	£1,165,000,000

Total employees: 119

Main locations: In the UK, the group has offices in London and Bury St Edmunds. It also has offices worldwide.

Community involvement

The group's charitable giving is channelled through its corporate charity, Music Sales Charitable Trust (Charity Commission no. 1014942).

Through its charity, the group seeks to relieve cases of need and hardship and further the education of people in the UK, particularly those in London and Bury St Edmunds.

According to the group's 2021 annual report, the group supports 'initiatives with organizations working in areas such as economic empowerment and business development; housing; legal services and bail; mental health services; legislative reform; physical health services; and voting resources and education.'

Employee-led support

The group supports staff in their charitable ventures and encourages participation in the Give A Day company volunteering initiative, which allows staff to take one day off a year to volunteer for a registered charity.

Applications

Contact the correspondent for more information.

Corporate charity

Music Sales Charitable Trust (Charity Commission no. 1014942) – see entry on page 261.

Community contributions

We were unable to determine a figure for the group's community contributions.

The financial figures have been converted from EUR to GBP using the exchange rate at the time of writing (October 2022).

WPP Group Ltd

General charitable purposes

Company registration number: 2670617

Correspondent: Andrea Harris, Head of Sustainability, Sea Containers, 18 Upper Ground, London SE1 9GL (tel: 020 7282 4600; email: sustainability@wpp.com; website: www.wpp.com/sustainability)

Directors: Roberto Quarta; Mark Read; John Rogers; Nicole Seligman; Angela Ahrendts; Jacques Aigrain; Sandrine Dufour; Terek Farahat; Tom Ilube; Cindy Rose; Sally Susman; Keith Weed; Jasmine Whitbread; Ya-Qin Zhang; Balbair Kelly-Bisla; Simon Dingemans (female: 44%; male: 56%).

Nature of business: WPP Group is an international group of companies providing a wide range of communications, management, advertising and public relations services.

Financial information

Year end	31/12/2021
Turnover	£12,800,000,000
Pre-tax profit	£950,800,000

Total employees: 109,382

Main locations: In the UK, WPP's office is in London.

Community involvement

WPP supports a variety of charities and causes through cash grants and pro bono work.

In-kind support

The group's support comes predominantly in the form of pro bono services. The group seeks to 'boost the impact' of charities and NGOs by providing communication and creative services for little or no fee.

WPP media agencies also secure free media space on behalf of pro bono clients.

Employee-led support

Staff are encouraged to undertake voluntary work, with half of WPP

companies having formal volunteering policies in place.

In 2021, VMLY&R, a subsidiary of WPP, closed all of its 82 offices for one day in September to enable 12,000 staff to volunteer their time in their local communities.

Applications

Most of the group's charitable giving and pro bono work is managed within WPP companies, based on 'their values and employees' passions'. Contact your local company for more information.

Community contributions

| Cash donations worldwide | £41,000,000 |

According to the group's 2021 annual report, the group made charitable donations totalling £41 million.

WPP valued its pro bono work at £7.6 million. The report also states that 'WPP media agencies negotiated free media space worth £17.3 million on behalf of pro bono clients.'

Xerox (UK) Ltd

Community enterprise and social entrepreneurship, community services and development, education and training, general charitable purposes, health, social welfare, STEM

Company registration number: 330754

Correspondent: The CSR Team, Building 4, Uxbridge Business Park, Sanderson Road, Uxbridge, Middlesex UB8 1DH (tel: 01895 251133; website: www.xerox.co.uk/en-gb/about/corporate-citizenship/uk-trust)

Directors: Anthony Arthurton; Darren Cassidy; David Dyas; Julie Ward; Richard Pitceathly (female: 20%; male: 80%).

Nature of business: The principal activity of the group is the marketing and financing of xerographic and electronic printing equipment, document managing systems and ancillary supplies in the UK. The ultimate parent company of Xerox (UK) Ltd is Xerox Corporation, incorporated in the USA.

Financial information

Year end	31/12/2021
Turnover	£305,600,000
Pre-tax profit	(£33,800,000)

Total employees: 23,300

Main locations: The group's UK headquarters is based in Uxbridge.

Community involvement

In the UK, the group's giving is predominantly channelled through its corporate charity, The Xerox (UK) Trust. The group also provides financial support to universities, colleges and other non-profit organisations across the world, with a particular interest in education and disaster relief.

Education

In other parts of the world, the group runs grassroots education programmes aimed at inspiring young people to take an interest in STEM.

As part of the Xerox Science Consultant Programme, employees visit schools in New York and teach science to students who may not have access to STEM education.

Disaster relief

Xerox champions several organisations that respond to natural disasters across the world. Xerox also provides aid to its employees and their neighbours in crises during natural disasters.

Employee-led support

Xerox allows staff paid time off to volunteer for registered charities. In 2021, staff completed over 11,454 hours of voluntary work.

Applications

For The Xerox (UK) Trust, contact xeroxuktrust@xerox.com. All other enquiries should be directed to the correspondent.

Corporate charity

The Xerox (UK) Trust (Charity Commission no. 284698) – see entry on page 287.

Community contributions

Cash donations worldwide	£1,117,000

The group's 2022 CSR Report states that it invested £1.12 million (USD 1.28 million) into charitable causes. We were unable to determine a figure for UK charitable contributions during the year.

Note: figures from the group's CSR report have been converted from USD using the exchange rate at the time of writing (October 2022)

Yorkshire Building Society

Community services and development, education and training, emergency response/relief, general charitable purposes, health, housing and homelessness, money and debt advice, social welfare

Company registration number: FCA 106085

Correspondent: CSR Team, Yorkshire House, Yorkshire Drive, Bradford BD5 8LJ (tel: 0345 120 0100; email: corporateresponsibility@ybs.co.uk; website: www.ybs.co.uk)

Directors: John Heaps; Guy Bainbridge; Alison Hutchinson; Angela Darlington; Mark Parsons; Dina Matta; Jennelle

Tiling; Alasdair Lenman; David Morris (female: 44%; male: 56%).

Nature of business: Yorkshire Building Society provides financial services, including mortgages, insurance products and financial advice.

Financial information

Year end	31/12/2021
Turnover	£577,600,000
Pre-tax profit	£320,000,000

Total employees: 3,300

Main locations: Yorkshire Building Society is headquartered in Bradford and has branches throughout the UK.

Community involvement

The group offers support for communities through its corporate charity, the Yorkshire Building Society Charitable Foundation (Charity Commission no. 1069082), as well as through charity partnerships, community programmes and fundraising activities, and by encouraging employee volunteering.

The group's Real Help for Real Lives strategy focuses the group's community investment on tackling youth homelessness and supporting the financial well-being of young people. In 2021, the group supported these two themes by continuing its partnership with End Youth Homelessness and delivering its financial literacy and employability programmes, Money Minds and Career Minds, to young people in schools across the UK. Money Minds mini-sessions were also rolled out into high-street stores during the school holidays, promoting discussions about finances between young people and their families.

Partnerships

In 2021, the group continued its partnership with End Youth Homelessness, a group of grassroots charities working together to end youth homelessness in the UK. Over the duration of the partnership, donations from the group, employees, customers, and the public raised over £1.1 million, helping more than 400 young people (aged 16 to 25) move into their own rented homes. By funding a rent deposit scheme and providing rental deposit guarantees, initial rent payments and grants for home essentials and furniture, the partnership helped homeless young people overcome financial barriers to living independently. According to its website, the group will continue to support End Youth Homelessness by funding the charity's Housing Fund, which provides bursary and bond schemes.

Yorkshire Building Society also partners with the charity Age UK. This

partnership supports the Age UK Building Better Lives programme. According to the group's Environmental, Social and Governance (ESG) Report 2021, this programme 'provides intensive one-to-one support sessions, local workshops, and tailored expert advice to older people in eight communities across the UK'. So far, the group and its employees have raised over £500,000 for the charity.

The group is also a long-standing corporate volunteering partner of The Silver Line, a helpline for older people that aims to reduce loneliness and isolation.

In-kind support

Yorkshire Building Society makes in-kind donations to charitable organisations and individuals every year. According to the group's ESG Report 2021, it made in-kind donations to the value of £102,000 during the year.

Employee-led support

All group employees are entitled to 31 hours of paid leave to take part in voluntary or charitable activities annually. In 2021, colleagues donated over 2,700 hours of volunteering in total, which was worth £50,400.

Employees volunteer for the group's Money Minds and Career Minds programmes to deliver financial literacy sessions, employability workshops and student mentoring. Employees volunteer as telephone befrienders for the group's partner Silver Line and teams of employees also volunteer together to provide practical support to local charities and community groups. Previous examples of team volunteering have included redecorating and rejuvenating community areas, hospices and older people's residential homes, and supporting homeless people at shelters and soup kitchens.

Commercially led support

Small Change Big Difference

The group's customers can choose to take part in the Small Change Big Difference scheme, whereby the annual pence interest on savings and mortgage accounts is donated to the group's corporate charity. A maximum of 99 pence per account per year is donated to the foundation.

Applications

General enquiries and questions about the group's volunteering programme can be submitted via email to community@ybs.co.uk. Alternatively, speak to a staff member in your local branch.

Corporate charity

Yorkshire Building Society Charitable Foundation (Charity Commission no. 1069082) – see entry on page 287.

Community contributions

Cash donations UK	£1,870,000

According to its ESG Report 2021, during the year the group made a charitable contributions totalling £1.87 million. The following breakdown was provided:

Other	£429,000
Age UK	£344,000
Financial resilience	£290,000
Yorkshire Building Society Foundation	£100,000
In-kind donations	£92,000
Bradford employability/digital skills	£76,000
Volunteering time	£54,000
Other charities	£10,000

As per our standard practice, we have not included customer or employee fundraising in our figure for the group's total contributions (£460,000).

Zurich Insurance Group

Community services and development, education and training, emergency response/relief, general charitable purposes, health, housing and homelessness, humanitarian aid, mental health and well-being, social welfare, work outside the UK

Company registration number: BR7985

Correspondent: Corporate Responsibility Team, The Zurich Centre, 3000 Parkway, Whiteley, Fareham, Hampshire PO15 7JZ (tel: 0800 096 6233; email: CRZurichUK@uk.zurich.com; website: www.zurich.co.uk/en/about-us/corporate-responsibility/community)

Directors: Michel Liès; Christoph Franz; Joan Amble; Catherine Bessant; Dame Alison Carnwath; Michael Halbherr; Sabine Keller-Busse; Monica Mächler; Kishore Mahbubani; Jasmin Staiblin; Barry Stowe (female: 50%; male: 50%).

Nature of business: Zurich is an insurance company headquartered in Zurich, Switzerland and, according to its website, has around 55,000 employees working in over 215 countries. The group's UK branch provides a range of personal, business, public sector and charity insurance products.

Financial information

Year end	31/12/2021
Turnover	£61,740,000,000
Pre-tax profit	£4,710,000,000

UK employees: Approx. 5,000

Total employees: 55,369

Main locations: Zurich has offices located throughout the UK and its head office is based in Fareham, Hampshire.

Community involvement

Zurich's UK community involvement is channelled through the Zurich Community Trust (Charity Commission no. 266983). The trust manages Zurich's grant-making, employee volunteering and pro bono activities in the UK. According to its website, the Zurich Community Trust works in partnership with over 100 charities across the UK every year.

Internationally, the group's community involvement is supported by the Zurich Foundation, registered in Switzerland. The foundation's local grant programmes give Zurich offices the opportunity to apply for funding to initiate long-term strategic relationships with local community organisations that tackle issues such as health and well-being, youth empowerment and disaster resilience. The foundation also funds the Zurich Flood Resilience Alliance, a multi-sector co-operation which focuses on finding practical ways to help communities in strengthening their resilience to flood risk.

Partnerships

In 2018, Zurich UK employees chose Dementia UK and Place2Be as their charity partners. Zurich UK fundraises and donates cash to the Zurich Community Trust to support these two charities. According to the trust's website, both charities receive £250,000 every year.

In-kind support

Zurich employees are encouraged to share their knowledge and skills through programmes involving national and local partners managed by the Zurich Community Trust.

Skillshare projects – the purpose of these projects is to allow employees to use their skills to make an important contribution to a community organisation in a short space of time. Projects are usually one-off and can cover a wide range of areas – from marketing to business and strategic planning to social media training – and range in length from 2 to 20 hours, either in one session or over a period of a few months.

Zurich Youth Skills – according to Zurich's website, the 'programme involves Zurich employees volunteering in schools to teach secondary school students about financial literacy and careers in financial services, as well as providing guidance on soft skills through CV and interview skills workshops, and mentoring'. The programme focuses on schools with higher deprivation indicators.

Employee-led support

Volunteering

Each year, Zurich employees in the UK give more than 4,000 days of volunteering time. All employees are entitled to three days' leave per year for volunteering. Employees take part in team challenges, skills-based volunteering and lunchtime volunteering. Examples include:

Challenge – Challenge is Zurich's biggest annual team volunteer event, bringing together employee teams from Zurich offices across the UK to complete a one-off project which benefits a local voluntary organisation or school.

Call in Time – employees volunteer to call an older person supported by Age UK to have a chat and check on their well-being.

Evolving – the programme gives people in the last six months of employment one half day a week to volunteer in their local community.

Employee fundraising

Payroll giving – voluntary donations can be made through payroll giving to support the work of the Zurich Community Trust.

Matched funding – the Zurich Cares initiative is half funded by employees and is matched by the Zurich Community Trust using the annual donation it receives from Zurich UK businesses.

Zurich Cares Lottery – employees can take part in a monthly lottery, the proceeds from which are contributed to the Zurich Cares initiative.

Commercially led support

Sponsorship

The Zurich Forest – in 2020, the group became the exclusive sponsor of a reforestation project with Brazilian-based non-profit Instituto Terra. According to the group's website, 'Zurich's grant covers the planting of one million seedlings of up to 120 scientifically selected native species, supporting the growth of healthy native forest.'

Support for the voluntary sector

Insurance and risk management guides – Zurich has worked with the Guardian and NCVO to produce free risk guides and webinars aimed specifically at the voluntary sector. The guides are available on the group's website (www.zurich.co.uk/en/charity-insurance/get-help/support-and-resources).

Applications

General enquiries regarding Zurich's corporate responsibility programme can be directed to the Corporate Responsibility team by email (CRZurichUK@uk.zurich.com).

ZURICH

If your organisation could benefit from the Skillshare volunteering initiative, email CRZurichUK@uk.zurich.com.

Corporate charity

Zurich Community Trust UK Ltd (Charity Commission no. 266983) – see entry on page 288.

Community contributions

Cash donations worldwide	£13,760,000

According to its 2021 annual report, during the year the group awarded £13.76 million in cash donations to charitable causes. We were unable to determine a figure for charitable contributions in the UK.

The financials from the group's 2021 annual report have been converted from EUR using the exchange rate at the time of writing (October 2022).

Corporate charities in alphabetical order

This edition of the guide provides a section containing information on 160 corporate charities (compared to 162 in the 13th edition), all of which have a close association with the company to which they are linked. Typically, corporate charities rely on their companies for a substantial part of their income.

Each entry provides an overview of charitable activities as well as details on grant-making such as the number of grants made, the total value of those grants, the beneficiaries and beneficial areas. This information can provide a useful starting point for any organisation considering applying to a corporate charity for funding.

abrdn Charitable Foundation

 Education; employment; financial wellness; the environment; climate change

UK and overseas where the company has a presence

(£) £1.28 million (2021)

OSCR number: SC042597

Trustees: Stephanie Bruce; Stephen Whitehead; Rene Buehlmann; Paul Aggett; David Gorman.

Correspondent: The Board of Directors, 10 Queen's Terrace, Aberdeen AB10 1XL (email: charitablefoundation@abrdn. com)

www.abrdn.com/corporate/ corporate-sustainability/abrdn- charitable-foundation

General information
Registered in 2011, this is the charitable foundation of abrdn plc (formerly known as Standard Life Aberdeen plc), a global investment management group, managing assets for both institutional and retail clients. The foundation's name

was changed from Standard Life Aberdeen Charitable Foundation in October 2021.

The foundation's support is separated into two categories, people and planet. People projects will focus on enabling education, employment and financial wellness. The planet category will focus on protecting nature and addressing climate change.

Emerging markets partnerships
In addition to its local grant-making, the foundation establishes partnerships with charities that are working to improve the needs of disadvantaged children in emerging market countries. In 2021, the foundation entered into a one-year partnership with Big Issue Invest to support its connecting futures programme.

Beneficiaries included: A list of beneficiaries was not available.

Financial information
Year end	31/12/2021
Assets	£1,310,000
Income	£2,220,000
Grant total	£1,280,000

Further financial information
In 2021, grants were broken down as follows: local community support (£1.05 million) and emerging markets projects (£238,800).

Exclusions
The foundation's local community funding does not support:
- Projects that promote religious or political views or discriminate against sexual orientation, gender, etc.
- Crowdfunding initiatives
- Individuals
- Capital build costs
- Projects that do not support at least one of the UN Sustainable Development goals
- Activities located outside a community local to an abrdn plc office

Applications
Complete an expression of interest form on the foundation's website. The board of directors meets and reviews funding requests on a quarterly basis.

Sources of information
Accounts; annual report; OSCR record; Companies House; funder's website.

abrdn Financial Fairness Trust

 Financial well-being; research, campaigning and policy work

UK, with a preference for Scotland

(£) £754,300 (2021)

OSCR number: SC040877

Trustees: Alistair Darling; James Daunt; Naomi Eisenstadt; Prof. David Hall; Prof. Wendy Loretto; Graeme McEwan; Keith Skeoch; Euan Stirling; Lucy Heller; Ella Hugh; Matthew Upton; Kate Bell; Jenny Marra.

Correspondent: The Trustees, 1 George Street, Edinburgh EH2 2LL (tel: 0131 528 4243; email: enquiries@ financialfairness.org.uk)

 www.financialfairness.org.uk/en

@finan_fairness

General information
This is one of the corporate charities of abrdn plc (formerly Standard Life Aberdeen plc). The trust's website explains its history as follows:

> We were established in 2009 and became Standard Life Foundation in 2017 upon receiving a substantial donation from the unclaimed assets following Standard Life's demutualisation. At this time, our constitution, governance structure and name were all revised to align with this change.

Standard Life plc merged in 2017 to become Standard Life Aberdeen, and in 2021 became abrdn plc. We took this opportunity to choose a new, more descriptive, name for the organisation. From December 2021 we became abrdn Financial Fairness Trust.

Our new, mission-led name, also recognises the help and support provided by the company, from which we receive in-kind donations of office space and professional support.

The trust's mission is to improve financial well-being in the UK. It achieves this by funding research, campaigning and policy work (it intends to award around £3 million per year). More specifically, the work it supports examines and promotes measures to:

- Increase incomes for those on low-to-middle incomes.
- Ensure people have an adequate safety net, building savings and assets.
- Reduce the cost of living, making sure those on lower incomes are not paying more.
- Address issues related to spending and borrowing, particularly where it becomes problematic.

The trust's funding programmes are focused on three areas that influence financial well-being:

- **Income** – wages, social security, pensions and taxation
- **Spending** – cost of living, consumer spending, problem gambling, borrowing and payment problems
- **Assets** – general saving, retirement saving, housing and taxation.

Applications are invited from organisations undertaking charitable activities, including charities, voluntary organisations, think tanks, campaigning groups, research bodies and universities. The foundation supports UK-wide organisations but is keen to support work within Scotland, or UK-wide work with a Scottish focus.

Grants are typically made for between one and three years, with grant sizes ranging from £10,000 to £200,000. Funding is given for specific projects or, in some cases, for ongoing costs, including staff salaries and overheads. Organisations are encouraged to include a reasonable amount of core costs to cover their overheads when applying for funding.

Beneficiaries included: University of York (£147,200 in two grants); University of Oxford (£123,000); University of Southampton (£90,800); Parenting NI (£77,000); Gingerbread (£74,800); Centrepoint (£60,100); Coventry University (£59,800); Resolution Foundation (£12,000).

Financial information

Year end	31/12/2021
Assets	£103,510,000
Income	£2,590,000
Grant total	£754,300
Organisations supported	23

Further financial information

During 2021, grants were awarded via the trust's three programmes as follows: Income (£405,900); Assets (£198,000); Spending (£135,000). A further £15,500 was awarded through a category titled 'Cross cutting'.

Exclusions

The trust's funding guidelines state that it will not support applications:

- For the direct delivery of services, unless this is testing a new approach which has good potential to lead to wider change and be of significant benefit.
- For work that does not address those on low-to-middle incomes living in the UK.
- For work that is not charitable.
- From individuals.
- For work that is primarily the responsibility of statutory authorities.
- From organisations which have fewer than three non-executive people on their governing body (trustees/directors). You must have at least three who are not employees of the organisation or affiliated to it in any other way.
- For work that has already taken place.
- For general appeals.
- From organisations seeking to distribute grants on our behalf.
- For the promotion of religion.
- From organisations who have been rejected by us in the last 12 months. We may accept a further application within a 12-month period from universities if the application is from a different department and addresses different subject matter.
- From organisations whose accounts are in serious financial deficit.
- Where organisations have significant unrestricted reserves (including those that are designated). Generally up to nine months' expenditure is normally acceptable. We will make exceptions for some institutions which need to holder larger reserves such as universities and housing associations.

Applications

Application forms and guidelines can be downloaded from the trust's website. When completed, applications should be sent to applications@financialfairness.org.uk. The trust has two annual deadlines (in February and June). See the website for details of upcoming deadlines.

Sources of information

Accounts; annual report; OSCR record; funder's website; guidelines for applicants.

The Addleshaw Goddard Charitable Trust

General charitable purposes; education; health; legal education and the legal profession; social welfare

In the UK, Greater London, Manchester, Leeds, Aberdeen, Glasgow and Edinburgh. Also, Paris, Hamburg, Hong Kong, Singapore, Tokyo, Doha, Dubai and Muscat

£91,600 (2020/21)

CC number: 286887

Trustees: Bruce Lightbody; Louise Cliffe; Jonathan Cheney; Lisa Rodgers; Pervinder Kaur.

Correspondent: Bruce Lightbody, Trustee, Addleshaw Goddard LLP, 3 Sovereign Square, Sovereign Street, Leeds LS1 4ER (tel: 0113 209 2578; email: jonathan.cheney@ addleshawgoddard.com)

General information

Registered in 1983, this is the charitable trust of Addleshaw Goddard LLP, a law firm with offices in Leeds, London, Manchester, Aberdeen, Edinburgh, Glasgow and several other locations across the world.

The trust tries to help the communities it works in by supporting local projects near each of its offices. As part of the trust's activities to achieve this, it operates a matched staff fundraising scheme.

The trust's objects, detailed in its 2020/21 annual report and accounts, state that support is given to: 'Promote any charitable object or purpose connected with the legal profession and in particular to assist the persons engaged in that profession and the husbands, wives, civil partners, widows, widowers, surviving civil partners, children and other dependents of such persons being in conditions of need, hardship or distress.'

Beneficiaries included: A list of beneficiaries was not available. Previous beneficiaries include: Centrepoint, Changing Faces, NSPCC and Street League.

Financial information

Year end	05/04/2021
Assets	£323,100
Income	£77,000
Grant total	£91,600

Applications

Apply in writing to the correspondent.

Sources of information

Accounts; annual report; Charity Commission record; funder's website; company's CSR report.

The Adnams Community Trust

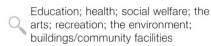 Education; health; social welfare; the arts; recreation; the environment; buildings/community facilities

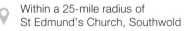 Within a 25-mile radius of St Edmund's Church, Southwold

£63,000 (2020/21)

CC number: 1000203

Trustees: Melvyn Horn; Simon Loftus; Andy Wood; Jonathan Adnams; Michael Heald; Joshua Freeman; Juliet Grimes; Geoffrey Stevens; Clare Teasdel; Samantha Crocker.

Correspondent: Rebecca Abrahall, Adnams Community Trust Administrator, Adnams plc, Sole Bay Brewery, East Green, Southwold, Suffolk IP18 6JW (tel: 01502 727200; email: communitytrust@adnams.co.uk)

http://adnams.co.uk/about/the-adnams-community-trust

facebook.com/Adnams

@adnams

General information

The Adnams Charity was founded in 1990 to mark the centenary of the Adnams brewing company and is funded mainly by the annual donation from the profits of Adnams plc. It supports a wide variety of organisations within a 25-mile radius of Southwold.

Applications from national charities which operate within a 25-mile area of Southwold may be considered if assurances can be given that the money will be used for a specific purpose within the area.

The charity prefers to make one-off grants for specific items which normally range from £100 to £2,500. The trustees expect to see the result of its donations within 12 months.

Areas of work

According to the charity's website, most grants are made in the following areas:

- Education
- Health and social welfare
- The arts
- Recreation
- Buildings and community facilities
- The environment/conservation
- History

Beneficiaries included: Harleston Church of England Primary Academy (£2,000); Tas Valley Pre-School (£1,500); Beccles Primary Academy (£1,200); Rural Coffee Caravan (£1,000); Martlesham Primary School (£320).

Financial information

Year end	31/08/2021
Assets	£9,200
Income	£62,200
Grant total	£63,000

Exclusions

The trust will not support:

- Individuals
- Religious organisations or private clubs unless they can demonstrate that the purpose of the grant is for something of clear public benefit, accessible to all
- Sponsorship, raffle prizes or the fundraising efforts of individuals
- Hardware associated with solar panels (though educational equipment linked to 'green energy' and energy conservation may be considered)

Grants are only made for specific purposes (ongoing running costs are rarely supported) and are not usually made to the same organisation two years in succession.

Applications

Application forms are available on request from the Charity Administrator. Grants are considered at quarterly meetings, in January, April, July and October. Application deadlines usually fall in the previous month and are listed on the charity's website.

Sources of information

Accounts; annual report; Charity Commission record; funder's website.

The Allen & Overy Foundation

 Disaster relief; access to justice; access to education, employment and training

 London; UK; worldwide

 £1.49 million (2020/21)

CC number: 1153738

Trustees: Hilde van der Baan; Franz Ranero; Mary Johnston; Joanna Page; Brendan Hannigan; Angela Clist; Mark Mansell; Phillip Mansfield; Andrew Wedderburn-Day.

Correspondent: The Trustees, One Bishops Square, London E1 6AD (tel: 020 3088 0000; email: allenoveryfoundation@allenovery.com)

www.allenovery.com/en-gb/global/about_us/corporate_responsibility/charitable_giving

General information

Allen & Overy is a large international law firm with its headquarters in London. Its foundation is funded by contributions from all Allen & Overy partners around the world. The core themes are: access to justice, and access to employment, education, and training.

Grants programmes

The following information about the two grants programmes has been taken from the foundation's website:

Local Charitable Giving

One example of our local charitable funds is the Allen & Overy Foundation's work in London. The Foundation, administered by the London Grants Committee, makes donations to charities that meet one or more of the following criteria:

- Charities which work to promote access to justice in the UK.
- Charities which support and develop projects focusing on issues of education, employment and training, based in or benefiting those in Tower Hamlets or Hackney.
- Charities to which Allen & Overy volunteers have made a significant contribution, by participating in their activities or providing pro bono and volunteering support.

The typical grant size is between £5,000 and £10,000.

Global Grants Programme

The Foundation is funded by contributions from Allen & Overy partners worldwide and, through the Global Grants Programme, supports:

- Our global charity partnership
- Disaster relief efforts
- Charities that address our core themes of access to justice, education and employment

Three charities are awarded grants of approximately £50,000 for one, two or three years. Charities may use 20% of the grant for core funding.

The staff at Allen and Ovary also select a global charity partner. The partnership helps raise money and support the charity over a period of two years.

Beneficiaries included: Hope and Homes for Children (£373,800); Charities Aid Foundation (£125,700); UN High Commissioner for Refugees (£75,000); The Redress Trust (£50,000); Law Centres Network (£25,000); Protect (£10,000); Prisoners' Advice Service (£5,000).

Financial information

Year end	30/04/2021
Assets	£813,700
Income	£1,620,000
Grant total	£1,490,000

Applications

Application guidelines and up-to-date information on application submission dates for each grants programme are available on the foundation's website.

Sources of information

Accounts; annual report; Charity Commission record; funder's website.

Alpkit Foundation

 Outdoor experiences

UK

£ £140,000 (2020/21)

CC number: 1162585

Trustees: David Hanney; Caroline Fry; Rehna Yaseen; Eloise Cundill; Pete Whittaker; Louise Bailey; Liam Reeves; Adge Last; Kenneth Stocker; Colin Stocker; Nicholas Smith.

Correspondent: The Trustees, Alpkit Ltd, Unit 12–14 Oak House, Moorgreen Industrial Park, Engine Lane, Newthorpe, Nottinghamshire NG16 3QU (email: akf@alpkit.com)

 www.alpkit.com/foundation

 facebook.com/alpkitfoundation

General information

The foundation was registered with the Charity Commission in July 2015 and is the charitable foundation of Alpkit, a technical outdoor clothing and equipment company.

The foundation's primary aim is to enable people to take part in outdoor experiences. The foundation meets this objective by making small grants in support of grass-roots projects that 'tackle issues such as diversity and inclusion in the outdoors, participation, education, conservation and protection of our natural environment and health and wellbeing'. Grants are awarded to individuals, groups and organisations.

Areas of work

According to its website, the foundation is particularly interested in projects that:

- Encourage responsible outdoor activity
- Have long-lasting benefits Introduce new people to get outdoors
- Demonstrate value for money

According to its website the foundation favours the following types of project:

- Diversity and Inclusion Projects that engage individual and groups from a diverse range of backgrounds
- Environmental Projects that seek to support, conserve, or generate understanding of our environment and wild places
- Health Projects enabling people to gain physical and mental wellbeing from the Great Outdoors
- Education Projects such as First Aid, D of E, Forest Schools and Mountain Leader
- Participation Projects that get more people experiencing the Great Outdoors

Beneficiaries included: A list of beneficiaries was not available.

Financial information

Year end	31/10/2021
Assets	£40,900
Income	£167,300
Grant total	£140,000
Organisations supported	534

Exclusions

The foundation's website states that it will not support:

- Holidays
- Charity challenges
- Commercially led travel Expeditions that are not focused the Great Outdoors (e.g. rebuilding schools, overseas medicine)
- Scout Jamborees – due to the large number of participants involved in Scout Jamborees, this is not something we are able to support. We do support the Scout Association through our Youth in Adventure Fund
- Retrospective applications – make sure you get your application in on time!

Applications

Application forms are available on the foundation's website. The trustees meet every two months to consider applications.

Sources of information

Accounts; annual report; Charity Commission record; funder's website.

Anglo American Foundation

 Accountability and policy advocacy; health and well-being; education; livelihoods; the environment and biodiversity

UK, Ireland, Australia, Botswana, Brazil, Canada, Chile, Colombia, Ecuador, Namibia, Peru, Sierra Leone, Singapore, South Africa and Zimbabwe

£ £3.41 million (2021)

CC number: 1111719

Trustees: Jonathan Samuel; Anik Michaud-Ahmed; Norman Mbazima; Yvonne Mfolo.

Correspondent: The Trustees, 17 Charterhouse Street, London EC1N 6RA (tel: 020 7968 8888; email: aagf@angloamerican.com)

www.angloamericangroup foundation.org

General information

The foundation was established in 2005 by Anglo American plc, a multinational mining company. The foundation's website states that:

The Foundation supports programmes aligned with the Group's Sustainable Mining Plan, focusing on the areas of accountability and policy advocacy, health and well-being, education, livelihoods and biodiversity. Our priorities are informed by the UN's Sustainable Development Goals and we aim to make progress against them in the countries we operate in.

The foundation receives donations from Anglo American and supports development initiatives in the areas where the company has operations, projects, or representative offices, these include the UK, Australia, Botswana, Brazil, Canada, Chile, China, Colombia, Peru and Zimbabwe.

The foundation's 2021 accounts provide the following information on its giving structure:

The Foundation seeks to develop continuing relationships with a select number of charitable organisations which contribute to its identified funding priorities and therefore mostly does not accept unsolicited funding applications. Through internal and external engagement, the Foundation identifies funding opportunities and develops joint solutions to foster sustainable socio-economic development (SED) in host communities. Resources are also allocated by way of matching funds raised for charities by employees who work in the Anglo American London office and through the employee volunteering programme Ambassadors for Good.

Beneficiaries included: Pyxera Global (£1.02 million); Anglo American Foundation (£953,700); Transparency International Australia (£611,300); Early Childcare Education Learning Centre Canada (£211,200); Gems and Jewellery Export Promotion Council (£97,100).

Financial information

Year end	31/12/2021
Assets	£77,330,000
Income	£80,300,000
Grant total	£3,410,000

Further financial information

Grants were broken down as follows:

Community development	£2.05 million
Capacity development	£611,300
Education and training	£569,200
Health and welfare	£151,500
Employee match funding	£22,300
Other social investment	£2,500

We were unable to determine the portion of grants awarded in the UK. Only a selection of larger grants was available to view in the 2021 accounts.

Applications

The foundation does not accept unsolicited applications.

Sources of information

Accounts; annual report; Charity Commission record; funder's website.

The Apax Foundation

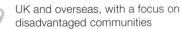

Social entrepreneurship; social mobility; social welfare; education; support for refugees

UK and overseas, with a focus on disadvantaged communities

£2.09 million (2021)

CC number: 1112845

Trustees: Sir Ronald Cohen; Roxana-Viorica Mirica; Jason Wright; Rohan Haldea; Shashank Singh; Mitch Truwit; David Marks; Dr Peter Englander.

Correspondent: Kate Albert, Foundation Manager, 33 Jermyn Street, London SW1Y 6DN (tel: 020 7872 6300; email: foundation@apax.com)

www.apax.com/responsibility/apax-foundation

General information

The Apax Foundation is the corporate charity of Apax Partners LLP and receives a percentage of the firm's profits to distribute to good causes. The foundation focuses its grant-making on charitable organisations and social enterprises which work with under-served communities to support:

- Relief of financial hardship
- Social mobility
- Entrepreneurship
- Education
- Helping refugees into work or entrepreneurship

As well as making grants, the foundation also runs a matched giving scheme for Apax employees.

Beneficiaries included: Breaking Barriers; Opportunity Network; Sponsors for Educational Opportunity.

Financial information

Year end	31/12/2021
Assets	£78,760,000
Income	£1,930,000
Grant total	£2,090,000

Applications

Apply in writing to the correspondent.

Sources of information

Accounts; annual report; Charity Commission record; funder's website.

Ardbarron Trust Ltd

Awareness and understanding of the Christian gospel; social welfare; health care; literacy

UK and the 'developing world'

£4.89 million (2021)

CCNI number: NIC101111

Trustees: Martin Agnew; Geoffrey Agnew; John Agnew; Malcolm Johnston.

Correspondent: The Trustees, 9 Hightown Avenue, Newtownabbey, County Antrim BT36 4RT (tel: 028 9034 2733)

General information

Ardbarron Trust Ltd is funded by donations from John Henderson (Holdings) Ltd.

The trust makes grants to UK-registered charities and charities operating in developing countries. It also supports worldwide relief organisations and responds to emergency appeals where practical and medical aid is needed.

The trust's 2021 accounts state: 'The Trust exists to promote the Christian Gospel in Word and Deed, to help the prevention and relief of poverty, the provision of healthcare and literacy, and the relief of those in need by reason of youth, age, ill-health, disability, financial hardship or other disadvantage.'

Beneficiaries included: A list of beneficiaries was not available. Previous beneficiaries have included: Christian Missions Charitable Trust; Echoes of Service; Operation Mobilisation; Strategic Resource Group; Tear Fund; Youth for Christ.

Financial information

Year end	31/12/2021
Assets	£219,110,000
Income	£5,360,000
Grant total	£4,890,000
Organisations supported	319

Applications

Apply in writing to the correspondent.

Sources of information

Accounts; annual report; CCNI record.

The Arsenal Foundation

Education; sport; health, medical; disability; social welfare

Barnet, Camden, Hackney, Islington, Walthamstow and Hertsmere

£230,300 (2020/21)

CC number: 1145668

Trustees: Svenja Geissmar; Alan Sefton; Andrew Jolly; Vinaichandra Venkatesham; Frederick Hudson.

Correspondent: Samir Singh, Highbury House, 75 Drayton Park, London N5 1BU (tel: 020 7704 4406; email: ssingh@arsenal.co.uk)

www.arsenal.com/thearsenalfoundation

facebook.com/TheArsenalFoundation

@AFC_Foundation

@arsenal_foundation

General information

The Arsenal Foundation was established in 2012 as 'the club's grant-giving organisation'. The foundation aims to help young people in North London and around the world fulfil their potential.

The Gunners Fund

The aim of The Gunners Fund is to support charities in the boroughs of Islington, Camden and Hackney by offering smaller grants of up to £2,500 that can make a big difference to the community.

The following information is taken from the fund's grant-making guidelines:

In line with the overall objectives of The Foundation, priority will be given to the following areas of need:

- Education (including academic, social, physical education, skills training and community engagement);
- Sports capable of improving health;
- Medical;
- Sickness and the relief of suffering;
- Disability;
- Poverty; and
- Individual misfortune.

The following is a non-exhaustive list of potential beneficiaries or groups of beneficiaries:

- Organisations connected to Arsenal FC;
- Charity or community projects connected to Arsenal FC;
- Community groups, societies or projects;
- Projects that have been developed by Arsenal FC's community team;
- Staff-initiated projects;
- Supporter-initiated projects;
- Projects where The Foundation's donation, even though relatively small, will make a difference;
- Projects where the gesture of support from a charity associated with Arsenal FC can have a greater effect than the money itself;
- Football-linked campaigns or public bodies;
- Projects where the person requesting a donation is doing something active to raise money for the cause;
- Projects where the person is playing a significant and voluntary role in raising money for the charity; and
- Awards to reward success or achievement in areas of endeavour that fall within the objectives of The Foundation.

The foundation has also partnered with Islington Giving, which makes grants to voluntary organisations.

Beneficiaries included: Save the Children (£192,000).

Financial information

Year end	31/05/2021
Assets	£1,040,000
Income	£266,900
Grant total	£230,300

Further financial information

In previous years, grants have totalled around £1 million. Only recipients of grants of over £10,000 were listed. Donations of less than £10,000 totalled £14,800.

Applications

Application forms for the Gunners Fund are available to download from the foundation's website, along with grant-making guidelines. The foundation states that it is unable to respond to all of the applications it receives, due to the high volume, so if you do not receive a response within two months, you should assume that you have been unsuccessful.

Sources of information

Accounts; annual report; Charity Commission record; funder's website.

The Artemis Charitable Foundation

 Health; social welfare; education and training; the environment; global disasters and emergency appeals

UK and overseas

£924,800 (2021)

OSCR number: SC037857

Trustees: Stephanie Sutton, Emma Maher, Yemi Emiola, Derek Stuart, Zuoyi Zhou, Maria Ryder, Mark Niznik.

Correspondent: Marisa Charosky, Foundation Coordinator, 6th Floor, Exchange Plaza, 50 Lothian Road, Edinburgh EH3 9BY (email: charitablefoundation@artemisfunds.com)

www.artemisfunds.com/en/about-artemis/artemis-charitable-foundation

General information

The Artemis Charitable Foundation was founded in 2007 as the charitable arm of Artemis Investment Management LLP. According to its website, the foundation awards grants to 'core' charities in the UK and internationally in the following key areas:

- Health
- Poverty
- Education
- The environment

The foundation also makes donations to global disasters and emergencies when they occur.

According to the foundation's 2021 accounts, the trustee's policy is to award one-off grants; however, multi-year grants have been awarded on a small number of occasions. The foundation's website states that initial grants are generally of between £1,000 to £10,000 but amounts can increase if a

partnership develops into a multi-year relationship.

The foundation will consider providing unrestricted funding.

Eligibility

Charities must be registered in the UK but can operate in the UK or internationally. Preference is given to small and medium-sized charities (those with an income of less than £2 million per year). Innovative and sustainable projects that can be scaled up/replicated are preferred.

Charity of the Year

In addition to its annual core charity partners, Artemis employees vote for a Charity of the Year. In 2020, employees chose to support Challenge Partners, an education charity, and in 2021, employees chose Children's Hospices Across Scotland.

Beneficiaries included: Shivia Microfinance (£60.000); Client Earth (£57,500); City Harvest (£50,500); Reach Academy (£50,000); Mary's Meals (£21,200); Beaver Trust (£2,500); Trussell Trust (£250).

Financial information

Year end	31/12/2021
Assets	£659,400
Income	£1,020,000
Grant total	£924,800

Applications

Apply in writing via email with a covering letter, a brief proposal (ideally no more than two to three pages) containing an overview of your organisation's work and funding priorities, and details of your organisation's basic financial information, including income and expenditure activity from your latest accounts.

The trustees meet at the end of every month to consider applications.

Sources of information

Accounts; annual report; Charity Commission record; funder's website.

The Ove Arup Foundation

The built environment; engineering; architecture; education

UK and overseas

£242,800 (2020/21)

CC number: 328138

Trustees: Gregory Hodkinson; Ricky Tsui; Kate West; Alan Belfield; Faith Wainwright; Tim Chapman; Caroline Cole; Terry Hill.

Correspondent: John Ward, Secretary, Ove Arup Foundation, 8 Fitzroy Street, London W1T 4BJ (tel: 020 7636 1531;

email: foundation@ovearupfoundation.org)

 www.ovearupfoundation.org

 @OveArupFdn

 @ovearupfoundation

General information

This foundation was established in 1989 in the memory of Sir Ove Arup, who was an engineer, designer and philosopher. The trustees of the foundation are appointed by the board of Arup Group Ltd.

The foundation's aim is: 'the advancement of education of the public directed towards the promotion, furtherance, and dissemination of knowledge of matters associated with the built environment'. It commissions research and funds educational programmes and initiatives, with a strong emphasis on sustainability and interdisciplinary collaboration.

The website states that the foundation is 'committed to the benefit of practitioners from different fields learning from each other. Through its actively inclusive work with universities, communities and organisations around the world, the Ove Arup Foundation strives to create a professional culture of multiple perspectives and skills across different disciplines within the built environment.'

Beneficiaries included: Sydney Opera House (£55,400); The Learning Partnership (£39,800); The Technical University of Munich (£26,200); Placed Education (£20,000); The Design and Technology Association (£10,000); The Designing and Making Educational Trust (£5,000); The Anglo-Danish Society (£2,500).

Financial information

Year end	31/03/2021
Assets	£3,610,000
Income	£588,100
Grant total	£242,800
Organisations supported	9

Exclusions

Grants are not made to individuals for private study.

Applications

Application forms are available to download from the website. Trustees' meetings are held quarterly, in early December, March, June and September. The trustees will consider applications received by the Secretary by the middle of the preceding month.

Sources of information

Accounts; annual report; Charity Commission record; funder's website.

Ove Arup Partnership Charitable Trust

Education; social care; health; social welfare; disaster relief and poverty alleviation; local community development; the environment

UK and overseas

£589,400 (2020/21)

CC number: 1038737

Trustee: Ove Arup Partnership Trust Corporation Ltd.

Correspondent: Stephanie Wilde, Ove Arup and Partners Ltd, 8 Fitzroy Street, London W1T 4BJ (tel: 020 7636 1531; email: stephanie.wilde@arup.com)

General information

The Ove Arup Partnership Charitable Trust was first established by a trust deed in January 1978. The annual report for 2020/21 explains that the trust 'is not in receipt of a regular income and relies on gifts from Arup Group Limited'.

Income from the company is used to make donations to charities. With respect to the trust's grant-making policy, the trust's 2020/21 annual report also states:

> The Trustee considers causes and charities that operate in areas related to Arup's skills and business activities where these are aligned with Arup's values, as expressed in Ove Arup's 'Key Speech', of doing socially useful work and of being engaged in activities for the benefit of society at large.

> In deciding on specific recipients, the Trustee has regard to the size and structure of the recipient organisation in relation to the size of donation order to maximise the impact and effectiveness of that donation

Grants have previously been made for a wide range of purposes including education, social care, health, welfare, disaster relief, poverty alleviation, local community development and the environment.

Beneficiaries included: The Ove Arup Foundation (£400,000); Drukpa Trust (£80,000); Bridges to Prosperity (£22,600); Social Mobility Foundation (£10,000); Theatre Artists Fund (£2,000); Mission Remission (£1,000); StreetVet (£800); Marmalade Trust (£500).

Financial information

Year end	31/03/2021
Assets	£41,800
Income	£616,200
Grant total	£589,400

Further financial information

Only organisations that received grants of over £500 were listed as beneficiaries in the charity's accounts. Grants of under £500 totalled £2,900.

Applications

Apply in writing to the correspondent.

Sources of information

Accounts; annual report; Charity Commission.

The Asda Foundation

General charitable purposes including: social welfare; education; religion; health; citizenship; community development

England and Wales

£3.96 million (2021)

CC number: 1124268

Trustees: John Cookman; Jane Earnshaw; Jason Martin; Jodie Tate; Helen Selby; Rukia Hussain; Simon Lewis; Patricia Mitchell; Susan Hennessey.

Correspondent: Grants Team, Asda House, Great Wilson Street, Leeds, West Yorkshire LS11 5AD (email: asdafoundation@asda.co.uk)

 www.asdafoundation.org

 @asdafoundation

General information

The Asda Foundation is the corporate charity of the supermarket Asda. The foundation supports small, grassroots organisations with the aim of transforming communities and improving lives.

Open grants programmes are advertised on the foundation's website.

In January 2023, grants for organisations listed on the website included:

Cost of Living Grant

These grants support local community groups with increasing running costs due to the rising cost of living. The application window for these grants was due to close in February 2023 or as soon as the budget cap was reached.

Empowering Local Communities Grant

Grants are awarded to local groups and groups supporting refugees in the UK in the provision of activities that help to transform communities and improve lives. Applications were not being accepted for this grant at the time of writing.

U18 Better Starts Grant

Through this grants programme, grants are made to local groups that provide activities which help to give children a better start in life. Applications were not being accepted for this grant at the time of writing.

See the website for up-to-date information on grants currently being offered by the foundation.

Green Token Giving

Asda customers can nominate a small, local grassroots charity or good cause to be put forward for a quarterly customer vote. Winners of the vote get £500 and runners up get £200. Since 2021 the programme has been delivered online rather than in store.

Emergency funding

The foundation can provide assistance during times of emergency. This includes emergencies on a personal level, such as a house fire, or a community wide disaster, such as flooding.

Other

The foundation matches Asda employees' fundraising efforts up to £300 per employee per year. It also works in partnership with other charitable organisations.

Beneficiaries included: University of Leeds (£180,000); Jane Tomlinson's Run for All (£139,000); The Duke of Edinburgh's Award Charter (£127,500); Breast Cancer Now (£17,500); Moordown Community Association (£15,000).

Financial information

Year end	31/12/2021
Assets	£4,470,000
Income	£3,750,000
Grant total	£3,960,000

Further financial information

Grants to organisations were broken down as follows:

Transforming Communities and Improving Lives	£1.95 million
Green Token Giving	£971,600
Partnerships	£446,500
Digital Inclusion	£438,000
Other	£56,000
Colleague matched funding	£36,000
Community projects	£29,000
Emergency grants	£24,000

In addition, hardship grants totalling £45,000 were awarded to Asda colleagues.

Only beneficiaries of grants of over £10,000 were listed in the foundation's accounts.

Exclusions

Each programme has specific exclusions – see the relevant guidance on the foundation's website.

Applications

Further information on eligibility and how to apply for grants can be found on the foundation's website. In most cases, applicants are encouraged to contact their local Asda Community Champion to discuss eligibility and to receive an application form. For emergency grants, contact your local Asda store.

Sources of information

Accounts; annual report; Charity Commission record; funder's website; guidelines for applicants.

The Ashmore Foundation

 Education and training; community development; social and local enterprise

Countries in which Ashmore has a presence. Priority countries are reviewed regularly but currently include Colombia, India, Indonesia and Peru

£154,900 (2020)

CC number: 1122351

Trustees: Matthew Hill; Alyssa Nolan; Jonathan Shingler; Nichole Yepes; Lydia Toisuta; Tim Jenkins; Oscar Espindola; Patrick Cadell; Cemil Urganci; Jennifer Bingham; Mark Coombs; James Carleton.

Correspondent: The Trustees, 5th Floor, 61 Aldwych, London WC2B 4AE (tel: 020 3077 6153; email: info@ashmorefoundation.org)

www.ashmorefoundation.org

General information

Established in 2008, the Ashmore Foundation is the corporate charity of the Ashmore Group, an emerging markets investment management company.

Areas of work

The foundation works with local NGOs in emerging markets communities where the Ashmore Group operates. According to its website, the foundation's main areas of interest are:

- **Education** – the foundation is particularly interested in working with organisations that bring 'marginalised' children and young people from mainstream education into regular education, improve educational attainment of children and young people through higher quality or more relevant learning, and those seeking to improve the quality of life and job prospects of young people and marginalised community members through functional education and skills training.
- **Livelihoods** – the foundation makes grants to organisations providing vocational training for disadvantaged young people, building community knowledge, resources and capabilities for sustainable local enterprise, and to those supporting effective social enterprise benefitting disadvantaged groups.

Funding

Grants are usually distributed on a multi-year basis and range in size depending on the scale and nature of the programme, and the organisation's capacity.

Typically, grants are in the range of £20,000 to £50,000 per year over three years.

STARS Foundation

Through its partnership with the STARS Foundation, the charity funds awards for NGO excellence.

Beneficiaries included: Salva Terra (£50,800); Aangan Trust (£44,200); Children Change Colombia (£35,000); Voice for the Free (£5,000).

Financial information

Year end	31/12/2020
Assets	£8,740,000
Income	£343,800
Grant total	£154,900
Organisations supported	9

Further financial information

Figures have been converted from USD using the conversion rate at the time of writing (November 2022).

Exclusions

According to its 2020 accounts, the foundation will not make grants to organisations that:

- Fail to meet eligibility requirements
- Fail to provide sufficient information to enable adequate assessment
- Have paid staff related to Ashmore employees
- Personal appeals
- Are overtly political or pursue political agenda
- Are religious and seek to evangelise or proselytise

Animal charities are not supported, nor are requests for retrospective funding.

Applications

Unsolicited applications are not accepted. The foundation sources new partners through recommendations from experts, suggestions from Ashmore staff and detailed research by the foundation team.

Sources of information

Accounts; annual report; Charity Commission record; funder's website.

Axis Foundation

 General charitable purposes; small/local projects or causes

London, the South of England, the Midlands and Wales

£108,400 (2020/21)

CC number: 1126117

Trustees: Peter Varney; John Hayes; Michael Hayes; Timothy Hayes; Maurice Gertski; Sandra Ryan; Yusef Ibrahim.

Correspondent: The Trustees, Tramway House, 3 Tramway Avenue, Stratford E15 4PN (tel: 0330 045 0030; email: info@axisfoundation.com)

www.axisfoundation.org

@axisfoundation

General information

The foundation is the corporate charity of Axis Europe, a contractor active in social housing, education, commercial and retail sectors. Each year the company donates a percentage of its profits to the foundation.

According to its website, the foundation's priority is to support small local causes in the areas in which the company operates (London, the South of England, the Midlands and Wales.) The website also states that the foundation is 'dedicated to supporting causes that help improve lives from the underprivileged, vulnerable and disabled, to those who just need a hand to help realise their potential.'

Beneficiaries included: Demelza Hospice (£46,700); Farm Ability (£7,000); Sussex EDS and Swale Gloves (£6,000 each); Lifelites and Literacy Pirates (£5,000 each).

Financial information

Year end	31/03/2021
Assets	£185,000
Income	£225,600
Grant total	£108,400

Exclusions

The foundation's website states:

- We do not support national appeals
- We will not support any group project that is non-inclusive and is not open to all individuals and communities irrespective of gender, race or faith. Nor we will fund the advancement of religion or religious groups unless they offer a non-religious service to the local community
- We do not support projects that take place outside the UK
- We do not support projects that are the responsibility of a statutory body
- We do not fund projects of a political nature
- We do not fund animal welfare projects

Applications

Applications can be made via the foundation's website.

Sources of information

Annual report; accounts; Charity Commission record; funder's website.

B&Q Foundation

 Community spaces; home improvements

UK and the Republic of Ireland

£1.07 million (2021/22)

CC number: 1183275

Trustees: Catherine Burge; Simon Hewett-Avison; Anna Peters; Aleah Truscott; Vicki Carroll; Antony Purnell; Andrew Moat; Paul Crisp.

Correspondent: The Trustees, B&Q House, Chestnut Avenue, Chandler's Ford, Eastleigh SO53 3LE (tel: 023 8069 0000; email: B&QFoundation@b-and-q.co.uk)

www.diy.com/corporate/bandq-foundation

General information

This foundation registered with the Charity Commission in May 2019. It is the corporate charity of B&Q, a British DIY and home improvement retailing company. It is supported by the fundraising efforts and volunteers from the company.

The foundation aims to makes grants to registered charities that work to improve housing and community spaces and support people who are experiencing poor quality housing and homelessness. Charities must be based in the UK or Ireland.

Grants are typically one-off and up to the value of £5,000. Occasionally, higher value grants may be awarded.

Beneficiaries included: A list of beneficiaries was not available.

Financial information

Year end	31/01/2022
Assets	£73,800
Income	£1,720,000
Grant total	£1,070,000
Organisations supported	242

Exclusions

The foundation does not give grants to individuals.

Applications

Register your interest by filling out the form linked to the website.

Sources of information

Charity Commission record; funder's website.

Bally's Foundation

 Mental health

UK. Also, Canada, Gibraltar, Hong Kong, Malta, the Philippines (Manilla), Sweden, Ukraine and the USA

£2.10 million (2021)

CC number: 1188099

Trustees: Christina Southall; Anita Iwugo; Kevin Hopgood; Neil Goulden; Holly Spiers.

Correspondent: The Trustees, 10 Piccadilly, London WJ10 0DD (email: a contact form is available on the website)

https://gamesysfoundation.org

General information

The Bally's Foundation (formerly known as The Gamesys Foundation) was established in February 2020 by Gamesys Group who are now owned by Bally's Corporation. The foundation supports the well-being of individuals with mental health issues.

Grants are made to UK-based organisations with a minimum annual income of £50,000, or a minimum annual income of €50,000 for territories outside the UK. Funding is prioritised for countries where Gamesys plc either trades or has offices.

Beneficiaries included: Mental Health Innovations (£600,000); Ambitious about Autism (£200,000); Women's Aid (£150,000); Smiles Campaign (£89,100); Orchard OCD (£40,000); Body and Soul (£10,000); Child Bereavement (£5,000).

Financial information

Year end	31/12/2021
Assets	£525,100
Income	£1,820,000
Grant total	£2,100,000

Exclusions

The following information was taken from the foundation's website:

We do not fund:

- Organisations dealing with physical health care, research, treatment and rehabilitation. For example, this includes areas such as cancer research and treatment, heart disease, dementia, epilepsy etc
- Applications relating to sports, such as sports scholarships, sponsorship, or sporting events
- Organisations or activities which preach or spread religious beliefs or attempt to convert people to their own belief or religious views
- Organisations or activities which adopt a partisan political stance, or which are party political
- Organisations that advocate the use of violence to campaign or influence public opinion
- One-off conferences or workshops even within the mental health field, as it is difficult to demonstrate the impact that such events are likely to achieve
- Funding can still be made available for conferences, workshops and other gatherings along as they form part of longer-term projects
- Appeals for the funding of study or the attainment of qualifications, whether by an individual or group sponsorship
- Organisations or applications focussed solely or primarily on raising public awareness of mental health issues via marketing campaigns. Funding can still be made available for such campaigns as part of a larger-scale project which will deal mainly with the alleviation, support and treatment of mental health

Applications

Apply via the foundation's website.

Sources of information

Charity Commission; funder's website.

Bank of Scotland Foundation

Social exclusion and disadvantage

Scotland

£5.02 million (2021)

OSCR number: SC032942

Trustees: Graham Blair; Alison Macdonald; Graeme Thompson; Karen Watt; Donald MacKechnie; Julianne Reddin; Jackie Leiper; Ken MacIntosh; Laura Armstrong; Jon Alexander.

Correspondent: The Trustees, The Mound, Edinburgh EH1 1YZ (tel: 07385 024428; email: enquiries@bankofscotlandfoundation.co.uk)

www.bankofscotlandfoundation.org

facebook.com/bankofscotlandfoundation

@bofsfoundation

General information

The Bank of Scotland Foundation was established in 2002 to disperse funds from an annual donation from Lloyds Banking Group to charities across Scotland. Over the past decade, the foundation has awarded over £14 million to almost 2,000 charities through its various grants programmes.

Eligibility

Eligible organisations must be a charity registered in Scotland and operational for more than one year. Organisations must have all regulatory returns up to date with OCSR and Companies House. See the foundation's grants programmes on its website for specific criteria.

Grants programmes

Launched in 2019, Supporting Positive Change Across Scotland is the foundation's five-year strategic plan which aims to focus its funds and impact on charities that address social exclusion or disadvantage. Charities supported may be addressing disadvantages such as homelessness, mental health, poverty, debt issues, learning disabilities, illiteracy, unemployment or poor health. They may also be addressing exclusionary challenges for minority groups including people with disabilities, LGBT people, drug users, institutional care leavers, older people or young people.

At the time of writing (November 2022), the foundation had three grants programmes:

▷ **Reach**: charities with an annual income of £1 million or less can apply for grants of between £1,000 and £25,000 to enable them to address social disadvantage or exclusion
▷ **Change**: charities with an income of between £500,000 and £5 million can apply for capital costs, project costs or unrestricted core costs of between £50,000 to £100,000 per annum, over the course of one to two years.
▷ **Invest**: charities with an income of between £50,000 and £1 million can apply for grants of between £10,000 and £50,000 per year for between two and five years. The grants, either for project, capital or core costs, aim to support different themes each year.

Further information on each of the funding streams is available on the foundation's website.

Employees of Lloyds Bank in Scotland can also claim up to £1,000 in matched giving funding. Up to £500 is available for fundraising events, as well as up to £500 for voluntary time given.

Beneficiaries included: LGBT Youth Scotland (£172,500); St Andrews Environmental Network (£134,600); Healthy 'n' Happy Community Development Trust (£107,600); Families Like Us (£70,500); Home-Start Lorn (£25,000); Street Soccer Scotland (£24,500); Cruse Bereavement Care Scotland (£23,200); Epilepsy Connections (£20,000).

Financial information

Year end	31/12/2021
Assets	£2,270,000
Income	£5,310,000
Grant total	£5,020,000
Organisations supported	168

Further financial information

In 2021, the foundation made 168 grants totalling £4.75 million under the theme of social exclusion and disadvantage. These grants ranged from £1,300 to £176,200. In addition, the foundation

awarded matched funding totalling £270,400. Only organisations that received grants of over £20,000 were listed as beneficiaries in the foundation's accounts. A full list of beneficiaries can be found on the foundation's website.

Exclusions

The foundation does not support the following organisations and causes:

▷ Political organisations
▷ Individuals
▷ Animal welfare
▷ The promotion of religion
▷ Medical research
▷ Charities that redistribute funding for subsequent grant-making to other organisations and/or individuals
▷ Advertising
▷ Sponsorship
▷ Foreign travel
▷ Overseas projects

Applications

Check the foundation's website for current deadlines and fund opening dates. A 'Hints and Tips' application guidance document can also be found on the website.

Sources of information

Accounts; annual report; OSCR record; funder's website.

The Barbour Foundation

 Social welfare; education; employability; homelessness; children and young people; older people; health; medical research; the environment; heritage; national and international crises

📍 UK, with a strong preference for North East England

£ £2.75 million (2020/21)

CC number: 328081

Trustees: Helen Barbour; Dame Margaret Barbour; Nichola Bellaby.

Correspondent: Edith Howse, Executive Secretary, Simonside, South Shields, Tyne and Wear NE34 9PD (tel: 0191 427 4217; email: barbour.foundation@barbour.com)

🌐 www.barbour.com/uk/the-barbour-foundation

General information

The foundation was established in 1988 and is the corporate charity of British luxury clothing and lifestyle brand, J. Barbour and Sons Ltd. It was set up by Dame Margaret Barbour, with a gift of 20% of the company shares. According to its website, the foundation supports charities and causes primarily in the North East (i.e. Tyne and Wear,

Northumberland, Durham and South Tyneside).

Areas of work

The foundation's website states:

> The Foundation has a diverse collection of objectives, including;
> ▷ The relief of persons in the North East of England who are in conditions of need, by reasons of their social and economic circumstances, hardship or distress.
> ▷ To assist organisations that provide services/projects for those with special needs.
> ▷ To help improve the employment prospects of young people and to alleviate their problems of homelessness in the North East of England.
> ▷ The promotion of research into the cause and treatment of chronic illnesses or diseases and the provision of medical equipment.
> ▷ The protection and preservation for the benefit of the public in the North East of England such features of cities, towns. Villages and the countryside as are of special environmental, historical and architectural interest.
> ▷ National and international crisis

Grants are available in the following categories: main grants of over £2,000 and small grants up to £2,000.

Beneficiaries included: Newcastle University Faculty of Medical Sciences (£1 million); North Music Trust (£150,000); Hospitality and Hope (£30,000); Veterans at Ease (£10,000); Single Homeless Action Initiative Durham and Versus Arthritis (£5,000 each); Together For Short Lives (£3,000); National Kidney Federation, Theatre Space and Wallsend Sea Cadets (£1,000 each).

Financial information

Year end	05/04/2021
Assets	£13,170,000
Income	£609,100
Grant total	£2,750,000
Organisations supported	311

Further financial information

According to the foundation's annual accounts, 311 grants were awarded during the year.

Exclusions

According to its website, the foundation will not give to the following:

▷ Requests from outside the geographical area
▷ Requests from educational establishments
▷ Capital grants for building projects
▷ Applications for/from individuals

Applications

Apply in writing to the correspondent. Full details of what should be included in an application can be found on the foundation's website. Applications for the main grants are considered at quarterly meetings and applications for the small grants applications are considered at meetings every six weeks.

The website states the following:

> In addition to the Grant Meetings, consideration is given to requests for prizes for charitable events. If successful a voucher will be issued. Applications for prizes should be made in writing to the correspondence address. Applications must include the full address, date and full details of the event.

Sources of information

Accounts; annual report; Charity Commission record; funder's website.

The Barratt Developments plc Charitable Foundation

 General charitable purposes

England, Wales and Scotland

£1.21 million (2020/21)

CC number: 1188447

Trustees: David Thomas; Jeremy Hipkiss; Kamalprit Bains; Mark Rolfe; Lord Gavin Barwell; Tim Collins.

Correspondent: The Trustees, Barratt House, Cartwright Way, Forest Business Park, Bardon Hill LE67 1UF (tel: 01530 278278; email: cf@barrattplc.co.uk)

General information

This foundation was registered with the Charity Commission in March 2020. It appears to be the corporate charity of Barratt Developments plc, the 'nation's largest housebuilder' with profits of over £811 million in 2021.

Before registering this foundation with Charity Commission, the firm has long supported various charitable organisations in accordance with its charitable giving policy. The policy states that the firm focuses on causes linked to the business, the communities it works with, and its business partners and employees. While the firm appears to have a preference for charities local to its areas of operation, it has supported national charities, but only when the proposed support is delivered locally within the firm's divisional areas.

Previous causes supported by the firm include:

- Diversity and inclusion
- The environment
- Mental health and well-being
- Homelessness
- Veterans

According to its Charity Commission record, the foundation will make grants to organisations in England, Wales and Scotland for general charitable purposes.

Beneficiaries included: Macmillan Cancer Support (£329,100); The Running Charity (£150,000); Dementia UK (£75,000); English Chamber Orchestra (55,000).

Financial information

Year end	30/06/2021
Assets	£722,300
Income	£1,980,000
Grant total	£1,210,000

Applications

Apply in writing to the correspondent.

Sources of information

Charity Commission record; Barratt Developments (website); Barratt Developments (annual report and accounts).

BC Partners Foundation

 Community development; environmental conservation; the arts; education

UK and overseas

£442,700 (2020)

CC number: 1136956

Trustees: Nikos Stathopoulos; Cedric Dubourdieu; Francesco Loredan; Laurian Douin; Matthew Evans.

Correspondent: The Trustees, BC Partners LLP, 40 Portman Square, London W1H 6DA (tel: 020 7009 4800)

www.bcpartners.com/about/foundation

General information

This foundation was established in 2010 and is the corporate charity of the private equity firm, BC Partners.

The firm's website states that the foundation focuses primarily on providing 'financial contributions to non-for-profit organisations worldwide that are important to the employees of BC Partners'.

The foundation is not restrictive in terms of the causes it supports; however, its funding priorities are:

- Community development including infrastructure advancements, development aid, healthcare improvements
- Conservation of the environment including endeavours related to pollution reduction, natural preservation, clean technologies
- The arts and education including support for educational, scholastic or artistic programmes

The foundation also matches donations made by employees.

Beneficiaries included: BCPF Inc. (£238,200); Private Equity Foundation (£110,500); Dolphin Society (£25,000); American School in London Foundation (£15,000); Kids Welcome (£3,600); MS Society (£950); Hertford College (£500); Northern Ireland Children's Hospice (£100).

Financial information

Year end	31/12/2020
Assets	£528,000
Income	£396,600
Grant total	£442,700
Organisations supported	29

Applications

The foundation does not accept unsolicited applications. Charities are nominated by BC Partners employees or trustees of the foundation.

Sources of information

Accounts; annual report; Charity Commission record; funder's website.

AJ Bell Trust

 Children and young people; disability; social welfare and inclusion; skills development; education and training; health and medical research

UK

£191,200 (2020/21)

CC number: 1141269

Trustees: Andrew Bell; Tracey Bell; Paul Clements; Paul Barrow.

Correspondent: Esther Speksnijder, Secretary, Blythe Hall, Blythe Lane, Lathom, Ormskirk, England L40 5TY (email: moorhall@outlook.com)

www.ajbell.co.uk/about-us/corporate-social-responsibility

General information

The trust has awarded grants and in-kind donations since 2011 and focuses on providing help and relief to people who are in need as a result of their age, financial hardship, poor health, disability or other disadvantages. The trust's primary focus is on children and young adults under 25 years of age.

The trust supports social welfare and inclusion in the following ways:

- Providing grants, goods and services to individuals and/or charities and organisations that work to prevent or relieve financial hardship
- Providing for people's care and upbringing, including the provision of accommodation
- Skills development and education and training, including the study of art, culture, heritage or science
- Employment advice and assistance
- Providing or subsidising recreational and leisure activities and encouraging participation in amateur sports
- Promoting healthcare projects and medical research

Beneficiaries included: A list of beneficiaries was not available.

Financial information

Year end	30/09/2021
Assets	£2,330,000
Income	£292,900
Grant total	£191,200

Applications

Apply in writing to the correspondent.

Sources of information

Accounts; annual report; Charity Commission record.

Benefact Trust Ltd

 Churches; social welfare; homelessness; mental health; social exclusion; ex-offenders; community health and well-being; substance misuse; heritage

 UK and Ireland

 £19.3 million (2021)

CC number: 263960

Trustees: Timothy Carroll; Stephen Hudson; Caroline Banszky; The Ven. Karen Lund; The Revd Jane Hedges; Chris Moulder; The Revd Paul Davis; Sir Stephen Lamport; David Smart.

Correspondent: Iain Hearn, Correspondent, Benefact House, 2000 Pioneer Avenue, Gloucester Business Park, Brockworth, Gloucestershire GL3 4AW (tel: 01452 873189; email: info@benefacttrust.co.uk)

 https://benefacttrust.co.uk

 facebook.com/benefacttrust

 @benefacttrust

General information

Formerly known as the Allchurches Trust, this trust was established in 1972. Its income is derived from its wholly owned subsidiary company the Benefact Group (formerly known as Ecclesiastical Insurance Group). According to its Charity Commission record, the trust's aims are 'to promote the Christian religion, to contribute to the funds of any charitable institutions, associations, funds or objects and to carry out any charitable purpose'.

Grant-making

Grants are available to churches and Christian charities, schools and colleges from all parts of the UK and Ireland, particularly from areas of deprivation. The trust's grants programmes are outlined below. Grants are typically for capital projects and equipment, not salaries or running costs, with the exception of the trust's Transformational Grants programme.

General Grants

The General Grants programme supports projects that demonstrate an impact on people and communities. These are typically capital grants that support the repair, restoration, protection and improvement of churches, cathedrals and other places of Christian worship where changes support wider community use and enable greater impact. The programme also supports projects that help tackle social issues, for example homelessness, poverty, climate change and cultural cohesion, and projects that support Christian leaders, and help to share the Christian faith.

These grants range from £1,000 up to £15,000 for projects with a total cost of up to £1 million. Churches, cathedrals, denominational bodies, Christian charities, and schools and educational institutions are all eligible to apply.

Methodist Grants

The Methodist Grants programme offers grants of up to £100,000 for building development projects that focus on church growth, community engagement and improving accessibility. Individual Methodist churches who are part of the Methodist Connexion are able to apply, along with Methodist Circuits and Districts and some key Methodist heritage sites.

Roof alarm Grants

The trust's Roof Protection Scheme 'provides grants to help churches install roof alarms in response to the issue of metal theft, which continues to be a very challenging issue across the UK', as stated on its website.

For more details on the trust's current grants programmes, see its website.

Beneficiaries included: Methodist Connexion (£1.4 million); The Diocese of London (£385,000); Diocese of Leeds (£285,000); The Cinnamon Network (£201,000); Betel UK – Birmingham (£120,000); Just Finance Foundation and The Keswick Convention Trust (£100,000 each).

Financial information

Year end	31/12/2021
Assets	£542,440,000
Income	£28,660,000
Grant total	£19,330,000
Organisations supported	900+

Further financial information

The following geographical analysis of grants was provided in the trust's 2021 accounts:

England	£14.70 million
National projects	£2.59 million
Ireland	£1.02 million
Wales	£575,000
Scotland	£402,000
Other	£40,000

According to the trust's accounts, under the trust's general grants programme,

697 small grants were awarded totalling £2.1 million and 24 large grants were awarded totalling £1.3 million.

Only beneficiaries of grants of £100,000 and above were listed in the accounts.

Exclusions

According to the trust's website it will not normally fund the following:

- Non-Christian charities
- Overseas projects or charities
- Charities with a political association
- Projects that benefit only a small part of a community
- Multiple applications from the same organisation in a 24-month period

Applications

Applications for the General Grants programme should be submitted via the trust's website using its online application form. Applications can be submitted at any time.

To apply for one of the trust's specific programmes, the relevant application form on the dedicated web page should be completed.

Sources of information

Accounts; annual report; Charity Commission record; funder's website.

The Berkeley Foundation

 Supporting young people with housing and homelessness; education, training and employment; health and well-being

 Berkshire, Birmingham, Buckinghamshire, Greater London, Hampshire, Hertfordshire, Kent, Oxfordshire, Surrey, Warwickshire and West Sussex

 £2.14 million (2020/21)

CC number: 1152596

Trustees: Robert Perrins; Wendy Pritchard; Elaine Driver; Alison Dowsett.

Correspondent: The Trustees, Berkeley House, 19 Portsmouth Road, Cobham, Surrey KT11 1JG (tel: 01932 584551; email: info@berkeleyfoundation.org.uk)

 www.berkeleyfoundation.org.uk

 @berkeleyfoundation/?hl=en

General information

This foundation was established in 2011 and became a registered charity in 2013. It is the corporate charity of the Berkeley Group, a property development company based in London.

The foundation aims to help young people and their communities across London, Birmingham and the south of England. According to its website, the foundation provides funding through the following channels:

Strategic Partnerships
Long-term, high value partnerships which operate on multiple levels.

Community Investment Fund
Targeting funding, aimed at supporting innovation and building evidence of what works.

Designated Charities
Partnership between Berkeley offices and local charities, focused on fundraising, volunteering and in-kind support.

The foundation also operates a Capacity Building Fund, available to all current charity partners, which aims to build resilience and capacity, enabling partners to overcome organisational challenges and operate more effectively.

Registered charities and CICs can apply for funding under the foundation's Community Investment Fund, which has the following focus areas:
- A safe place to call home
- The skills to succeed
- Access to employment
- Health and well-being

Beneficiaries included: Imperial College (£600,000); The Change Foundation (£230,100); Richard House (£180,000); New Horizon Youth Centre (£150,000); Khulisa (£120,000); MAC-UK (£102,300); Oaresome Chance (£15,000); No.5 Young People (£10,000).

Financial information

Year end	30/04/2021
Assets	£1,820
Income	£2,590,000
Grant total	£2,140,000

Exclusions
The trust does not make grants to individuals.

Applications
Applications are typically made online through the foundation website. The foundation welcomes Expressions of Interest at any time during the year.

Sources of information
Accounts; annual report; Charity Commission record; funder's website.

The Bestway Foundation

 Education and training; social welfare; health; emergency relief

UK and overseas, particularly India, Pakistan, Bangladesh and Sri Lanka

£82,000 (2020/21)

CC number: 297178

Trustees: Mohammed Younus Sheikh; Sir Anwar Pervez; Lord Zameer Choudrey; Dawood Pervez; Rizwan Pervez; Hon. Haider Choudrey.

Correspondent: The Trustees, Bestway Foundation, 2 Abbey Road, London NW10 7BW (tel: 020 8453 1234; email: zulfikaur.wajid-hasan@bestway.co.uk)

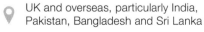 www.bestwaygroup.co.uk/responsibility/bestway-foundation

General information
This foundation was registered with the Charity Commission in 1987. It is the corporate charity of the Bestway Group, which owns the UK's second largest wholesaler. Each year the group contributes approximately 2.5% of its post-tax profits to the foundation.

The foundation aims to empower disadvantaged sections of the local community through economic regeneration and employment creation.

According to its website, the foundation's objectives are:
- The advancement of education for public benefit in both the UK and overseas by providing assistance through promotion of local schools; provision of scholarships to universities; supporting education initiatives and endowing universities
- The relief of sickness and the preservation of health for public benefit in both the UK and overseas by way of grants and endowments to existing hospitals, clinics, medical research establishments and by establishing new health facilities
- The provision of financial and material to support victims of natural disasters
- To have a significant impact on poverty reduction in Pakistan through strategic investments in affordable financial and social services catering to the poor
- The development of technical skills within the local communities in which we operate through structured apprenticeship and training programmes

Grants are awarded to both organisations and individuals, although donations on behalf of students are usually made directly to academic institutions.

Beneficiaries included: Crimestoppers (£40,000); Queen Elizabeth's Foundation for Disabled People (£20,000); The Duke of Edinburgh's Award (£15,000); The Drink Trust (£1,000).

Financial information

Year end	30/06/2021
Assets	£5,470,000
Income	£49,100
Grant total	£82,000

Applications
Apply in writing to the correspondent. The foundation has previously noted that telephone calls are not invited.

Sources of information
Accounts; annual report; Charity Commission record; funder's website.

Biffa Award

 Biodiversity; community buildings; recreation

 UK. Projects should be located near a Biffa operation and any licensed landfill site – there is a postcode checker on the website

£3.62 million (2020/21)

Trustees: Andrew Moffat; Patience Thody; Simon Rutledge; Jackie Doone; Mick Davis; Debbie Tann.

Correspondent: The Grants Team, The Wildlife Trusts, The Kiln, Mather Road, Newark, Nottinghamshire NG24 1WT (tel: 01636 670000; email: biffa-award@wildlifetrusts.org)

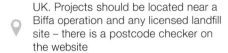 www.biffa-award.org

@BiffaAward

General information
Biffa plc is a waste management company headquartered in High Wycombe. The Biffa Award is an environmental fund managed by the Royal Society of Wildlife Trusts (RSWT) and funded through landfill tax credits donated by Biffa Waste Services.

Main Grants Scheme
The main grants scheme makes grants under four main themes, details of which have been taken from the Biffa Award guidance notes:
- **The Community Buildings theme** aims to improve community buildings such as village halls, community centres and church halls to act as mechanisms for community involvement
- **The Rebuilding Biodiversity theme** supports a variety of living things and includes all species of plants and animals and the natural systems (or habitats) that support them.
- **The Recreation theme** generally covers projects which will benefit people within their free time, but also includes renovations of clubhouses which have a wider community use outside of sporting activities.
- **The Cultural Facilities** theme aims to improve recreation, interest and education. The project could be based within a theatre, gallery, museum, concert hall, arts or heritage centre. It must be open to the general public for published periods of not less than 104 days each year and must attract tourists or day visitors.

Grants of between £10,000 and £75,000 are awarded for projects with a total cost of less than £200,000 including VAT.

Partnership Projects
Grants of between £250,000 and £750,000 are available for partnership projects. Organisations should work in partnership on brand new projects of regional or national significance which

look to improve the built or natural environment.

Each grant scheme has its own eligibility criteria – see the organisation's website for further details.

Beneficiaries included: Wiltshire Wildlife Trust (£442,900); RSPB (£433,500); Boston Spa Village Hall (£50,000); War Memorial Playing Fields Committee (£70,000); Ulster Wildlife (11,800).

Financial information

Year end	30/03/2021
Grant total	£3,620,000

Further financial information

A breakdown of grant distribution by both theme and grant scheme was provided in the Biffa Award annual review for 2020/21, including the number of projects supported during the year:

Natural Environments	5	£2.3 million
Community Building	13	£667,900
Biodiversity	7	£337,700
Recreation Building	5	£252,400

Exclusions

For full exclusions, see the organisation's guidance notes.

Applications

The main grants programme is a rolling programme with no deadlines. Applicants must first submit an expression of interest form on the organisation's website. If successful, within five days you will be invited to submit a full application, which must be submitted within six weeks of the invitation being made. If you have been unsuccessful, you will receive a letter by email.

Sources of information

Annual report; funder's website.

The Birmingham International Airport Community Trust Fund

Community; the environment; heritage; health and well-being; sport

The areas affected by the airport's operation, particularly east Birmingham and north Solihull – a full list of postcodes is provided on the website

(£) £62,500 (2020/21)

CC number: 1071176

Trustees: Cllr Michael Ward; Robert Sleigh; Martin McCarthy; Diane Donaldson; Cllr Robert Grinsell; David Cuthbert; Margaret Kennett; Andrew Holding.

Correspondent: Andy Holding, Trust Fund Secretary, Birmingham Airport Ltd, Diamond House, Birmingham Airport, Birmingham, West Midlands B26 3QJ (tel: 0121 767 7448; email: andy.holding@birminghamairport.co.uk)

www.birminghamairport.co.uk/about-us/community-and-environment/community-investment/community-trust-fund

General information

Established in 1998, the trust aims to compensate those communities most affected by Birmingham International Airport. Each year, the airport invests in excess of £80,000 into the trust fund. Charges made to airlines in breach of night noise regulations are also donated to the fund.

Eligibility

A full list of postcode areas within the trust's area of benefit can be seen on the website. Your project must operate from one of these areas.

Your organisation must have a constitution or a set of rules, be locally managed and must be able to provide basic income and expenditure, preferably in form of annual accounts.

According to its guidelines, the trust will support projects in any of the following areas:

- Heritage conservation
- Environment improvement, improving awareness of environmental issues, environmental education and training, encouraging and protecting wildlife
- Bringing the Community closer together through facilities for sport, recreation and other leisure time activities
- Improving health and wellbeing through the promotion of healthy lifestyles and employment opportunities

Work should benefit a substantial section of the community rather than less inclusive groups, although work with older people or people with special needs is positively encouraged.

The maximum grant made is for £3,000. Grants may be for capital or revenue projects, although the trust will not commit to recurrent or running costs, such as salaries.

Beneficiaries included: A list of beneficiaries was not available.

Financial information

Year end	31/03/2021
Assets	£62,500
Income	£90,000
Grant total	£62,500

Exclusions

The trust will not support:

- Running costs, such as salaries or expenses
- Individuals
- Medical treatment
- Organisations with statutory responsibilities, unless the project is clearly above their obligations
- Purchase of land and buildings, or general repair and maintenance (adaptions for disability or security may be supported)
- Uniforms or sports kits
- Short-term projects, such as events or trips
- Projects which have already taken place

Branches of national or international organisations are not usually supported.

Applications

After reading through the guidelines, application packs can be requested by emailing the Trust Fund Secretary. The following information has been taken from the website:

Your email must include:

- The name of your project or organisation
- The address and postcode from where the project operates
- A brief outline of what your project is about
- What you are applying for – you must be specific: 'to fund our project to reduce social isolation' is not sufficient. We need to know exactly what you would spend the money on.

Grants are awarded twice per year in April and October.

Sources of information

Accounts; Charity Commission record; funder's website; guidelines for applicants.

Blakemore Foundation

General charitable purpose including: sport and recreation; health; medical research; housing and homelessness; emergency services and the armed forces; the environment

England and Wales, excluding parts of the South West and northern England. See the map on the foundation's website for details

(£) £87,900 (2020/21)

CC number: 1015938

Trustees: Peter Blakemore; Ita McAuley.

Correspondent: Kate Senter, Community Affairs Officer, A.F. Blakemore & Sons Ltd, Longacre, Willenhall, West Midlands WV13 2JP (tel: 0121 568 2910; email: Blakemore.Foundation@afblakemore.co.uk)

www.afblakemore.com/blakemore-foundation/blakemore-foundation

General information

This is the charitable trust of A.F. Blakemore and Son Ltd, a food retail, wholesale and distribution company based in the UK. The trust was established in 1992 by the Blakemore family to support good causes across the company's trading area.

According to its website, the foundation offers support in four ways:

- **In-Kind donations** – Donations which are given in the form of food, drink or supplies from our Blakemore Retail SPAR stores or Philpotts stores
- **Monetary donations** – Donations given to good causes up to the value of £200 to help towards projects, events, workshops and ongoing charitable work
- **Match fund donations** – Donations for causes supported by employees of A.F. Blakemore and Son Limited up to the value of £200
- **Independent retail donations** – Grants which allow SPAR retailers to apply for a donation for a good cause of their choice

Beneficiaries included: A list of beneficiaries was not available.

Financial information

Year end	30/04/2021
Assets	£78,800
Income	£344,500
Grant total	£87,900

Further financial information

'Other charitable contributions' totalled £123,400.

Exclusions

The foundation's guidelines state that the following are not supported:

- Salaries
- National charities (unless directly linked to an A.F. Blakemore employee or local branch)
- Grants for an individual
- Good causes that fall outside of A.F. Blakemore's trading area
- Overseas appeals
- Expeditions or overseas travel
- Sponsorship and marketing promotions
- Endowment and hardship funds
- Political causes

Applications

Applications can be made through the foundation's website.

Sources of information

Accounts; annual report; Charity Commission record; funder's website.

The Boodle & Dunthorne Charitable Trust

 General charitable purposes

 UK and overseas

£ £268,000 (2020/21)

CC number: 1077748

Trustees: Nicholas Wainwright; Michael Wainwright.

Correspondent: The Trustees, Boodles House, 35 Lord Street, Liverpool, Merseyside L2 9SQ (tel: 0151 224 0580)

General information

Established in 1999, the Boodle & Dunthorne Charitable Trust is the corporate charity of Boodles, a family jewellers based in North West England. The trust supports general charitable causes and provides grants to UK based organisations.

Beneficiaries included: Shining Faces in India (£75,000); The Message Trust (£55,000); NSPCC (£30,000); Rainbow Trust (£25,000); Hope and Homes for Children (£20,000); I Can and I Am (£10,000).

Financial information

Year end	05/04/2021
Assets	£1,200,000
Income	£119,600
Grant total	£268,000

Exclusions

The trust's annual report and accounts do not evidence donations to individuals.

Applications

Contact the correspondent for further information. The 2020/21 annual report states that the trustees 'have discretion over where and when grants are made. Grants will be made by the Trustees as and when they identify a suitable and deserving cause'.

Sources of information

Accounts; annual report; Charity Commission record.

Boots Charitable Trust

 Health; lifelong learning; community development; social care

 Nottinghamshire

£ £250,000 (2020/21)

CC number: 1045927

Trustees: Lucy Reynolds; Stuart Buchanan; Lavinia Moxley; Felicity Walton-Bateson.

Correspondent: The Trustees, Boots UK Ltd, D90E S09, 1 Thane Road West, Nottingham, Nottinghamshire NG90 1BS (email: feelgoodworks@boots.co.uk)

 www.boots-uk.com/corporate_social_responsibility/boots-charitable-trust.aspx

General information

Boots Charitable Trust was registered with the Charity Commission in 1995 and is wholly funded by Boots UK Ltd, a health and beauty retailer and pharmacy chain.

It provides funding to registered charities that benefit the people of Nottinghamshire, the location of the first Boots store and head office. The trust also makes grants to smaller voluntary organisations in the county that are too small to qualify for charitable status, but still need support.

According to its website, the trust has donated over £10 million to charities in Nottinghamshire. Around 50 grants are awarded per year ranging from £100 to £10,000; however, applications for larger amounts will be considered.

The trust's charitable giving policy states:

> The Trust will consider applications for funding for most expenditure items, including salary and running costs. Where a general overhead allocation is part of the funding requested, the method of calculation must be included. Generally, large building or construction projects will not be funded although minor structural improvements and refurbishments would be considered.

To be considered for support, applicants must meet at least one of the trust's funding priorities. Current priorities are as follows:

- Health
- Lifelong learning
- Community development
- Social care

Beneficiaries included: Dance4, Nidas and Refugee Roots (£10,000 each); Framework (£8,800); Home-Start Nottingham (£7,000); Good Vibrations (£6,200); Good Companions (£4,400); Read Easy Nottingham (£2,000).

Financial information

Year end	31/08/2021
Income	£266,800
Grant total	£250,000
Organisations supported	31

Further financial information

Grants were broken down as follows:

Social care	14	£117,550
Health	8	£61,200
Lifelong learning	5	£39,600
Community development	4	£31,600

Exclusions

The trust's charitable giving policy states that it will not fund the following:

- Projects benefitting those people outside of Nottinghamshire
- Individuals
- Organisations which are not registered charities and have an income or expenditure of more than £5,000 per year
- Charities seeking funds to re-distribute to other charities
- Projects for which there is a legal statutory obligation or which replace statutory funding

Applications

Applications can be made using an online application form on the website. Further guidance and eligibility criteria are also available to view. Paper application forms can also be requested by contacting feelgoodworks@boots.co.uk.

The trustees review applications on a bi-monthly basis. Applications should be received by the seventh day of February, April, June, August, October and December.

Sources of information

Accounts; annual report; Charity Commission record; guidelines for applicants; funder's website.

BRIT Trust

Music; performing arts; young people

UK

£1.07 million (2021)

CC number: 1000413

Trustees: Geoff Taylor; Tony Wadsworth; David Sharpe; William Rowe; David Munns; Angela Watts; Gerald Doherty; Rita Broe; Henry Semmence; Paul Burger; Caroline Dollimore; Mulika Sannie; Kwame Kwaten.

Correspondent: The Trustees, Level 21, 40 Bank Street, Canary Wharf, London E14 5DS (email: brittrust@bpi.co.uk)

 www.brittrust.co.uk

 facebook.com/thebrittrust

 @thebrittrust

General information

Established in 1989, the BRIT Trust is entirely funded by the British music industry and receives a large part of its income from the profits of the annual BRIT Awards. Its mission is 'improving lives through the power of music and the creative arts', which it does principally through its commitments to the BRIT School in Croydon – the UK's only non-fee paying performing arts school – and to Nordoff-Robbins, which is the UK's leading independent provider of music therapy.

The trust mainly supports The Brit School and Nordoff Robbins; however, the trustees sometimes make smaller donations to support additional charitable organisations and activities. These applications are considered at the November meeting of the trustees.

Beneficiaries included: The BRIT School (£452,000); Nordoff Robbins Music Therapy (£400,000); BPI BRITs Apprentice Scheme (£194,300).

Financial information

Year end	31/12/2021
Assets	£12,620,000
Income	£1,690,000
Grant total	£1,070,000

Further financial information

Only organisations that received grants of over £10,000 were listed as beneficiaries in the trust's accounts. Grants of under £10,000 totalled £25,000.

Applications

See the trust's website for the latest information on applications.

Sources of information

Accounts; annual report; Charity Commission record; funder's website.

British Gas Energy Trust

Fuel debt advice

England, Wales and Scotland

£3.56 million (2020/21)

CC number: 1179578

Trustees: Helen Charlton; William Gillis; Albert Chong; Sheila Wheeler; Laurie Lee; Hardial Bhogal; Christina Thwaite; Mark McGillicuddy; Susan Deacon.

Correspondent: The Trustees, Farrer & Co., 65–66 Lincoln's Inn Fields, London WC2A 3LH (tel: 020 3375 7496; email: contact@britishgasenergytrust.org.uk)

 www.britishgasenergytrust.org.uk

 @EnergyBritish

General information

The British Gas Energy Trust, which incorporates the Scottish Gas Energy Trust, was established as an independent charity in 2004 and is funded entirely by British Gas. In August 2018, the trust re-registered with the Charity Commission as a CIO.

Organisational grants

The trust's website states:

> The Trust funds a number of organisations across England, Wales and Scotland to provide a wide range of specialist fuel debt advice services including:
> - Budget planning
> - Benefit/income maximisation checks
> - Energy supplier/tariff switching exercises
> - Resolution of energy debt problems
> - Negotiating with energy suppliers
> - Completing applications to British Gas Energy Trust and other grant giving schemes, e.g. Warm Home Discount and ECO schemes and energy companies' Priority Services Registers
> - Desktop Home Energy Efficiency Surveys and specific energy efficiency advice

> - Generalist advice on subjects including housing, employment and discrimination, helping to overcome other barriers to financial well-being.

Individual Families Fund

Both British Gas customers and non-customers can apply for grants to clear domestic gas and electricity debts owed to British Gas or suppliers other than British Gas. The trust's website states:

> To be considered for a grant you must meet the following criteria, if you cannot tick all these boxes your application will not progress to assessment:
> - You live in England, Scotland, or Wales
> - You have not received a grant from the British Gas Energy Trust within the last 2 years
> - You must be seeking a grant to clear an outstanding debt on a current or open gas, electricity, or dual fuel energy account in your name or be a member of that household, the energy account must relate to your main residence
> - You have electric and/or gas debt
> - You do not have savings above £1,000
> - You have received help from a money advice agency

British Gas Energy Support Fund

This fund is open to British Gas customers with an energy debt of £250 to £1,500. To be eligible, applicants must live in England, Scotland or Wales and have not received a grant from the trust in the last 12 months. The fund is open to both Credit and PPM customers with a previous outstanding credit account debt.

Beneficiaries included: A list of beneficiaries was not available.

Financial information

Year end	31/03/2021
Assets	£2,620,000
Income	£6,000,000
Grant total	£3,560,000

Applications

Applications can be made online via the trust's website.

Sources of information

Accounts; annual report; Charity Commission record; funder's website.

Bupa UK Foundation

Children and young people's mental health

UK

£984,400 (2021)

CC number: 1162759

Trustees: Siobhan Moynihan; Robert Edmundson; Alexandra Cole; Mark Callister-Davies; Thomas Webber; Sally Pain; Dr Helen Cliffe; Andrea Spyropoulus; Dr Paula Franklin.

Correspondent: The Trustees, Battle Bridge House, 300–306 Gray's Inn Road, London WC1X 8DU (email: bupafoundation@bupa.com)

 www.bupaukfoundation.org

 @bupafoundation

 @bupafoundation

General information

This is the charitable foundation of Bupa Ltd, an international healthcare provisioning and multi-insurance group based in the UK. It was established in 2015 to replace the group's previous charity, The Bupa Foundation.

The foundation runs and funds projects that aim to have a positive impact on people's mental health.

Well-being for educators – the foundation's flagship programme helps educators manage their energy levels and provides practical methods to improve well-being in schools.

Community Committees – employees run local Community Committees in Bristol, Manchester, Leeds, London and Staines. Through a mixture of grants, volunteering and fundraising, the committees help support vulnerable people in local areas.

Charity partnerships – the foundation has partnerships with several charities with the aim of supporting young people's mental health.

Beneficiaries included: A list of beneficiaries was not available. Previous beneficiaries include: Asthma UK (£115,000); Muscular Dystrophy UK (£45,300); Single Homeless Project (£23,000); Cruse Bereavement Care (£22,800); Salford Foundation (£22,300); Bike for Good and Cardiff Community Trust (£1,000 each).

Financial information

Year end	31/12/2021
Assets	£138,800
Income	£1,190,000
Grant total	£984,400
Organisations supported	82

Applications

Contact the correspondent or your local Community Committee for further information.

Sources of information

Accounts; annual report; Charity Commission record; funder's website.

The Burberry Foundation

STEAM education; educational equality; waste reduction; social and economic development

Worldwide, with a strong preference for communities where Burberry employees live and work

£3.62 million (2020/21)

CC number: 1154468

Trustees: Christopher Holmes; Edward Rash; Dr Gerard Murphy.

Correspondent: Pamela Batty, Secretary, Burberry Ltd, Horseferry House, Horseferry Road, London SW1P 2AW (tel: 020 7806 1328; email: enquiries@burberryfoundation.com)

 www.burberryplc.com/en/responsibility/policies/communities/the-burberry-foundation.html

General information

The Burberry Foundation is an independent charity established in 2008 by Burberry Group plc, the British luxury fashion house.

According to its website, the foundation wishes to drive positive change and, through innovation, promote a sustainable future in communities that are affected by the luxury industry. Its grant-making policy is focused on supporting the communities located in key Burberry supply chain locations.

The foundation has partnered with leading organisations to address educational inequality, support social and economic development, reduce waste and promote the STEAM agenda.

The 2020/21 annual report states that, when considering requests for support, the foundation will consider projects that:

- are managed competently through accountability, cost effectiveness, strong leadership and creativity
- provide a significant and measurable impact
- are located in a community where Burberry Group employees live and work
- have the potential to offer volunteering opportunities for Burberry Group employees

Beneficiaries included: Oxfam (£839,300); Royal College of Art (£412,700); Teach First (£300,000); London Youth (£285,000); MyKindaCrowd (£69,700); King's College (£50,000); California Association of Foodbanks (£5,000).

Financial information

Year end	31/03/2021
Assets	£3,590,000
Income	£2,550,000
Grant total	£3,620,000

Further financial information

In 2020/21 the foundation awarded grants totalling £3.62 million. Within this, £2.79 million was awarded in the UK.

Applications

Apply in writing to the correspondent.

Sources of information

Accounts; annual report; Charity Commission record; funder's website.

The Cadbury Foundation

Skills development; health

Charities close to Cadbury sites in the UK and Ireland

£484,700 (2021)

CC number: 1050482

Trustees: Eoin Kellett; Lisa Crane; Louise Stigant; Clive Jones; Joshua Townson; Denise Chester.

Correspondent: The Trustees, PO Box 12, Bourneville, Birmingham, West Midlands B30 2LU (tel: 0121 787 2421; email: kelly.farrell@mdlz.com)

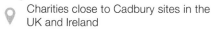 www.cadbury.co.uk/cadbury-foundation

General information

The Cadbury Foundation was established in 1935 in recognition of the founders of the Cadbury's chocolate company, George and Richard Cadbury. In 2010 Kraft Foods Inc. gained control of Cadbury plc and two years later, divided the corporation into Kraft Food Group plc and Mondelez, the latter of which now funds the Cadbury Foundation.

According to its website, the foundation's ethos is 'helping people to help themselves'. It achieves this by supporting a number of charities in the UK and Ireland that are located in the communities in which the company operates.

The foundation's website states:

Investment is focused in three key areas:

Health and wellbeing
We encourage local communities to lead healthier lifestyles through cooking, food growing, physical activity and social cohesion.

Skills
We inspire the next generation of talent by developing their transferable skills to help them succeed in the workplace.

Colleague Passions

We care about the local charities our employees are passionate about, supporting local causes close to their hearts through our 'Your Charity Your Choice' and 'Cashmatch' programmes.

Beneficiaries included: Health for Life in Primary Schools (£100,000); Grocery Aid (£50,000); St Francis Hospice (£43,700); Age Action, Cardiac Risk in Young, Mountain Rescue, Sense and The Turning Tides Project (£5,000 each).

Financial information

Year end	31/12/2021
Assets	£380,700
Income	£649,400
Grant total	£484,700

Further financial information

Grants were distributed as follows: health and well-being (£308,700); colleague passions (£126,000); skills (£50,000).

Applications

The foundation actively seeks out projects to support and therefore does not accept any unsolicited requests for funding.

Sources of information

Accounts; annual report; Charity Commission record; funder's website.

Cadent Foundation

Social welfare; environment; community development; sustainable energy projects

North West England, the East of England, the West Midlands and North London

£ £3.88 million (2021)

CC number: 327489

Trustees: Advisory Board: Sir Adrian Montague; Dr Catherine Bell; Mark Braithwaite; Linda Minnis.

Correspondent: Julia Dwyer, Cadent Foundation Director, Pilot Way, Ansty Park, Coventry CV7 9JU (email: enquiries@cadentfoundation.com)

 https://cadentgas.com/cadent-foundation

 @cadentfund

General information

The Cadent Foundation was established in March 2020. The Charities Trust administers the foundation and manages the grant applications and giving process. Cadent owns and manages four gas distribution networks and projects must take place in these areas. The geographical areas are the East of England, North London, North West England and the West Midlands.

Grants

According to its website the foundation makes grants in the following areas:

- **Research and Innovation (RandI)** – Projects that help eliminate harmful emissions and support sustainable energy
- **People** – Projects that help alleviate suffering and hardship of people in vulnerable situations
- **Environment** – Projects that will help protect and preserve the environment
- **Communities** – Projects that provide a better and healthier community to live in and use

Partnerships

The foundation will also partner with organisations that are working to advance sustainable energy and create innovative ways to tackle the climate crisis.

Beneficiaries included: A list of beneficiaries was not available.

Financial information

Year end	31/12/2021
Assets	£101,650,000
Income	£164,280,000
Grant total	£3,880,000

Further financial information

Full financial information was not available as the foundation is administered by the Charities Trust and is not a registered charity. The foundation's grant total has been taken from its 2021 Impact Report.

Grants were broken down as follows:

North West England	£1.05 million
West Midlands	£1 million
North London	£931,800
East of England	£893,500

Exclusions

The foundation's website states:

Unfortunately, we cannot accept applications or grant funds to any of the following groups or related:

- Animal groups
- The benefit of individuals
- The purpose of repaying loans
- Sponsorship of events or activities
- Religious or faith-based groups
- Overseas travel or groups
- Political or lobbyists groups
- Sporting groups
- Natural disaster relief
- Heritage and historic buildings
- Projects that are not sustainable
- Refurbishment of buildings (we may consider community spaces)
- Schools
- Medical
- Projects that are outside Cadent's region

Applications

Applications for grants can be made through the online form. There are detailed grant application guidelines available on the website. For partnership projects contact the foundation via email, including an outline of your project idea and purpose, details of your organisation and the breakdown of costs.

Sources of information

Charity Commission record; funder's website; guidelines for applicants.

The Cadogan Charity

Social welfare; medical research; military charities; animal welfare; education; conservation and the environment

UK, with a preference for London and Scotland

£ £2.48 million (2020/21)

CC number: 247773

Trustees: The Rt Hon. Earl Cadogan; Viscount Chelsea; William Cadogan; Countess Cadogan; Lady Anna-Karina Thomson.

Correspondent: Paul Loutit, Secretary to Trustees, 10 Duke of York Square, London SW3 4LY (tel: 020 7730 4567; email: paul.loutit@cadogan.co.uk)

General information

The charity was established in 1966 for general charitable purposes. The charity currently operates two funds, the general fund and the rectors' fund. The rectors' fund was created with a gift from Cadogan Holdings Company in 1985 to pay an annual amount to one or any of the rectors of Holy Trinity Church – Sloane Street, St Luke's Church and Chelsea Old Church. The general fund provides support for registered charities in a wide range of areas. These grants are only given to recognised national charities, particularly those based in London and Scotland.

Beneficiaries included: Natural History Museum (£250,000); Royal College of Surgeons (£100,000); Missing Salmon Alliance (£50,000); The Prince's Trust (£20,000); SeeSaw (£5,000); Dogs Trust (£1,000).

Financial information

Year end	05/04/2021
Assets	£54,880,000
Income	£2,590,000
Grant total	£2,480,000
Organisations supported	41

Further financial information

Grants were broken down as follows in 2020/21:

Social welfare	£1 million
Military charities	£460,500
Medical research	£380,000
Animal welfare	£296,000
Education	£273,000
Conservation and the environment	£65,000

Applications

The charity's 2020/21 annual report states: 'Although the trustees make some grants with no formal applications, they normally require organisations to submit a request saying how the funds could be used, what would be achieved, and how this would add to public benefit.'

Sources of information

Accounts; annual report; Charity Commission record.

Card Factory Foundation

 General charitable purposes

 UK

£367,300 (2020/21)

CC number: 1180081

Trustees: Caroline Thompson-Hayes; Julie Hardy; Nicola Rogerson; Jane Rowney; Susan Glass; Stephen Gleadall.

Correspondent: The Trustees, Century House, Brunel Road, Wakefield 41 Industrial Estate, Wakefield, West Yorkshire WF2 0XG (tel: 07933 399645; email: trustees@cardfactoryfoundation. org)

 www.cardfactoryinvestors.com/ foundation

General information

The foundation was registered with the Charity Commission in September 2018 as is the corporate charity of Card Factory, a national retailer of greetings cards based in Wakefield.

The foundation has three funds, details of which have been taken from the foundation's website:

Community Grant Fund

Card Factory Foundation supports projects and charitable causes to benefit the communities of our colleagues and stores. The Trustees welcome applications that support the Foundation's funding priorities from not-for-profit organisations, community groups and individuals based in the United Kingdom.

The maximum award for a Community Funding application is £2,500. Applications over £2,500 will be made at the discretion of the Charity Trustees.

All funding awarded by the Foundation must be used to cover the costs of the charitable activities the Trustees have agreed to fund. Funds will not be provided to meet salary or overhead costs.

Match Fund

Card Factory Foundation provide match-funding contributions for money raised by colleagues for charitable causes. Match funding is available to all colleagues who are directly employed by a Card Factory group company or an agency engaged by Card Factory.

Applicants must raise a minimum of £50 to be eligible for match funding and the maximum contribution for each successful application is £2,500. Applications for match funding beyond £2,500 shall be made at the discretion of the Charity Trustees.

Family Fund

Card Factory Foundation is committed to offering a helping hand to colleagues and their families in time of hardship. If you or your family have experienced or are experiencing hardship following a life-changing event. The maximum award for a Family Fund application is £2,000.

Beneficiaries included: Alzheimer's Society; British Heart Foundation; Macmillan Cancer Support; NSPCC.

Financial information

Year end	31/01/2021
Assets	£1,640,000
Income	£711,400
Grant total	£367,300

Further financial information

According to its annual statement, the foundation donated £131,500 between Alzheimer's Society, the British Heart Foundation, Macmillan Cancer Support and the NSPCC. In addition, it awarded £130,300 in COVID-19 grants to organisations during the year.

Applications

Applications can be made via the foundation's website.

Sources of information

Charity Commission record; funder's website.

CareTech Charitable Foundation

 Disability; skills development; local communities

 UK and Pakistan

£525,000 (2020/21)

CC number: 1182567

Trustees: Haroon Sheikh; Farouq Sheikh; Nicholas Cheffings; Nash Jaffer; Jessica Taplin; Christopher Dickinson; Farzana Ali; Prof. Moira Livingston; Hamza Sheikh; Claire Marshall; Lisa Stafford.

Correspondent: The Trustees, Metropolitan House, 3 Darkes Lane, Potters Bar EN6 1AG (tel: 01707 601800; email: info@caretechfoundation.org.uk)

 www.caretechfoundation.org.uk

 facebook.com/CareTechFoundation

 @CareTechFdn

General information

Established in 2017, this foundation is the corporate charity of CareTech Holdings plc, which provides social care for children and adults below retirement age. The foundation's current areas of work are physical and learning disabilities and mental health, skills development (in the care sector) and local communities.

Grants programmes

There are four types of funding available:

» **Partnership grant-giving** – the foundation supports a small number of significant partnerships with charities and social enterprises which coincide with its three focus areas

» **Matched funding** – CareTech staff can apply for matched funding of up to £350 per year for any charitable fundraising activity undertaken

» **Community grants** – under this grant scheme, CareTech staff can apply for funding for causes in their local communities. Previous beneficiaries have included Addaction Dumfries, Dudley Town FC, Edmonton Scouts and Sport Birmingham.

» **Staff hardship fund** – CareTech staff experiencing significant hardship, or at risk of hardship, can apply for a grant from the foundation. This grant scheme is also open to previous staff who may have recently left the company.

Beneficiaries included: Birkbeck College (£83,300); Barnardo's (£75,000); British Asian Trust (£50,000); Autistica (£37,500); Care First (£22,000); Open University (£20,000); Onside Youth Zones (£12,500); Birmingham Disability Resource Centre (£11,300).

Financial information

Year end	30/09/2021
Assets	£7,100,000
Income	£1,440,000
Grant total	£525,000
Organisations supported	13+

Further financial information

Grants awarded to organisations were broken down as follows in 2020/21: skills and development in the care sector (£248,200); disabilities and mental health (£229,900); supporting communities (£47,000). In addition, grants totalling £145,100 were awarded to individual CareTech employees.

Applications

Each grants programme has an eligibility test, which should be completed by prospective applicants before making an application. If deemed eligible, applications can be made online. Paper or digital/Word copies of the application form can be requested by email. The foundation can also offer applicants support filling in their application.

Sources of information

Accounts; annual report; Charity Commission record; funder's website.

The Clarkson Foundation

 General charitable purposes, including: people affected by COVID-19; social welfare; health; homelessness; community development; maritime charities; and disaster relief

 Worldwide

£ £86,500 (2021)

CC number: 1191357

Trustees: Jeffrey Woyda; Richard Haines; Dharani Sridharan; Alexander Gray; Lily-Rose Bagshaw; Robert Knight; Katharine Thompson.

Correspondent: The Trustees, Commodity Quay, St Katharine Docks, London E1W 1BF (email: foundation@clarksons.com)

🌐 www.theclarksonfoundation.com

General information

The foundation was established is 2020 and is the corporate charity of Clarkson plc, a provider of shipping services headquartered in London.

Grants are made worldwide. The foundation's website states: 'We strive to make a tangible difference by supporting causes with a localised focus, anywhere in the world.'

According to its 2021 annual report, the foundation had seven main focus areas during the year:
- Charities which support those in need caused directly or indirectly by the impact of COVID-19
- Relief of poverty
- Relief of sickness and preservation of health
- Homelessness
- Community charities
- Maritime-related charities
- Disaster relief

Beneficiaries included: Samaritans; Street Child; The Valley Hospital Charity; The Wave Project; The Whitechapel Mission; Willow Foundation.

Financial information

Year end	31/12/2021
Assets	£294,600
Income	£381,800
Grant total	£86,500
Organisations supported	16

Applications

The foundation's website states: 'If you think the foundation can help with charitable causes you are involved with, or you have an idea of ways the foundation can help – get in touch.'

Sources of information

Accounts; annual report; charity Commission record; funder's website.

The Keith Coombs Trust

 General charitable purposes; children and young people; health; education; the arts

 UK, with a preference for the West Midlands

 £ £73,300 (2020/21)

CC number: 1149791

Trustees: Anthony Coombs; Graham Coombs; Demetrios Markou; Christine Ingram; Chris Redford; Manjeet Bhogal.

Correspondent: Christine Ingram, Trustee, c/o S&U plc, 2 Stratford Court, Cranmore Boulevard, Solihull, West Midlands B90 4QT (tel: 0121 705 7777; email: christineingram@suplc.co.uk)

General information

The trust was established in 2012 after the death of Keith Coombs, the West Midlands businessman who set up S&U. Mr Coombs was a specialist motor finance and bridging lender and also spent a decade as the chair of Birmingham City Football Club. His sons Anthony and Graham Coombs are trustees of the charity. The trust receives funding from S&U and its employees.

According to its Charity Commission record, the objects of the trust are:
- The funding and support of exclusively charitable purposes, particularly those related to children, young people, people with disabilities, education and the arts
- Providing support to children and young people to develop their skills and capabilities, in order for their education to advance and so they may participate in society as mature individuals
- The relief of sickness and improvement of health in people in the West Midlands
- To promote and protect the health of those with cerebral palsy, Parkinson's disease and those who have suffered strokes
- To advance public knowledge in the area of conductive education
- To advance the education of pupils at Red Boots School by providing educational facilities
- Promotion of the arts to the general public

Beneficiaries included: A list of beneficiaries was not available.

Financial information

Year end	12/09/2021
Assets	£9,200
Income	£78,000
Grant total	£73,300

Applications

Apply in writing to the correspondent.

Sources of information

Accounts; annual report; Charity Commission record.

Co-op Foundation

 Community enterprise; community development; health; community safety; sustainability

UK

£ £2.53 million (2021)

CC number: 1093028

Trustees: Jamie Ward-Smith; Peter Batt; Mahalia Flasz; Latefa Mansarit; Hope Levy-Shepherd; Ewansiha George Edenene Imafidon; Sharon Jones; Sheila Malley.

Correspondent: The Trustees, 9th Floor, 1 Angel Square, Manchester M60 0AG (email: foundation@coop.co.uk)

🌐 www.coopfoundation.org.uk

f facebook.com/Co-op-Foundation-156348321640279

🐦 @Coop_Foundation

General information

Established in 2000, the Co-operative Community Investment Foundation is administered by the Co-operative Group and funded by its members who have agreed to donate some of their profit share to the foundation.

According to its 2022–27 strategy, the foundation will help to create:
- Prosperous communities with access to opportunity
- Safe communities
- Diverse, equitable and inclusive communities
- Healthy communities
- Sustainable communities
- Communities that prioritise youth activism, shared power and transparent governance

Visit the foundation's website to see current funding and support available.

Beneficiaries included: A list of beneficiaries was not available. Previous beneficiaries include: Envision (£132,500); The Children's Society (£69,800); Women's Technology Centre (£50,000); White Rock Neighbourhood Ventures (£40,000); Changing Our Lives (£35,000); Scotswood Garden (£21,200); UK Youth (£20,000).

Financial information

Year end	31/12/2021
Assets	£28,920,000
Income	£4,540,000
Grant total	£2,530,000

Applications

Funding rounds for specific programmes open periodically during the year and will be advertised on the foundation's website. Alternatively, subscribe to the foundation's blog for updates.

Sources of information
Accounts; annual report; Charity Commission record; funder's website.

Coutts Charitable Foundation

 Women and girls; projects empowering young people through the performing arts

 UK

£746,600 (2020/21)

CC number: 1150784

Trustees: Lord Waldegrave of North Hill; Dr Linda Yueh; Alison Rose-Slade; Peter Flavel; Camilla Stowell; Rachel Harrington; Judith McNeill; Laura Lines; Linda Urquhart.

Correspondent: The Trustees, c/o Coutts & Co., 440 Strand, London WC2R 0QS (tel: 020 7753 1000; email: coutts. foundation@coutts.com)

 www.coutts.com/coutts-foundation. html

General information
Established in 2013, this foundation is the charitable arm of Coutts & Co., a private bank and wealth manager. Coutts & Co. is one of the world's oldest banks (founded 1692) and is wholly owned by the Royal Bank of Scotland Group.

The foundation's website states:

> The mission of the Coutts Foundation is to support sustainable approaches to tackle the causes and consequences of poverty, in the communities where Coutts has a presence. Building on the legacy of Thomas Coutts and Angela Burdett-Coutts, the grand-daughter of Thomas Coutts, who was a progressive 19th-century philanthropist – The Foundation currently focuses on work that supports vulnerable women and girls and work that empowers young people through the performing arts. The Coutts Foundation is an independent corporate foundation, supported by Coutts.

According to its website, the foundation's current focus is 'UK organisations or programmes that support women and girls and organisations that empower young people through the performing arts, with a particular focus on addressing the causes and consequences of poverty.' The foundation makes significant commitments to a small number of organisations that reflect its mission.

Beneficiaries included: Contact and Immediate Theatre (£150,000 each); The Magdalene Group (£128,200 in two grants); Clore Social Leadership

Programme (£24,000); The Theatre Artists Fund (£20,000); The Nelson Trust (£10,000); Women's Resource Centre (£250).

Financial information
Year end	01/04/2021
Assets	£4,000,000
Income	£316,300
Grant total	£746,600
Organisations supported	15

Further financial information
In 2020/21, the foundation awarded 16 grants to 15 organisations, of which 9 were COVID-19 emergency grants.

Applications
The foundation does not accept unsolicited applications. However, its website states, 'if you wish to bring information about your organisation or programmes that fit with our funding priorities to our attention, please complete the information submission form and either email it to us or post it.'

The foundation will then get in touch if it wishes to learn more. Refer to the foundation's website for more details.

Sources of information
Accounts; annual report; Charity Commission record; funder's website.

Coventry Building Society Charitable Foundation

 Groups or activities aimed at improving the quality of life and opportunities in communities affected by disadvantage, deprivation and social exclusion

 Coventry and Warwickshire

£300,000 (2021)

CC number: 1072244

Trustees: Matthew Mannings; Tina Jones; Kevin Purvey.

Correspondent: The Trustees, Coventry Building Society, Oak Tree Court, Harry Weston Road, Coventry, Warwickshire CV3 2UN (tel: 0800 121 8899)

 www.coventrybuildingsociety.co.uk/ consumer/who-we-are/charities/ charitable-foundation.html

General information
The foundation was launched in 1998 and is entirely funded by the Coventry Building Society.

Grants are distributed by from the Heart of England Community Foundation to organisations in Coventry and Warwickshire.

Beneficiaries included: Coventry Citizens Advice, Grapevine and Positive Youth Foundation (£50,000 each);

Central England Law Centre and The Belgrade Theatre Trust (£40,000 each); Age UK and St Francis Employability (£35,000 each).

Financial information
Year end	31/12/2021
Assets	£15,400
Income	£388,700
Grant total	£300,000
Organisations supported	7

Further financial information
According to the foundation's annual accounts for 2021, the foundation awarded seven grants to organisations, totalling £300,000.

Applications
Applications can be made online through the Heart of England Community Foundation.

Sources of information
Accounts; annual report; Charity Commission record; funder's website.

The Cranswick Charitable Trust

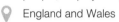 Food poverty; children and young people; employability

England and Wales

£8,000 (2021/22)

CC number: 1192296

Trustees: Miranda Spencer; Andrew Napthine; Michael De-Villamar Roberts; Steven Glover.

Correspondent: The Trustees, Cranswick plc, Crane Court, Ferriby Road, Hessle, East Riding of Yorkshire HU13 0PA (email: charitable.trust@cranswick.co.uk)

https://cranswick.plc.uk/ responsibility/cranswick-charitable-trust

General information
The trust was registered with the Charity Commission in 2020 and is the corporate charity of Cranswick plc, a food producer based in Yorkshire.

The trust will focus on the areas of food poverty, children's charities and employability. It will also support individuals who are facing hardship, including former employees of Cranswick plc.

Beneficiaries included: UNICEF (£4,000); Bundles of Joy, ENYP, The Exodus Project and The Kinetic Science Foundation (£1,000 each).

Financial information
Year end	31/03/2022
Assets	£14,300
Income	£530,500
Grant total	£8,000
Organisations supported	4

Applications
Apply in writing to the correspondent.

Sources of information
Accounts; annual report; Charity Commission record; funder's website.

Credit Suisse EMEA Foundation

The education and training of children and young people; financial inclusion

Countries where Credit Suisse has offices in Europe, the Middle East and Africa

£1.1 million (2021)

CC number: 1122472

Trustees: Colin Hely-Hutchinson; Samantha Ruston; Raminder Bath; Jeremy Lewis; Katarsyna Sejwa; Mark Walsh; Katarsyna Jozefowicz; Matthew Watson; Ian Hale; Sean Alleyne; Caroline Waddington; Karen Newton; Guy Varney; Marc Pereira-Mendoza; Mark Ellis.

Correspondent: Corporate Citizenship Team, Credit Suisse, 1 Cabot Square, London E14 4QJ (tel: 020 7888 8888; email: emea.corporatecitizenship@credit-suisse.com)

www.credit-suisse.com/about-us/en/our-company/corporate-responsibility/economy-society/emea.html

General information
The foundation was established by Credit Suisse AG and channels the group's corporate citizenship activities in Europe, the Middle East and Africa. It supports general charitable purposes in the areas where the company has a presence, but has a preference supporting organisations that improve the educational attainment, employability and aspirations of disadvantaged young people. The foundation also makes grants to the employee-nominated Credit Suisse Charity of the Year.

The foundation's 2021 annual report states the following about its grant-making:

> The Foundation looks for opportunities to provide multi-year funding where possible... The Foundation will support proposals, which meet its priority areas of work. This may be a specific project or ongoing costs including staff salaries and overheads. It also encourages any organisation seeking funding to include a reasonable amount of core costs to cover overheads if applying for project funding.

Beneficiaries included: City Year UK (£296,800); ThinkForward UK (£200,000); Learning with Parents (£100,000); Young Enterprise (£50,000); Cancer Research UK (£31,000).

Financial information
Year end	31/12/2021
Assets	£2,190,000
Income	£1,430,000
Grant total	£1,100,000
Organisations supported	11

Exclusions
According to the foundation's 2021 annual report, it will not support applications:

- that directly replace or subsidise statutory funding;
- that are the primary responsibility of statutory funders such as local and central government and health authorities;
- for administration and costs not directly associated with the application;
- from individuals, or which are for the benefit of one individual;
- for the promotion of religious or political causes;
- for holidays;
- for work that has already taken place;
- for general appeals;
- for animal welfare;
- for festivals, sports and leisure activities.

Exceptions may be made to the above exclusions in relation to Credit Suisse's Charity of the Year and under other exceptional circumstances.

Applications
Credit Suisse coordinates grant-making on a regional basis within four regions across the globe. Contact your local Credit Suisse office for further information.

Sources of information
Accounts; annual report; Charity Commission record; funder's website.

The Peter Cruddas Foundation

Disadvantaged and disengaged young people aged 16 to 30

England and Wales

£313,300 (2020/21)

CC number: 1117323

Trustees: Lord Peter Cruddas; Martin Paisner; Rt Hon Lord Young of Graffham.

Correspondent: Stephen Cox, Company Secretary and Foundation Administrator, 133 Houndsditch, London EC3A 7BX (tel: 020 3003 8360; email: s.cox@petercruddasfoundation.org.uk)

www.petercruddasfoundation.org.uk

General information
Established in December 2006, this is the charitable foundation of Peter Cruddas, founder of the UK-based financial trading group CMC Markets plc, who has pledged to donate at least £100 million to good causes during his lifetime.

The foundation's website provides the following information about its funding:

> The foundation supports programmes designed to help disadvantaged and disengaged young people in the age range of 16 to 30, to pursue pathways to Education, Training and Employment with the ultimate aim of helping them to become financially independent.

> Preference will be given to the support of projects undertaken by charitable organisations registered with The Charity Commission of England and Wales benefitting young people in England and Wales only.

The foundation's priority funding streams are listed on its website as:
- Pathways/support for young disadvantaged or disengaged young people in the age range 16 to 30 into education, training or employment
- Work experience/skills projects for young people aged 16 to 30
- Youth work in London; particularly evening work for disadvantaged young people aged 16 to 30

Beneficiaries included: The Scout Association (£100,000); GOSH Charity (£35,000); The Amber Trust (£10,000); Yes Futures (£5,000); Tall Ships Youth Trust (£3,000); The Childhood Trusts (£2,000).

Financial information
Year end	31/03/2021
Assets	£161,500
Income	£437,500
Grant total	£313,300

Applications
The foundation operates an invitation-only application scheme. As of January 2023, the foundation's website stated:

> At a recent Trustee meeting, concern was raised over the time it takes a charity to apply to The Foundation and subsequently receive a decision on their application. With this in mind and wishing to avoid any lengthy period between application submission and receiving an outcome, it has been decided that from 1st September 2021, The Foundation will go to an "Invitation Only" application scheme.

> The current backlog of applications received prior to this date will be processed and then The Foundation will review past applications as a resource to reach out to those charities working in our area of interest. This will be the case for the foreseeable future.

> We know this will be a disappointment to charities only recently finding The Peter Cruddas Foundation but we hope you will

understand this as a necessary step to take following an unprecedented time caused by COVID-19. Please do revisit the website for future updates.

Sources of information
Accounts; annual report; Charity Commission record; funder's website; guidelines for applicants.

Cruden Foundation Ltd

 Social welfare; medical support and research; arts; education; conservation

Scotland

£346,700 (2021/22)

OSCR number: SC004987

Trustees: John Rafferty; Kevin Reid; Alison Paul; Dr Angus Campbell.

Correspondent: The Trustees, 16 Walker Street, Edinburgh EH3 7LP (tel: 0131 442 3862; email: info@ crudenfoundation.org)

 https://crudenfoundation.org

General information
Cruden Foundation Ltd is the corporate charity of the Cruden Group, one of the largest independent development and construction groups in Scotland.

The object of the foundation is to support and contribute to institutions for the benefit of the community. According to the foundation's website, it makes donations to small and medium-sized charities in Scotland, with a focus on the areas of community welfare, medical support and research, the arts, education and conservation.

The foundation's website states:

The Trust is keen to support charities involved in one, or more, of the following areas:

- Activities relating to community healthcare services including home care, aftercare, sufferers of long-term medical conditions and the continuing care of disabled people.
- Health education and prevention – promoting knowledge and awareness of specific diseases or medical conditions.
- Research in preventative or curative medicine.
- Lifelong learning projects helping people of any age to achieve their educational potential through supplementary schools, literacy and numeracy projects, community education, vocational/restart education for the unemployed, and alternative education for excluded school pupils.
- Community development by helping groups to organise and respond to problems and needs in their communities.
- Social services including organisations assisting individuals or families to overcome social deprivation e.g. people who are homeless or disabled

and their carers, single parent and childcare groups and other family support groups.
- Social preventive schemes covering activities which prevent crime, 'dropping out' and general delinquency, provide social care outreach services, deliver social health and safety awareness schemes.
- Community social activities which promote social engagement for vulnerable people, mitigating against isolation and loneliness.
- Artistic activities that are supportive of cultural enhancement in the community.
- Advancing public participation in a sport that involves physical skill and physical exertion.

Beneficiaries included: Edinburgh International Festival (£25,000); Pitlochry Festival Theatre (£15,000); Street Soccer – Scotland (£10,000); Horatio's Garden (£5,000); Scottish Chamber Orchestra (£3,000); Borders Children's Charity, Sepsis Research – FEAT and St Andrew's Hospice (£2,500 each).

Financial information
Year end	31/07/2022
Assets	£13,430,000
Income	£391,600
Grant total	£346,700
Organisations supported	164

Further financial information
During 2021/22, grants were distributed as follows:

Social welfare	£132,000
Medical causes	£104,200
Arts	£90,500
Education	£11,000
Heritage conservation	£9,000

A total of 164 grants were awarded during the financial period. Of these grants, 18 were of over £5,000 and 20 were of between £2,500 and £4,999. Only organisations that received grants of over £2,500 were listed as beneficiaries in the charity's accounts. Grants of less than £2,500 totalled £144,700.

Exclusions
The foundation will not support individuals or activities that are generally the responsibility of the local health authority, education authority or similar body. It does not tend to support capital development projects.

Applications
Applications can be made via the foundation's website at any time of the year. The board meets three times a year to consider applications, usually in November, February and June.

Sources of information
Accounts; annual report; Companies House; funder's website; OSCR record.

Cumberland Building Society Charitable Foundation

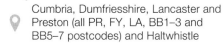 General charitable purposes

Cumbria, Dumfriesshire, Lancaster and Preston (all PR, FY, LA, BB1–3 and BB5–7 postcodes) and Haltwhistle

£23,900 (2020/21)

CC number: 1072435

Trustees: Claire Deeks; Rebecca Towns; Lewis Benson.

Correspondent: Annalee Holliday, Senior Grants, Programmes and Communications Officer, Cumberland House, Cooper Way, Parkhouse, Carlisle, Cumbria CA3 0JF (tel: 01900 825760; email: annalee@cumbriafoundation.org)

 www.cumbriafoundation.org/fund/ cumberland-building-society

General information
The Cumberland Building Society Charitable Foundation is a registered charity set up by Cumberland Building Society in November 1998. Although the foundation was established by the society, they are separate organisations.

The foundation has two main grants programmes, details of which have been taken from its website.

Strategic grants
- Larger, multi-year grants of up to £25,000 to improve or maintain the capacity of organisations promoting the financial wellbeing of people.
- Funding can be used to provide an opportunity to scale up promising innovations and/or improve existing initiatives.
- Strategic grants of up to £25,000 for three years.

Community grants
- Grants of up to £5,000 to community organisations that improve the life skills, education, employability and enterprise of disadvantaged people or support vulnerable, older people.
- These are likely to be one-off grants.
- Priority will be given to projects that can demonstrate a clear need and/or demand for their service.
- Community grants of up to £5,000 over one year.

Beneficiaries included: A list of beneficiaries was not available.

Financial information
Year end	31/03/2021
Assets	£0
Income	£23,900
Grant total	£23,900

Applications
Applications can be made via the Cumbria Community Foundation website.

237

Sources of information

Accounts; annual report; Charity Commission record; funder's website.

The DWF Foundation

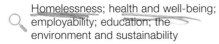

🔍 Homelessness; health and well-being; employability; education; the environment and sustainability

📍 UK, Ireland, Australia, Canada, France, Germany, India, Italy, Poland, Qatar, Spain, the United Arab Emirates and the USA

£ £127,300 (2019/20)

CC number: 1191347

Trustees: Sir Duncan Nichol; Carolyn Ferber; Zelinda Bennett; Peter Holland; Sean Monks; Robert Binns; Edwin Oliver; Mark Stanbury; Lindsay Ogunyemi; James Davies; Jewels Chamberlain.

Correspondent: Clare Bevan, Foundation Manager, 5 St Paul's Square, Old Hall Street, Liverpool, Merseyside L3 9AE (tel: 07736 121046; email: clare. beavan@dwf.law)

🌐 www.dwf.law/About-us/DWF-Foundation

General information

The DWF Foundation was established by DWF LLP, a multinational law firm based in Manchester.

Areas of work

The foundation's areas of interests are:
- Homelessness
- Health and well-being
- Employability
- Education
- Environment and sustainability

According to its website, grants are made specifically to initiative that develop and improve local communities by:
- Tackling a specific community issue
- Helping voluntary and community groups become more effective and efficient
- Encouraging the involvement in the community of those too often excluded
- Enabling young people to develop skills for benefit of the community

Eligibility

Grants are awarded to registered charities only. Eligible organisations must operating in countries in which DWF offices are located. A full list of eligible locations can be seen on the website. Grants typically fall under £5,000.

Financial information

Year end	31/03/2020
Assets	£1,850,000
Income	£336,700
Grant total	£127,300

Further financial information

The foundation has recently re-registered with the Charity Commission; therefore, full financial information was not available. This financial information relates to the previous charity, The DWF Charitable Foundation (Charity Commission no. 1157229).

Exclusions

The foundation does not support:
- Academic research
- Activities for which a statutory body is responsible
- Activity taking place in school time that is a statutory responsibility
- Animal welfare
- Evaluation which is not related to the funded work
- Everyday running costs and core salaries
- General fundraising appeals
- Individuals
- Loans or business finance
- Other grant-making bodies
- Professional fundraisers or bid writers
- Professional qualifications
- Recurrent funding
- Redundancy payments
- Religious or political causes
- Sponsorship, marketing appeals or fundraising costs
- Start-up costs for new organisations
- The advancement of religion
- Universities/higher education facilities
- Vehicles and minibuses
- Work that has already taken place

Applications

Applications can be submitted using an online form on the foundation's website.

Sources of information

Accounts; annual report; Charity Commission record; funder's website.

The James Dyson Foundation

🔍 Medical research; engineering education; projects in Malmesbury

📍 Worldwide, with a preference for the UK and in particular the local area around Dyson's UK headquarters in Malmesbury, Wiltshire

£ £2.34 million (2021)

CC number: 1099709

Trustees: Lady Deirdre Dyson; Sir James Dyson; Valerie West.

Correspondent: The Trustees, Tetbury Hill, Malmesbury, Wiltshire SN16 0RP (tel: 01666 746802; email: info@ jamesdysonfoundation.com)

🌐 www.jamesdysonfoundation.com

 facebook.com/ JamesDysonFoundation

 @foundationdyson

 @jamesdysonfoundation

General information

The James Dyson Foundation is the charitable foundation of the British technology company Dyson Ltd. The foundation was established in 2002 to promote charitable giving, especially to charities working in the fields of science, design, engineering education and medical research. The foundation is almost exclusively funded by donations from Dyson Ltd.

Charitable support

According to its website, the foundation can provide small financial donations to charitable causes that fall within its three areas of focus:
- Engineering education
- Medical or scientific research
- Projects and organisations in Malmesbury, Wiltshire, where Dyson's head office is based

The James Dyson Award

The foundation runs the James Dyson Award, an annual international design competition that aims to inspire and encourage the next generation of design engineers. The award is open to current and recent design or engineering students.

Beneficiaries included: A list of beneficiaries was not available.

Financial information

Year end	31/12/2021
Assets	-£1,060,000
Income	£1,110,000
Grant total	£2,340,000

Further financial information

Grants were distributed as follows: science and medical research (£1.16 million); education and training (£1.15 million); social and community welfare (£32,300).

Exclusions

According to its website, the foundation will not fund any of the following:
- Animal welfare
- Loans or funding for individuals or companies
- Sports team sponsorship

Applications

To apply, organisations should complete the online contact form on the foundation's website. The foundation aims to respond within two weeks.

Sources of information

Accounts; annual report; Charity Commission record; funder's website.

The Economist Charitable Trust

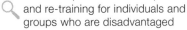 Education; communication; literacy and re-training for individuals and groups who are disadvantaged

UK

£121,400 (2020/21)

CC number: 293709

Trustees: Ada Simkins; Kiran Malik; Susan Clark; Jamie Credland; Ursula Esling.

Correspondent: The Trustees, The Adelphi, 1–11 John Adam Street, London WC2N 6HT (tel: 020 7576 8000)

General information

The Economist Charitable Trust is the charity of The Economist Newspaper Ltd, a multinational media company specialising in international business and world affairs.

The trust was established in 1985 to distribute funds received from the Economist Newspaper Ltd to various charities. Around 60 to 70% of the trust's donations go to charities in the fields of communication, education, literacy and re-training for individuals and groups who are disadvantaged in some way. These charities are nominated to the trustees for a screening process to make sure the projects align with the goals of the trust. A staff vote determines the amount each charity receives. Approximately 30 to 40% of funds are used to match donations made by employees of The Economist Group. The remaining funds are utilised to make small donations to small and local charities.

Beneficiaries included: Staff Matching (£19,200); One Acre Fund (£18,000); Room to Read (£16,400); Village Enterprise (£13,200); Build on Belief (£8,900); Yes, Futures (£8,100).

Financial information

Year end	31/03/2021
Assets	£9,500
Income	£112,000
Grant total	£121,400

Applications

The trust does not accept unsolicited applications.

Sources of information

Accounts; annual report; Charity Commission record.

The Fairness Foundation

 General charitable purposes; a fairer society

UK

£942,800 (2020/21)

CC number: 1044174

Trustees: Julian Richer; Frances Crook; Emma Revie; Peter Gladwell.

Correspondent: R. Bamforth, Secretary, Gallery Court, Hankey Place, London SE1 4BB (tel: 020 7173 4393; email: info@persula.org)

 https://fairnessfoundation.com

General information

The foundation changed its name from The Persula Foundation to The Fairness Foundation in December 2020. It was established in 1994 by Richer Sounds plc, the UK home entertainment retailer. Trustees include Julian Richer, founder of the company, who donates 15% of the yearly profit to the foundation. The foundation supports general charitable purposes, but its main aim is to address unfairness and inequality in society. At present, the foundation is focusing on providing funding for charities that are supporting the following causes:

- A fairer society
- Human rights
- Animal welfare
- The environment
- Women
- LGBTQ+
- People with disabilities
- Mental health and medical causes
- Migrants and refugees
- Domestic abuse
- Older people
- Support for prisoners
- Citizenship
- Children

The foundation also has a preference for managing its own projects. Examples include: the 'National Storytelling Tour', which annually provides 100 free sessions of storytelling and music to people with visual impairments, older people, and children and adults with disabilities; and 'ASB Help' which provides advice and support to victims of anti-social behaviour.

Beneficiaries included: Good Business Foundation (£175,000); ASB Help (£140,000); Tax Watch (£60,000); Hickman and Rose (£42,000); Prisoners' Advice Service (£35,000); Parallel Histories (£25,000); Shelter (£10,000).

Financial information

Year end	30/04/2021
Assets	£500,000
Income	£1,420,000
Grant total	£942,800

Further financial information

Grants are broken down as follows:

A fair society	£449,600
Human rights	£137,700
Animal welfare	£98,900
Prisoners' support	£81,500
Women's support	£50,200
Children	£41,600
Medical causes	£30,000
Migrants/refugees	£24,100
Disabilities	£20,000
Mental health	£6,000
Bullying	£3,000
Miscellaneous	£220

Applications

According to the 2020/21 annual report, the foundation considered applications from a variety of charitable organisations. Contact the correspondent for more information.

Sources of information

Accounts; annual report; Charity Commission record.

The Fidelity UK Foundation

 Disadvantaged children and young people; health and well-being; arts, culture and heritage

UK

£9.51 million (2021)

CC number: 327899

Trustees: Anthony Bolton; John Owen; Sally Walden; Abigail Johnson; Elizabeth Johnson; Dr Malcolm Rogers; Sanjeev Gandhi; Peter Goldsbrough; Edward Johnson.

Correspondent: The Trustees, Beech Gate, Millfield Lane, Lower Kingswood, Tadworth, Surrey KT20 6RP (tel: 01732 777364; email: foundation@fil.com)

 https://filfoundations. fidelityinternational.com

General information

The Fidelity UK Foundation is the charitable foundation of the financial services company Fidelity Worldwide Investments. The foundation was established in 1988 and primarily supports UK-registered charities.

Grants are generally made to organisations with an annual operating budget in excess of £1 million. Grants are made for IT projects, organisational development, capital costs and core costs.

The foundation has three priority programme areas:

- Enabling disadvantaged children and young people to achieve their potential
- Health and well-being
- Arts, culture and heritage

Fidelity also has three international foundations: The Fidelity Bermuda Foundation; The Fidelity Europe Foundation; The Fidelity Asia Pacific Foundation. They make grants to organisations in countries where the company has operations and which serve beneficiaries in Austria, Belgium, Ireland, Italy, France, Germany, Luxembourg, Netherlands, Poland, Spain, Sweden, Switzerland, Australia, Bermuda, China, Hong Kong, India, Japan, Korea, Singapore and Taiwan.

Beneficiaries included: The Prince's Trust (£500,000); Asthma UK and British Lung Foundation Partnership (£450,000); Midlands Arts Centre (£332,300); MyBNK (£255,000); The Nelson Trust (£161,000); FARE – Scotland (£87,700); City Year UK (£52,000); Breaking Barriers (£10,000).

Financial information

Year end		31/12/2021
Assets		£338,800,000
Income		£4,340,000
Grant total		£9,510,000
Organisations supported		71

Further financial information

Grants were broken down as follows:

Disadvantaged children and young people	41	£6.37 million
Health and well-being	14	£3.38 million
Arts, culture and heritage	14	£1.81 million
Cross sector	1	£240,000
Grants from the W. L. 'Bill' Byrnes Global Scholarship Fund	1	£129,100

Applications

Unsolicited applications are not accepted. The foundation's website states:

> The Foundation does not seek unsolicited proposals and has an invitation-only application process. The Foundation's team pro-actively identifies organisations that we would like to learn more about through research, seeking insights from funders who have shared interests, and insights from the organisations we support. Where appropriate, organisations are invited to submit a short concept note, which we aim to respond to within four weeks. If a concept note is approved, a full application is invited at which point the formal application process begins. This two-stage process is designed to help ensure the application process is efficient for everyone involved.

Sources of information

Accounts; annual report; Charity Commission record; funder's website.

The Sir John Fisher Foundation

 General charitable purposes with a preference for maritime causes; medicine; people with disabilities; education; music; the arts; community projects

UK, with a strong preference for charities in the Furness peninsula and Cumbria

£2.76 million (2020/21)

CC number: 277844

Trustees: Julie Barton; Daniel Tindall; Michael Shields; Thomas Meacock; Christopher Batten; Chris Tomlinson; Dr David Jackson.

Correspondent: David Dawson, Executive Officer, c/o Hart Jackson and Sons, 8–10 New Market Street, Ulverston, Cumbria LA12 7LW (tel: 07464 504756; email: www. sirjohnfisherfoundation.org.uk)

www.sirjohnfisherfoundation.org. uk

General information

The foundation registered with the Charity Commission in 1979 after it was established by Sir John and Lady Maria Fisher. The foundation is closely associated with James Fisher and Sons plc which provides marine engineering services.

Areas of work

The foundation's website states that it supports charitable causes in the six following categories:

▶ Maritime
▶ Medical and disability
▶ Education
▶ Music
▶ Arts
▶ Community projects in Barrow-in-Furness and the Furness Peninsula.

Capital and revenue funding is available for up to three years. Most grants are for less than £30,000. In the past, larger grants have also been awarded for major one-off projects or research.

The foundation's website states:

> The Foundation gives priority to applying its income to projects and causes based in Barrow-in-Furness and the Furness Peninsula. Exceptionally, occasional community projects from the remainder of Cumbria and North Lancashire will be considered. Some projects are supported nationally, particularly Maritime projects and a few educational Music projects.

Beneficiaries included: The Lady Maria Fisher Foundation (£1 million).

Financial information

Year end		31/03/2021
Assets		£124,480,000
Income		£58,260,000
Grant total		£2,760,000
Organisations supported		96

Further financial information

During 2020/21, grants were broken down as follows:

Lady Maria Fisher Foundation	2	£1 million
Community	46	£649,000
Medical research	6	£398,700
Medical causes	17	£242,900
Education	14	£251,700
Arts	6	£160,400
Maritime causes	3	£31,500
Music	2	£17,500

Exclusions

According to the foundation's website, it will not make grants for:

▶ Sponsorships
▶ Individuals
▶ Expeditions
▶ The promotion of religion or places of worship (except when acting as a community centre)
▶ Animal welfare
▶ Retrospective funding
▶ Pressure groups
▶ Community projects outside Barrow-in-Furness and the Furness Peninsula (except occasional projects in Cumbria or North Lancashire or if they fall within one of the other categories supported by the Foundation)

Applications

Application forms are available from the correspondent or to download from the website, where guidelines can also be found. Applications should be made by submitting a completed application form, together with all relevant information (set out on the application form) to the Secretary by e-mail or post. The Trustees meet at the beginning of May and the beginning of November each year. The closing dates for applications are posted on the foundation's website.

Sources of information

Accounts; annual report; Charity Commission record; funder's website.

Ford Britain Trust

 Community; education and schools; people with special needs; people with disabilities; arts and culture; the environment; homelessness

Areas in close proximity to Ford Motor Company Ltd's locations in the UK; these include Essex (including East London), Bridgend, Daventry, Liverpool, Manchester and Southampton

£ £125,500 (2020/21)

CC number: 269410

Trustees: Lara Nicoll; David Russell; Wendy James; Dr June-Alison Sealy; Paul Bailey; Jenny Ball; Jane Skerry.

Correspondent: The Trustees, 15–02B D20-B, Ford Dunton Technical Centre, Laindon, Basildon, Essex SS15 6EE (email: fbtrust@ford.com)

www.ford.co.uk/fbtrust

General information

The Ford Britain Trust serves the communities in which Ford Motor Company Ltd and its employees are located. The trust provides grants mainly to registered charities and schools in support of: youth development; schools and education, with particular emphasis on special educational needs; disabilities; and community-related services.

The trust particularly encourages applications from Ford employees, but is open to all, provided that applicants meet the selection criteria.

Grants

The website states that grants are typically one-off, provided for specific capital projects or parts of a project and fall into two categories:

- Small grants of up to £250, available four times a year
- Large grants of over £250 and usually up to £3,000, available twice a year

Grants can be made to registered charities, schools or PTAs, and other non-profit organisations. Support is given in the following categories:

- Local community/environment
- Young people and children
- Education and schools
- Special education needs
- People with disabilities
- Arts and culture

Grants can be given for the following purposes:

- Contributions to capital projects (e.g. refurbishments)
- Capital expenditure items (e.g. furniture/equipment/computers)
- Contributions towards the purchase of a new vehicle (maximum grant £3,000*)

*See the website for full conditions.

Beneficiaries included: Action for Family Carers and Blind in Business (£3,000 each); Bygrave Primary School (£2,900); The CommunityHub (£2,700); City Gateway (£2,300); Scampdoodles (£2,000).

Financial information

Year end	31/03/2021
Assets	£345,900
Income	£256,900
Grant total	£125,500

Further financial information

Only organisations that received grants of over £1,000 were listed as beneficiaries in the charity's accounts. Grants of under £1,000 totalled £44,200.

Exclusions

The trust's website states:

Grants cannot be provided to:
- Individuals
- CICs
- Local Authorities, Councils, Government and Government Departments

Grant applications are NOT considered if they support the following purposes or activities:
- Core funding; General running costs
- Major building works
- Sponsorship or advertising
- Research
- Overseas projects ; Travel
- Religious projects ; Political projects
- Purchase of second-hand vehicles
- Third party fundraising initiatives (exceptions may be made for fundraising initiatives by Ford Motor Company Limited employees and retirees)

Applications

Application forms are available to download from the website, where guidance notes are also available. The trust's website states: 'The Ford Britain Trust particularly encourages applications supported by Ford employees, but is open to all, provided that the qualifying organisations meet our selection criteria.'

Sources of information

Accounts; annual report; Charity Commission record; funder's website.

Gatwick Airport Community Trust

 Children and young people; art; sports facilities; the environment and conservation; community facilities; people with disabilities; older people; development of volunteering

Parts of East and West Sussex, Surrey and Kent, but particularly communities directly affected by operations at Gatwick Airport

£ £205,700 (2021)

CC number: 1089683

Trustees: Joanna Rettie; Andrew Lynch; Angela Baker; Helyn Baker; Elizabeth McDermid; Alan Jones; Julie Ayres; Richard Burrett.

Correspondent: Rosamund Quade, Administrator, GACT, PO Box 783, Chichester, West Sussex PO19 9TY (tel: 07444 737518; email: mail@gact.org.uk)

www.gact.org.uk

General information

The trust was launched in 2001 and the first grants were awarded in May 2002. It is an independent charity set up by legal agreement between West Sussex County Council, Crawley Borough Council and Gatwick Airport Ltd.

The following was taken from the trust's website:

Grants are currently awarded annually for such charitable purposes as the trustees determine within the area of benefit which covers parts of East and West Sussex, Surrey and Kent. They adopt strict criteria and channel funds for deserving projects, particularly in those areas where people are directly affected by operations at Gatwick Airport.

The minimum grant is £250. The Trust's normal level of grants is from £1000–£5,000. Occasional larger grants may be considered if the impact is targeted to benefit a significant number of people and is considered to make a valuable and noticeable difference longer term.

The following are listed as priority areas for funding:

- Development of young people
- Art projects including amateur drama, music, art
- Sporting facilities
- Environmental improvement and conservation
- Improvements to community facilities such as village halls
- Support for the disabled
- Support for the elderly
- Encouragement of additional volunteering or giving in the area

Beneficiaries included: Crawley Youth Centre and Surrey East Girlguiding (£5,000 each); Crawley Film Initiative

CIC (£3,500); Ifield Tennis Club and YMCA East Surrey (£3,000 each).

Financial information

Year end		31/12/2021
Assets		£50,400
Income		£236,000
Grant total		£205,700
Organisations supported		96

Further financial information

Only organisations that received grants of over £3,000 were listed as beneficiaries in the charity's accounts.

Exclusions

According to the trust's website it will not support the following:

- Individuals
- Projects or beneficiaries that are outside the area of benefit
- Salaries, recurrent expenditure and running costs
- Ongoing costs, maintenance, or deficits
- Repeat annual applications for similar projects
- The purchase of land or buildings
- Organisations that are working to make a profit for shareholders, partners or sole owners
- Organisations with excess 'free' reserves
- Costs that should be funded from other sources e.g., public bodies
- Applications from organisations that have statutory responsibilities such as local authorities, hospitals, schools, unless it is a project that is over and above their core activities. This would include one off projects or capital projects, e.g., playground equipment, or a green heating system in a community building.
- Grants will NOT normally be made where it is evident that little or no effort has been made or is being made to raise funds elsewhere or to demonstrate match funding.

Applications

Application forms can be downloaded from the trust's website. Completed forms should be returned by post (Royal Mail standard first or second class). Note: The trust does not accept applications by email.

Sources of information

Accounts; annual report; Charity Commission record; funder's website.

Global Charities

 Inclusion, diversity and equality; physical and mental health; safety and shelter; life skills; reducing isolation

 UK

 £2.36 million (2020/21)

CC number: 1091657

Trustees: Michael Connole; Jonathan Norbury; Joanne Kenrick; Ulrika Hogberg; Sally Cairns; Marcia Asare; Jennifer Stubbs; Shalni Sood; Martin Allen.

Correspondent: Grants Team, 30 Leicester Square, London WC2H 7LA (tel: 0345 606 0990; email: grants@makesomenoise.com)

 www.makesomenoise.com

facebook.com/globalsmakesomenoise

@makenoise

@globals_make_some_noise

General information

Global Charities is the charitable arm of Global, the media and entertainment group which operates some of the UK's largest and most well-known radio stations, including Heart, Capital and Classic FM.

Global's Make Some Noise

The charity's flagship grant-giving programme Global's Make Some Noise raises money from Global Radio listeners, customers and the entertainment and music industries, which the charity then distributes to support projects undertaken by small community charities. The programme supports charities working in the following areas:

- Providing shelter and safety
- Physical and mental health
- Preventing isolation
- Improving life skills

In 2022, the programme offered one-year grants of between £20,000 and £30,000. The programme does not award grants of more than 40% of a charity's annual income.

To be eligible for funding, applicants must be registered a charity delivering a project or service that addresses one or more of the programme's key outcomes. Charities must have been registered for at least one year, have an annual income of between £30,000 and £1 million and have at least one set of full submitted accounts. Full eligibility criteria are available to view on the charity's website.

Beneficiaries included: A full list of beneficiaries is available on the charity's website.

Financial information

Year end		31/03/2021
Assets		£3,200,000
Income		£4,880,000
Grant total		£2,360,000
Organisations supported		91

Further financial information

In 2020/21, grants were broken down as follows:

Lack of opportunity	20	£441,600
Disability	17	£428,200
Illness	16	£422,700
Mental health	10	£353,800
Bereavement	9	£187,100
Carers	5	£143,900
Poverty	3	£100,000
Homelessness	4	£90,000
Domestic abuse	2	£80,000
Loneliness and isolation	3	£72,000
Other	2	£40,000

A full list of beneficiaries is available on the charity's website.

Applications

The charity has a three-stage application process. These are:

1. **Expression of interest:** an online form can be completed when funding rounds open.
2. **Invitation to apply:** the Grants Team will shortlist charities to apply based on how well they meet the funding objectives. A full application form will need to be completed with relevant documents attached (including your safeguarding policy, current financial information and your constitution or governing document).
3. **Panel assessment:** Applications will be assessed by the Grants Panel. All applicants will be notified of the outcome and will be given feedback.

There is one funding round per year. Check the website for upcoming funding rounds.

Sources of information

Accounts; annual report; Charity Commission record; funder's website.

The Golden Bottle Trust

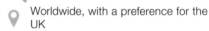 General charitable purposes

Worldwide, with a preference for the UK

£1.40 million (2021)

CC number: 327026

Trustee: Messrs Hoare Trustees.

Correspondent: Messrs Hoare Trustees, c/o C. Hoare & Co., 37 Fleet Street, London EC4P 4DQ (tel: 020 7353 4522)

 www.hoaresbank.co.uk/golden-bottle-trust

General information

The trust was established in 1985 for general charitable purposes by C. Hoare and Co. bankers, the oldest remaining private bank in the UK. The trust is managed by the company Messrs. Hoare Trustees and continues to receive most of its income from C. Hoare and Co.

The objective of the trust is the continuation of the philanthropic commitments and ideals of the Hoare family. According to the trust's 2020/21 annual report, traditionally the trust has supported causes in the spheres of:

- The arts
- Education
- Health
- The environment/sustainability
- Social investment

The trust's website states that in recent years its giving has focused on:

- Prisons and early intervention
- Financial and income inequality
- The refugee crisis
- The environment

The minimum grant amount is £250, rising to a maximum of £100,000, but occasionally larger sums are considered. The trust's 2021 annual report states that 'the preference of the trustee is to build trusted partnerships that allow for the donation of unrestricted funding.'

Beneficiaries included: RefuAid (£120,000); Key 4 Life (£102,000); Think Forward UK (£100,000); The Henry C. Hoare Charitable Trust (£60,000); Tree Council (£50,000); Kids Network (£25,000); Dementia Adventure and Jubilee Centre (£10,000 each).

Financial information

Year end	30/09/2021
Assets	£18,160,000
Income	£1,640,000
Grant total	£1,400,000

Further financial information

Grants paid during the year totalled £1.4 million. The following breakdown was provided in the trust's 2021 annual report:

The environment	£245,000
Relief in need	£232,750
Health and saving lives	£204,600
Staff matched giving	£186,600
Education	£154,000
Charitable trusts	£139,000
Citizenship and community development	£121,000
Religion	£114,000
Arts, culture, heritage and science	£100,800
Prevention and relief of poverty	£38,250
Children	£33,750
Armed forces and emergency services	£9,000
Human rights, racial harmony and equality	£7,250
Animal welfare	£1,000
Amateur sports	£500

Only beneficiaries of grants of £10,000 and above were listed in the accounts.

Applications

The trust's website states that it prefers to use trusted partners and networks to identify suitable causes to help. For this reason, unsolicited grant requests are not accepted.

Sources of information

Accounts; annual report; Charity Commission record; funder's website.

The Goldman Sachs Charitable Gift Fund (UK)

 General charitable purposes, including community development, education, health, social welfare, arts and culture, religion and humanitarian relief

UK and overseas

£2.95 million (2020/21)

CC number: 1120148

Trustees: Jennifer Evans; Graham Shaw; Robert Katz; Peter Fahey.

Correspondent: The Trustees, Goldman Sachs International, 25 Shoe Lane, London EC4A 4AU (tel: 020 7774 1000)

General information

The Goldman Sachs Charitable Gift Fund (UK) was established in 2007 for general charitable purposes. It is the UK charity of the multinational investment bank and financial services company The Goldman Sachs Group Inc., and is the wholly owned subsidiary of the Goldman Sachs Charitable Gift Fund, which has been recognised by the United States Internal Revenue Service as a tax-exempt organisation.

Grants are awarded worldwide and are used to support a wide range of charitable activities including, community development, education, health, social welfare, arts and culture and humanitarian relief.

The foundation stated the following in its 2020/21 annual report: 'The ongoing strategy of the Fund is to make grants pursuant to its objects from donated funds solicited from The Goldman Sachs Group, Inc, and its predecessors, subsidiaries, affiliates and successors ("Goldman Sachs"), and current and former senior employees of Goldman Sachs.'

Beneficiaries included: Princeton University (£867,300); Elsai Foundation (£246,000); Groton School (£165,400); Boston Higashi School, College of the Holy Cross and Worthless Foundation (£82,700 each).

Financial information

Year end	30/06/2021
Assets	£25,780,000
Income	£8,470,000
Grant total	£2,950,000
Organisations supported	108

Further financial information

A total of 108 grants were awarded during the year. According to the charity's annual report:

Grants were made to support charities that build and stabilise communities, increase educational opportunities, advance health, relieve poverty, promote the arts and culture, provide humanitarian relief and to further other exclusively charitable purposes under English and Welsh law and American law. All grants were made to institutions.

Note: the financial information was converted from USD using the exchange rate at the time of writing (November 2022). Only organisations that received grants of over $100,000 were listed as beneficiaries in the charity's accounts. Grants of under $100,000 totalled $1.1 million (£911,700).

Applications

The charity's 2020/21 annual report explains that it 'operates as a donor-advised fund whereby the directors establish donor accounts for individual donors to make recommendations, although the ultimate decision for the distribution of funds rests solely with the directors of the fund'.

Sources of information

Accounts; annual report; Charity Commission record.

Goldman Sachs Gives (UK)

General charitable purposes including arts and culture, community, education, humanitarian causes and medical causes

Worldwide

£25.47 million (2020/21)

CC number: 1123956

Trustees: Jenny Evans; Robert Katz; Graham Shaw; Peter Fahey.

Correspondent: The Trustees, Goldman Sachs, Peterborough Court, 133 Fleet Street, London EC4A 2BB (tel: 020 7774 1000)

www.goldmansachs.com/ citizenship/goldman-sachs-gives

General information

Goldman Sachs Gives (UK) was established and registered with the Charity Commission in 2008. The income of the fund is made up of donations from affiliate and subsidiary companies of Goldman Sachs Group Inc. and also from past and present senior employees of these companies.

The charity's 2020/21 annual accounts state:

The objects of the Fund are to promote for the public benefit the advancement of education, the relief of poverty, the advancement of religion and any other exclusively charitable purpose. In furtherance of those objects the Fund focuses on supporting charities and charitable activities that build and stabilise communities, increase educational opportunities, advance health, relieve poverty, promote the arts and culture, provide humanitarian relief and further any other charitable purposes.

Beneficiaries included: A list of beneficiaries was not available. Previous beneficiaries include: Greenhouse Sports Ltd (£854,000); Mind (£590,000); Fondation de l'Assistance Publique (£518,000).

Financial information

Year end	30/06/2021
Assets	£107,500,000
Income	£42,750,000
Grant total	£25,470,000

Further financial information

Grants were broken down as follows:

Education	£10.53 million
Community	£8.99 million
Medical	£2.08 million
Arts and culture	£1.67 million
Other	£1.22 million
Humanitarian	£980,000

Applications

Apply in writing to the correspondent. Be aware, however, that this is a donor-advised fund. The trustees do not utilise key performance indicators to measure the activity of grant-making.

Sources of information

Accounts; annual report; Charity Commission record; funder's website.

The Mike Gooley Trailfinders Charity

🔍 Medical research; community projects for young people; the armed forces

📍 UK

£ £3.57 million (2021)

CC number: 1048993

Trustees: Fiona Gooley; Tristan Gooley; Bernadette Gooley; Michael Gooley.

Correspondent: The Trustees, 9 Abingdon Road, London W8 6AH (tel: 020 7938 3143)

General information

The charity was founded by Mike Gooley, the owner of the travel company Trailfinders Ltd. The charity was established in 1995 and according to its 2020/21 annual report, it supports young people and education, the armed forces and public services such as medical research.

Beneficiaries included: A list of beneficiaries was not available.

Financial information

Year end	30/06/2021
Assets	£24,120,000
Income	£6,180,000
Grant total	£3,570,000

Applications

Apply in writing to the correspondent.

Sources of information

Accounts; annual report; Charity Commission record.

Gowling WLG (UK) Charitable Trust

🔍 General charitable purposes, particularly young people, older people, health, disability and social/economic disadvantage

📍 UK in practice, but there is a preference for Birmingham, Coventry, Dudley, London, Sandwell, Solihull and Walsall

£ £173,200 (2020/21)

CC number: 803009

Trustees: Lee Nuttall; Philip Clissitt; Andreas Stylianou.

Correspondent: The Trustees, c/o Gowling WLG (UK) LLP, Two Snowhill, Snow Hill Queensway, Birmingham B4 6WR (tel: 0121 233 1000)

General information

Registered in 1990, the trust is the corporate charity of Gowling WLG LLP.

While the trust is not restrictive in terms of the causes it supports, grants are generally made to charities supporting young people, older people, those suffering ill-health, people with disabilities and people who are socially and/or economically disadvantaged. Other causes noted on the trust's Charity Commission page include education and training and the advancement of arts, culture, heritage or science.

In its 2020/21 annual report, the trust states that it supports a 'wide range of local and national charities', but preference is given to the following areas:

▪ London
▪ Birmingham
▪ Coventry
▪ Dudley
▪ Sandwell
▪ Solihull
▪ Walsall

Beneficiaries included: Cancer Research UK (£21,500); The Brain Tumour Charity (£10,000); The KEHS Trust (£7,000); Ladywood Community Project (£5,000); Royal British Legion (£3,000); The Salvation Army Social Work Trust (£2,500); The PSP Association (£1,000); The Lily Mae Foundation (£300).

Financial information

Year end	05/04/2021
Assets	£107,100
Income	£175,000
Grant total	£173,200

Exclusions

The trust does not usually award grants to individuals or organisations which are not charities.

Applications

Apply in writing to the correspondent.

Sources of information

Accounts; annual report; Charity Commission record.

The Greggs Foundation

🔍 Social welfare; people with disabilities; homelessness; voluntary carers; older people; isolated people; school breakfast clubs

📍 North East England, (Northumberland, Tyne and Wear, Durham and Teesside)

£ £1.84 million (2021)

CC number: 296590

Trustee: The Greggs Foundation Trustee.

Correspondent: The Trustees, Greggs House, Quorum Business Park, Newcastle upon Tyne, Tyne and Wear NE12 8BU (tel: 0191 212 7626; email: grants@greggsfoundation.org.uk)

🌐 www.greggsfoundation.org.uk

General information

The Greggs Foundation was registered with the Charity Commission in 1987. It is the corporate charity of Greggs plc, the food retail group known for its baked goods.

According to the website, the foundation provides grants to charitable organisations with a focus on:
▪ Addressing issues of poverty and inequality
▪ Ensuring food is at the heart of communities
▪ Supporting local community organisations to make a real difference

According to its website, the foundation distributes 'over £3 million per year to charitable organisations throughout England, Scotland and Wales'.

Programmes

North East Core Fund – grants of up to £60,000 (up to £20,000 per year) are awarded to organisations working with the community's 'most deprived and excluded members' to help cover core running costs, as stated on the website.

Applications are particularly welcomed from organisations serving the following groups: people with disabilities; people who are currently homeless; voluntary carers; older and isolated people.

Eligible organisations must be able to provide at least one full year's set of accounts. Applications from organisations with more than six month's running costs in free reserves will not be considered.

Breakfast Clubs – the breakfast club programme was established to help primary schoolchildren to get a nutritious start to their day. Through the scheme, schools are provided with fresh bread from their local Greggs store, as well as grants to support start-up and ongoing costs.

Hardship fund – this fund provides grants to people in need in the North East of England through recognised social organisations like housing associations, social services and registered charities that are acting on behalf of an individual/family in need.

The foundation also donates unsold food to local charities.

Beneficiaries included: A list of beneficiaries was not available.

Financial information

Year end	31/12/2021
Assets	£29,020,000
Income	£3,310,000
Grant total	£1,840,000

Further financial information

Grants were distributed as follows:

Hardship*	£1.69 million
Breakfast clubs	£943,200
North East Core Fund	£401,500
Community hubs	£240,000
Community	£100,800
Food poverty	£99,700
Environmental grants	£50,000

*Note: these were grants paid to organisations for distribution to individuals.

Exclusions

A full list of exclusions for each grants programme can be seen on the website.

Applications

Apply online via the foundation's website. Each grants programme has its own criteria, guidelines and application process, all of which are available to view on the website.

Sources of information

Accounts; annual report; Charity Commission record; funder's website.

Halifax Foundation for Northern Ireland

Social and community needs, including: community services, advice services, people with special needs; health, civic responsibility, cultural enrichment; education and training, including employment and life skills

Northern Ireland

£1.04 million (2021)

CCNI number: NIC101763

Trustees: Barry Connolly; Gillian Boyd; Áine McCoy; Michael Prendergast; Ken Simpson; Melvin Slaine; Brenda Kelly; Dionne Darragh; Jenny Ebbage; Niall Parfitt; Becca Hume.

Correspondent: The Trustees, Clifton House Heritage Centre, 2 North Queen Street, Belfast BT15 1ES (tel: 028 9032 3000; email: grants@halifaxfoundationni. org)

 www.halifaxfoundationni.org

General information

This foundation is one of four Lloyds Banking Group charities, covering England and Wales, Scotland, Northern Ireland and the Channel Islands. The four charities together receive 0.5% of the group's pre-tax profits.

Areas of support

The foundation supports a wide range of activities and the following examples are listed on the website as a guide:

- **Advice services** – homelessness, addictions, bereavement, family guidance, money advice, helplines and suicide awareness.
- **Community services** – family centres, youth clubs, older people's clubs, after-school clubs, self-help groups, childcare provision, preschools and playgroups.
- **People with educational special needs** – residences, day centres, transport, carers, information, advice and advocacy.
- **Promotion of health** – information and advice, mental health, hospices, day care, home nursing, and independent living for older people.
- **Civic responsibility** – young people at risk, crime prevention, promotion of volunteering, victim support, mediation, and rehabilitation of offenders.
- **Cultural enrichment** – improving access and skills development in the arts and national heritage for disadvantaged people and those with special needs.
- **Employment** – project which help disadvantaged people develop their potential and secure employment.

- **Life skills** – promotion of life skills, and independent living skills for people with special needs.
- **Training and education** – accredited, vocational or personal development training.

Grants programmes

The Community Grants Programme is the foundation's main focus through which grants are made within its funding objectives. Grants currently average between £3,000 and £4,000.

In order to be eligible to apply, organisations must have an income of less than £1 million in the previous 12 months. For registered charities which have a headquarters based outside Northern Ireland, the foundation will use the figure of the income of their Northern Ireland operation to determine eligibility.

Beneficiaries included: A list of beneficiaries was not available.

Financial information

Year end	31/12/2021
Assets	£2,830,000
Income	£1,600,000
Grant total	£1,040,000

Exclusions

See the foundation's website for a full list of exclusions.

Applications

All applications must be made online via the foundation's website, where full guidelines, including a list of supporting documentation required, are available.

Sources of information

Accounts; annual report; CCNI record; funder's website; funding guidelines.

Heathrow Community Trust

Community development; young people; education; skills and employment; sport/recreation; environmental protection

The areas surrounding Heathrow Airport (Ealing, Hillingdon, Hounslow, Richmond, Runnymede, Slough, South Bucks, Spelthorne and the Royal Borough of Windsor and Maidenhead)

£194,700 (2021)

CC number: 1183004

Trustees: Dr Prabhjot Basra; Nigel Milton; Aled Patchett; Jason Knight; David Cottrell; Alison Keeley; Gennie Dearman; Richard de Belder; Michael Murphy.

Correspondent: The Trustees, c/o Groundwork South, Colne Valley Park Centre, Denham Court Drive, Denham, Middlesex UB9 5PG (tel: 01895 839916; email: HCT@Groundwork.org.uk)

www.heathrowcommunitytrust.org

General information

The trust is an independent charity which receives funding from Heathrow Airport Ltd, airline noise fines, other funders and airport staff. Its grants programmes look to improve the quality of life for communities near the airport.

Grants programmes

In support of its objectives, the Heathrow Community Trust (HCT) makes grants through six programmes.

There are three routes to funding for external applicants:

▶ **Projects for Young People** – grants of up to £7,500 for projects that raise aspirations, increase resilience or increase employability in children and young people up to age 24.
▶ **Environment and Sustainability** – grants of up to £7,500 for projects focused on the environment and sustainability.
▶ **Communities Together** – grants of up to £2,500 for small community projects.

More information on these programmes, including full eligibility criteria and guidelines, is available from the charity's website.

There are also two funds to which employees can apply for support with their own charitable involvement:

▶ **Heathrow Active People Initiative (HAPI):** grants of up to £2,500 are open to Heathrow Airport employees who are regular volunteers with non-profit organisations anywhere in the UK.
▶ **Matched funding:** employees are also supported in their fundraising with a Matched Fund scheme in which the trust will match funds raised for charity.

Beneficiaries included: A list of beneficiaries was not available. Previous beneficiaries include: The Eikon Charity (£47,400); Fine Futures (£45,200); Oxfordshire Crossroads (£22,500); West London River Group (£20,900); Stanwell Village Hall (£17,000); Slough West Indian People's Enterprise (£15,000); Spark! – Hounslow Education Business Charity (£9,400); Victoria Junior School (£5,000); The Manor Friends Charity (£2,100).

Financial information

Year end	31/12/2021
Assets	£343,500
Income	£431,400
Grant total	£194,700

Exclusions

Refer to the trust's website. Each of the grants programmes are subject to their own eligibility criteria and restrictions.

Applications

Application forms and guidance notes for each of the grants programmes are available from the HCF website, where important dates for application submissions and decision-making are also listed.

Sources of information

Accounts; annual report; Charity Commission record; guidelines for applicants; funder's website.

The Hiscox Foundation

 General charitable purposes, including: education; medical science; the arts; independent living for older, disadvantaged or vulnerable members of society

⚲ Worldwide, but primarily the UK

£ £1.34 million (2020/21)

CC number: 327635

Trustees: Lucy Hensher; Nick Orton; Lee Turner; Craig Martindale; Robert Childs; Keely Davies; Vanessa Newbury.

Correspondent: The Trustees, Hiscox Underwriting Ltd, 1 Great St Helen's, London EC3A 6HX (tel: 020 7614 5299)

🌐 www.hiscoxgroup.com/hiscox-foundation-uk

General information

The Hiscox Foundation is the corporate charity of Hiscox Group, a specialist insurance provider.

According to its website, the foundation's charitable giving is divided into three key pillars:

▶ Social mobility and entrepreneurship
▶ Protecting and preserving the environment
▶ Causes that Hiscox employees are passionate about

Focus is given to education, medical science, the arts, independent living for older, disadvantaged or vulnerable members of society.

Eligibility

Preference is given to organisations local to the Hiscox office (no more than around 25 miles away), or those that have a presence in the communities that it serves.

Although the foundation will fund organisations of all sizes, preference is given to those with an annual income of under £10 million.

The foundation will also provide match funding to its employees raising money for good causes.

Beneficiaries included: Alzheimer's Society (£101,500); Action for Children (£100,000); Crisis UK (£50,000); HART (£30,000); I Can (£25,000); Masks for

NHS Heroes (£20,500); KEEN London (£16,900); Andover RDA (£6,000); Barnardo's (£4,000); City Music Foundation (£2,000); Pancreatic Cancer UK (£500).

Financial information

Year end	05/04/2021
Assets	£9,680,000
Income	£1,030,000
Grant total	£1,340,000

Exclusions

The foundation will not fund the following:

▶ Scholarships
▶ Event sponsorship
▶ New business start-up funding
▶ Carbon offset schemes
▶ Requests from other charitable foundations

Applications

Applications can be made at any time using the foundation's online application form. Unsolicited applications are not accepted for multi-year grants.

Sources of information

Accounts; annual report; Charity Commission record; funder's website.

The Hudson Foundation

⚲ General charitable purposes, particularly the relief of older people

⚲ Wisbech

£ £84,900 (2020/21)

CC number: 280332

Trustees: David Ball; Stephen Layton; Edward Newling.

Correspondent: The Trustees, 1–3 York Row, Wisbech, Cambridgeshire PE13 1EA (tel: 01945 461456)

General information

This foundation was registered with the Charity Commission in 1980. It is the corporate charity of Alan Hudson Ltd, which trades as a fruit farm. The foundation's income derives solely from Alan Hudson Ltd.

Grant-making policy

Grants are awarded to other charitable organisations assisting older people in the Wisbech area. Grants have also been made for community development purposes within the area of benefit.

Beneficiaries included: Wisbech Regeneration Group (£25,000); Gorefield Playing Field Association (£20,000); Methodist Homes for the Aged (£11,000); Wisbech Swimming Club (£10,000); Wisbech St Mary Church of England Primary School (£6,000); Wisbech Sea Cadets (£2,000); Murrow Primary Academy (£1,500).

Financial information

Year end	31/07/2021
Assets	£3,130,000
Income	£1,720,000
Grant total	£84,900

Applications

Apply in writing to the correspondent.

Sources of information

Accounts; annual report; Charity Commission record.

IBM United Kingdom Trust

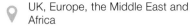 An IT-driven approach to causes such as: education; research; disability; poverty; health; the environment; charitable sector efficiency; emergency response

UK, Europe, the Middle East and Africa

£2.78 million (2020/21)

CC number: 290462

Trustees: Prof. Derek Bell; Naomi Hill; Anne Wolfe; Andrew Fitzgerald; Juliet Upton; Bryan Berry; Kuljit Takhar.

Correspondent: The Trustees, IBM United Kingdom Ltd, 1PG1, 76 Upper Ground, London SE1 9PZ (tel: 020 7202 3608; email: wakefim@uk.ibm.com)

www.ibm.org

General information

This trust was established in 1984. It is the corporate charity of IBM, the global technology company specialising in hardware, software and cloud-based services.

According to its Charity Commission record and 2020/21 annual report, the trust strives to meet the following objectives through the use and understanding of information technology:

- The advancement of education
- The advancement of research (with emphasis, although not exclusively, on information technology)
- The improvement of life for people with disabilities and/or those who are disadvantaged
- The relief of poverty
- Support for disaster relief efforts
- Encouraging the use/understanding of IT in the charitable sector
- The advancement of health in the community
- The preservation of the environment

Grant-making policy

The trust's grant-making falls into two key areas:

- The provision of grants to advance both the aims of the trust and support IBM programmes
- The provision of small grants in support of charitable organisations in the communities surrounding IBM sites

In 2020/21, the trust had one primary focus area – education and skills – and two secondary focus areas – health, and human trafficking and modern slavery.

While a crucial part of meeting the trust's objectives is to make direct financial contributions, it also encourages relationships between charitable organisations, educational organisations and IBM itself.

Note: the trust's 2020/21 annual report states that the trustees are likely going to wind down the trust because its principal source of income, the IBM International Foundation, will no longer be providing funding. However, the annual report states that 'this will not take within 12 months from the date of signing these financial statements.'

Beneficiaries included: Education Development Trust (£165,000); Enabling Enterprise (£102,000); Ada National College and STEM Learning (£100,000 each); Code Door (£80,000); UK Youth (£70,000); Purple Unicorn and Stop the Traffik (£46,000 each); Law Works (£35,000).

Financial information

Year end	31/03/2021
Assets	£916,000
Income	£95,000
Grant total	£2,780,000
Organisations supported	206+

Further financial information

Grants awarded to organisations in 2020/21 were broken down as follows in the trust's accounts:

Provision of IT and other services	£1.63 million
Increasing the use of technology in education	£822,000
Digital skills	£150,000
Research	£100,000
Miscellaneous	£77,000
Promoting volunteering	£1,000

Only beneficiaries of grants of £30,000 and above were listed in the accounts. Grants of under £30,000 were broken down as follows: 23 grants of between £10,000 and £29,999 (£375,000) and 164 grants of below £10,000 (£148,000).

Applications

Apply in writing to the correspondent.

Sources of information

Accounts; annual report; Charity Commission record.

The Innocent Foundation

Food poverty

Worldwide

£1.44 million (2021/22)

CC number: 1104289

Trustees: Adam Balon; Richard Reed; Christina Archer; Douglas Lamont; Sarah-Jane Norman; Jonathan Wright; Camilla Clarke.

Correspondent: Kate Franks, Foundation Director, The Innocent Foundation, 342 Ladbroke Grove, London W10 5BU (tel: 020 3235 0352; email: hello@innocentfoundation.org)

 www.innocentfoundation.org

 @innocentfdn

General information

This foundation was established in 2004. It is the corporate foundation of Innocent, the drinks brand specialising in juices and smoothies. Since the company's inception, Innocent's founder pledged to donate 10% of its profits to charity.

According to its website, the foundation aims to 'create a world where every person has enough food to live'. So far, the foundation has spent over £8.88 million on charitable activities and helped 1 million people directly through its projects in 42 countries.

Grants programmes

All grants go towards helping resolve world hunger. Funding is awarded for projects that align with the foundation's two goals:

- Stop children dying of hunger: the foundation makes grants for projects which diagnose and treat children whose lives are in immediate danger because of severe hunger. Cutting-edge research with the same potential (i.e. to prevent children from dying) is also funded.
- Help the poorest families feed themselves: funding is awarded for agricultural projects which make sure families have enough food to feed themselves. Under this scheme, the foundation also helps families to tackle problems surrounding harvesting food and climate change.

According to its 2020/21 annual report, the foundation looks for partnerships with organisations 'from UK-based charities to organisations from around the world, who may be charities, but could also be universities, research institutes, or other innovators, who need our support to test and scale their great ideas'.

Beneficiaries included: Action Against Hunger (£568,000); ALIMA (£218,300); MyAgro (£66,700); Send a Cow (£44,400); Semilla Nueva (£30,000). Kickstart International (£26,500).

Financial information

Year end	04/08/2022
Assets	£2,420,000
Income	£999,900
Grant total	£1,440,000

Applications

According to the foundation's 2019/20 annual report, it has strong global research connections, through which charities are selected for Goal 1, and an annual application cycle is available for Goal 2. Contact the foundation for more information.

Sources of information

Accounts; annual report; Charity Commission record; funder's website.

JD Foundation

🔍 Disadvantaged children and young people including in the areas of mental health and homelessness; the environment

📍 UK

💷 £397,700 (2020/21)

CC number: 1167090

Trustees: Siobhan Mawdsley; Traci Corrie; Julie Blomley; Nigel Keen; Neil Greenhalgh.

Correspondent: The Trustees, JD Sports Fashion, Edinburgh House, Hollins Brook Way, Bury, Greater Manchester BL9 8RR (tel: 0161 767 1000; email: thejdfoundation@jdplc.com)

🌐 www.jdsports.co.uk/page/jd-foundation

f facebook.com/TheJDFoundation

🐦 @JDFoundationUK

📷 @thejdfoundation

General information

The JD Foundation was founded in October 2015 by JD Sports Fashion plc. The JD Foundation receives 100% of proceeds from the carrier bag charges from JD Sports with funds donated to Mountain Rescue and to charities chosen by the group's employees, that work with young people in the UK. The foundation also receives financial contributions from employee fundraising.

In 2022 the foundation committed its support to 19 charity partners listed below:

- Blueprint 4 All
- Bolton Wanderers in the Community
- Buddies of the Birches
- C.R.Y. (Cardiac Risk in the Young)
- Harmony Youth Project
- HideOut
- Kidscape
- Manchester Youth Zone
- Mountain Rescue England and Wales
- Once Upon A Smile
- Papyrus
- Sacriston Youth Project
- Salford Foundation
- Scottish Mountain Rescue
- Smiling Families;
- Sport 4 Life UK
- Unseen
- The Wellspring
- YoungMinds

Financial information

Year end	31/01/2021
Assets	£263,500
Income	£631,100
Grant total	£397,700

Further financial information

Grants were broken down as follows: youth (£225,200); health (£87,800); mountain rescue (£67,000); social services (£43,700); other (£29,400); education (£22,500).

Applications

Support is provided to charity partners. Contact the foundation for further information.

Sources of information

Accounts; annual report; Charity Commission record; guidelines for applicants; further information provided by the funder; funder's website.

KFC Foundation

🔍 Children and young people (11 to 25 years old)

📍 UK

💷 £1.24 million (2021)

CC number: 1163560

Trustees: Clara Widdison; Daniel Carr; Michael Williams; Nichola Newman; Simon Coates; Neil Morrison; James Fletcher.

Correspondent: The Trustees, Orion Gate, Guilford Road, Woking GU22 7NJ (email: a contact form is available on the website)

🌐 www.kfc.co.uk/kfc-foundation

General information

The foundation provides grants to grassroots organisations that support young people in the UK fulfil their potential by providing safe social spaces, mentoring and work or social skills. The foundation is focused on supporting young people in a position of social disadvantage (i.e. care leavers, those experiencing homelessness, young carers, young parents, young people at risk of or with experience of the criminal justice system).

The foundation had previously supported charities through partnerships with regional charities. However, these partnerships were concluded in May 2020 in order to move to a more locally focused community grants programme.

Community grants

The KFC Foundation provides grants to support grass roots organisations in the heart of its restaurant's communities.

Grants of up to £2,000 are made to registered charities, registered community interest companies, unincorporated clubs or associations or unregistered charities with a turnover of less than £300,000.

The following information has been taken from the foundation's website:

The KFC Foundation welcomes funding applications from organisations which:

- Benefit young people aged 11–25 years old.
- Support those in a position of social disadvantage (i.e. care leavers, those experiencing homelessness, young carers, young parents, young people at risk of or with experience of the criminal justice system).
- Empower young people to fulfil their potential and build a positive future by providing spaces that allow young people to feel safe and secure, helping them to unlock talent, build life skills, provide mentoring and improve their chances to gain meaningful employment.
- Are local to a KFC restaurant.
- Will demonstrate positive results from their project within 12 months of our funding being received.

Beneficiaries included: Comic Relief (£990,000); Action for Youth, Childhood Trust, Focus Charity, Include Youth and Young Lives Foundation (£10,000 each).

Financial information

Year end	31/12/2021
Assets	£898,300
Income	£1,460,000
Grant total	£1,240,000

Exclusions

According to the foundation's FAQs document, the following will not be funded:

- General fundraising or sponsorship appeals
- Political campaigns
- Promotion of religion
- Overseas travel
- Curricular activities taking place during the school day
- Research
- Repayment of loans
- Purchase of vehicles
- Medical equipment
- Major capital projects

- Interventions which fail to provide long-term impact or support
- Projects focused on a one-off event such as a residential
- Generic youth work activities (i.e. those not aimed at the foundation's priority groups)

Applications

Apply via the foundation's website where application deadlines and further guidance can be found.

Sources of information

Accounts; annual report; Charity Commission record; guidelines for applicants; funder's website.

The KPMG Foundation

 Children and young people; education and training; social care; employment

UK

£797,500 (2020/21)

CC number: 1086518

Trustees: Sherrylyn Peck; Kamini Mehta; Corrine Harms; David Bartram; David Woodward; Peter Sherratt.

Correspondent: Judith McNeill, Chief Executive, 15 Canada Square, Canary Wharf, London E14 5GL (tel: 020 7311 4217; email: kpmgfoundation@kpmg.co. uk)

 https://kpmgfoundation.org.uk/ index.html

 @kpmg_foundation

General information

Established in 2001, the KPMG Foundation is the corporate charity of the audit, tax and advisory services company KPMG LLP.

According to its website, the foundation's focus is 'on helping the most vulnerable children, through their early years, including through "whole family" approaches; in school, in care, and through adolescence, wherever, whenever and however the greatest benefits can be achieved.'

Grant-making policy

The foundation works with selected partners. According to the foundation's website, its priorities are:

- Care experienced children and young people, and on the edge of care (and those who can help make the most positive difference in their lives)
- Children under 5 (including the first 1001 days) in families and communities facing the toughest challenges

The website also states that the foundation will use its resources to 'help catalyse great ideas and organisations, build evidence for sustainability and

scale, and influence systems through collaboration'.

An overview of some of the programmes supported by the foundation can be seen on its website.

Beneficiaries included: Education Endowment Foundation (£250,000); Reach Foundation (£100,000); Family Rights Group and School Home Support (£75,000 each); The Lucy Faithfull Foundation (£59,500); Anna Freud Centre for Children and Families (£50,000); Family Action (£33,000); University of Oxford (£30,000); Buttle UK (£25,000).

Financial information

Year end	30/09/2021
Assets	£6,190,000
Income	£939,200
Grant total	£797,500
Organisations supported	11

Applications

The foundation pro-actively identifies organisations to support and therefore does not accept unsolicited applications; however, the foundation's website states the following:

If you share our purpose, our priorities and approach, please provide a brief description of your work and a link to your own website. Most of the organisations we support are specialists in the areas we are most interested in, currently:

- Care experienced children and young people (and their foster or kinship families)
- Children in their early years (under 5's) and their families in the most vulnerable communities in areas of high deprivation

If you do get in touch, where there is a strong alignment, we will respond.

Sources of information

Accounts; annual report; Charity Commission record; funder's website.

Ladbrokes Coral Trust

 Healthcare; education; community projects; social welfare; the environment and animals

UK

£364,600 (2021)

CC number: 1101804

Trustees: Karen Thraves; Nick Batram; Jay Dossetter; Craig Watson; Simon O'Halloran; Steve Humphries; Simon Burnell.

Correspondent: The Trustees, c/o GVC Holdings plc, 3rd Floor, One New Change, London EC4M 9AF (tel: 020 3938 0000; email: charity@ ladbrokescoral.com)

General information

Ladbrokes Coral Trust was established in 2003. Formerly known as Ladbrokes in the Community Charitable Trust, the charity changed its name to Ladbrokes Coral Trust in May 2017, following the merger between Ladbrokes and certain businesses of Gala Coral Group Ltd. Its funding comes not from the Ladbrokes company, but via the fundraising efforts of the head office and shop staff and customers.

The trust's record on the Charity Commission's website states that support can be given to a range of causes 'with the overriding requirement being that the causes supported operate and serve the community in which the shops and businesses of Ladbrokes Coral group plc operate'.

According to the trust's annual report for 2021, grants are commonly given in the following categories:

- Health – principally research/treatment, hospice services and disability support
- Education – supporting the disabled/ disadvantaged and sports services in deprived areas or for disadvantaged persons
- Community – focusing on projects for the homeless and aged or social activity projects for those at risk

Beneficiaries included: A list of beneficiaries was not available.

Financial information

Year end	31/12/2021
Assets	£286,000
Income	£224,700
Grant total	£364,600

Further financial information

Grants awarded in 2021 were broken down as follows:

Medical causes	£103,700
Hospices and hospitals	£17,600
Youth support	£15,600
Other	£12,900
Social welfare	£4,900
The environment and animals	£400

Applications

Apply in writing to the correspondent. The trust's Charity Commission record states that 'the Trustees meet every 4–6 weeks to consider grant requests from shop and head office fundraisers and registered charities.'

Sources of information

Accounts; annual report; Charity Commission record.

The Lancashire Foundation

 Children and young people; people who are disadvantaged; social isolation

 UK; Bermuda; worldwide

£ £515,800 (2021)

CC number: 1149184

Trustees: Derek Stapley; Louise Wells; Emma Grimes; Robert Kennedy.

Correspondent: The Trustees, Lancashire Insurance Company (UK), Level 29, 20 Fenchurch Street, London EC3M 3BY (tel: 020 7264 4056)

 www.lancashiregroup.com/en/responsibility/lancashire-foundation.html

General information

This foundation is the corporate charity of the Lancashire group of insurance companies which operates in Bermuda and London. It receives 0.75% of Group profits.

Areas of work

Initially, when the foundation was established in 2007, donations were made with an emphasis on supporting communities in Bermuda. Now, the foundation has a strong focus on supporting work addressing social exclusion and issues that affect children and young people.

According to its 2021 annual report, the foundation provides grants to organisations in the UK, Bermuda and other parts of the world, 'whose work reflects and is aligned to the values and interests of the people and businesses within the Lancashire group of insurers'. Applications are also welcomed from members of staff on behalf of charities in which they have an interest or involvement.

Beneficiaries included: The Family Centre (£60,000); St Giles Trust (£40,000); Cancer Research UK (£25,000); The Poppy Factory (£10,000); Victor Scott Primary School (£6,000); Carers Choices, The Living Paintings Trust and St Luke's Hospice (£4,000 each); BTA Youth Squad (£2,900); Macmillan Cancer Support (£2,000).

Financial information

Year end	31/12/2021
Assets	£1,930,000
Income	£196,600
Grant total	£515,800
Organisations supported	57

Applications

Apply in writing to the correspondent. Grants are also made to organisations recommended by employees.

Sources of information

Accounts; annual report; Charity Commission record; funder's website.

Leeds Building Society Foundation

 Social welfare; people with disabilities; homelessness; health

 UK

£ £142,200 (2021)

CC number: 1074429

Trustees: Carla Marshall; Gary Hetherington; Timothy Steere; Susan Moreland; Emma Woods-Bolger.

Correspondent: The Trustees, Leeds Building Society, 26 Sovereign Street, Leeds, West Yorkshire LS1 4BJ (tel: 0113 225 7518; email: foundation@leedsbuildingsociety.co.uk)

 www.leedsbuildingsociety.co.uk/your-society/about-us/foundation

General information

The foundation was established by and is closely associated with the Leeds Building Society. It was registered with the Charity Commission in 1999 and supports the communities around the nationwide branches of the society. The foundation primarily provides funding for practical items that directly support those in need including those with disabilities, affected by homelessness, or with serious health issues.

In July 2022, the foundation shifted its focus to supporting those in need of a safe and secure home. According to its website, the foundation will prioritise charities that share this goal. It aims to give grants to projects that fall within the following criteria themes:

▷ Health
▷ Sustainability
▷ Accessibility
▷ Financial stress
▷ Security and refuge
▷ Education and advice

The foundation states the following on its website:

For our small grants (up to £1,000), we only accept requests to fund capital expenditure. This means that we fund the purchase of items used to directly help those in need, rather than contributing to a charity's running costs.

The foundation will only accept applications from UK registered charities with a turnover of less than £1 million.

Beneficiaries included: A list of beneficiaries was not available.

Financial information

Year end	31/12/2021
Assets	£3,200
Income	£152,100
Grant total	£142,200

Further financial information

Grants are broken down as follows:

Mental or physical disability	£41,900
Disadvantage	£27,500
Social inclusion	£22,500
Poverty	£20,900
Homelessness	£14,300
Caring responsibilities	£8,200
Illness	£6,900

Exclusions

The foundation's website states:

The Foundation is unable to support:
▷ Religious, military or political projects
▷ Charities based overseas
▷ Individuals (including sponsorship)
▷ Animal welfare projects
▷ Medical research
▷ Administrative costs including salaries, rent or promotional materials
▷ General fundraising appeals
▷ Building restoration
▷ Items for staff use

Applications

Apply online through the foundation's website. The foundation will only accept applications from UK registered charities with a turnover of less than £1 million.

Sources of information

Accounts; annual report; Charity Commission record; funder's website.

John Lewis and Partners Foundation

 Education and training; employability; healthcare; community development; the environment; children and young people; recreational facilities; childcare facilities

 UK and overseas (particularly areas that support the John Lewis business)

£ £475,000 (2021/22)

CC number: 1118162

Trustees: Margaret Porteous; Paul Buchanan; Sarah Gillard; Simon Bishop; Christine Kasoulis; Johnathan Marsh; Nyika Brain; Andrew Hoad; Marija Rompani; Louise Stuart.

Correspondent: The Trustees, 171 Victoria Street, London SW1E 5NN (tel: 020 7592 5658; email: trustsandfoundations@johnlewis.co.uk)

 www.johnlewisfoundation.org

General information

The John Lewis and Partners Foundation was established in 2007 to benefit communities in the UK and overseas within which the retailer John Lewis and Partners operates.

At the time of writing the John Lewis Partnership was conducting a review of its philanthropic giving and therefore the foundation had suspended all new funding.

According to its 2020/21 annual report the foundation makes grants to improve the well-being of communities in the UK and overseas in which those who produce products supplied to John Lewis and Partners live and work. These projects may include:

▶ Funding to improve schools and education projects
▶ Funding to improve children's welfare
▶ Funding for medical centres and healthcare initiatives
▶ Funding for childcare facilities to enable women with young children to work
▶ Funding for training facilities to help people improve their employability skills
▶ Funding for community and recreational facilities
▶ Funding to help protect the environment and biodiversity

Beneficiaries included: Grassmarket Community Project; Pop Up Enterprises; Smartworks; The Feed; Voices of Hope.

Financial information

Year end	31/01/2022
Assets	£1,020,000
Income	£853,600
Grant total	£475,000

Applications

At the time of writing (November, 2022), the foundation's website continues to state that the foundation is conducting a review of its giving and has therefore suspended all new funding. The application form and guidance pack are therefore temporarily unavailable. See the foundation's website for updates.

Sources of information

Accounts; annual report; Charity Commission record; funder's website.

Lloyds Bank Foundation for England and Wales

 Work addressing one of the following social issues: addiction and dependency; asylum seekers and refugees; care leavers; domestic abuse; homelessness and people who are vulnerably housed; learning disabilities; mental health; offending, prison or community service; sexual abuse and exploitation; trafficking and modern slavery; young parents; racial equity

England and Wales

£15.88 million (2021)

CC number: 327114

Trustees: Catharine Cheetham; Joanna Harris; Neil Wooding; Dame Gillian Morgan; Gareth Oakley; Rebecca Shaw; Darren Knight; Kamran Mallick; Ruth Sutherland; Dame Ann Limb; Bushra Ahmed.

Correspondent: Grants Team, Second Floor, Society Building, 8 All Saints Street, London N1 9RL (tel: 0370 411 1223; email: enquiries@ lloydsbankfoundation.org.uk)

www.lloydsbankfoundation.org.uk

facebook.com/ lloydsbankfoundation

@LBFEW

General information

The foundation is principally funded from Lloyds Banking Group receiving a share of the group's profit under a deed of covenant.

Funding for complex social issues

According to its 2021 annual report, the foundation funds small and local charities working on one of the following complex social issues:

▶ Addiction or dependency on alcohol, drugs and/or gambling
▶ Asylum seekers and refugees
▶ Care leavers
▶ Domestic and sexual abuse
▶ Homelessness/vulnerably housed
▶ Learning disabilities
▶ Mental health
▶ Offending, prison or community service
▶ Sexual exploitation
▶ Trafficking and modern slavery
▶ Young parents
▶ Racial equity

The foundation offers unrestricted funding, including around core costs, and tailored development support to help charities be more effective.

Beneficiaries included: Examples of projects the foundation has funded can be found on its website.

Financial information

Year end	31/12/2021
Assets	£33,480,000
Income	£19,360,000
Grant total	£15,880,000
Organisations supported	899

Exclusions

The foundation has previously stated that it does not provide funding for the following organisations:

▶ Community Interest Companies, or any other organisations that are not charities or CIOs registered in England and Wales
▶ Infrastructure or 'umbrella' organisations
▶ Organisations whose primary purpose is to give funds to individuals or other organisations. This means organisations using more than 50% of annual expenditure as grants
▶ Hospitals, health authorities or hospices
▶ Rescue services
▶ Nurseries, pre-schools or playgroups
▶ Schools, colleges or universities
▶ Animal charities
▶ Charities working predominantly outside England and Wales
▶ Organisations that do not have a purpose/benefit beyond the promotion of religion

Check the website for up-to-date exclusions.

Applications

Applications can be made via the foundation's website. At the time of writing (November 2022), the foundation's website stated that it was 'closed to new funding applications until later this year'.

Sources of information

Accounts; annual report; Charity Commission record; funder's website.

Lloyds Bank Foundation for the Channel Islands

 Health and disability; homelessness; drug and alcohol dependency; carers; disadvantage and discrimination; literacy; domestic violence; care leavers

Channel Islands

£1.04 million (2021)

CC number: 327113

Trustees: John Henwood; Gavin Ferguson; Heather MacCallum; Tracey Johnson; Neil Fellows; Brian Heath; Alasdair Gardner; Philippa Stahelin; Poppy Murray.

Correspondent: Johanna Le Poidevin, Executive Director, 1 Smith Street,

St Peter Port, Guernsey GY1 4BD
(tel: 01481 706360; email: jlepoidevin@
lloydsbankfoundation.org.uk)

 www.lloydsbankfoundationci.org.
uk

 facebook.com/
lloydsbankfoundationci

 @lloydsbfci

General information

The foundation was set up by Lloyds Bank in 1986. The foundation derives its income almost entirely from Lloyds Banking Group but is an independent entity with policies determined by a board of trustees which meets three times each year, to agree on strategic priorities and to distribute funding. According to the foundation's Grant Programme Guidelines, grants are given to 'charities helping disadvantaged people play a fuller role in the community'.

Areas of work

According to its website, the foundation provides support for the following areas:
▹ Health, including mental health or disability
▹ Homelessness
▹ People leaving institutional care to live independently
▹ Addiction and dependency
▹ Loneliness and isolation
▹ Employment, literacy, financial literacy and debt problems
▹ Domestic violence
▹ Human rights

The foundation also supports the charitable sector through information and mentoring.

Beneficiaries included: GROW – Guernsey (£100,000); Autism Guernsey (£71,900); Jersey Childcare Trust (£59,400); The Shelter Trust (£35,000); Jersey Action Against Rape (£33,000); Centrepoint Trust – Jersey (£28,900); Family First – Jersey (£25,000); Trauma Recovery Centre – Guernsey (£14,100).

Financial information

Year end	31/12/2021
Assets	£1,650,000
Income	£892,300
Grant total	£1,040,000

Exclusions

The following information has been taken from the foundation's website:

What we can't fund:
▹ Organisations which are not registered charities.
▹ Individual requests
▹ Sponsorship requests
▹ Animal welfare
▹ Environmental charities
▹ International appeals
▹ Expeditions or overseas travel

▹ The promotion of religion. We might not exclude charities which have a religious element, if their objectives demonstrate a wider benefit to people experiencing disadvantage Schools and colleges (except for projects that will benefit disadvantaged students and are clearly additional to statutory responsibilities)
▹ Large capital projects (small capital projects e.g. renovations, improvements will be considered)
▹ Purchase of vehicles.
▹ Activities which are the responsibility of a statutory body or the islands' governments.
▹ Activities which duplicate or overlap a service already provided.
▹ Applications for salaries which would apply to the applicant.
▹ Charities which have received one of our grants in the previous 12 months or have received three years continuous funding.

Applications

Applications can be made via the foundation's website. Applicants are encouraged to discuss their project with the Executive Director before completing an application form.

Sources of information

Accounts; annual report; Charity Commission record; funder's website.

Lloyd's of London Foundation

 Disasters and emergencies; social welfare; education and training

Worldwide; UK, with a preference for East London

£890,000 (2021)

CC number: 207232

Trustees: Victoria Carter; David Ibeson; Andrew Brooks; Oliver Ferrari; Amy Bumstead; Mark Fidler; Caroline Klein; Claire O'Meara; Elizabeth Cabrera; Hannah-Polly Williams; Raza Hassan; Ola Jacob-Raji.

Correspondent: The Trustees, Lloyd's Building, 1 Lime Street, London EC3M 7HA (tel: 020 7327 1000; email: responsiblebusiness@lloyds.com)

www.lloyds.com/about-lloyds/responsible-business/community-involvement/lloyds-charities-trust

General information

The charity was set up in 1953 and is the charitable arm of Lloyd's insurance market in London. The trust makes grants on behalf of the Society of Lloyd's.

The trust's website states:

As the Lloyd's market responds to emerging risks and the challenges that these pose to communities around the

world, it becomes increasingly important that Lloyd's Charities Trust supports projects that aim to reduce the risk of devastation to the people who need it most. Through our charity partnerships, we work with organisations who help the most vulnerable groups with disaster risk reduction globally.

Lloyd's Charities Trust also supports causes close to the hearts of our people in the Lloyd's market in London. Recognising the voluntary and fundraising efforts of individuals from across the market, we reward their chosen charities with unrestricted grants to help maintain stability and resilience in a changing world through an annual campaign.

Lloyd's Market Charity Awards

The awards are donations to charities supported by individuals from across the Lloyd's market. Donations are given to charities and CICs supported by individuals working in the market in recognition of their fundraising and voluntary work, and to charities that have given invaluable support to those in the market whose lives have been affected by difficult circumstances. In 2021, the trustees increased the potential award from £4,000 to up to £25,000 depending on the size of the charity.

Lloyd's Community Programme

Through longstanding relationships with local delivery partners, this programme supports projects that tackle disadvantages. Grants are awarded to a small number of delivery partners each year to enable them to run projects. These projects provide volunteering opportunities to employees in the Lloyd's market.

Beneficiaries included: A list of beneficiaries was not available.

Financial information

Year end	31/12/2021
Assets	£3,610,000
Income	£1,090,000
Grant total	£890,000

Further financial information

Grants were awarded to organisations as follows:

Lloyd's Market Charity Awards	£498,000
Lloyd's Community Programmes	£238,000
Habitat for Humanity	£130,000

In addition, £109,000 was awarded to individuals through the Lloyd's Education Fund, which provides university bursaries to young people from schools in London.

Applications

Applications for the Lloyd's Market Charity Awards can be made via the trust's website, where guidelines and application deadlines can also be found. Applicants must be permanent employees working in the Lloyd's market. They must demonstrate direct and sustained personal engagement with their nominated charity during the past 12 months, for example as a volunteer, fundraiser, trustee, or beneficiary of services provided.

Sources of information

Accounts; annual report; Charity Commission record; funder's website.

Lloyd's Patriotic Fund

 The armed forces

England and Wales

£170,000 (2020/21)

CC number: 210173

Trustees: Alexander Findlay; Richard Williams; Air Cdre Wendy Rothery; William Roscoe; Bruce Carnegie-Brown; Duncan Welham; Edward Butler; Caroline Sandeman-Allen; Michelle Alston; Neil Maidment.

Correspondent: Corporate Social Responsibility Manager, Lloyd's, One Lime Street, London EC3M 7HA (email: globalcommunityengagement@lloyds.com)

www.lloyds.com/lpf

General information

Established in 1803 following the Napoleonic Wars, the Lloyd's Patriotic Fund focuses on improving the transition to civilian life for veterans and their families. The fund provides long-term support to a number of partner organisations as well as smaller one-off grants of £10,000.

Beneficiaries included: Combat Stress and Regular Forces Employment Association (£50,000 each); Felix Fund (£11,000); Supporting Wounded Veterans (£10,000).

Financial information

Year end	30/06/2021
Assets	£2,690,000
Income	£470,000
Grant total	£170,000
Organisations supported	8

Applications

See the charity's website for the latest information on grants.

Sources of information

Accounts; annual report; Charity Commission record; funder's website; further information provided by the funder.

Making a Difference Locally Ltd

 General charitable purposes, including community projects and causes spanning health and well-being, education, employment, good food and nutrition, shelter and security

 UK, in areas local to Nisa Retail Ltd stores – see the store locator on the website

 £1.06 million (2020/21)

CC number: 1123800

Trustees: Valerie Aston; Mohammed Aslam; Kathryn Marsden; John McNeill; David Stokes; Andrew Barber; Mike Gisby.

Correspondent: The Trustees, Waldo Way, Normanby Enterprise Park, Scunthorpe, North Lincolnshire DN15 9GE (tel: 01724 282028; email: makingadifference@nisaretail.com)

www.nisalocally.co.uk/community

facebook.com/MADLcharity

@madlcharity

General information

Making a Difference Locally Ltd is the corporate charity of Nisa Retail Ltd, the groceries retailer.

The charity was established to allow the group's retail members to make donations to local charities and causes, such as local sports teams, hospices and charities. Retailers and partners of Nisa raise funds through the sale of specific products in their stores and then choose a local beneficiary for the funds.

Eligibility

The charity's overall mission is to invest in building stronger local communities. Funding areas span health and well-being, education, employment, good food and nutrition, shelter and security. Its criteria for funding are outlined below:

- Requests must be local to a Nisa store (ideally within ten miles)
- Requests must be from a registered charity or good cause with a dedicated business bank account
- The registered charity or good cause must be transparent and accountable; this means that it must be able to confirm what any donation would be used for on request

There is no minimum or maximum turnover restrictions for the charity or cause.

Heart of the Community Awards

This initiative was launched in October 2020 and supports community projects with donations totalling £150,000 (up to

£3,000 each). Nominations are accepted by Nisa partners via a dedicated website when funding rounds open.

Check the website for future funding rounds.

Beneficiaries included: The Trussell Trust (£17,500).

Financial information

Year end	30/06/2021
Assets	£1,450,000
Income	£1,200,000
Grant total	£1,060,000
Organisations supported	1,725

Further financial information

In 2021 1,725 grants were awarded. Grants were distributed as follows: retailers nominated organisations (£868,600); national organisations (£137,800); local organisations (£51,700). Grants ranged from £1.30 to £17,500. Only beneficiaries of grants of £10,000 and above were listed in the accounts.

Exclusions

The charity website states that it will not make donations to the following groups:

- Any group which is involved in the abuse of human rights;
- Any group which discriminates on the grounds of race, sexual orientation, religion, gender, disability or age;
- Any group which causes harm to animals for the purposes of either entertainment or sport;
- Any group which has as its main purpose the dissemination of political or religious information;
- Any group that will spend the funds directly in a Nisa partner's store;
- Any group that sends its funds out of the UK, even if it is a UK-registered charity.

Applications

Use the store locator on the Nisa website to contact your local store. Individual retailers can then submit a form to the MADL committee for approval.

Any enquiries should be sent via the contact form on the website.

Sources of information

Accounts; annual report; Charity Commission record; funder's website.

Man Group plc Charitable Trust

Literacy and numeracy

UK

£702,800 (2021)

CC number: 275386

Trustees: Carol Ward; Lydia Bosworth; Keith Haydon; Steven Desmyter; Christopher Pyper; Angus Jacobs; Abby King.

Correspondent: The Trustees, Man Group plc, Riverbank House, 2 Swan Lane, London EC4R 3AD (tel: 020 7144 1734; email: charitable.trust@man.com)

 www.man.com/responsibility

General information

This trust, which was registered in 1978, is the corporate charity of the investment management firm Man Group plc. The trust is the vehicle for most of the company's charitable donations and operates as an independent charity.

The trust has two main aims: firstly, it looks to support organisations working to raise literacy and numeracy levels in the UK and, secondly, it looks to facilitate opportunities for Man Group employees to share their time and expertise for charitable causes. It works to achieve these aims by carrying out the following activities, which are outlined on the trust's web page:

- Providing grants via a two-stage application process, or through negotiated partnerships with selected charities
- Tracking success by measuring impact, carefully monitoring all grants to ensure progress against agreed objectives
- Providing volunteering opportunities to Man Group UK employees via the Trust's community volunteering programme, ManKind
- Supporting Man Group UK employees' fundraising activity and charitable donations via the Trust's Sponsorship Matching and Give As You Earn schemes

Funding criteria

The trust supports small to medium-sized charities registered in the UK whose work is focused on the promotion of literacy and/or numeracy. There is a document available to download from the website which sets out full criteria and guidelines for applying for support. It states that, in order to be eligible, a charity must:

- Have an annual income greater than £500,000 and less than £10 million
- Raise levels of education with evidence of an increase in attainment
- Have a significant impact; changing wider policy and practice or having the potential to be mainstreamed or replicated
- Have clear and measurable outcomes and benefits and use evidence of results to improve performance
- Lead to leverage of additional funding wherever possible

The document further explains that applicants must be able to show that they are 'well run, with good governance and financial management' and that they 'have an ambitious approach to tackling social issues'. The trustees prefer to support activities that provide assistance

directly to individuals, families and communities and also those that increase the capacity of organisations and individuals.

The trustees also consider the interest and involvement of Man Group employees and hold an interest in finding out about volunteering opportunities; however, no preference is given to organisations or projects that can offer such opportunities.

Grant-making

At the time of writing (November 2022), the trust is currently funding one-year grants of up to £100,000 but will consider longer-term support for applications that are deemed by trustees to have particular merit.

Grants are typically given to fund core costs (including salaries and overheads) and project costs.

Beneficiaries included: Man US Charitable Foundation (£136,900); The Auditory Verbal Centre (£50,000); Read Easy UK (£41,600); Greenhouse Sports Ltd (£40,500); NSPCC (£35,000); Tower Hamlets Education Business Partnership (£28,800); Children's Discovery Centre East London (£25,000); Middlesbrough Football Club Foundation (£10,000).

Financial information

Year end	31/12/2021
Assets	£2,920,000
Income	£3,090,000
Grant total	£702,800

Exclusions

The trust's guidelines state:

The Trust does not as a rule support, through its grants programme or its broader giving:

- Large national charities (unless in relation to a specific education project)
- Charities which use external fundraising agencies
- Charities primarily devoted to promoting religious beliefs
- Endowment funds
- Requests to directly replace statutory funding
- Individual beneficiaries
- General media campaigns or campaigning or advocacy work to influence policy debates
- Applicants which have been successful during the last twelve months
- Work which has already been completed
- Capital projects and appeals
- Sponsorship or funding towards marketing appeals or fundraising events
- Organisations or projects whose primary purpose is political

Applications

In the first instance, see the trust's page on the Man Group website, where a document detailing eligibility criteria and guidelines on how to apply is available.

The document states that the trust has a two-stage application process. After reading the trust's eligibility criteria and exclusions, a brief expression of interest (not exceeding one side of A4) should be sent by email. Information on what should be included in the expression of interest can be found in the guidelines document on the trust's website.

Sources of information

Accounts; annual report; Charity Commission record; funder's website.

Manchester Airport Community Trust Fund

🔍 The environment; social welfare; community development and services

📍 Within a 10-mile radius of Manchester Airport, concentrating on the areas most exposed to aircraft noise

£ £110,400 (2020/21)

CC number: 1071703

Trustees: Paul Andrews; John Taylor; Cllr Don Stockton; Michael Whetton; Wendy Sinfield; John Twigg; Bill Fairfoull; Bob Rudd.

Correspondent: The Trustees, Manchester Airport plc, Olympic House, Manchester Airport, Manchester M90 1QX (tel: 0161 489 3853; email: trust.fund@manairport.co.uk)

 www.manchesterairport.co.uk/community/working-in-our-community/community-trust-fund

 @macomrels

General information

Registered with the Charity Commission in 1998, the Manchester Airport Community Trust Fund is a corporate charity of Manchester Airports Group plc. The trustees are employees of Manchester Airport, as well as trustees appointed by the Manchester Airport Consultative Committee from the council areas of Stockport, Manchester, Trafford, Tameside, Cheshire East, Cheshire West and Chester. The trust receives £100,000 each year from Manchester Airport Group, as well as the proceeds of fines charged for aircraft which exceed noise limits.

The following information has been taken from the fund's website:

Funding Criteria

The Community Trust Fund award grants to a maximum of £3,000. To be successful a group MUST:

- Carry out positive work in the community and be of charitable nature and be 'Not for Profit' status.

- Be Community, Socially or Environmentally focused
- Based within the area of benefit

The website states that projects should do one of the following:

- Improve, enhance, protect and conserve the natural and built environment
- Offer heritage conservation
- Promote or advance social welfare
- Provide better appreciation of the natural and urban environment
- Create a safe habitat for flora and fauna

Projects should also:

- Demonstrate lasting benefit to the community.
- Benefit all members of the community regardless of race, gender or religion.
- Be from an established group or charity able to demonstrate clear banking or financial records, and not an individual or commercial organisation working for profit.

Beneficiaries included: Cranford Bowling (£3,000); Styal Tennis Club (£2,800); Stockport Wheelchair Races (£2,600); Barnardo's Wythenshawe Centre (£2,000); 4th Newall Green Rainbows (£1,500); Active Communities Experiences Ltd (£1,000); Manchester Basketball Club (£400).

Financial information

Year end	31/03/2021
Assets	£37,600
Income	£126,400
Grant total	£110,400
Organisations supported	63

Applications

Apply online via the fund's website. The trustees meet four times a year; application deadlines are published on the fund's website.

Sources of information

Accounts; annual report; Charity Commission record; funder's website.

The Mansfield Building Society Charitable Trust

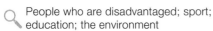 People who are disadvantaged; sport; education; the environment

 Nottinghamshire, Derbyshire, Lincolnshire and South Yorkshire

£ £46,700 (2021)

CC number: 1177151

Trustees: Irvin Robinson; Lady Diana Meale; Tony Sale; Paul Wheeler; Victoria Preston.

Correspondent: The Trustees, Mansfield Building Society, Regent Street, Mansfield, Nottinghamshire NG18 1SS (tel: 01623 676300; email: enquiries@ mansfieldbs.co.uk)

 www.mansfieldbs.co.uk/charitable-trust

General information

This trust was registered with the Charity Commission in February 2018. The trust is the corporate charity of The Mansfield Building Society. It is exclusively for the benefit of registered charities in its core operating territory of Nottinghamshire, Derbyshire, Lincolnshire and South Yorkshire. The trustees consider applications from sustainable charitable causes that benefit the local community.

The trust's website states:

As well as working in the local area, the trust's objective is to create a legacy of giving to support projects with enduring benefit which:

- support the disadvantaged (e.g. young, elderly, disabled or the homeless)
- promote and encourage sporting activity
- support education and/or development
- benefit the environment (e.g. conservation)

Beneficiaries included: Bluebell Children's Hospice; Derbyshire Wildlife Trust; Panathlon; Sherwood Forest Trust.

Financial information

Year end	31/12/2021
Assets	£222,600
Income	£77,900
Grant total	£46,700

Exclusions

The trust will not normally sponsor individuals, party political activities, promotion of religious causes, animal charities or commercial enterprises.

Applications

If you currently work or volunteer for a registered charity in Nottinghamshire, Derbyshire or South Yorkshire, the trust asks you to email community@mansfieldbs.co.uk in the first instance with details of your charity and the project you'd like support for; the trust will then let you know how to apply.

Sources of information

Charity Commission record; funder's website.

D. G. Marshall of Cambridge Trust

 Aviation; children and young people; health and disability; education; community projects

Cambridgeshire

£ £40,000 (2020/21)

CC number: 286468

Trustees: Sarah Moynihan; Robert Marshall; Julie Ingham.

Correspondent: The Trustees, Airport House, The Airport, Newmarket Road, Cambridge CB5 8RY (tel: 01223 373737)

General information

The trust was established in December 1982 by its settlor, Marshall of Cambridge Aerospace Ltd (referred to in the trust's annual report and accounts as 'the Company'), Marshall of Cambridge (Holdings) Ltd and Marshall Motor Group Ltd. The trust's annual report for 2020/21 explains that 'initially the trust capital was £100 but since then further donations have been paid into the Trust by the settlor'.

The trust's 2020/21 annual report states that the trust's primary objectives are to support:

- needy and deserving cases arising anywhere but in particular among employees or ex-employees or their relatives or dependants of the Company or any subsidiary or associated company
- local charities
- local educational institutions as are charitable in nature

Beneficiaries included: Form the Future (£10,000); The Arthur Rank Hospice (£6,000); Air League, Cambridge United Community Trust and Parkinson's UK (£3,000 each); Ely Cathedral Restoration Trust and Mind (£1,000 each); Bobby Moore Bowel Cancer Fund (£500); Cancer Research UK (£150); Crisis (£90).

Financial information

Year end	05/04/2021
Assets	£2,630,000
Income	£169,500
Grant total	£40,000

Further financial information

Grants were broken down as follows:

Local community	£13,000
Hospitals and related organisations	£13,000
Children's charities	£5,500
Education	£3,000
Aviation	£3,000
Disability and health	£2,500

Applications

Apply in writing to the correspondent. The trust will consider all applications for funding as received.

Sources of information
Accounts; annual report: Charity Commission record.

Dr. Martens Foundation

 Human rights; social justice; social welfare

Worldwide

£753,800 (2021/22)

CC number: 1194513

Trustees: Emily Reichwald; Pamela Shores; Darren Campbell; Tuze Schwank; Paul Armstrong.

Correspondent: The Trustees, 28 Jamestown Road, Camden, London NW1 7BY (tel: 020 3995 2626; email: dmfoundation@drmartens.com)

www.drmartensplc.com/sustainability/people

General information
The charity was established in 2021 and is the corporate foundation of Dr. Martens plc, a British-based footwear producer. The foundation supports causes that advance social justice.

The foundation's website states:

> What the Foundation stands for:
>
> We will put our best foot forward and lead the way for what is fair. We will support social justice causes, which empower rebellious self-expression and drive forward positive change for society.
> - Human Rights – Protecting and respecting everyone's human rights.
> - Participation – Social justice is not possible if only some voices are heard and the marginalised are silent.
> - Equity – Tackling the structural inequality and embedded bias that exists across society.
> - Access – Ability to access essentials like shelter or opportunities in education, music or creative industries.

Beneficiaries included: A list of beneficiaries was not available.

Financial information
Year end	31/03/2022
Grant total	£753,800
Organisations supported	41

Further financial information
As the foundation is a newly-registered charity, full accounts were not available to view on the Charity Commission website. However, Dr. Martens plc's 2021/22 annual report states that the foundation made 41 grants totalling £753,800 during the year. Grants were broken down as follows:

LGBTQ+	5
Gender justice	5
Anti-racism	5
Mental health	4
Refugees and asylum seekers	4
Trafficking	3

Homelessness	3
Multiple themes	3
Access to music or arts	2
Criminal justice	2
Climate change	1

Applications
The foundation isn't accepting unsolicited applications as grant-making is currently by invitation only.

Sources of information
Charity Commission record; Dr. Martens plc annual report; Dr. Martens plc website.

Mazars Charitable Trust

 General charitable purposes

UK

£108,600 (2020/21)

CC number: 1150459

Trustees: Tracey Marshall; Lesley Fox; Philip Verity; Kim Hurst; Janine Fox; Jonathan Bennett.

Correspondent: The Trustees, Mazars LLP, Merck House, Seldown Lane, Poole, Dorset BH15 1TW (tel: 07756 323888; email: mazarscharitabletrust@gmail.com)

General information
The firm Mazars LLP specialises in audit, tax, and advisory services across a range of markets and sectors. This associated charitable trust was registered with the Charity Commission in January 2013 and makes grants to charitable organisations in the UK and Ireland. In 2018/19 the majority of the trust's income was received from Mazars LLP. It does not respond to unsolicited applications; however, applications can be made through a team member of Mazars LLP.

The trust's 2020/21 annual report states:

> The Trustees have determined that all grants are to be based on nominations by team members of Mazars LLP, the donor firm, and reflect criteria developed by the Trustees.
>
> All the Major grants were reviewed by the Management Committee prior to Trustee approval. The remainder of funds allocated to each Mazars LLP office pro rata to headcount are approved by each office potholder.

The Mazars Charitable Trust grants awards to charities that work in sectors including: mental health and well-being; research and support for physical health conditions; the arts; palliative care/hospices; food banks; and sports.

Beneficiaries included: A list of beneficiaries was not available. Previous beneficiaries include: Friends of Asha (£25,000); Erskine Hospital Ltd (£14,400); Muntada Aid (£10,000);

King's Arms Project Bedford (£9,000); Burning Nights CRPS Support (£5,000); The RAF Association (£2,000).

Financial information
Year end	31/03/2021
Assets	£473,200
Income	£452,600
Grant total	£108,600

Applications
The trustees do not respond to unsolicited applications. All nominations for grants have to be proposed by staff members of Mazars LLP and no grant applications should be submitted directly to the trust.

Sources of information
Accounts; annual report; Charity Commission record; funder's website.

The Robert McAlpine Foundation

Children and young people; social welfare; older people; medical research; disability

UK

£645,600 (2020/21)

CC number: 226646

Trustees: Adrian McAlpine; The Hon. David McAlpine; Cullum McAlpine; Gavin McAlpine.

Correspondent: Appeals Manager, Eaton Court, Maylands Avenue, Hemel Hempstead, Hertfordshire HP2 7TR (tel: 0333 566 2069; email: foundation@srm.com)

www.robertmcalpinefoundation.org

General information
Sir Robert McAlpine Ltd is a family owned UK construction and civil engineering company. The foundation was established by the family of Sir Robert McAlpine and gives grants to support small charities situated throughout the UK that fall within specific categories, namely:
- Children with disabilities or life-limiting illnesses
- Social welfare
- Older people
- Young people
- Medical research

To be eligible, charities must meet the following criteria:
- Have a total income of less than £1 million per annum
- Be intending to use the funding for a UK-based project
- Work in one of the trust's areas of interest

The foundation's 2020/21 accounts state: 'The policy of the Trustees is to make grants to charitable institutions of amounts from £5,000 upwards in the specific categories of objectives which they support.'

Beneficiaries included: A list of beneficiaries was not available.

Financial information

Year end	31/03/2021
Assets	£19,220,000
Income	£678,500
Grant total	£645,600

Exclusions

The foundation will not fund fundraising activities or support fundraising by established charities for a target sum.

Applications

Apply by post or via email to the correspondent. The foundation's website states that appeals should be no more than two A4 pages and outline:

- Who you are
- Your charity number
- What work your charity does
- Details of the specific project for which you require funding
- The amount of funding you are looking for
- Your contact details, together with website address if you have one

The foundation also asks that applicants enclose a copy of their most recent accounts. The trustees meet annually in November to approve grants. Applications must be received no later than 31 August to be considered in the next meeting. The foundation is unable to accept any appeal requests by telephone.

Sources of information

Accounts; annual report; Charity Commission record; funder's website.

The Medicash Foundation

 Health and well-being

 North West England, Derbyshire and North Wales

(£) £371,900 (2021)

CC number: 257636

Trustee: Medicash Health Benefits Ltd.

Correspondent: Linda Traynor, Medicash Ltd, 1 Derby Square, Liverpool L2 1AB (tel: 0151 702 0334; email: linda. traynor@medicash.org)

 www.medicash.org/charity

General information

In 2019, the foundation's name was changed from Medicash Charitable Trust to The Medicash Foundation. The foundation is the corporate charity of Medicash Health Benefits Ltd and

receives a large proportion of its income from the company.

Grants are made to support a range of health and well-being causes. In the past, grants have been given for the following:

- Children's charities, including mental health and support for disadvantaged children
- Health and well-being projects
- People with disabilities
- Local hospitals, hospices and charities that support people who are ill
- Educational organisations such as universities and schools

In the past, grants have been give to organisations in the region covering Merseyside, Wirral, Cheshire, Lancashire, Greater Manchester, Derbyshire, North Wales and Cumbria.

Beneficiaries included: Northern Vision (£17,500); St Helens Christian Life Centre (£10,000); The Hope Centre (£7,500); Compassionate Friends (£6,000); Roy Castle Lung Cancer Foundation and Voice for Change (Domestic Violence) (£5,000 each); Henshaws Society for the Blind (£2,000); Litherland High School (£1,000); Radio City Cash for Kids (£480).

Financial information

Year end	31/12/2021
Assets	£2,030,000
Income	£924,900
Grant total	£371,900

Further financial information

Grants were distributed as follows:

Children's charities	£93,700
Health and well-being	£76,100
Illness or medical condition	£59,600
Disability	£15,000
Hospices	£12,000
Education	£11,300

Applications

Application forms can be downloaded from the foundation's website.

Sources of information

Accounts; annual report; Charity Commission record; funder's website.

Melton Mowbray Building Society Charitable Foundation

 Community development; children and young people; people who are disadvantaged; health

Organisations within a 15-mile radius of the building society's branches in Melton Mowbray, Grantham and Oakham

(£) £20,000 (2021/22)

CC number: 1067348

Trustees: Martin Reason; Rachel Kolebuk; Simon Taylor; Vicki

Williamson; David Wood; Robert Brownlow; Keith Hallam.

Correspondent: The Secretary to the Trustees, Mutual House, Leicester Road, Melton Mowbray, Leicestershire LE13 0DB (tel: 01664 414141; email: c.ritchie@mmbs.co.uk)

www.themelton.co.uk/community-support/charitable-foundation

General information

The foundation was established in 1998 and supports people and projects within a 15-mile radius of the building society's branch offices in Melton Mowbray, Grantham and Oakham.

According to its website, the foundation divides its resources between the following two areas of activity:

Community Projects
The Foundation commits at least 33% and up to 50% of the annual contribution made by the Society to either kickstart a community project or to establish an enduring activity or initiative for the benefit of the community. Any donations made from sources other than the Society's own contributions will be matched by the Society, subject to a maximum level at the discretion of the Society's Board of Directors.

Community Activities
The Foundation also supports a variety of local worthwhile needs. Types of request considered by the Foundation will be from:
- Young people, particularly those who are disadvantaged
- Vulnerable groups such as the frail elderly, people with physical disability, people with learning difficulties or those who are mentally ill
- Small neighbourhood groups in areas experiencing the greatest disadvantage
- Communities and voluntary organisations seeking assistance in the achievement of social and community development.

Financial information

Year end	31/03/2022
Income	£8,300
Grant total	£20,000

Further financial information

Full accounts were not available to view on the Charity Commission website due to the foundation's low income. We have therefore estimated the foundation's grant total based on its total expenditure.

Exclusions

According to its application guidelines, the foundation is unlikely to make grants for the following:
- Running costs such as rent or staff wages
- Expeditions or overseas travel

- Entities or individuals who have applied to the foundation within the previous 12 months
- The restoration or upgrade of buildings, including churches
- Sponsorship of individuals
- National charities or funding requests which do not have direct relevance to the local community

Applications

Apply in writing to the correspondent.

Sources of information

Charity Commission record; funder's website.

Mills and Reeve Charitable Trust

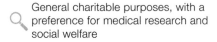 General charitable purposes, with a preference for medical research and social welfare

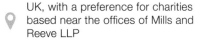 UK, with a preference for charities based near the offices of Mills and Reeve LLP

 £125,400 (2020/21)

CC number: 326271

Trustees: Greg Gibson; Tom Pickthorn; Dawn Brathwaite; Justin Ripman; Sarah Seed; Alison Bull; Neil Howes; Stuart Thompson; Richard Santy.

Correspondent: The Trustees, Botanic House, 100 Hills Road, Cambridge, Cambridgeshire CB2 1PH (tel: 01223 222273)

🌐 www.mills-reeve.com/about-us/ making-a-positive-impact

General information

Mills and Reeve Charitable Trust was established in 1982 and is the corporate charity of Mills and Reeve LLP, a law firm with offices in London, Birmingham, Cambridge, Leeds, Manchester and Norwich. The trust receives a substantial amount of its income from members of the firm.

The trust provides funding for a range of causes, with a particular interest in charities working with disadvantaged people or funding medical research. Usually, supported causes will be local to one of the firm's offices.

The 2020/21 annual report states the following: 'Smaller donations were made on an ad hoc basis – again for local projects or to support staff initiatives. The trustees intend to continue with this approach for the future.'

Beneficiaries included: Kids Out (£6,000); Romsey Mill Trust Ltd (£5,800); EACH (£5,000); Tommy's (£4,300); Safe Lives (£4,000); Leeway Domestic Violence and Abuse Services (£3,000); Cats Protection (£2,500);

Manchester Central Foodbank (£2,000); Solicitors Benevolent Association (£1,500); Leeds South and East Foodbank (£1,000).

Financial information

Year end	31/05/2021
Assets	£281,500
Income	£132,600
Grant total	£125,400

Applications

Apply in writing to the correspondent.

Sources of information

Accounts; annual report; Charity Commission record; funder's website.

The Steve Morgan Foundation

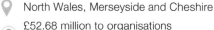 Children and young people; families; older people; health and disability; people who are socially isolated

🌐 North Wales, Merseyside and Cheshire

£ £52.68 million to organisations (2021/22)

CC number: 1087056

Trustees: Vincent Fairclough; Stephen Morgan; Rhiannon Walker; Ashley Lewis; Sally Morgan; Jonathan Masters; Brian Clark.

Correspondent: The Trustees, PO Box 3517, Chester CH1 9ET (tel: 01829 782800; email: hello@ stevemorganfoundation.org.uk)

🌐 https://stevemorganfoundation.org. uk

f facebook.com/Steve-Morgan-Foundation-106137272803911

🐦 @stevemorganfdn

📷 @stevemorganfoundation

General information

The Steve Morgan Foundation was established in 2001 with an endowment of over £2 million from Stephen Morgan CBE, founder of Redrow plc.

Areas of work

The foundation's website states:

All requests which would result in a positive effect on people's welfare or quality of life or improves opportunities and life choices, are considered.

We are interested in receiving applications from organisations which help:

 children
 children and families
 the elderly
 those with disabilities
- the socially isolated

Types of grant

Funding provided by the foundation typically falls into one of the following four categories:

- **Regional grants** – multi-year revenue grants for core funding, salaries and ongoing running costs
- **Major grants** – grants of over £100,000 including awards for capital costs
- **Enable** – funding for specialised disability equipment for people of all ages
- **Smiley Bus** – funding for both standard and wheelchair-accessible minibuses and other essential transport vehicles including bikes and vans

Beneficiaries included: Diabetes UK/ Juvenile Diabetes UK (£50 million); Reader Organisation (£120,000); The Duke of Edinburgh's Award (£100,000); Creating Adventures (£60,000); Warrington Youth (£50,000).

Financial information

Year end	31/03/2022
Assets	£255,150,000
Income	£6,510,000
Grant total	£52,680,000

Exclusions

Application guidelines and criteria for each funding programme can be found on the foundation's website.

Applications

For regional, major and Smiley Bus grants, applicants are requested to first check their eligibility against the criteria listed on the foundation's website. Eligible organisations are then asked submit an expression of interest via email.

Sources of information

Accounts; annual report; Charity Commission record; funder's website.

Morgan Stanley International Foundation

🔍 Education and children's health

📍 Europe, the Middle East and Africa. Local projects in Tower Hamlets and Glasgow

£ £2.13 million (2021)

CC number: 1042671

Trustees: Sue Watts; Russell Weinberg; Emily Laino; Dorothee Fuhrmann; Josephine Harriman; Zoe Parish; Caroline Nicholls; Aidan Armstrong; Maro Gregotti; Sacha Anselm; Jamie Glynn; Norbert Fogarasi; Stephen Mavin; Oliver Stuart; Clare Woodman.

Correspondent: The Trustees, Morgan Stanley & Co. International plc, 20 Bank

Street, London E14 4AD (email: communityaffairslondon@ morganstanley.com)

 www.morganstanley.com/pub/ content/msdotcom/en/about-us/ giving-back/msif-guidelines.html

General information

The Morgan Stanley International Foundation was registered with the Charity Commission in 1994. It is the corporate charity of Morgan Stanley and Co. International plc, a financial services corporation.

The foundation's goal is to make a sustainable impact on children's welfare in the communities in which it operates across Europe, the Middle East and Africa. According to its website, the foundation is primarily focused on providing funding in the following areas:

Children's Health – The Foundation looks to invest in innovations and development in children's healthcare. Working with charitable organisations, hospitals and community based initiatives, the MSIF focuses on supporting young people. The MSIF strives to ensure that more children have access to quality healthcare to enable them to have a more meaningful life.

Education – The MSIF aims to work with registered charities and state-funded schools which provide benefit to communities across EMEA. The MSIF works with organisations that increase access and opportunity for young people, supporting programmes that address academic achievement and employability skills, by inspiring talented but underserved young people.

According to the 2021 annual report, the foundation makes grants through three different channels:

- Direct charitable grant applications are invited for the funding of projects in the EMEA region, and are reviewed at the Trustees' meetings against specific grant objectives. Multi-year grants are monitored on an annual basis to ensure the grant criteria continue to be met
- Employee nominated charity partnerships are voted for by Morgan Stanley employees, and the Foundation matches employee fundraising and donations up to a pre-determined amount.
- Employee matching grants recognise Morgan Stanley employees' fundraising and volunteering efforts in their local communities. The Foundation currently matches fundraising efforts by an employee for a charitable organisation up to a maximum of £500 per employee in one given year. In addition, grants in recognition of certain employees' volunteering efforts are awarded of £500 per employee, to a charity of the employee's choice in one given year.

Beneficiaries included: Place2Be – London (£252,700); Great Ormond Street Hospital (£107,400); Save the Children (£91,000); CHAS – Glasgow (£90,000); PEEK – Glasgow (£84,300).

Financial information

Year end	31/12/2021
Assets	£3,450,000
Income	£2,690,000
Grant total	£2,130,000

Exclusions

According to its website the foundation does not provide grants for any of the following:

- Organisations which are not registered as a non profit organisation with the appropriate regulatory agencies in their country (unless a state funded school).
- National or International charities which do not operate in the regions we are located.
- Grants will not be made to either political or religious organisations, "pressure groups" or individuals outside the Firm who are seeking sponsorship either for themselves (e.g. to help pay for education) or for onward transmission to a charitable organisation.
- Programmes that do not include opportunities for Morgan Stanley employee volunteer engagement.

Applications

The foundation's website gives the following details on making an initial approach for funding:

The Morgan Stanley International Foundation takes a proactive approach to grant making and therefore does not accept unsolicited proposals. If you think your organisation is a match for the criteria set out below, please send an email to communityaffairslondon@morganstanley.com with the following information:

- Program description, including mission, goals and numbers served
- Measurement strategies
- Geographic scope

Please note that due to the large number of quality proposals we receive, only applications that have been reviewed and are considered to fit within the MSIF priorities will be contacted directly.

Sources of information

Accounts; annual report; Charity Commission record; funder's website.

The Morris Charitable Trust

 Social welfare; health; education; community

 UK and overseas, with a strong preference for Islington

 £139,600 (2020/21)

CC number: 802290

Trustees: Paul Morris; Jack Morris; Alan Stenning; Dominic Jones; Gerald Morris; Linda Morris; Lucie Grant.

Correspondent: Linda Morris, Secretary, Business Design Centre, 52 Upper Street, Islington Green, London N1 0QH (tel: 020 7359 3535; email: info@ morrischaritabletrust.com)

 www.morrischaritabletrust.com

facebook.com/morrischaritabletrust

@theMorrisCT

@morrischaritabletrust

General information

The Morris Charitable Trust was established in 1989 by the Morris Family and is funded by companies within the BDCG Holdings Ltd group. The family's primary company is the Business Design Centre, a multipurpose trade centre and events venue based in London, that donates a significant portion of its profits to the trust. The trustees are made up of members of the Morris family as well as several of the board of directors at the Business Design Centre.

The trust funds projects and other charitable causes within the community of the London Borough of Islington, with a focus on the following:

- **Education** – promoting the advancement of education both in schools and community-based projects
- **Hardship** – projects that enable people in need to access services and resources they may not have access to otherwise
- **Health** – projects that aim to enhance the enjoyment of life for individuals who are older or experiencing ill health
- **Community** – improving the financial circumstances of worthwhile causes, for the benefit of community groups

According to its website, the trust offers funding for capital and one-off projects; however, 'consideration is occasionally given to other innovative community projects as well as exceptional crisis funds.'

The trustees select national and international charities to support on an ad hoc basis.

The key aims of the trust are 'to focus funding towards those in disadvantaged groups, the elderly or isolated and in particular towards the advancement of education and community facilities. Particular emphasis is placed on alleviating social hardship and deprivation.'

To be considered for funding, charities must be registered with the Charity Commission. The website states the following:

> Grants can vary between hundreds and several thousands of pounds at the discretion of the Trustees. Occasionally the Trust makes major donations for local projects which it considers to be particularly worthy of support. The Trustees consider very carefully how the Trust's donations will make a real difference to the charity or project applying. Only a limited number of selected charities are chosen for support each year.

Beneficiaries included: A list of recent beneficiaries can be found on the trust's website.

Financial information

Year end	31/03/2021
Assets	£177,700
Income	£100,100
Grant total	£139,600
Organisations supported	24

Further financial information

Grants can be broken down as follows:

Donation band	No. of grants	Amount
£5,001+	4	£81,000
£1,001 to £5,000	18	£56,400
£501 to £1,000	2	£2,000
£0 to £500	0	£0

Exclusions

The following information has been taken from the trust's website:

> We do not generally make donations to applications from individuals. Requests for subsidising the annual, recurring running costs of organisations (e.g. staffing, salaries, or equipment hire) will not be considered either. We do not generally make donations to applicants not registered with The Charity Commission.

Applications

Application forms are available to complete online on the trust's website. The trustees meet throughout the year to consider applications. Grants are generally not repeated within a 12-month period.

Sources of information

Accounts; annual report; Charity Commission record; funder's website.

The Morrisons Foundation

 General charitable purposes; the arts and culture; health; education; social welfare; community

England, Wales and Scotland

£3.04 million (2020/21)

CC number: 1160224/SC045634

Trustees: Charles Jones; Charles Dacres; Kate Bratt-Farrar; Sarah Wilkinson; David Scott; Guy Hurlstone; Jonathan Burke.

Correspondent: The Trustees, Hilmore House, Gain Lane, Bradford, West Yorkshire BD3 7DL (tel: 0845 611 5364; email: foundation.enquiries@ morrisonsplc.co.uk)

 www.morrisonsfoundation.com

General information

The Morrisons Foundation was established in 2014 and is fully funded by Wm Morrison Supermarkets plc, one of the biggest supermarket chains in the UK.

It supports registered charities that are making a difference in local communities across England, Scotland and Wales by awarding grants for charitable projects. Applications can be made for grants of up to £25,000 to fully-fund projects that will help to improve people's lives. Occasionally, the foundation awards high-value grants to support larger projects and initiatives.

The foundation supports a wide range of causes including health care, social inclusion, mental health, arts and culture, education, the armed forces, the environment and people with disabilities.

The foundation also supports charities by match funding the money raised by Morrisons employees for their chosen organisations.

Beneficiaries included: A list of beneficiaries was not available. Previous beneficiaries include: Ickle Pickles and The Children's Trust (£25,000 each); Dentaid (£20,000); Emmaus Oxford (£18,400); Lincolnshire Emergency Blood Bikes Service (£14,700); British Disabled Angling Association (£7,400); Pinpoint (£5,000); Disability Snowsport UK (£4,600).

Financial information

Year end	04/02/2021
Assets	£2,270,000
Income	£3,690,000
Grant total	£3,040,000

Exclusions

According to the foundation's guidance for applicants, it will not generally consider supporting the following:

- Staff costs, rent costs, utilities, administration costs or any other running costs;
- Support of ongoing services
- Grants, bursaries etc. to individuals;
- Expeditions, recreation or overseas travel;
- Fundraising events or grants to ongoing appeals;
- Work that is primarily the statutory responsibility of public agencies;
- Promotion of religious or political messaging;
- Part-funding or contributions towards projects or grants in excess of £25,000;
- Advertising, promotion or marketing of events or services;
- Part-funding or contributions towards projects or grants in excess of £25,000;
- Advertising, promotion or marketing of events or services;
- Overseas appeals;
- Conferences or seminars;
- Charities that are newly listed on the Charity Commission/OSCR, or whose accounts are overdue or filed late;
- Organisations that are not registered with the Charity Commission or OSCR;
- Equipment which will be retained by individuals rather than the charity;
- Animal charities, unless the objective is to improve the lives of vulnerable or disadvantaged individuals;
- Projects being delivered outside England, Scotland or Wales;
- Sports-based charities, unless the objective is to improve the lives of vulnerable or disadvantaged individuals;
- Projects which could harm the reputation of the Foundation.

Applications

Applications can be completed online through the foundation's website. Applications are accepted and reviewed on a continual basis. Applicants will be notified of a decision by telephone or email, even if the application is unsuccessful.

Sources of information

Accounts; annual report; Charity Commission record; funder's website; 2019/20 annual review.

The MSE Charity

 Financial education and improving financial literacy

UK

(£) £172,900 (2021/22)

CC number: 1121320

Trustees: Tony Tesciuba; Katie Davies; Vanessa Bissessur; Teej Dew; Clarissa Coleman; Marcus Herbert.

Correspondent: Katie Davies, Operations Manager, c/o Tesciuba Ltd, 72 Cavendish Road, Salford M7 4WA (tel: 0161 211 0205; email: info@ msecharity.com)

 www.msecharity.com

 @msecharity

General information

The charity was launched in 2007 by founder of the Money Saving Expert website, Martin Lewis. According to its website, the charity is dedicated to supporting UK voluntary groups deliver financial life skills which make a lasting impact on the way people think, behave and manage their money.

The trustees prefer to fund small to medium-sized non-profit organisations with a constitution. Organisations should have an income under £750,000 and have less than six months free reserves.

There are two grant rounds per year. Each funding round has a different theme and will focus on delivering financial life skills to different defined groups. Themes rotate through a two-year cycle. The main emphasis is that all projects must increase the personal financial/money life skills of the beneficiaries. See below for examples of 2023/24 grant round themes.

Grant round themes

- **Life Changing Transitions** – projects focused on building financial capability skills assisting groups who support bereavement, redundancy, retirement, relationship breakdown, homelessness, offenders and resettlement. Applications accepted between 4 September and 29 September 2023.
- **Living with Long Term Challenges** – projects focused on building financial capability skills assisting groups who support dementia, autism, learning difficulties, disabilities, caring responsibilities, mental illness, brain injury and stroke. Applications accepted between 2 January and 31 January 2024.

- **Building and Developing Resilience** – projects focused on building financial capability skills that support people recovering from the results of the pandemic and help them move forward. Applications accepted between 2 September and 27 September 2024.

Beneficiaries included: Hull Kingston Rovers Community Trust (£7,500); Kith and Kin Financial Well-being CIC (£6,600); Citizens Advice Wokingham (£5,800); The Family Trust (£5,000); Transitions UK (£4,500); Happy Days Ministries UK (£3,000); CAP Larne (£2,100).

Financial information

Year end	31/03/2022
Assets	£21,100
Income	£121,400
Grant total	£172,900

Exclusions

The charity will not fund individuals or organisations with an annual income of over £750,000. The charity only funds activities in England, Wales, Scotland and Northern Ireland.

For a full list of exclusions, see the FAQs section of the grant-giver's website (www.msecharity.com/how-to-apply/faqs).

Applications

Applicants should complete an online application form when the relevant funding round opens. A template can be found on the website which previews the questions that will need to be answered. Each grant round is limited to the first 40 applicants.

An eligibility quiz is available on the charity's website which organisations can take to see if they are eligible for a grant. Full application details can be found on the website.

Sources of information

Accounts; annual report; Charity Commission record; funder's website; further information provided by the funder.

Music Sales Charitable Trust

General charitable purposes; health; the arts and culture; education and training; religion; overseas and famine relief; disability; children and young people

UK, with a preference for London and Bury St Edmunds

(£) £165,100 (2021)

CC number: 1014942

Trustees: Christopher Butler; Ian Morgan; Robert Wise; Mildred Wise; Mr M. Wise; Nicholas Kemp; David Stock.

Correspondent: The Trustees, c/o Music Sales Ltd, 14–15 Berners Street, London W1T 3LJ (tel: 020 7612 7400; email: neville.wignall@musicsales.co.uk)

General information

Music Sales Charitable Trust was registered with the Charity Commission in 1992. It is the corporate charity of Wise Music Group, formally known as the Music Sales Group, a global music publisher. The trust's primary activity is to make donations to a range of organisations, with a preference for those that benefit the residents of London and Bury St Edmunds.

Funding is given for a wide range of causes including education, social welfare, medicine and health, religion, the arts and culture, people with disabilities and overseas aid.

Beneficiaries included: East Anglia's Children's Hospices, LIFEM, Médecins Sans Frontières, St Nicholas Hospice Care and Westminster Synagogue (£5,000 each).

Financial information

Year end	31/12/2021
Assets	£223,100
Income	£102,400
Grant total	£165,100
Organisations supported	80

Further financial information

Only organisations that received grants of over £5,000 were listed as beneficiaries in the trust's accounts. Grants of under £5,000 totalled £130,100 and were awarded to 73 organisations. Overall, grants were distributed within the following categories:

General	£76,700
Disability	£37,400
Art and culture	£22,100
Religion	£11,000
Medical health and sickness	£7,600
Education and training	£6,300
Overseas and famine relief	£4,000

Applications

Contact the correspondent for further information.

Sources of information

Accounts; annual report; Charity Commission record.

The National Express Foundation

 Young people aged 15 to 24; education, especially bursaries for disadvantaged students; social welfare; sport; community; general charitable purposes

Priority is given to the West Midlands Combined Authority area and surrounding districts

£ £202,700 (2021)

CC number: 1148231

Trustees: Ian Fraser; Thomas Stables; Ian Austin.

Correspondent: The Trustees, c/o National Express Ltd, National Express House, Mill Lane, Birmingham B5 6DD (tel: 0121 803 5650; email: foundation@ nationalexpress.com)

www.nationalexpressgroup.com/ national-express-foundation

General information

Established in 2011 following the summer riots in the UK, the charitable foundation is a key part of the National Express Ltd's community support in the UK and is entirely funded by the company. Trustees include directors of the National Express Group. The group's employees play a central role in its community involvement through volunteering, fundraising activities and a payroll giving scheme.

The National Express Foundation's objectives are to promote education, including by awarding scholarships, maintenance allowances or grants to those in higher or further education, as well as to provide grants for recreational activities for disaffected and disadvantaged young people, aged 15 to 24, which will, in turn, develop their skills and harness their potential.

Although the foundation has previously given support more broadly in areas where National Express Group operates, the foundation's 2021 annual report explains that 'To maximise the impact of the available funding in 2021, the trustees agreed to focus solely on community groups in the West Midlands alone.' The foundation's website further defined the area of benefit for the 2022 funding programme as 'the areas served by the West Midlands Combined Authority constituent members* and surrounding districts which are served by National Express West Midlands/ Coventry bus routes and National Express Accessible Transport services'.

* Birmingham, Coventry, Dudley, Sandwell, Solihull, Walsall and Wolverhampton.

The foundation makes grants to:
- Individual students with challenging personal and financial circumstances to enable them to advance their further and higher education. All support for students is provided via academic partners, not directly to individuals.
- Charitable and community groups for projects which support children and young people and promote cross-community cohesion and understanding

Grants are typically awarded to contribute towards project costs or to help an organisation deliver a particular service. Grants tend to be of £2,500, £5,000, £10,000 or £20,000, although many are of less than £10,000.

The trustees note the following in the application guidance: 'While we do not propose to set restrictions on how the funding would be applied, we will be seeking evidence of innovation in how the projects will be delivered.'

Beneficiaries included: Employability UK, Friar Park Millennium Centre and Loaves n Fishes (£10,000 each); Blessed to Bless, Excite Active CIC and Longford Short Football (£5,000 each); Inspired2Connect (£2,500).

Financial information

Year end	31/12/2021
Assets	£13,800
Income	£240,000
Grant total	£202,700

Further financial information

Grants are given for two categories: community and education. The foundation funds student bursaries for individuals with challenging personal and financial circumstances.

Exclusions

The guidance notes state that the foundation will reject applications that:
- Involve one-off activities – one day/ weekend/week, and therefore lack key milestones for the project
- Only benefit a small number of young people – less than ten
- Are seeking part-funding towards a larger project
- Seek sponsorship for an event
- Offer little opportunity for stakeholder or Foundation engagement
- Do not provide evaluation or measurement for impact of the activity

Furthermore, the foundation does not support projects that are unsustainable.

Applications

Application forms and guidance can be downloaded from the foundation's website, where applicants can find further information on successful projects and deadlines. Check the website for up-to-date information on funding rounds.

Sources of information

Accounts; annual report; Charity Commission record; funder's website.

The Nationwide Foundation

 Community development; affordable housing; social welfare

UK

£ £1.32 million (2020/21)

CC number: 1065552

Trustees: Sarah Mitchell; Antonia Bance; Sara Bennison; Saphie Ashtiany; Terrie Alafat; Judith McNeill; Gill Leng; Baroness Usha Prashar; Robert Collins.

Correspondent: The Trustees, Nationwide House, Pipers Way, Swindon, Wiltshire SN38 2SN (tel: 0330 460 0709; email: enquiries@ nationwidefoundation.org.uk)

 www.nationwidefoundation.org.uk

@NationwideFdtn

General information

The Nationwide Foundation was established as an independent charity in 1997. It receives the majority of its funding from the Nationwide Building Society, which makes an annual lump sum donation of 0.25% of its pre-tax profit. According to its 2020/21 annual report, 'at its heart, the Nationwide Foundation seeks to tackle the root causes of social problems that lead to disadvantage, poverty, and inequality.' It aims to ensure that everyone in the UK has access to decent, affordable housing.

Grants programmes

The foundation provides support through three programmes:

Nurturing Ideas to Change the Housing System

This programme supports projects that are working to tackle systemic failings in the housing system. On its website, the foundation states that this programme funds the researching, testing, developing, piloting and evaluation of new ideas.

Backing Community-Led Housing

This programme aims to support the growth of community-led housing. The foundation's website clarifies: 'Community-led housing schemes come in a variety of forms, shapes and sizes. They can build new homes, create homes from empty properties, protect existing decent, affordable homes and provide homes of all types of tenure.'

This programme funds organisations that provide information, support, advice and technical expertise to help community-led housing schemes progress.

Transforming the Private Rented Sector

This programme aims to 'transform the private rented sector so that it provides homes for people in need that are more affordable, secure, accessible and are better quality', as stated on the foundation's website.

This programme supports projects that are working to build an understanding of life in the private rented sector, in particular for people who are vulnerable, disadvantaged or at risk of harm. It also supports a number of tenant's voice projects across the country.

Beneficiaries included: Wales Co-operative Centre (£225,100); Communities Housing Trust (£90,000); Affordable Housing Commission (£63,100); Citizens Advice (£43,800); Tenants Union (£25,300); University of Huddersfield (£10,500); Indigo House (£1,000).

Financial information

Year end	31/03/2021
Assets	£4,230,000
Income	£2,280,000
Grant total	£1,320,000
Organisations supported	28

Exclusions

The foundation will not consider funding for the following:

- The promotion of religion or politics
- Applications which do not comply with the foundation's funding criteria/guidelines.

Applications

As of January 2023, the foundation was not accepting unsolicited applications for funding. See the website for up-to-date information.

Sources of information

Accounts; annual report; Charity Commission record; funder's website.

The NFU Mutual Charitable Trust

 Community development; education; social welfare; research focusing on initiatives that will have a significant impact on rural communities

UK, with a preference for rural areas

£1.10 million (2021)

CC number: 1073064

Trustees: James McLaren; David Brown; Aled Jones; Martin Kennedy; Nicholas Turner; Minette Batters; Dr Harriet Kennedy; Meurig Raymond.

Correspondent: Jim Creechan, Secretary to the Trustees, Tiddington Road, Stratford-upon-Avon, Warwickshire CV37 7BJ (tel: 01789 204211; email: nfu_mutual_charitable_trust@ nfumutual.co.uk)

 www.nfumutual.co.uk/about-us/ charitable-trust

General information

The NFU Mutual Charitable Trust was established in 1998 and is the corporate charity of the National Farmers Union Mutual Insurance Society Ltd (NFU Mutual), one of the UK's leading insurers.

According to its website, the trust makes one-off grants to charities that work in the areas of agriculture, rural development and insurance, particularly those working to:

- Advance the education of the public by means of research and dissemination of information in relation to agriculture
- Advance the education of young people within rural areas
- Relieve poverty within rural areas
- Promote the benefit and social welfare of inhabitants of rural communities by associating together with the inhabitants and local authorities, voluntary and other organisations to advance education and leisure
- Promote research into agriculture associated activities
- Advance the education of the public by means of research and dissemination of information in relation to insurance provided that the charity may also promote, facilitate and support any such other purposes as are exclusively charitable according to the laws of England and Wales

The trustees are particularly interested in initiatives in the areas of education of young people in rural areas and relief of poverty within rural areas.

Grants can range from £1,000 to £150,000; however, the trustees prefer to fund larger projects that will have a significant impact on the rural community.

Non-charitable organisations can also apply, but the funding request needs to be for charitable purposes.

Beneficiaries included: FareShare (£150,000); Farming Community Network, Rural Support and Samaritans (£100,000 each); Royal Scottish Agricultural Benevolent Institution (£80,000); Young Farmers' Clubs of Ulster (£30,000); Farms for City Children and Open Farm Weekend – Northern Ireland (£10,000 each); The Wales Federation of Young Farmers Clubs (£7,000).

Financial information

Year end	31/12/2021
Assets	£285,300
Income	£1,110,000
Grant total	£1,100,000
Organisations supported	31

Further financial information

During the year the trust made grants totalling £1.1 million to 31 organisations. Included in the grant total is £27,000 paid to universities to fund postgraduate bursaries.

Exclusions

The trust does not provide funding for university fees, salaries or overseas appeals. Generally, the trustees will not consider funding initiatives over multiple years.

Applications

Application forms are available from the trust's website and should be sent to the correspondent either via post or email.

The website states that applications should include details of the following:

- The project, initiative or organisation for which funding is sought
- An indication of the amount of the donation requested
- Any business plans
- Details of any other funding sought and or obtained
- Any recognition which would be given to the trust in recognition of its support
- Confirmation of whether or not the applicant is a registered charity

The trustees meet twice a year to consider applications. These meetings are currently held in June and November. Applications should be submitted by the 27th of the previous month.

Sources of information

Accounts; annual report; Charity Commission record; funder's website.

The Norton Rose Fulbright Charitable Foundation

 Education; social welfare; medical; disaster relief; legal projects

Worldwide

£419,300 (2020/21)

CC number: 1102142

Trustees: Patrick Farrell; Ffion Flockhart.

Correspondent: The Trustees, c/o Norton Rose Fullbright, 3 More London Riverside, London SE1 2AQ (tel: 020 7283 6000)

www.nortonrosefulbright.com/ corporate-responsibility

General information

The Norton Rose Fulbright Charitable Foundation was established in 2004 and is funded by Norton Rose Fulbright LLP, an international law firm, and its employees.

The trust's principal activity is to make charitable donations. It supports a wide range of causes, notably medicine, education and social welfare. Many of the charities supported by the trust are nominated by employees of Norton Rose Fulbright. Funding is donated to charities alongside donations raised by the activities Norton Rose Fulbright staff.

Beneficiaries included: Action for Children (£45,000); Child's i Foundation (£25,000); Advocates for International Development (£15,000); Barretstown (£10,000); Beanstalk (£5,000).

Financial information

Year end	30/04/2021
Assets	£21,800
Income	£451,200
Grant total	£419,300

Applications

Apply in writing to the correspondent. Regarding the grant-making policy, the 2020/21 annual report states the following:

In many cases, the charities we support are those we have supported in the past, but new charities are considered at Trustee meetings. The Trustees also meet on an ad hoc basis to consider specific urgent requests such as the support of major disaster relief appeals.

Sources of information

Accounts; annual report; Charity Commission record; funder's website.

Oglesby Charitable Trust

 The arts; the environment; health; social inequalities; health

 Mainly northern England

 £2.24 million (2020/21)

CC number: 1026669

Trustees: Jane Oglesby; Chris Oglesby; Jean Oglesby; Katharine Vokes; Kathryn Graham.

Correspondent: Louise Magill, Trust Manager, Union, Albert Square, Manchester M2 6LW (email: welcome@ oglesbycharitabletrust.org.uk)

 https://oglesbycharitabletrust.org.uk

General information

The Oglesby Charitable Trust was established in 1992 and has been active since the early 2000's. The trust is funded by annual contributions from

Bruntwood Ltd, a company which is part of a group of North West England-based property investment companies owned by the founding trustees.

The trust make grants across four broad areas:

- The arts
- The environment
- Health
- Social inequalities

The trust makes grants ranging from under £1,000 to over £1 million. Grants can be one-off but the majority are multi-year. Funding proposals are considered by invitation only.

Grant holders can also access 'Funding Plus', a range of non-financial resources including access to advice, training, networking, signposting, complimentary meeting room hire and opportunities to advertise volunteer roles and opportunities to Bruntwood staff.

Beneficiaries included: Shared Health UK (£350,000); Blood Cancer UK (£150,000); Care for Social Justice (£50,000); Think Ahead Stoke (£35,000).

Financial information

Year end	30/09/2021
Assets	£11,060,000
Income	£1,510,000
Grant total	£2,240,000
Organisations supported	54

Further financial information

Grants were broken down as follows:

Social and health inequalities	£1.1 million
Environmental improvement	£482,200
Education	£363,700
Artistic development	£220,000
Medical aid and research	£212,500

Only grants over £35,000 were included in the annual accounts.

Applications

The trust's website states:

The Oglesby Charitable Trust is an invitation-only funder. A small team with a focused approach, we want to ensure that we use our resources, and those of others, effectively. This is why we limit the time and energy spent on preparing applications to those most likely to be successful.

We find our grantees through our collective professional and personal networks. Each Trustee has an active role in one or more of our giving areas, and all those involved in decision-making have extensive experience of working with charitable and community organisations across our region.

Sources of information

Accounts; annual report; Charity Commission record; funder's website.

The Ovo Charitable Foundation

 Sustainability; the environment; climate change; children and young people; increasing access to green spaces and opportunities in education, employment and health

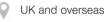 UK and overseas

£799,100 (2021)

CC number: 1155954

Trustees: Gina Cicerone; Katherine Goldsmith; Phillip Kerry; Charlotte Eaton; Oluwakemi Akindele; Thomas Wilson.

Correspondent: The Trustees, 1 Rivergate, Bristol BS1 6ED (tel: 0800 599 9440; email: hello@ovofoundation. org.uk)

www.ovofoundation.org.uk

General information

The foundation is the corporate charity of Ovo Energy, an energy supply company based in Bristol. It was established in 2014 and is funded by customer donations, which are then matched by the company. Ovo also covers the running costs of the foundation.

The foundation's website states that its vision is to 'create a greener, brighter future for every child'.

According to its 2021 annual report, the foundation's long-term outcomes are to:

- Equip disadvantaged children and young people with improved skills, knowledge and confidence to take action on sustainability issues and contribute to building sustainable communities.
- Ensure disadvantaged children and young people live in a sustainable community with increased access to green spaces and opportunities in education, employment and health.

Beneficiaries included: Energy 4 Impact (£202,600); Energy Sparks (£114,200); Action for Conservation (£55,000); The Wildlife Trusts (£48,000); Roundabout Ltd (£35,900); End Youth Homelessness (£20,600); FareShare (£8,300); Doorstep Library (£3,000).

Financial information

Year end	31/12/2021
Assets	£1,770,000
Income	£999,700
Grant total	£799,100
Organisations supported	14+

Applications

At the time of writing (November 2022), the foundation was not accepting new grant applications; however, its website stated that 'this may change soon'. The website also states: 'We're always looking for other organisations and charities to help fight the climate crisis with. If you know a great project, we'd love to hear from you.'

Sources of information
Accounts; annual report; Charity Commission record; funder's website.

Parabola Foundation

🔍 General charitable purposes, with a particular focus on the arts, culture and music

📍 England and Africa

£ £617,000 (2020/21)

CC number: 1156008

Trustees: Deborah Jude; Anne Millican; Peter Millican.

Correspondent: The Trustees, Broadgate Tower, 20 Primrose Street, London EC2A 2EW (tel: 0191 500 8571)

General information
This foundation is the corporate charity of Parabola Land Ltd, a real estate and property development company. Trustee Peter Millican serves as a director of the company. Peter Millican has had a well-publicised involvement in the arts and was responsible for the development of Kings Place, a London concert venue and office space.

Parabola Foundation operates with general charitable purposes, although there is a particular focus on art, music and culture. Grants are made to UK-based organisations and some grants are made to organisations operating in Africa. The annual report 2020/21 states: 'The objectives of the charity are to further charitable and cultural projects that will bring benefit to the public. It has been particularly keen to support music and the arts in a way that benefits the community.'

The foundation gives regular support to a number of charities, such as Kings Place Music Foundation and Ruwenzori Sculpture Foundation. However, the foundation carefully evaluates all applications for funds based on merit.

Beneficiaries included: Kings Place Music Foundation (£565,000); Ruwenzori Sculpture Foundation (£36,000); Edinburgh Leisure; Health In Mind; Grizedale Arts; People Know How; St Columbus Hospice.

Financial information

Year end	31/03/2021
Assets	-£677,900
Income	£863,000
Grant total	£617,000

Further financial information
Grants awarded in support of creative arts totalled £611,000 and other grants totalled £6,000. Only two grant amounts were listed in the accounts.

Applications
Apply in writing to the correspondent.

Sources of information
Accounts; annual report; Charity Commission record; funder's website.

The Performing Right Society Foundation

🔍 Music

📍 UK

£ £1.93 million to organisations (2021)

CC number: 1080837

Trustees: Richard King; Mark Poole; Caroline Norbury; Chris Butler; Susannah Simons; Lorna Clarke; Michelle Escoffery; Christine Geissmar; Nitin Sawhney. Yolanda Brown.

Correspondent: Fiona Harvey, Secretary, 41 Streatham High Road, Streatham, London SW16 1ER (tel: 020 3741 4233; email: info@prsfoundation.com)

 www.prsfoundation.com

 facebook.com/ PRSforMusicFoundation

 @PRSFoundation

 @prsfoundation

General information
The PRS Foundation is an independent charitable foundation established in 2000 by the UK's largest collection society, PRS for Music Ltd, from which it receives an annual donation of around £3 million.

The foundation is currently the UK's largest independent funder of new music of any genre. The principal objectives of the foundation are to support, sustain and further the creation and performance of new music and to educate the public in order to augment its appreciation in the UK. The foundation awards grants and works in strategic partnerships with like-minded organisations.

Grants programmes
The foundation awards grants under a variety of themes, which are listed on its website. Of these, four are available for charities and not-for-profit organisations:

The Open Fund
This fund supports new music projects across all genres led by promoters, talent development organisations, venues, curators and large performance groups (which includes orchestras, choirs, jazz bands or folk groups with 12 or more

performers). Projects must involve the creation, performance and promotion of new music and enable songwriters, composers, solo artists, bands and performers of all backgrounds to develop creatively and professionally. Grants of up to £10,000 are available and can be provided to support the creation, performance, touring, recording, marketing and commissioning of new music by UK-based creators, community projects, residencies, and live programmes. This fund prioritises not-for-profit organisations and tends not to support organisations limited by shares.

Beyond Borders
Grants of up to £15,000 are available to organisations working with partners based in the UK or Ireland that want to co-commission or tour new music across the UK. Funding is available for projects that include new commissions, recordings and repeat performances of music written in the past five years. Support is given to around eight to ten projects per year.

Resonate
Grants of up to £10,000 are available to orchestras who commit to exploring contemporary UK repertoire as part of a season/tour and longer-term audience development programmes. The programme supports projects that benefit audiences, composers and players in the UK and overseas.

New Music Biennial
Grants are available to organisations which are developing local and regional audiences for new music. The aim of the programme is to reach new audiences for contemporary music and encourage ideas for short works no longer than 15 minutes' duration which could be performed in a range of settings.

Full details of the foundation's grant schemes including grant-making priorities and application forms are available on the website.

Beneficiaries included: A list of beneficiaries was not available. Previous beneficiaries include: Apples and Snakes; Chamber Music Scotland; Dante or Die Theatre; Horniman Museum and Gardens; Kings Place Music Foundation; National Youth Orchestra of Great Britain; Presteigne Festival; The Belfast Ensemble; The Old Vic Theatre Trust 2000.

Financial information

Year end	31/12/2021
Assets	£1,220,000
Income	£4,180,000
Grant total	£1,930,000
Organisations supported	222

Exclusions
See the relevant funding programme on the website for exclusion criteria.

Applications
Apply via the foundation's website, where full guidelines for each programme are available. Deadlines for applications vary from programme to programme.

Note: organisations can only apply to the Open Fund once per calendar year.

Sources of information
Accounts; annual report; Charity Commission record; funder's website.

The Persimmon Charitable Foundation

 General charitable purposes, including: community and economic development; the environment; education; young people; sport; the arts and culture; health; social welfare

Areas of company presence in England, Scotland and Wales

£1.81 million (2021)

CC number: 1163608

Trustees: Roger Devlin; Joanna Place; Dean Finch; Anthony Vigor; Tracy Davison.

Correspondent: The Trustees, Persimmon plc, Persimmon House, Fulford, York, North Yorkshire YO19 4FE (tel: 01904 642199; email: contact@persimmonhomes.com)

 www.persimmonhomes.com/charity

General information
Established in 2015, this foundation is the corporate charity of Persimmon plc, a large housebuilding company. The foundation receives its income from independent financial advisers (IFAs) and the Persimmon group. The IFAs that make donations are those companies or firms who give advice on mortgage products to customers of the group.

Funding
The foundation makes grants to charities, particularly small local charities, and community groups to promote urban regeneration in areas of economic and social deprivation. The trustees' aim is to improve local communities in the UK by improving health, relieving poverty, advancing amateur sport, improving the local environment and supporting the arts and culture.

There are two programmes: the Community Champions campaign, which supports grassroots groups and charities, and the Building Futures campaign, which supports children's health, sport, education and the arts. The Persimmon Group matches donations made by the foundation under the Community Champions campaign.

Community Champions
Every month the company makes 60 donations of up to £1,000 each to local groups and charities.

Building Futures
Launched in 2019, in partnership with the British Olympic Association, the £1 million scheme supports projects for young people under 18 across three categories: education and the arts, sport and health. In each of the three categories, awards of £100,000, £50,000 and £20,000 are made. There are also smaller awards of £5,000 available to shortlisted projects.

Eligibility
The foundation will support a range of organisations, including charities, sports groups, Scouts and Brownies, hospices, foodbanks, theatres and art projects.

Beneficiaries included: Change of Scene, The Children's Hospital Charity and Wotton Community Sports Foundation (£100,000 each); Great Melton Cricket Club, Senses Well-being Centre CIC and Warren Association Trust (£50,000 each); Islastones Foundation, Newcastle Powerchair Football Club and Sandwell Young Carers (£20,000 each).

Financial information

Year end	31/12/2021
Assets	-£177,500
Income	£1,550,000
Grant total	£1,810,000

Further financial information
Beneficiaries of Building Futures and Community Champion funding in 2021 can be found on the foundation's website.

Applications
Community Champions
Applications can be made via the company's website, as well as details of what to include.

The trustees prefer to support local charities. Go to www.persimmonhomes.com/contact to find your nearest Persimmon office.

Building Futures
Details of how to apply can be found on Persimmon plc's website.

Sources of information
Accounts; annual report; Charity Commission record; funder's website.

Personal Assurance Charitable Trust

General charitable purposes; social welfare; health

There are no geographical restrictions

£116,700 (2021)

CC number: 1023274

Trustees: Sarah Mace; Justine Woolf; Julie Stayte.

Correspondent: The Trustees, c/o Personal Group Holdings plc, John Ormond House, 899 Silbury Boulevard, Milton Keynes, Buckinghamshire MK9 3XL (tel: 01908 605000; email: hayley.wheatley@personalgroup.com)

General information
The Personal Assurance Charitable Trust (PACT) was registered with the Charity Commission in 1993. It is the corporate charity of Personal Group Holdings plc, a financial services company.

According to its Charity Commission record:

> The object of the charity is to make donations to registered charities and non-charitable bodies from funds supplied by Personal Assurance Plc. There are no restrictions on the type of donations that can be made although preference will be given to recommendations made by policyholders of Personal Assurance Plc and employees of Personal Group Holdings Plc.

Beneficiaries included: Memusi Foundation (£66,400); Winter Night Shelter Milton Keynes (£17,700); Milton Keynes Community Foundation (£10,000); Willen Hospice (£3,300); Children in Need (£3,000); Victory Outreach (£2,100); St Luke's Hospice (£1,100); Wolverhampton Wanderers Foundation (£1,000).

Financial information

Year end	31/12/2021
Assets	£146,100
Income	£169,900
Grant total	£116,700

Further financial information
Only organisations that received grants of over £1,000 were listed as beneficiaries in the trust's accounts. Grants of under £1,000 totalled £12,100.

Exclusions
Grants are rarely made to individuals.

Applications
The trust makes grants to charities recommended by staff and policyholders. The trust's 2021 accounts state:

> In view of the limited sources of income available the trustees have restricted donations to other charities and charitable organisations recommended by policyholders of Personal Assurance plc,

their employers and employees of Personal Group Holdings plc and its subsidiary undertakings.

Sources of information

Accounts; annual report; Charity Commission record.

Petplan Charitable Trust

 The promotion and improvement of the welfare of animals (dogs, cats, horses or rabbits) and the relief of their suffering; veterinary research and education

UK and overseas

£1.14 million (2020)

CC number: 1032907

Trustees: David Simpson; Isabella Von Mesterhazy; Irene Pinto dos Santos; Alan Farkas; Prof. The Lord Trees; Jamie Critall; Kathryn Willis; Ted Chandler; Clarissa Baldwin; John Bower.

Correspondent: Catherine Bourg, Trust Administrator, Great West House (GW2), Great West Road, Brentford, Middlesex TW8 9EG (email: info@ petplancharitabletrust.org.uk)

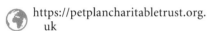 https://petplancharitabletrust.org.uk

 facebook.com/ PetplanCharitableTrust

 @petplan_charitable_trust

General information

The trust was established in 1994 by pet insurance company Petplan Ltd, a subsidiary company of Allianz Insurance plc., to provide funds to promote the health and welfare of dogs, cats, horses and rabbits. Petplan gives its policy holders the option of making a small annual donation to the trust, which they are able to increase from the suggested £2 per year if they wish.

The trust has two active grant rounds each year:

Scientific grants

The trust awards two types of scientific grants:

▹ Full grants for in-depth research, tenable for up to three years
▹ Pump priming/pilot grants of up to £10,000 to fund initial research over a period of no more than one year

Welfare grants

According to the trust's Terms and Conditions document, applicants must have registered charity status and must demonstrate a direct benefit species supported by Petplan (i.e. dogs, cats horses or rabbits). Grants to human charities may be considered when it can

be clearly demonstrated that the grant will enhance/give support to the animals' best interest.

Welfare grants can include items such as neutering, kennelling and veterinary costs and animal housing and repairs, but not general overheads. Requests for funding for education in animal welfare will also be considered.

Check the website for up-to-date guidance.

Beneficiaries included: ADCH Emergency Fund (£150,000); Lead Up International (£111,500); Birmingham Dogs Home (£25,000); Dogs Trust (£19,000); Our Special Friends (£5,000); Rain Rescue (£500).

Financial information

Year end	31/12/2020
Assets	-£95,300
Income	£986,900
Grant total	£1,140,000

Further financial information

Grants were broken down as follows: scientific grants (£601,300); special grants (£288,500); welfare and educational grants (£248,800).

Applications

Application forms, eligibility criteria, full terms and conditions and the dates for application rounds for each grants programme are available via the trust's website.

Sources of information

Accounts; annual report; Charity Commission record; funder's website; guidelines for applicants.

The Pets at Home Foundation

Animal welfare

UK

£2.98 million (2021/22)

CC number: 1104152

Trustees: Louise Stonier; George Lingwood; Jill Shields; Dan Laurence; Adrian Bates; Andrew Bickerton; Claire Gavin; Dr Catriona Curtis.

Correspondent: The Charity Team, c/o Pets at Home, Chester House, Epsom Avenue, Stanley Green Trading Estate, Handforth, Cheshire SK9 3DF (tel: 0161 486 6688; email: info@ petsathomefoundation.co.uk)

 www.petsathomefoundation.co.uk

 facebook.com/ PetsAtHomeFoundation

 @PetsAtHomeFDTN

 @petsathomefdtn

General information

The Pets at Home Foundation (formerly known as Support Adoption for Pets) was established in 2006 by Pets at Home, a pet supplies retailer.

Rescue Centres

According to the foundation's website, it provides funding to organisations whose main activity is the rescue and rehoming of UK pets.

Grants range from £250 upwards and can be used to fund the following:
▹ Vet bills
▹ Boarding fees
▹ Trap and neuter schemes for feral or stray cats
▹ Food
▹ Equipment
▹ Vehicles
▹ Building work

Helping People Through Pets

The foundation will also support organisations providing temporary or ongoing assistance to ensure pets can remain with their owners, or organisations changing the lives of children and adults through the provision of animal-based activities and practical assistance. These grants typically range from £250 to £50,000 and can be used to fund:
▹ Building work
▹ Vehicles
▹ Equipment
▹ Vet bills
▹ Salaries
▹ New initiatives directly involving pets and people

For full eligibility criteria, see the foundation's guidelines on its website.

Charity of the Year

The foundation also runs a Charity of the Year scheme, supporting rescue centres that are local to Pets at Home stores. Rescue centres interested in learning more about the scheme are encouraged to contact the foundation.

Beneficiaries included: Birmingham Dogs Home (£242,700); RSPCA (£193,100); Canine Partners (55,700); Support Dogs (£51,900); Dogs for Autism (£41,600); HorseWorld Trust (£37,200); Dog Assistance in Disability (£30,000); Appledown Rescue and Rehoming Kennels (£27,300); Seeing Dogs Alliance (£20,000); London Inner City Kittens (£10,000)

Financial information

Year end	25/03/2022
Assets	£4,390,000
Income	£5,690,000
Grant total	£2,980,000

Exclusions

The foundation will not fund:

- Salaries, uniforms or expenses
- The cost of leasing a vehicle, road tax, insurance or petrol costs
- The purchase of land or buildings
- Any costs associated with a charity shop
- Fundraising costs such as marketing materials

Applications

Prospective applicants should first check the grant criteria to confirm their eligibility and then complete the online request for an application form. The foundation's website notes that a virtual or in person visit may be requested. There are no deadlines for Rescue Centre grants. Applications for Helping People Through Pets grants are considered three times a year – contact the foundation for information on timescales.

Sources of information

Accounts; annual report; Charity Commission record; funder's website; guidelines for applicants.

The DLA Piper Charitable Trust

 Health and social welfare

UK

£33,600 (2020/21)

CC number: 327280

Trustees: Sean Mahon; Sandra Wallace; Liam Cowell; Amanda Pilkington.

Correspondent: Sue Greaves, c/o Wrigleys Solicitors LLP, Derwent House, 150 Arundel Gate, Sheffield, South Yorkshire S1 2FN (tel: 0114 267 5596; email: sue.greaves@wrigleys.co.uk)

General information

The DLA Piper Charitable Trust is the corporate charity of the law firm DLA Piper.

Its 2020/21 accounts state that its grants policy aims to support registered charities through grants which:

- Stimulate and support the charity fundraising efforts of members and employees of DLA Piper UK LLP
- Support, for example, a charity project selected by a DLA Piper office for fundraising activities throughout a financial or calendar year; and
- Give significant support to a charity or charities offering service to particular communities or needy groups (for example, by reason of ill health or other disadvantage).

The trust was registered with general charitable purposes; however, it appears to give in two main areas: medical research and social welfare. Grants are usually of less than £1,000, although larger grants can be made.

Beneficiaries included: Leeds Cares (£5,000); The UK Sepsis Trust (£3,500); Morley and District Lions Club (£2,500); Action for Children (£2,000); Whitechapel Mission (£1,500).

Financial information

Year end	05/04/2021
Assets	£141,600
Income	£104,100
Grant total	£33,600
Organisations supported	21

Exclusions

Individuals.

Applications

Apply in writing to the correspondent. The trustees meet four times a year to discuss applications. Applications from members, partners and employees of DLA Piper for grants in support of charities are encouraged.

Sources of information

Accounts; annual report; Charity Commission record.

The Pret Foundation

 Homelessness; social welfare; food poverty; education, training and employment

 UK, in communities local to Pret shops

£190,700 (2020)

CC number: 1050195

Trustees: Clive Schlee; Andrea Wareham; Valerie Cuminet; Pano Christou; Dilys Winterkorn; Dulcie McDermott.

Correspondent: The Trustees, 10 Bressenden Place, London SW1E 5DH (tel: 07584 213354; email: pret.foundationuk@pret.com)

 www.pret.co.uk/en-GB/the-pret-foundation

 @PretFoundation

 @thepretfoundation

General information

The Pret Foundation, formerly known as Pret Foundation Trust, was founded in 1995 and its aim is the alleviation of poverty, hunger and homelessness. It does this in four main ways:

- Delivering surplus foods from its shops to hostels and charities supporting people experiencing homelessness

- Making grants of cash, food and equipment to small grassroots homelessness charities
- Supporting smaller charities working with people who are experiencing homelessness and poverty
- Running the Rising Stars Initiative, which helps vulnerable people off the streets and into work, and the Shooting Stars Initiative, which offers Rising Stars graduates a seven-month career development programme
- In partnership with West London Mission, the foundation also established 'The Pret House at St Luke's', a shelter in Kennington with 26 rooms, of which the foundation has access to at least 6. The house is available to current or graduated Rising and Shooting Stars who work in Pret shops nearby

Beneficiaries included: Genesis Trust, InHope, Off the Fence Trust, Shelter from the Storm and The 999 Club (£10,000 each); Salford Loaves and Fishes (£7,700); Bethany Christian Trust (£7,000); Cardboard Citizens (£5,000).

Financial information

Year end	31/12/2020
Assets	£2,020,000
Income	£2,800,000
Grant total	£190,700
Organisations supported	25

Further financial information

The 2020 accounts were the latest available at the time of writing (November 2022). Only organisations that received grants of over £5,000 were listed as beneficiaries in the charity's accounts. Grants were awarded to 25 organisations during the year. Grants of under £5,000 totalled £7,500 and were awarded to four organisations. In addition to grants, food donations totalled £3,800 and equipment donations totalled £10,700.

Applications

Apply in writing to the correspondent.

Sources of information

Accounts; annual report; Charity Commission record; funder's website.

The PwC Foundation

 Social inclusion through employability and education; mental health and healthcare; general charitable purposes

UK

£1.57 million (2020/21)

CC number: 1144124

Trustees: Kevin Ellis; David Adair; Zelf Hussain; Kalee Talvitie-Brown; David Walters; Emma Cox.

Correspondent: Community Engagement Team, PricewaterhouseCoopers, 1 Embankment Place, London WC2N 6RH (tel: 07764 902846; email: uk_pwcfoundation@pwc.com)

 www.pwc.co.uk/corporate-sustainability/the-pwc-foundation.jhtml

General information
The PwC Foundation was established in 2011 and is the corporate charity of PricewaterhouseCoopers LLP (PwC).

The objectives of the foundation are to promote sustainable development and social inclusion and environmental awareness for public benefit. Grants are made under the following themes:

- Social inclusion through employability
- Social inclusion through education
- Healthcare
- Environmental and other general charitable purposes

The foundation is also the company's vehicle for providing matched funding whereby the foundation matches employees' fundraising to a maximum of £250 per person, per year.

Grants can be made to registered charities, CICs and social enterprises.

Beneficiaries included: Wellbeing of Women (£136,400); School for Social Entrepreneurs (£104,500); Samaritans (£97,000); The World's Big Sleep Out Trust (£54,000); Teach First (£36,000); National Literacy Trust (£14,900); Mind (£6,200); Barnardo's Northern Ireland (£40).

Financial information
Year end	30/06/2021
Assets	£3,550,000
Income	£4,311,000
Grant total	£1,570,000

Further financial information
Grants were broken down as follows:

Social mobility	187	£747,000
Healthcare	228	£409,000
Other charitable activities	97	£245,000
Education	9	£59,000

Exclusions
The foundation will not fund political organisations, lobbying groups, animal rights groups or religious bodies.

Applications
The foundation's 2021 accounts state:

There is no current requirement for a formal open grant application process. The Steering Committee and trustees can independently identify recipients for funding who meet the charitable objectives of the Foundation. Recipients are approved by the trustees.

Sources of information
Accounts; annual report; Charity Commission record; funder's website.

The Quilter Foundation

 Young people: young carers; education; employment; health and well-being

UK and the Isle of Man

£458,200 (2021)

CC number: 1175555

Trustees: Steven Levin; Stephen Gazard; Tosin James-Odukoya; Richard Breen; Timothy Childe; Philippa Foster Back.

Correspondent: The Trustees, c/o Quilter plc, Senator House, 85 Queen Victoria Street, London EC4V 4AB (tel: 020 7778 9614; email: responsiblebusiness@quilter.com)

 www.quilter.com/responsible-business/the-quilter-foundation

General information
The foundation was established in 2018 by Quilter plc, a wealth management company. It provides funding to selected charity partners that support young people in three areas: financial education and empowerment; sustainable employment; raising awareness of young carers and supporting their health and well-being.

Beneficiaries included: Carers Trust (£211,000); Disasters Emergency Committee (£96,000); Local Community (£50,000); Safe New Futures (£26,000); School of Hard Knocks (£25,000); Street League (£24,000); Kickstart Money (£20,000).

Financial information
Year end	31/12/2021
Assets	£9,750,800
Income	£521,900
Grant total	£458,200
Organisations supported	8

Further financial information
During the year grants made in support of young carers totalled £340,000 and grants made in support of employment totalled £11,000. In addition, a grant of £96,000 was awarded to the Disasters Emergency Committee.

Exclusions
The foundation does not provide funding to political, religious or profit-making organisations.

Applications
The foundation makes grants to selected charity partners. Contact the correspondent for further information.

Sources of information
Annual report and accounts; Charity Commission record; Quilter plc's Responsible Business Report 2020.

The Rathbones Group Foundation

Disadvantaged young people

Areas where the company has an office

£205,200 (2021)

CC number: 1150432

Trustees: Geoffrey Powell; Paul Stockton; Rathbone Trust Company Ltd; Richard Lanyon; Stuart Furzer.

Correspondent: Sophie Boyd-Willis, Head of Communications, Rathbone Bros plc, 8 Finsbury Circus, London EC2M 7AZ (tel: 020 7399 0000; email: rathbonefoundation@rathbones.com)

General information
This foundation was established in November 2012 and is the associated charitable foundation of Rathbone Brothers plc, one of the UK's leading providers of investment management services for private clients, charities and professional advisers. Until January 2022, it was known as The Rathbone Brothers Foundation.

Grants programme
The main objective of the foundation is to help disadvantaged young people in the areas the company has a presence. The following offices receive money from the foundation to be distributed to local charities:

- Aberdeen
- Birmingham
- Bristol
- Cambridge
- Chichester
- Edinburgh
- Exeter
- Glasgow
- Jersey
- Kendal
- Liverpool
- London
- Lymington
- Newcastle
- Winchester

Beneficiaries included: Paul Lavelle Foundation (£14,300); Envision – Birmingham (£10,000); Their Voice – London (£6,000); Teenage Cancer Trust (£5,000); Sussex Snowdrop Trust (£4,000); Winchester Young Carers (£2,000); Brathay Trust – Cumbria (£1,500); We Can Dance – Exeter (£200).

Financial information

Year end	31/12/2021
Assets	£1,430,000
Income	£325,200
Grant total	£205,200
Organisations supported	38

Applications

Apply in writing to your local Rathbones office or directly to the trustees.

Sources of information

Accounts; annual report; Charity Commission record; funder's website.

RSM UK Foundation

 The environment; citizenship and community development; the advancement of education and relief of poverty in the context of access to employment

 UK and overseas

(£) £536,300 (2020/21)

CC number: 1179349

Trustees: David Gwilliam; Nicholas Sladden; Kelly Adams; John Taylor; Joy Welch; Catherine Riches.

Correspondent: The Trustees, 6th Floor, 25 Farringdon Street, London EC4A 4AB (tel: 020 3201 8313; email: info@rsmukfoundation.com)

 www.rsmukfoundation.com

General information

The foundation was registered with the Charity Commission in July 2018 and is the corporate charity of RSM UK, a global provider of audit, tax and consulting services. The foundation supports four core charities (The Duke of Edinburgh's Award, Anthony Nolan Trust, Trees for Cities, and Leadership through Sport and Business) but also makes grants to other organisations in accordance to the trustees' current funding priorities, which are:

- Environmental protection or improvement
- Advancement of citizenship or community development
- Advancement of education and relief of poverty in the context of access to employment

Beneficiaries included: Anthony Nolan (£222,000); The Duke of Edinburgh's Award (£200,000); Great Western Air Ambulance (£40,000); Leadership Through Sport and Business (£20,000); Trees for Cities (£15,000).

Financial information

Year end	31/03/2021
Assets	£407,700
Income	£774,800
Grant total	£536,300
Organisations supported	56

Further financial information

Grants were awarded to 56 organisations during the financial period.

Exclusions

Grants are not normally made to individuals, nor for projects in countries in which another RSM Group corporate foundation is based.

Applications

Apply by email to the correspondent. Applications must be received by the trustees between January and March for a decision in April, or between July and September for a decision in October.

Sources of information

Accounts; annual report; Charity Commission record.

The Rugby Group Benevolent Fund Ltd

 Community projects

Barrington (Cambridgeshire), Chinnor (Oxfordshire), Kensworth (Bedfordshire), Lewes (Sussex), Rochester (Kent), Rugby and Southam (Warwickshire), South Ferriby (North Lincolnshire) and Tilbury (Essex)

(£) £162,600 to organisations (2021)

CC number: 265669

Trustees: Nigel Appleyard; Graeme Fuller; Norman Jones; Ian Southcott; Geoff Thomas; John Brooks; David Holton; Kevin Murch.

Correspondent: The Trustees, Cemex UK, Cemex House, Evreux Way, Rugby, Warwickshire CV21 2DT (tel: 01788 517000; email: info@rugbygroupbenevolentfund.org.uk)

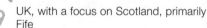 www.rugbygroupbenevolentfund.org.uk

General information

This fund was originally established in 1955 to support employees and former employees of Rugby Cement Group Ltd, and their dependants. Today, the Rugby Group is part of CEMEX UK; however, the fund remains independent. The fund has retained its original objectives but has widened its scope to support other charitable causes within the same area of benefit.

Eligibility

The fund provides support for projects in communities where former Rugby Cement plants were once located. These include:

- Barrington, Cambridgeshire
- Chinnor, Oxfordshire
- Kensworth, Bedfordshire
- Lewes, Sussex
- Rochester, Kent
- Rugby, Warwickshire
- Southam, Warwickshire
- South Ferriby, North Lincolnshire
- Tilbury, Essex

Prospective projects must be able to demonstrate benefits to the community as a whole, including past employees of the Rugby Group and their families.

Eligible organisations do not have to be registered charities but must have charitable objectives.

Grants are made towards project-related capital costs.

Beneficiaries included: Friends of St Cross (£20,000); Parenting Project – Rugby (£10,000); Friends of Barrington School (£7,000); Rugby Theatre (£5,000); Winterton Bowls Club (£4,000); Muscular Dystrophy Support Centre (£3,000); Southam Albion FC (£2,000); Woodland Singers (£1,000).

Financial information

Year end	31/12/2021
Assets	£1,100,000
Income	£36,700
Grant total	£162,600
Organisations supported	42

Further financial information

Only organisations that received grants of over £1,000 were listed as beneficiaries in the charity's accounts. Grants of under £1,000 totalled £3,600 and were awarded to eight organisations.

Exclusions

The fund does not normally provide funding to meet day-to-day revenue costs.

Applications

Potential applicants must first complete an expression of interest form, available to download from the fund's website. Applicants must be able to demonstrate that the project has been properly costed and that any other support funding is in place or in prospect. Evidence of self-help is important. The trustees meet several times a year to consider applications, meaning that applications are considered on a rolling basis.

Sources of information

Accounts; annual report; Charity Commission record; funder's website.

Russell Trust

 General charitable purposes

 UK, with a focus on Scotland, primarily Fife

(£) £171,300 (2020/21)

OSCR number: SC004424

Correspondent: The Secretary, 2.19, 2nd, Block B, 1 Summerhall, Edinburgh EH9 1PL

General information

The Russell Trust was established in 1985. It is endowed by shares in Tullis Russell Group Ltd, an environmentally responsible coatings company specialising in silicone, adhesive coatings and lamination.

The trust supports a range of charitable causes and organisations in Fife, Scotland. According to its 2020/21 annual report, the trust prioritises projects which are 'new and require initial rather than continuing support'.

Beneficiaries included: The Adam Smith Foundation (£15,000); University of St Andrews (£10,000); Demelza Hospice Care for Children (£6,300); The Phaeo and Para Cancer Charity (£6,000); Iona Village Hall (£5,000); Edinburgh Art Festival, Guide Dogs for the Blind Association and Young Enterprise Scotland (£2,000 each).

Financial information

Year end	05/04/2021
Assets	£6,120,000
Income	£296,800
Grant total	£171,300

Further financial information

Only organisations that received grants of over £2,000 were listed as beneficiaries in the trust's accounts. Grants of under £2,000 totalled £46,500.

Applications

Apply in writing to the correspondent.

Sources of information

Accounts; annual report; OSCR record.

The RWS Foundation

 Sustainable community and economic development; overseas aid; social welfare; education and training

 Worldwide

£ £110,000 (2021)

CC number: 1127138

Trustees: Dorte Schou; James McHugh; Kathleen Matthews; David Shrimpton; Maria Schnell.

Correspondent: The Trustees, Europa House, Chiltern Park, Chalfont St Peter SL9 9FG (tel: 01753 480200; email: connect@rws.com)

 www.rws.com/about/corporate-sustainability/social/community

General information

This foundation was established in 2008 as the corporate charity of SDL plc. In 2020, SDL plc was bought by RWS plc and the name of the foundation was changed along with it. The group provides filing and search services, technical and commercial translation and localization, and develops and supports translation productivity and management software. The global nature of the group's business is reflected in the activities and aspirations of the foundation.

The objectives of The RWS Foundation are to promote sustainable development in order to relieve poverty and improve the lives of disadvantaged communities, and to promote sustainable means of achieving economic growth and regeneration.

The foundation encourages RWS plc employees to identify charities and causes that are involved in structural and sustainable projects which improve the lives of disadvantaged people through education, improved living conditions, and income generation projects. Partners receive financial support and participation from employees, and they are often supported over a number of years.

Beneficiaries included: A list of beneficiaries was not available. Previous beneficiaries include: Street Business School (£38,900); Brighter Children (£25,600); Food for the Hungry UK (£20,100); Sportable (£12,900); St Wilfrids (£10,000); Akshaya Patra Foundation (£5,000); Big Brothers Big Sisters of New York City (£1,600); Losev (£840); Sandblast (£500).

Financial information

Year end	31/12/2021
Income	£1,100
Grant total	£110,000

Further financial information

Full accounts were not available to view on the Charity Commission website due to the foundation's low income. We have therefore estimated the foundation's grant total based on its total expenditure.

Exclusions

The foundation does not support political or religious causes. The projects it funds tend to be small but with lasting impact.

Applications

Only causes supported and sponsored by RWS employees will be considered by the RWS Foundation. Contact the foundation by email for further information on how to request the support of staff and application procedures.

Sources of information

Accounts; annual report; Charity Commission record; funder's website.

The Samworth Foundation

 Causes addressing the root causes of sexual exploitation and climate change/environmental issues

Worldwide. In the UK, there is a preference for the East Midlands

£ £5.1 million (2021/22)

CC number: 265647

Trustees: Belinda Gordon; Sarah-Jane Keer; Prof. Neil Gorman; Dr Daniela Lloyd-Williams; Susan Ralphs; Mark Samworth.

Correspondent: The Trustees, Chetwode House, 1 Samworth Way, Melton Mowbray, Leicestershire LE13 1GA (tel: 01664 414500; email: admin@samworthfoundation.org.uk)

https://samworthfoundation.org.uk

General information

The Samworth Foundation, formerly known as the Samworth Cadell Trust, was established in 1973. The foundation has grown over the years with annual donations from Samworth Brothers Ltd and the Samworth family.

Grants are made in the UK and abroad to organisations that address the environment/climate change and sexual exploitation. The foundation supports organisations tackling the root causes of these issues. In the UK, preference is given to work based in the East Midlands.

The foundation offers multi-year grants for core costs and projects. Its website states: 'We look to invest in organisations and their people rather than just the specific projects they deliver.'

Occasionally, the foundation operates specific special-interest grants programmes. More information on the foundation's grant-making strategy can be found on its website.

Beneficiaries included: Uppingham School (£500,000); Climate Outreach and Information Network (£244,400); University of Bedfordshire (£138,300); New Futures Project (£100,000); Tearfund (£90,000); WWF-UK (£70,000); Green New Deal UK Ltd (£50,000); Climate Alliance CIC (£30,000); Médecins Sans Frontières (£25,000); Climate Emergence (£1,000).

Financial information

Year end	05/04/2022
Assets	£70,910,000
Income	£516,100
Grant total	£5,110,000
Organisations supported	142

Further financial information

Grants were made in five categories:

Core grants	41	£2.57 million
Transformation and Innovation Fund	19	£2.18 million
Family and exceptional donations	71	£869,800
Humanitarian crisis response grants	3	£250,000
COVID-19 emergency response grants	8	£222,300

Applications

The foundation does not accept unsolicited applications. Causes are researched and identified by the trustees and organisations that meet the foundation's criteria are invited to apply.

Sources of information

Accounts; annual report; Charity Commission record; funder's website.

Santander UK Foundation Ltd

 Financial and digital empowerment

 UK, Guernsey and Jersey, and the Isle of Man

£2.12 million (2021)

CC number: 803655

Trustees: Sue Willis; Christopher Fallis; John Collins; Danny Jones; Judith Moran; Christopher Anderson.

Correspondent: The Trustees, Santander UK plc, Santander House, 201 Grafton Gate East, Milton Keynes, Buckinghamshire MK9 1AN (email: grants@santander.co.uk)

 www.santanderfoundation.org.uk

General information

The Santander Foundation was established by Santander bank and supports disadvantaged people throughout the UK.

The foundation's Financial and Digital Empowerment Fund aims to help disadvantaged people become more digitally and financially empowered. The foundation's website states:

There are millions of people in our society that are already at a disadvantage – through age, education, income, disability, or unemployment. Without the right support for them, the social inequality gap will only widen.

Many charitable and community interest organisations work with such groups; with people that feel the impacts of financial or digital exclusion the most.

We want to reach lone parents, single pensioners, migrants and refugees, those with long term illnesses and disabilities, those struggling to find sustained employment and households headed by students or part-time workers. These are among the groups most commonly excluded from financial services.

People with low or unstable incomes, or those who have experienced a significant life shock, are particularly affected by financial exclusion. The pandemic will only have made this situation worse, as more and more basic services have moved to the web. We want to help charities build their capacity to help people to become digitally and financially empowered.

Beneficiaries included: Code Your Future, Create Arts and Social Action for Health (£100,000 each); Share Community Ltd and Willowacre Trust (£75,000 each); Key Unlocking Futures (£40,000).

Financial information

Year end	31/12/2021
Assets	£21,800,000
Income	£3,680,000
Grant total	£2,120,000
Organisations supported	383

Further financial information

Grants were broken down as follows:

Santander Digital and Financial Empowerment Fund	21	£1.67 million
Social inclusion	227	£366,000
Health	129	£83,200
Other	6	£760

Only grants of over £10,000 were listed in the accounts. Grants awarded with amounts totalling to less than £10,000 totalled £300,100.

Applications

Visit the foundation's website for up-to-date information regarding open grants programmes.

Sources of information

Accounts; annual report; Charity Commission record; funder's website.

The Scott Bader Commonwealth Ltd

 Social welfare; people who are disadvantaged; children and young people; disability; education

UK and areas near to where companies in the Scott Bader Group are located

£331,000 (2021)

CC number: 206391

Trustees: Robert Gibson; Richard Tapp; Andrew Bell; David Black; Jessica Clark; Paul Smith; Agne Bentsson; Hansi Mannng; David Harris.

Correspondent: The Trustees, Scott Bader Commonwealth Ltd, PO Box 36, Wollaston, Wellingborough, Northamptonshire NN29 7RL (tel: 01933 663 100 or 01933 666 755; email: use the contact form on the website)

www.scottbader.com/humanity/our-society/how-to-access-funds

General information

The Scott Bader Commonwealth Ltd was established in 1967. It is a registered charity and a company limited by guarantee, which owns the share capital of the global chemical company, Scott Bader Company Ltd and receives a minimum of 5% of Scott Bader's operating profit each year.

The charity is a membership organisation and everyone employed by The Scott Bader Commonwealth Ltd or any of its subsidiaries may become a member of the charity.

Grants programmes

The charity's grants programmes are structured as follows:

Global Strategy Fund – Each site receives an allocation based on the number of colleagues at the site, enabling them to support local projects that address social and environmental issues.

Commonwealth Community Hardship Fund – Any site can apply for a grant of £500 to £10,000 (or the equivalent) to address local financial distress from COVID-19.

Honorary Life President's Fund – A £7,500 fund that is awarded to charities chosen by Godric Bader, who is the son of the company's founder.

Eligibility

The charity's website states:

▶ We will only consider applications for funding of projects overseas from Charities that are registered in the UK or from charities who are already known to us.

▶ We will only consider applications for funding from Charities who have been operational for over two years.

▶ We recommend that first time applicants only apply for between £2,000 and £4,000.

▶ Our preference is that if you have recently received a grant from us, you do not reapply for two years.

Beneficiaries included: Ace Africa (£10,000); Busy Bees Pre School (£5,000); Action for Asperger's (£4,500); London Hearts (£3,000); Living Without Abuse (£2,900); Autism East Midlands (£2,000); Compassionate Friends (£750); Fondation René Verrier (£250).

Financial information

Year end	31/12/2021
Assets	£2,030,000
Income	£589,000
Grant total	£331,000

Exclusions

The fund does not support animal charities; individual sponsorships; travel or adventure schemes; art projects; any form of advertising; medical research and equipment; general charitable appeals; or construction/renovation/maintenance of buildings in the UK.

Applications

Details of how to apply and upcoming deadlines can be found on the company's website. When the application window is open, applications can be made online.

Sources of information

Accounts; annual report; Charity Commission record; funder's website.

ScottishPower Foundation

 General charitable purposes, including: education; the environment; the arts, heritage and culture; science; social welfare; citizenship and community development

UK

£1.57 million (2021)

OSCR number: SC043862

Trustees: Mike Thornton; Melanie Hill; Sarah Mistry; Keith Anderson; Anita Longley; The Revd Stuart MacQuarrie; Louise Smith.

Correspondent: Rebecca Fairley, Secretary, 320 St Vincent Street, Glasgow G2 5AD (email: scottishpowerfoundation@scottishpower.com)

 www.scottishpower.com/pages/the_scottishpower_foundation.aspx

General information

This foundation was established in 2013. It is the corporate charity of ScottishPower, the UK-wide gas and electricity supplier based in Glasgow.

According to its website, the foundation awards funding to registered charities for the following causes:

- The advancement of education
- The advancement of environmental protection
- The advancement of the arts, heritage, culture or science
- The prevention or the relief of poverty and the relief of those in need by reason of disability or other disadvantage
- The advancement of citizenship and community development

Awards

Each year, the foundation also delivers the ScottishPower Foundation Awards during which charities are shortlisted by a panel of experts, comprised of professionals from various sectors. A number of different awards are available, including the Education Award; the Community Engagement Award; the Innovation Award and the Charity

Champion Award, details of which can be found on the foundation's website.

Beneficiaries included: Scottish Autism (£158,700); Museum of East Anglian Life (£122,000); The Single Homeless Project (£98,600); Dynamic Earth Charitable Trust (£76,000); Action for ME (£64,700); Street League (£56,100); Drake Music (£50,000); Dangerpoint Ltd (£36,600).

Financial information

Year end	31/12/2021
Assets	£71,700
Income	£1,370,000
Grant total	£1,570,000
Organisations supported	17

Further financial information

Grants were awarded to 17 organisations during the year totalling £1.57 million. In addition, ScottishPower Foundation Awards totalled £30,000.

Applications

Check the foundation's website for updates on opening dates for grants programmes.

Sources of information

Accounts; annual report; OSCR record; funder's website.

The Screwfix Foundation

 Repairing, maintaining, constructing and improving charity and community facilities

UK

£2.17 million (2021/22)

CC number: 1151375

Trustees: Jonathan Mewett; Lindsay Haselhurst; Elizabeth Bell; Caroline Welsh; Darren Worth; Philip Barr; Kelvin Jackson; Nicholas Boyd.

Correspondent: The Trustees, Trade House, Mead Avenue, Houndstone Business Park, Yeovil, Somerset BA22 8RT (tel: 01935 414100; email: foundation@screwfix.com)

 www.screwfix.com/help/screwfixfoundation

General information

The foundation was established in 2013 and supports projects that will fix, repair, maintain and improve properties and community facilities for those in need throughout the UK. The foundation's website explains:

The Screwfix Foundation currently offers local registered charities and not-for-profit organisations funding up to the region of £5,000.

Eligibility

To be eligible to apply, organisations must be:

- A registered charity or not for profit organisation.
- Helping those in need by reason of financial hardship, sickness, disability, distress or other disadvantage in the UK
- Looking for funding to support projects that relate to the repair, maintenance, improvement or construction of homes, community buildings and other buildings.

Beneficiaries included: A list of beneficiaries was not available.

Financial information

Year end	31/01/2022
Assets	£655,100
Income	£2,340,000
Grant total	£2,170,000
Organisations supported	395

Further financial information

During 2021/22, grants to local charities totalled £2.03 million. Additionally, a grant of £143,000 was awarded to Macmillan Cancer Support in support of its community build projects.

Exclusions

The foundation does not provide support for projects that will be used by general members of the public e.g. sports clubs and associations, uniformed groups such as scout and girl guide groups or organisations that support wildlife or animals as their main beneficiary. Further exclusions can be found on the foundation's website.

Applications

Applications can be made via the foundation's website. Applications are reviewed quarterly, usually in March, June, September and December.

Sources of information

Accounts; annual report; Charity Commission record; funder's website.

The Serco Foundation

Healthcare; transport; defence; prison management; immigration services; skills and training; waste collection and recycling

Europe, Asia-Pacific, North America and the Middle East

£579,100 (2021)

CC number: 1150338

Trustees: Kate Steadman; Brigadier John Weller; David Richardson; Keith Archer Jones.

Correspondent: The Trustees, Serco House, 16 Bartley Wood Business Park, Bartley Way, Hook, Hampshire RG27 9UY (email: info@sercofoundation.org)

www.sercofoundation.org

General information

The Serco Foundation is the corporate foundation of Serco Group plc, a government services contractor based in Hampshire. The foundation works internationally to enhance public service outcomes for vulnerable citizens.

The foundation's website states:

> The Foundation supports not-for-profit organisations which operate in the public service sphere, across Europe, Asia-Pacific, North America, and the Middle East, including:
>
> ▶ new and innovative approaches to the delivery of public services;
> ▶ programmes and charities supporting vulnerable citizens;
> ▶ academic research for public benefit; and
> ▶ programmes that foster skills development in the public sector.
>
> We particularly, but not exclusively, welcome applications relating to Defence, Justice and Immigration, Transport, Health, and Citizen Services.

Beneficiaries included: A list of beneficiaries was not available.

Financial information

Year end	31/12/2021
Assets	£5,960,000
Income	£120,300
Grant total	£579,100

Applications

Application forms can be downloaded from the foundation's website. The trustees review applications for support quarterly, normally in February, May, September and December. The foundation has a strong preference for applications that are sponsored by a Serco employee or group of employees.

Sources of information

Accounts; annual report; Charity Commission record; funder's website.

The Shoe Zone Trust

🔍 Education and training; social welfare; children and young people

📍 There is a preference for Leicestershire and Rutland and for certain charities operating in the Philippines and elsewhere

£ £237,600 (2021)

CC number: 1112972

Trustees: Anthony Smith; John Smith.

Correspondent: The Trustees, c/o Shoe Zone, Haramead Business Centre, Humberstone Road, Leicester, Leicestershire LE1 2LH (tel: 0116 222 3000)

 www.shoezone.com/OurCharities

General information

Founded in 2005, this trust is the corporate charity of Shoe Zone Retail Ltd, a UK footwear retailer. Since its inception, the charity has donated over £350,000 to good causes.

The trust's 2021 annual report states that its objectives are to: 'Make grants and donations to other charities to relieve financial hardship and poverty and/or advance education, mainly for children and young persons under age 18 particularly in Leicestershire and Rutland and for certain charities operating in the Philippines and other countries.'

Beneficiaries included: Shepherd of the Hills (£73,600); Cord (£25,000); Amantani (£17,200); Leicester Charity UK (£10,000).

Financial information

Year end	31/12/2021
Assets	£336,900
Income	£319,900
Grant total	£237,600
Organisations supported	10

Applications

Apply in writing to the correspondent.

Sources of information

Accounts; annual report; Charity Commission record; Shoe Zone (website)

The Simmons and Simmons Charitable Foundation

🔍 General charitable purposes, particularly causes relating to social exclusion

📍 Worldwide, in areas local to the Simmons & Simmons' offices

£ £317,600 (2020/21)

CC number: 1129643

Trustees: Richard Dyton; Fiona Loughrey; Julian Taylor; Devarshi Saksena; Stefania Bergia.

Correspondent: The Trustees, Citypoint, 1 Ropemaker Street, London EC2Y 9SS (tel: 020 7628 2020; email: responsible. business@simmons-simmons.com)

 www.simmons-simmons.com/en/ about-us/responsible-business

General information

The foundation was established in 2009 by the law firm Simmons & Simmons LLP.

According to its Charity Commission record, the foundation 'seeks to provide support to smaller charitable organisations which are local to the Simmons & Simmons' offices in which the firm's staff can have an active

involvement and which address social exclusion by helping the less privileged to access opportunity'. Pro bono legal advice is also available.

The foundation also provides grants to individuals to help access 'justice, work and opportunities'.

Beneficiaries included: Battersea Legal Advice Centre (£46,000); Young Talent Programme (£30,000); British Red Cross (£20,000); Justice Without Borders (£19,800); Bristol Law Centre and Jigme Singye Wangchuck School of Law (£10,000 each); Envision (£6,500).

Financial information

Year end	30/04/2021
Assets	£105,300
Income	£216,700
Grant total	£317,600

Further financial information

The annual return for 2021 provides a breakdown of the foundation's grant-giving by category:

Social inclusion	£102,000
Pro bono	£98,000
International donations	£43,600
Access to justice	£39,800
Other donations	£20,400

Applications

Apply in writing to the correspondent by email.

Sources of information

Accounts; annual report; Charity Commission record.

Skipton Building Society Charitable Foundation

🔍 The education and welfare of children; older people

📍 UK, with a preference for areas near the society's principal office or one of its branches

£ £236,800 (2021/22)

CC number: 1079538

Trustees: Amelia Vyvyan; Alison Davies; Debra Ewing; Kitty North; John Dawson; The Revd and Rt Hon. Lord Hope of Thornes; Gregory Bell.

Correspondent: The Trustees, The Bailey, Skipton, North Yorkshire BD23 1DN (tel: 01756 705000; email: charitablefoundation@skipton.co.uk)

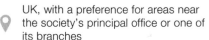 www.skiptoncharitablefoundation. co.uk

General information

The Skipton Building Society Charitable Foundation was established in 2000. It is funded by an annual donation from the building society. Since its inception, the foundation has awarded over £2.5 million to charitable causes.

Eligibility

The foundation awards grants of up to £3,000 to registered charities based in the UK. Priority is given to charities based in areas near the building society's principal office in Skipton, or any one of its branches. The foundation only supports charities with at least one year of published accounts covering a 12-month period.

Areas of work

Consideration will be given to charities whose objectives are:

▶ To benefit children (aged under 16), through their education and or welfare, i.e. literacy, numeracy and reducing poverty.

▶ To provide youth schemes and projects supporting those in their late teens/early 20s in socially deprived areas with literacy, numeracy and employment.

▶ To support the older people by reducing isolation, helping reduce the effects of dementia and Alzheimer's

Beneficiaries included: Frodsham Youth Association and Helping Disabilities (£3,000 each); Home-Start Kirklees (£2,500); Bolton Deaf Society (£2,300); The Happy and Healthy Trust (£1,300); Swansea Music Art Digital (£940); Willowbrook Hospice (£750); Walthew House – Cheshire (£470).

Financial information

Year end	28/02/2022
Assets	£48,300
Income	£200,200
Grant total	£236,800

Exclusions

According to its website, the foundation will not support:

▶ Applications for general on-going funding, running costs, rent, utility costs medical research, sponsorship, payment of salaries, counselling or expenses.

▶ Requests for administration equipment such as telephones, security systems or computers, for a charity's own use.

▶ [The] restoration and upkeep of buildings or maintenance of vehicles.

▶ Causes serving only a specific sector of the community selected on the basis of ethnic, racial, political or religious grounds/advancement.

▶ Overseas travel, expeditions or educational expenses, including causes that would otherwise qualify for support but require funds for activities outside the UK.

▶ Non-registered charities, individuals or large national charities.

▶ Activities which fall within an existing statutory funded budget or are the responsibility of central or local government even if the budget is insufficient to fund the activity applied for.

Applications

Application forms can be downloaded on the website. The trustees usually meet at the beginning of March, June, September and December. Submission deadline dates are the first of the month prior to each meeting.

Sources of information

Accounts; annual report; Charity Commission record; funder's website.

The Slaughter and May Charitable Trust

 General charitable purposes, particularly causes relating to children and young people

England and Wales — UK and occasionally other parts of the world

£526,900 (2020/21)

CC number: 1082765

Trustee: Slaughter and May Trust Ltd

Correspondent: The Trustees, Slaughter and May (Trust Ltd), 1 Bunhill Row, London EC1Y 8YY (tel: 020 7090 5286; email: corporateresponsibility@slaughterandmay.com)

www.slaughterandmay.com

General information

This trust was registered with the Charity Commission in 2000. It is the corporate charity of Slaughter and May, a law firm.

According to its 2020/21 annual report:

Direct charitable grants are made to selected applicants for charitable purposes for the benefit of the public at the discretion of the trustee. Further grants are made to miscellaneous charities for other reasons but particularly to incentivise Slaughter and May employees in charitable deeds.

The trust also offers gifts in kind, usually in the form of pro bono work.

Beneficiaries included: The Access Project (£60,000); National Literacy Trust (£51,000); Islington Law Centre (£35,000); St Luke's Community Centre (£25,000); Legal Advice Centre (£15,000); The BIG Alliance (£12,000); St Luke's Primary School (£10,000); Mencap (£5,000).

Financial information

Year end	05/04/2021
Assets	£120,000
Income	£412,100
Grant total	£526,900

Applications

The trust does not generally accept unsolicited applications.

Sources of information

Accounts; annual report; Charity Commission record.

The DS Smith Charitable Foundation

 Education and training; environmental conservation

England and Wales

£350,000 (2021/22)

CC number: 1142817

Trustees: Emma Ciechan; Mark Reeve; Giulio Giannini; Dana Ciuraru; Wouter van Tol.

Correspondent: The Trustees, 7th Floor, 350 Euston Road, London NW1 3AX (tel: 020 7756 1823; email: charitablefoundation@dssmith.com)

www.dssmith.com/sustainability/ building-strong-foundations/ looking-after-people-and-our-communities/responsible-neighbour/charitable-foundation

General information

The DS Smith Charitable Foundation is the charity of the British-based international packaging business DS Smith plc. Registered in 2011, the foundation supports charities engaged in conservation of the environment and training or education.

The following information was taken from the foundation's website:

Please note that only charities in the fields of environmental improvement and of education and training, will be considered, so please ensure that any application fulfils this criteria. The charity aims to make a combination of small donations (£1,000 or less) and larger donations each year. We particularly welcome opportunities to develop multi-year partnerships with key selected charities.

Beneficiaries included: A list of beneficiaries was not available. Previous beneficiaries include: Ellen MacArthur Foundation (£150,000); UNICEF (£42,600); The Royal Institute (£10,000); Litter Angels (£6,000); Earth Restoration (£2,000).

Financial information

Year end	30/04/2022
Income	£11,600
Grant total	£350,000

Further financial information

Full accounts were not available to view on the Charity Commission website due to the foundation's low income. We have therefore estimated the grant total based on its total expenditure.

Applications

Application forms are available on the foundation's website.

Sources of information

Accounts; annual report; Charity Commission record; funder's website.

The WH Smith Group Charitable Trust

 General charitable purposes; community services and development

UK

£90,400 (2021)

CC number: 1013782

Trustees: Faye Sherman; Natalie Davidson; Sharon Appleton; Clare O'Grady; Nicki Woodhead; Lisa Barrett; Mitchell Hunt; Paul Johnson; Wendy Stroud; John Pouton; Danielle Richards.

Correspondent: The Trustees, WHSmith Ltd, Greenbridge Road, Swindon, Wiltshire SN3 3JE (tel: 01793 616161; email: corporate.responsibility@whsmith.co.uk)

 www.whsmithplc.co.uk/corporate_responsibility/whsmith_trust

General information

The trust was registered with the Charity Commission in 1992. According to its website, the trust aims to support good causes in the local communities where WHSmith operates and also to promote literacy and a love of reading. Each year, the trust supports employees by matching their fundraising and volunteering for charities and schools. The Trust also makes donations to hundreds of schools across the UK and funds large scale literacy projects through its long-standing partnership with the National Literacy Trust. The trust benefits from the fundraising efforts WHSmith Group employees and donations.

Beneficiaries included: Young Readers Programme 2021 (£80,000); Read Easy UK (£5,000); The White Horse Federation (£2,000); 1st Lydiate Scout Group, Antony Nolan Trust and Macmillan Cancer Support (£1,000 each).

Financial information

Year end	31/12/2021
Assets	£170,600
Income	£93,400
Grant total	£90,400
Organisations supported	8

Further financial information

Only organisations that received grants of over £1,000 were listed as beneficiaries in the charity's accounts. Grants of under £1,000 totalled £1,400.

Applications

Apply in writing to the correspondent.

Sources of information

Accounts; annual report; Charity Commission record; funder's website.

Social Tech Trust

 Technology projects

Undefined; in practice, UK

£4,500 (2020/21)

CC number: 1125735

Trustees: Bill Liao; Nicolas Temple; Russell Johnstone; Sunil Suri; Robert Tashima; Nicholas Wise; Anisah Britton; Maria Nelson.

Correspondent: The Trustees, Social Tech Trust, Invicta House, 4th Floor, 108–114 Golden Lane, London EC1Y 0TL (tel: 01865 334000; email: hello@socialtechtrust.org)

 https://socialtechtrust.org

@SocialTechTrust

General information

This trust was established in 2008 as the corporate charity of Nominet, the official registry for UK domain names. Today, the trust is fully independent and has recently formed a new strategic partnership with Social Investment Business. The trust also works in partnership with the UK government to 'increase access to capital to enable the strongest social tech ventures to scale'. Over the past decade, the trust has supported around 800 initiatives in the UK, having awarded over £31 million in funding.

Grant-making policy

According to its website, the trust provides grants to organisations that are 'addressing social challenges using tech to transform lives'. The trust is particularly interested in projects that apply tech into the following areas/fields:

- Communities
- Health
- Wealth

The trust has various grants programmes which are subject to change. However, the trust states that it generally looks for:

- A social mission embedded in your governance
- Potential to deliver transformative social impact at scale through a deep understanding of the critical social challenge that drives your innovation and an ambition to make a difference
- An innovative approach to tackling a social challenge in the areas of communities, health and wealth
- A working product or service that you will continue to test and iterate

- Evidence of your potential to create user, social and financial value; for example, a theory of change; user co-design and testing; identified social KPIs; prospective partnerships or routes to market
- An experienced and aligned team with the in-house tech capabilities
- Registration as a UK-based organisation and the potential for social impact in the UK

Beneficiaries included: A list of beneficiaries was not available. Previous beneficiaries include: Beam Up Ltd, Bronze Software Labs Ltd, Carefreebreaks, Feebris and On Our Radar (£45,000 each); The Future Fox Ltd (£44,400); Twelve Two Ltd (£40,000).

Financial information

Year end	31/03/2021
Assets	£4,300,000
Income	£389,000
Grant total	£4,500

Applications

Applications are currently closed. See the website for updates on open grant schemes as well as detailed guidelines and deadlines. Alternatively, prospective applicants may wish to sign up for the trust's newsletter, or follow the trust on Twitter and LinkedIn, to be the first to hear about new opportunities.

Sources of information

Accounts; annual report; Charity Commission record; funder's website.

Societe Generale UK Foundation

Education and employability

UK and overseas

£577,900 (2020)

CC number: 1196579

Trustees: Ben Higgins; Jasvant Singh; Elise Sabran; John Oberman; Louise Redmond; Hannah Mackenzie.

Correspondent: The Trustees, 1 Bank Street, London E14 4SG (tel: 020 7597 3065; email: rachel.iles@sghambros.com)

General information

This foundation is the corporate charity of Societe Generale, the investment bank of the same name.

According to its 2020 annual report, the foundation's main objective is to support Societe Generale's global citizenship guidelines of inclusion through education and employability. Although, the foundation will occasionally make grants for more general charitable purposes.

Grants are made to UK registered charities with beneficiaries either overseas or here in the UK, as well as organisations with a charitable purpose such as schools, hospitals (including social enterprises).

Types of funding
The foundation's main funding streams include:
- **Matched funding** – Societe Generale staff can apply for matched funding either linked to fundraising organised by the group itself for its charity partner, or for other fundraising efforts within the foundation's criteria.
- **Key projects** – one-off or rolling donations to strategic education/employability projects which link to the bank's citizenship programme.
- **Specific projects** – this funding is reserved for the Shake Climate Change project, a new nine-year programme established by Rothamsted Research, in conjunction with leading academic institutions, to support entrepreneurs combatting climate change in agriculture and food production.
- **Ad hoc donations** – Exceptional one-off donations and matching to support emergency appeals.

Beneficiaries included: CLIC Sargent (£198,500); East London Business Alliance (£41,000); National Emergencies Trust (£25,000); Alzheimer's Society (£11,100); Bristol Black Carers (£2,800); The Old Church (£2,000).

Financial information

Year end	31/12/2020
Assets	£6,860,000
Income	£292,800
Grant total	£577,900

Further financial information
Full accounts were not available to view on the Charity Commission website as the foundation had recently re-registered. This financial information relates to the previous foundation, the Societe Generale UK Foundation (Charity Commission no. 1039013).

Exclusions
According to its 2020 annual report the foundation does not support:
- Organisations which are concerned solely with promoting religious beliefs, political parties and affiliated groups, drugs or research and animals.
- Organisations with overseas beneficiaries which are registered in the UK and work outside the scope of education and employment.
- Organisations with overseas beneficiaries which are not registered in the UK whether they work within or outside the scope of education and employment.
- Organisations whose work does not fit with Societe Generale's values and who could damage the reputation of the Societe Generale Group

Applications
The foundation does not accept unsolicited applications.

Sources of information
Accounts; annual report; Charity Commission record.

Sodexo Stop Hunger Foundation

 Hunger and malnutrition; healthy lifestyles; life skills

UK and Ireland

£351,200 (2020/21)

CC number: 1110266

Trustees: Gareth John; David Forbes; Laura Brimacombe; Simon McCluskey; Samantha Scott; Sean Haley; Patrick Forbes; David Mulcahy.

Correspondent: The Trustees, Sodexo, 1 Southampton Row, London WC1B 5HA (tel: 020 7404 0110; email: stophunger@sodexo.com)

 http://uk.stop-hunger.org/home.html

 facebook.com/SodexoUKIreland

 @stop_hungeruk

General information
Registered with the Charity Commission in June 2005, the Sodexo Stop Hunger Foundation is the corporate charity of the food services and facilities management company, Sodexo Ltd.

According to its website, the foundation is a grant-maker that works with the 'very best charities' to:
- Tackle hunger and malnutrition
- Promote healthy lifestyles
- Develop life skills such as cooking.

The foundation provides regular support to a number of organisations such as FareShare and the Trussell Trust, but is open to grant applications from other charities which meet the foundation's criteria. Grantees can also receive volunteer support from Sodexo employees.

Beneficiaries included: FareShare (£85,900); SSAFA Forces Help (£35,000); Coram Life (£22,000); Wycombe Food Hub (£10,000); Alexander Rose Charity (£5,000).

Financial information

Year end	31/08/2021
Assets	£175,500
Income	£595,900
Grant total	£351,200
Organisations supported	20

Applications
For further information on the support available, complete the contact form on the foundation's website.

Sources of information
Accounts; annual report; Charity Commission record; funder's website.

SPAR Charitable Fund

General charitable purposes

UK

£65,600 (2020/21)

CC number: 236252

Trustees: Peter Dodding; Patrick Doody; Dominic Hall; Mohammed Sadiq; Paul Stone; Justin Taylor; Peter McBride; Mike Boardman; Julian Green; Mark Cleary; Louis Drake; Rodney Tucker; Steven Irons.

Correspondent: The Trustees, SPAR (UK) Ltd, Hygeia Building, 66–68 College Road, Harrow, Middlesex HA1 1BE (tel: 020 8426 3670; email: michelle.geraghty@spar.co.uk)

General information
This fund was registered with the Charity Commission in 1964. It is the corporate charity of the food retail chain, SPAR (UK) Ltd. Its purpose is to provide funding to charities and charitable causes in the UK and abroad. Support is also given to retail industry charitable organisations. It has been partnered with Marie Curie since 2017 and has raised £2 million; the equivalent of 100,000 hours of care from a Marie Curie Nurse.

According to the charity's Charity Commission record, 'Through the charity's donations to other charities and to emergency appeals, the SPAR Charitable Fund has provided support to communities both in the UK and around the world. Through the support it provides to the SPAR Benevolent Fund and the Retail Trust, it has assisted retailers experiencing hardship and thus enabled them to continue serving their local communities.'

Beneficiaries included: Grocery Aid (£46,800); Drinkaware (£15,100); Marie Curie (£3,400).

Financial information

Year end	28/04/2021
Assets	£465,500
Income	£52,600
Grant total	£65,600

Applications
Apply in writing to the correspondent.

Sources of information
Accounts; Annual report; Charity Commission record.

The Vichai Srivaddhanaprabha Foundation

 General charitable purposes

 Leicestershire and Rutland

£ £698,400 (2020/21)

CC number: 1144791

Trustees: Susan Whelan; Simon Capper; Tony Lander; Alan Birchenall.

Correspondent: The Trustees, King Power Stadium, Filbert Way, Leicester, Leicestershire LE2 7FL (tel: 0116 229 4737; email: VSFoundation@lcfc.co.uk)

🌐 www.lcfc.com/fans-community/ foundation/foundation-overview

General information

The foundation was established in 2011 as the LCFC Foxes Foundation. In November 2018 it was renamed The Vichai Srivaddhanaprabha Foundation in honour of Leicester City's late Chair, Khun Vichai, who died in a helicopter accident. The foundation is primarily operated by employees of Leicester City Football Club.

The foundation's website states:

Money raised over the years has gone towards a number of important causes, including the funding of a renovation of Leicester Royal Infirmary's Children's Outpatient Ward and life-saving equipment desperately needed by the Children's Intensive Care Unit.

The Vichai Srivaddhanaprabha Foundation has supported dozens of local causes throughout its seven years, including Leicester Hospitals Charity, LOROS, Rainbows Children's Hospice, Leicestershire Children's Holiday Centre and by installing life-saving defibrillators in key areas around the county.

The foundation's annual Gift of a Wish programme supports a range of community causes throughout Leicestershire and Rutland.

Beneficiaries included: Gift of a Wish (£507,200); Leicester Hospitals (£162,000); Royal British Legion (£29,200).

Financial information

Year end	31/05/2021
Assets	£147,000
Income	£311,200
Grant total	£698,400
Organisations supported	3

Applications

See the foundation's website for further information on open grants programmes.

Sources of information

Accounts; annual report; Charity Commission record; funder's website.

St James's Place Charitable Foundation

 Supporting disadvantaged young people; combating cancer; supporting hospices; mental health

 UK and overseas

£ £6.64 million (2021)

CC number: 1144606

Trustees: Malcolm Cooper-Smith; Andrew Croft; Ian Gascoigne; Sonia Gravestock; Andrew Humphries; Robert Edwards; Sir Mark Weinberg.

Correspondent: The Trustees, St James's Place House, 1 Tetbury Road, Cirencester, Gloucestershire GL7 1FP (tel: 01285 878037; email: sjp.foundation@sjp.co.uk)

 www.sjpfoundation.co.uk

General information

The foundation is the corporate charity of St James's Place Wealth Management, a leading UK wealth management group. The foundation's grant-making in the UK is guided by four themes:

▶ **Supporting Young People (special needs or disadvantaged)** – focuses on supporting children and young people under the age of 25 who are disadvantaged, who are young carers, or who have physical or mental health difficulties or life-threatening degenerative conditions. Grants are made for small capital items, support for staff working directly or hands on with beneficiaries and support for projects of direct benefit to beneficiaries.

▶ **Supporting People with Cancer** – grants are given for capital items of direct benefit to patients with cancer, towards the salary of staff working directly with patients with cancer and for projects aimed at increasing the quality of life for cancer patients.

▶ **Supporting Hospices** – grants are given to hospices working with all age ranges. The foundation is currently working with Hospice UK, which will distribute funds to hospices on the foundation's behalf and, therefore, does not invite applications from hospices directly.

▶ **Mental Health** – according to the website, grants are awarded to allow 'organisations to scale their resources and create greater access to the right support'.

Funds are administered via two grants programmes:

▶ **Small Grants Programme:** grants of up to £10,000 are available to UK charities with an annual income of up to £1 million (this restriction does not apply to special needs schools or

mainstream schools with a special needs unit).

▶ **Major Grants Programme:** grants for up to two or three years for capital items or revenue. The programme is by invitation only.

The foundation's website states: 'Approximately 90% of the money raised goes to supporting UK charities, with the remaining 10% being allocated to charities overseas, particularly those helping children and young people to escape poverty, malnutrition and neglect. The Overseas grants programme is open via invitation only through the St James's Place Community.'

Beneficiaries included: Panathlon Foundation (£1 million); The OnSide Foundation (£500,000); School-Home Support (£120,000); Meningitis Now (£80,000); Centrestage Communities Ltd (£40,000); ThinkForward UK (£20,000); The Music Works (£5,000).

Financial information

Year end	31/12/2021
Assets	£6,110,000
Income	£8,570,000
Grant total	£6,640,000

Further financial information

The foundation's accounts report that 88% of grants awarded was in the UK.

A sample of recent UK beneficiaries is available on the foundation's website.

Exclusions

The foundation does not provide support for:

▶ Charities with reserves of over 50% of income
▶ Administrative costs
▶ Activities primarily the responsibility of statutory agencies
▶ NHS charities
▶ Pilot programmes
▶ Retrospective funding
▶ Research
▶ Events
▶ Advertising
▶ Holidays
▶ Sponsorship
▶ Contributions to large capital appeals
▶ Charities that are raising funds on behalf of another charity
▶ Community interest companies

The Small Grants Programme has a policy of not granting more than £10,000 to an organisation in any two-year period.

Applications

Applications for the Small Grants Programme should be made using the form on the foundation's website. Check the foundation's website for updates and information on how to apply.

The Stewarts Law Foundation

 Alleviating poverty; access to justice; supporting disability; providing educational opportunity

UK

£633,100 (2020/21)

CC number: 1136714

Trustees: John Cahill; Julian Chamberlayne; Stuart Dench; Stephen Foster; Daniel Herman; Paul Paxton; Clive Zietman; Sean Upson; Emma Hatley; Debbie Chism; Keith Thomas; Ian Gatt; Kathryn Pollock; Mohan Bhaskaran; James Price; Fiona Gillett; Alex Jay; Sam Longworth; Richard Hogwood; Muiris Lyons.

Correspondent: The Trustees, 5 New Street Square, London EC4A 3BF (tel: 020 7822 8000)

www.stewartslaw.com/about/social-impact/the-stewarts-foundation

General information
The foundation was established in 2010 to manage the charitable giving of Stewarts Law, the UK's largest litigation-only law firm.

According to its website, the foundation's vision is to:
- Create opportunities for the disadvantaged in our society
- Treat people less fortunate than ourselves with compassion and respect
- Make a substantial social impact

It achieves this by making grants to a handful of UK-registered charities, as chosen by the trustees. The foundation focuses its grant-making on the following four principles:
- Alleviating poverty
- Enabling access to justice
- Supporting disability
- Providing educational opportunity

The foundation has a long-term partnership with the Access to Justice Foundation.

Beneficiaries included: Access to Justice Foundation (£251,000); Centrepoint (£50,000); Wheelpower (£30,000); Finito (£9,000); JUSTICE (£6,000).

Financial information

Year end	30/04/2021
Assets	£235,400
Income	£812,400
Grant total	£633,100

Further financial information
Only organisations that received grants of over £3,000 were listed as beneficiaries in the foundation's accounts (20 organisations). Grants of under £3,000 totalled £9,100. The foundation has a partnership with the Access to Justice Foundation, to which it awards a large grant each year. In addition, employees of Stewarts Law are given the opportunity to vote for a charity to be supported each year.

Applications
Charities are chosen by the trustees. The 2021/22 annual report states: 'It is not the policy of the Trustees to accept direct applications for funds.'

The Stobart Newlands Charitable Trust

 Christian and missionary causes

Worldwide

£891,500 (2021)

CC number: 328464

Trustees: Ronnie Stobart; Linda Rigg; Peter Stobart; Richard Stobart.

Correspondent: The Trustees, Millcroft, Newlands, Hesket Newmarket, Wigton, Cumbria CA7 8HP (tel: 01697 478631)

General information
Established in 1989, the trust is the corporate charity of J Stobart and Sons Ltd, a manufacturer and retailer of animal feedstuffs. The trustees are directors and shareholders of J Stobart and Sons Ltd, which is the source of almost all of the trust's income. This family trust makes up to 60 grants a year, nearly all on a recurring basis to Christian religious and missionary bodies.

Beneficiaries included: World Vision (£250,000); Operation Mobilisation (£142,000); Every Home Crusade (£28,500); Logos Ministries (£16,500).

Financial information

Year end	31/12/2021
Assets	£348,300
Income	£1,040,000
Grant total	£891,500

Further financial information
Only beneficiaries of grants of £10,000 and above were listed in the accounts. Grants of under £10,000 totalled £155,300.

Applications
Unsolicited applications are unlikely to be successful.

The Swire Charitable Trust

 General charitable purposes, with a focus on creating opportunities, the environment and heritage

UK

£3.5 million to organisations (2021)

CC number: 270726

Trustees: Samuel Swire; Rupert Hogg; Martha Allfrey; Barnaby Swire.

Correspondent: Sarah Irving, Grants Manager, Swire House, 59 Buckingham Gate, London SW1E 6AJ (tel: 020 7834 7717; email: info@scts.org.uk)

www.swirecharitabletrust.org.uk

General information
The trust was established in 1975 as an independent grant-making charity. It receives its funding from John Swire & Sons Ltd, a diversified group of global companies and parent company of the Swire Group.

Its website states that the trust makes grants to charities 'supporting some of the UK's most vulnerable people to overcome barriers and realise their potential, and to charities who are protecting our precious environment and heritage'.

Grants programmes
Currently, grants are made through the following programmes:
- **Opportunity** – grants are given to charities that are directly addressing challenges faced by marginalised and disadvantaged people. The programme aims to improve life chances for the following: ex-Servicepeople; victims of slavery and trafficking; and children and young people who are in the care of their local authority, involved with the criminal justice system or from the most socio-economically disadvantaged backgrounds.
- **The environment** – funding is given to charities that can connect people to the environment and that support the UK's biodiversity.
- **Heritage** – funding is given to projects that can deliver social and economic benefits to deprived communities or disadvantaged people and charities working to safeguard endangered skills. Preference is given to grassroots organisations that engage with the local community.

COVID-19 Recovery Programme – one-year grants of £25,000 are given to charities providing a unique response to the pandemic or facing severe short-term funding pressures. The programme is a £1.5 million fund.

Eligibility

The trust's website states that across these programmes priority is given to charities that:

- Operate in some of the most economically disadvantaged parts of the UK
- Try to engage the most marginalised and vulnerable in their work
- Can clearly demonstrate the needs they are addressing
- Know what they are aiming to achieve and plan to monitor and evaluate outcomes
- Are well placed and qualified to deliver the work
- Can show a proven track record as well as solid ambitions
- Have the potential to change the way issues are tackled more widely
- Take an effective approach to using volunteers and mentors (where appropriate)
- Are seeking to make their income streams more sustainable
- Have strong and quality leadership
- Manage their finances prudently

The website also notes the following: 'We fund individual projects that are aligned with our funding priorities, although we also recognise that charities are often best placed to allocate resources within their organisations. We therefore award many grants on an unrestricted basis and are willing to support core costs, capital expenditure and salaries.'

There is no maximum or minimum grant size and multi-year grants may be considered if a longer-term commitment (up to three years) can be clearly justified.

As well as the core programmes, the trust's Discretionary Fund makes donations to charities that fall outside the funding criteria, at the suggestion of the companies' stakeholders.

Beneficiaries included: Combat Stress (£40,000); Heritage Crafts Association (£30,000); Mission to Seafarers (£25,000); Chichester Ship Canal Trust (£20,000); E:Merge (£15,200); EP Youth Ltd (£10,000); Cathedral Music Trust (£2,500); Macmillan Cancer Support (£1,000).

Financial information

Year end	31/12/2021
Assets	£9,010,000
Income	£3,230,000
Grant total	£3,500,000
Organisations supported	240

Exclusions

According to its website, the trust will not provide support for the following:

- Applications received by post or email, i.e. not via our online funding request form
- Organisations that are not UK registered charities
- Activities taking place outside England, Scotland, Wales or Northern Ireland
- Individual applicants or proposals that will benefit only one person
- Requests from charities that have applied to us in the last 12 months
- Work that has already taken place
- Work targeted towards people who are primarily disadvantaged due to the following:
  - physical health issues, disabilities or sensory impairments
  - learning disabilities or special educational needs
- Statutory bodies or work that is primarily the responsibility of statutory authorities (e.g. residential, respite and day care, housing)
- Activities of local organisations which are part of a wider network doing similar work (e.g. uniformed youth groups, YMCA, MIND, Mencap, Home-start, RDA, Relate, Citizens Advice Bureau, Age UK etc)
- Scholarships or bursaries

Note: the trust's Discretionary Fund is not subject to all of these exclusions.

Applications

Applicants should read the guidelines and FAQs on the website first, then complete the eligibility test. If eligible, applications can be made using the online form. Applications are considered throughout the year. Requests of less than £25,000 are considered at monthly meetings, with larger requests being considered quarterly (usually in January, April, July and October). Applications sent by post or email will not be considered.

Note: general correspondence is preferred by email rather than by post.

Sources of information

Accounts; annual report; Charity Commission record; funder's website.

The Syncona Foundation

🔍 Medical causes, particularly oncology

📍 UK

£ £442,800 (2020/21)

CC number: 1149202

Trustees: James Maltin; Thomas Henderson; Rupert Adams; Nigel Keen; Lucie Kitchener.

Correspondent: The Trustees, c/o Couch Bright King & Co., 2 Tolherst Court Turkey Mill, Ashford Road, Kent

ME14 5SF (tel: 020 7387 4264; email: th@bacit.co.uk)

 www.synconaLimited.com/about-us/charities

General information

This foundation was registered with the Charity Commission in 2012. It is funded by Syncona Ltd, a FTSE 250 life sciences investment company that is focused on founding, building and funding companies working in innovative areas of healthcare. Each year, the company donates a percentage of its net assets to charity with half of the funds going to cancer research and the other half to the Syncona Foundation.

The foundation makes grants to a number of charities a year. Its focus is on the prevention, treatment, cure and eradication of cancer and other diseases.

According to its 2020/21 accounts, the objectives of the foundation are to:

- support the prevention, treatment, cure and ultimately the eradication of cancer in all of its forms and any allied diseases;
- promote and assist
  - the study of and research into the nature, causes, diagnosis and pathology of cancer and any allied diseases
  - the development and provision of all forms of preventive, curative, management and palliative treatment of cancer and any allied diseases
  - education and training in subjects relevant to the study of cancer and any allied diseases
- co-operate with, and to promote and assist the work of, The Institute of Cancer Research ("the ICR") and, or alternatively, such other charitable organisations whose objects include any of those specified above as the Foundation may determine in addition to or in substitution for the ICR; and
- promote and assist such other charitable objects and charitable organisations as the Foundation may from time to time consider desirable.

Beneficiaries included: Place2Be (£60,000); The Listening Place (£33,300); Heritage of London Trust and Matt Hampson Foundation (£30,000 each); Trinity College Cambridge (£10,000).

Financial information

Year end	31/03/2021
Assets	£2,640,000
Income	£2,820,000
Grant total	£442,800

Applications

Charities are selected by Syncona shareholders from a list proposed by the trustees.

Sources of information

Accounts; annual report; Charity Commission record; funder's website.

The T.K. Maxx and Homesense Foundation

 Children, young people and families

UK, in communities local to T.K. Maxx stores

£1.48 million (2021/22)

CC number: 1162073

Trustees: Maureen Dunn; Michael Munnelly; Rachel Barber; Erica Michelle; Deborah Dolce.

Correspondent: The Trustees, 73 Clarendon Road, Hertfordshire WD17 1TX (tel: 01923 47300; email: TJX_Foundation@tjxeurope.com)

www.tkmaxx.com/uk/en/tkmaxx-and-homesense-foundation

General information

Established in 2015, this foundation is the corporate charity of TJX, the parent company of T.K. Maxx and Homesense, and is funded through donations from the company. It makes grants to organisations supporting vulnerable children and young people in the UK and Ireland, Germany and Poland. Grants are made to national and local charities.

Community Fund

The foundation funds and administers the Community Fund, which enables TJX, T.K. Maxx and Homesense staff to nominate charities they are passionate about, to receive a donation of £500 to make a difference in their local communities. A proportion of these grants is dedicated to charities supporting racial justice, mental health, disability and the LGBTQI+ community.

According to the website, the Community Fund delivered £1 million of COVID-19 emergency grants. This was in addition to the Tackle COVID-19 Fund, which delivered £700,000 to frontline mental health and medical charities.

Beneficiaries included: British Red Cross (£180,000); The Prince's Trust (£175,000); Retail Trust (£100,000); Stephen Lawrence Trust (£75,000); Mind (£50,000); School Without Racism (£40,000); Access UK (£35,000).

Financial information

Year end	30/01/2022
Assets	£7,480,000
Income	£2,240,000
Grant total	£1,480,000

Further financial information

Donations to national charities totalled £570,000 and donations to local charities totalled £905,000. Only a small list of large donations was given in the accounts.

Applications

Contact the correspondent for further information.

Sources of information

Accounts; annual report; Charity Commission record; funder's website.

The Thales Charitable Trust

 General charitable purposes; health; young people

UK

£175,900 (2021)

CC number: 1000162

Trustees: John Howe; Michael Seabrook; Craig Stevenson; Stuart Boulton; Stephen Murray.

Correspondent: Michael Seabrook, Trustee and Secretary, c/o Thales UK Ltd, 350 Longwater Avenue, Green Park, Reading, Berkshire RG2 6GF (tel: 0118 943 4500; email: mike.seabrook@uk. thalesgroup.com)

 www.thalesgroup.com/en/thales-solidarity-charitable-fund

General information

The Thales Charitable Trust was registered with the Charity Commission in 1990. It is the corporate charity of Thales UK Ltd, a major electronic systems company that provides services in areas such as defence, airlines security and safety, information technology and transportation.

The trust makes grants to charitable organisations, primarily for causes related to young people, technology and education and care for those with permanent or terminal conditions. The trustees may occasionally consider requests from other causes at their discretion.

Beneficiaries included: British Heart Foundation; Civil Service Benevolent Fund; Combat Stress; Primary Engineers; Railway Benefit Fund; Railway Children; The Service Benevolent Fund.

Financial information

Year end	31/12/2021
Assets	£42,400
Income	£165,000
Grant total	£175,900
Organisations supported	52

Further financial information

Grant totals for each beneficiary were not included in the 2021 accounts.

Applications

Apply in writing to the correspondent. The trustees meet on a quarterly basis. The annual return for 2021 states that the trust does not generally solicit requests unless for major donations.

Sources of information

Accounts; annual report; Charity Commission record.

the7stars Foundation

 Young people who are experiencing abuse, addiction or homelessness; young people who are carers

UK

£50,500 (2020/21)

CC number: 1168240

Trustees: Nick Maddison; Liam Mullins; Rhiannon Murphy; Jenny Biggam; Helen Rose; Anuschka Clarke.

Correspondent: The Trustees, Bush House, North West Wing, Aldwych, London WC2B 4PJ (email: info@ the7starsfoundation.co.uk)

 www.the7starsfoundation.co.uk

 facebook.com/the7starsfoundation

 @_the7starsfoundation

General information

Established in 2016, the7stars foundation is the corporate charity of the7stars UK Ltd, the UK's largest independent media agency. The foundation supports disadvantaged young people in the UK and has four priority areas for its grant funding:

- Abuse
- Addiction
- Child carers
- Homelessness

Grants programmes

The foundation operates four funding streams, detailed on the foundation's website as follows.

Project funding

- Project grants awarded up to £2,500.
- To organisations with a turnover of under £1.5M.
- Supporting young people aged 16 years and under.
- Projects enabling young people to have the best start in life- to reach for the stars.
- Projects which have a direct impact and respond to a need in an immediate manner.
- Projects hosted in geographical areas of deprivation and socioeconomic disadvantage.
- Projects which respond to (one of the/ multiple) funding priorities of the7stars foundation (Abuse; Addiction; Homelessness; Child Carers).
- Projects which address a lack of provision (due to a lack of funding from alternative sources).

- Projects which provide immediate support not just in the short term but with long-term benefits too.
- Regarding projects for Child Carers, preference will be given to projects offering long-term impact and/or sustainable support (such as mentoring or outreach programmes) over recreational trips.

Shine Bright funding

Shine Bright funding enables charities across the UK to purchase items and resources to protect and support the children they serve through the cost of living crisis.

Charities are asked to provide details of how our funding can assist, and which items would be purchased through an award. Grants are available up to £1,500 per successful application.

Please note, we are only able to fund charitable organisations with a turnover below £1.5m.

Direct funding

Requests on behalf of individual young people by outreach/social/care workers and legal professionals.

Beneficiaries included: A list of beneficiaries was not available.

Financial information

Year end	31/03/2021
Assets	£219,900
Income	£152,100
Grant total	£50,500

Exclusions

Organisations with a turnover of above £1.5 million for project funding and Shine Bright funding.

Applications

Apply using the form for the relevant funding stream on the foundation's website.

Sources of information

Accounts; annual report; Charity Commission record; funder's website.

Toyota Manufacturing UK Charitable Trust

 Community; road safety; social inclusion; social welfare; health and medical research

Burnaston and Deeside

(£) £144,300 (2021)

CC number: 1124678

Trustees: Sarah Overson; Kevin Reader; Sharon Wilson; Gary Shrimpton; Kevin Potter; Tim Freeman.

Correspondent: The Trustees, c/o Toyota Motor Manufacturing (UK) Ltd, Derby, Derbyshire DE1 9TA (tel: 01332 283611; email: charitabletrust@toyotauk.com)

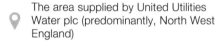 www.toyotauk.com/the-toyota-charitable-trust/charitable-trust-overview.html

General information

Registered in 2008, this is the charitable trust of Toyota Motor Manufacturing UK (TMUK) Ltd. Its income is largely derived from company employees through fundraising activities. The trust makes donations to local organisations in the Burnaston (Derbyshire) and Deeside (North Wales) areas.

The website notes that the trust has a preference for supporting the following areas:

Road Safety

- To fund projects which aim to improve the safety of roads in our local community, through either preventative or reactive measures.
- Provide support and resources to reduce road collisions and to reduce recovery time at scene.

Social Inclusion/Deprivation

- Encourage people to realise their potential by making opportunities possible that are not ordinarily available.
- To support projects providing opportunities to address inequalities in our society and enabling people to improve their social status.

Health

- Supporting projects aiming to promote knowledge of and research into diseases or medical conditions.
- Funding to support those suffering from medical conditions or illness.

Member Grants Scheme

The Member Grant Scheme awards grants of up to £5,000 to charities where a TMUK employee holds 'a recognised role' within the charity. Members who undertake a sponsored activity on behalf of a charity are able to request Member Match-Funding, where the trust will match up to £1,000 of any sponsorship raised. The website provides a detailed overview of the grants scheme and what the trust is willing to support.

Community Grant Awards

During the year, TMUK employees fundraise to support Toyota's Charity of the Year and other local charities.

Beneficiaries included: The Welsh Ambulance Charitable Trust (£5,000); Derbyshire Mind (£3,000); Quarrydale Utd (£2,000); Neston Nomads (£1,500); Prostate Cancer UK (£800).

Financial information

Year end	31/12/2021
Assets	£402,300
Income	£217,300
Grant total	£144,300

Further financial information

Grants were broken down as follows: Community Grants (£86,300); Member Grants (£55,300); Member Match Funding (£12,400). Funding was also awarded for three apprentice volunteering projects (£2,800).

Applications

Applications forms for Member Grants can be downloaded from the website. Beneficiaries of Community Grant Awards are nominated by company employees. Contact the trust for further information.

Sources of information

Accounts; Charity Commission record; funder's website.

United Utilities Trust Fund

Money advice; debt counselling; financial literacy

The area supplied by United Utilities Water plc (predominantly, North West England)

(£) £51,900 (2020/21)

CC number: 1108296

Trustees: Deborah Morton; Alastair Richards; Simon Dewsnip; Lynne Heath; Sandra McCaughley.

Correspondent: Company Secretary, c/o Auriga Services Ltd, Emmanuel Court, 12–14 Mill Street, Sutton Coldfield, West Midlands B72 1TJ (email: communitygrants@aurigaservices.co.uk)

 www.uutf.org.uk/information-for-organisations/organisational-grant-funding/grant-funding

 facebook.com/United-Utilities-Trust-Fund-110494273750171

General information

United Utilities Trust Fund is an independent grant-making charity established in early 2005. Its income largely comes from an annual donation from United Utilities Water plc.

Grants are mainly awarded to individuals in financial hardship who have a liability to pay water charges to United Utilities Water (directly or indirectly) and who are unable to pay.

Grants are also given to organisations that can deliver money advice and financial literacy services. The trustees' annual report and accounts for 2020/21 provides the following information: 'Trustees recognise the value of offering long-term help and support to individuals experiencing hardship and have adopted a policy of making grants available to organisations that provide free money advice and debt counselling services.

Beneficiaries included: Citizens Advice Halton (£15,100); Citizens Advice Preston (£13,100); The Oaks (£11,100); Liverpool Community Advice (£9,200); Institute of Money Advisors (£3,400).

Financial information

Year end	31/03/2021
Assets	£589,200
Income	£3,770,000
Grant total	£51,900
Organisations supported	5

Applications

Details of open funding rounds can be found on the fund's website.

Sources of information

Accounts; annual report; Charity Commission record; funder's website.

UPP Foundation

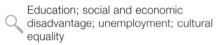 Education; social and economic disadvantage; unemployment; cultural equality

 UK

£ £226,000 (2020/21)

CC number: 1166323

Trustees: Prof. Mary Stuart; Jonathan Wakeford; Chris Skidmore; Alexandra Slater; Karen Morgan; Ellie Rapley.

Correspondent: The Trustees, 12 Arthur Street, London EC4R 9AB (tel: 020 7398 7200; email: upp-foundation@ upp-Limited.com)

 http://upp-foundation.org

 @upp_foundation

General information

This foundation was registered with the Charity Commission in April 2016 and aims to tackle issues facing the UK higher education sector. It was established and is fully funded by University Partnerships Programme (UPP), a UK company which provides student accommodation infrastructure and support services.

Grants

The trustees are focusing on four main themes:

- Increasing access and retention to higher education
- Improving employability
- Enhancing civic universities
- Developing global citizens

Further detail on each of these priorities is provided in the eligibility guide on the foundation's website.

Grants can be provided to registered charities and universities, but applications from other organisations with a clear social purpose, such as social enterprises and community groups, will also be considered. Grants are generally between £5,000 and £25,000.

The foundation's website says it supports applications which can demonstrate:

- A new or innovative approach to tackling relevant issues
- A commitment to collaboration and/or working in partnership
- How the UPP Foundation can measurably add value to the project
- A clear plan for long-term sustainability independent of support from the UPP Foundation

Beneficiaries included: A list of beneficiaries was not available.

Financial information

Year end	31/08/2021
Assets	£273,000
Income	£365,000
Grant total	£226,000

Exclusions

Individuals.

Applications

Application forms can be downloaded from the foundation's website. Check the website for upcoming deadlines and further information on eligibility.

Sources of information

Charity Commission record; funder's website; guidelines for applicants.

The Virgin Money Foundation

 Community development and regeneration; social enterprise; children and young people

 UK, with a preference for Glasgow, Sheffield, Edinburgh, Norwich, Manchester, Cardiff, London, Leeds and North East England

£ £1.46 million (2020/21)

CC number: 1161290

Trustees: Laura Christer; Abigail Walker; Alison Kidd; Amanda Jordan; Edward Spencer; Keith Merrin; Hannah Underwood; Keith Burge; Lorna Bennie; Joanne Curry.

Correspondent: Richard Walton, Programme Manager, Jubilee House, Gosforth, Newcastle upon Tyne, Tyne and Wear NE3 4PL (tel: 0330 123 3624; email: info@virginmoneyfoundation.org. uk)

 https://virginmoneyfoundation.org. uk

 @VMFoundation

General information

The foundation was registered with the Charity Commission in April 2015. It was established following the demise of the Northern Rock Foundation (established by the Northern Rock Bank which was purchased by the Virgin Money bank) to work 'in partnership with organisations who are committed to regenerating their area by investing in community activities that have a meaningful impact', as stated on the foundation's website.

Grants programmes

The foundation has a range of grants programmes. At the time of writing (November 2022), these included:

- **The Community Anchors Fund** – the foundation defines Community Anchor organisations, on its website, as 'vital, independent, locally led organisations, committed to driving positive economic, social or environmental change within a community'. The website further notes, 'They provide local people with support, services, activities, and volunteering opportunities. Local people shape their work and inform their activities.' Usually, Community Anchors are expected 'to work with a broad cross-section of the community'. The fund offers grants of up to £30,000 to organisations from the North East of England. Grants can be used to cover core costs, to continue to pay for existing work or to design and launch a new project. The award can be spent over one, two, or three years.
- **The Community Anchors Fund Glasgow** – in 2020, the Community Anchors Fund was expanded to support independent, community-led organisations in Glasgow. As the fund first opened during the COVID-19 pandemic, grants have initially focused on activity in response to COVID-19. Check the foundation's website for the latest information. At the time of writing (November 2022), the fund was only accepting applications by invitation.
- **The #iwill Take Action Fund** – this fund supports youth-led social action projects that create positive change in local communities. The fund offers grants of up to £50,000 to organisations from the North East.

For more open funds, see the foundation's website.

Beneficiaries included: West End Women and Girls Centre (£50,000); The Junction Foundation (£46,600); Youth Focus: North East (£40,900); South West Arts and Music Project (£30,000); Rosemount Lifelong Learning (£27,500); 3D Drumchapel (£20,000); Crossroads Youth and Community Association (£17,200); Cassiltoun Housing Association Ltd (£10,000); Bright Minds Big Futures (£1,000); British Octopush Association (£500).

Financial information

Year end	30/09/2021
Assets	£2,050,000
Income	£2,050,000
Grant total	£1,460,000
Organisations supported	140

Further financial information

Grants were broken down as follows:

Community Anchors' Fund – North East	21	£585,300
Community Anchors' Fund – Glasgow	19	£389,100
National Lottery Community Fund #iwill Fund Grant	9	£317,000
National Lottery Community Fund Partnerships England Wide	9	£100,800
Colleagues in the Community Fund	82	£40,700
Community Resilience Fund	-	£20,000
Social and Sustainable Capital Fund	-	£2,900

Exclusions

See the individual grants programmes on the foundation's website for specific exclusions.

Applications

Some grants programmes are open to applications and others are by invitation only. For those open to applications, an online form can be accessed through the foundation's application portal on its website. The foundation's website provides further information on each fund, including application deadlines and detailed eligibility criteria.

Sources of information

Accounts; annual report; Charity Commission record; funder's website.

The Vodafone Foundation

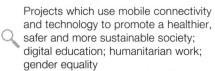

Projects which use mobile connectivity and technology to promote a healthier, safer and more sustainable society; digital education; humanitarian work; gender equality

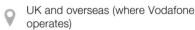

UK and overseas (where Vodafone operates)

£12.6 million (2020/21)

CC number: 1089625

Trustees: Nick Land; Elizabeth Filkin; Patricia Ithau; Amparo Moraleda; Rosemary Martin; Joakim Reiter; John Otty; Leanne Wood.

Correspondent: The Trustees, 1 Kingdom Street, Paddington Central, London W2 6BY (tel: 07824 342833; email: groupfoundation@vodafone.com)

 www.vodafonefoundation.org

 facebook.com/VodafoneFdn

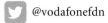 @vodafonefdn

 @vodafonefoundation

General information

The Vodafone Foundation was established in 2001 and received the majority of its funding from Vodafone plc. The foundation's website states that its aim is

> connecting communities around the world to improve lives. There is a unique network of 27 local foundations and social investment programmes that Vodafone Foundation works through.
>
> The underlying belief of this network of foundations is that connectivity drives change. By using this network Vodafone Foundation aims to connect people with the necessary tools to make a difference in the world.

The foundation currently provides funding and other support under the following headings:

- **Connected learning** – programmes and partnerships that enable some of the most vulnerable communities living in the areas Vodaphone operates to access quality learning
- **Connected health** – programmes that use technology to connect some of the people in greatest need to health and well-being information and services
- **Connected living** – a programme that uses technology to improve the lives of people with a learning disability, their families and carers
- **Apps** – a range of apps that address some of the world's most pressing problems, from domestic violence and abuse to cancer and COVID-19
- **Take action** – employee fundraising and volunteering

Grant-making approach

The foundation's 2020/21 annual report states:

> The Vodafone Foundation directs its grants to projects and partners that align with our strategic objectives with a main focus on programmes in countries where Vodafone Group companies operate. We prioritise programmes that leverage technology for public benefit, based on the social benefits offered by digital and communications technology and their potential to deliver public benefit through innovation, scale and sustainability

Beneficiaries included: Vodafone Germany Foundation (£1.61 million); Vodafone UK Foundation (£431,800); TecSOS – Thames Valley Partnership (£421,200); National Emergencies Trust (£228,900); Code Like a Girl (£14,600).

Financial information

Year end	31/03/2021
Assets	£5,560,000
Income	£15,990,000
Grant total	£12,630,000

Further financial information

The financial information has been converted from Euros using the exchange rate at the time of writing (May 2022). During 2020/21, grants were distributed as follows:

Vodafone/Vodacom Local Foundations	£7.75 million
Digital health	£2.08 million
Humanitarian Fund	£785,100
Digital education	£726,212
Gender equality	£680,700
Other activities	£439,900
UK employee matched funding	£169,800

Applications

The foundation usually approaches charitable organisations which it believes can help with the delivery of its charitable aims.

Sources of information

Accounts; annual report; Charity Commission record; funder's website.

Wates Family Enterprise Trust

Life opportunities for young people; sustainability and climate change; housing and homelessness

UK

£478,500 (2021)

CC number: 1126007

Trustees: Tim Wates; Paul Wates; Andrew Wates; Sir James Wates; Michael Wates; Andy Wates; Charles Wates; Jonathan Wates.

Correspondent: Rebecca Ray, Grants Officer, Wates House, Station Approach, Leatherhead, Surrey KT22 7SW (email: director@watesfoundation.org.uk)

 www.wfet.org.uk

General information

Registered in 2008, the trust is the vehicle for the philanthropic and charitable activities of the Wates family, owners of the Wates Group.

The trust has three main themes:

- **Life opportunities for young people** – improving the life chances of disadvantaged young people through training and education
- **Housing** – exploring the housing sector to consider issues around housing and homelessness
- **Sustainability** – supporting programmes that promote public engagement with the issue of climate change

According to the trust's 2020 annual report, there are three types of grant which may be made by the trust:

- **Major/group awards** – in support of bids originating from initiatives of the Wates Group and its business units.

- **Family awards** – in support of bids which are the initiative of the Wates family
- **Employee awards** – in support of initiatives of employees of the Wates businesses including staff fundraising efforts, Give As You Earn donations through payroll and volunteering, among other things.

The trust matches funds raised by Wates Group employees up to £500 per individual each year. One-off Community Awards of between £500 and £1,500 are also made to charitable organisations that employees volunteer for in their own time.

Beneficiaries included: The Difference (£100,000); Look Ahead (£30,000); Smith Institute (£27,500); Starlight Children's Charity (£10,000); Bridge the Gap and Carlisle Key (£5,000 each); Brixton Soup Kitchen and The Sick Children Fund (£1,000 each).

Financial information

Year end	31/12/2021
Assets	£478,500
Income	£825,000
Grant total	£478,500
Organisations supported	131

Applications

Unsolicited applications are not accepted. The trust's website states:

All proposals for awards are generated from the research and ideas from our own working groups or are proposed by Wates employees. As a result, we are unable to accept direct requests for funding.

Sources of information

Accounts; annual report; Charity Commission record; funder's website.

The Wates Foundation

 Building social values; education and employment; community health; life transitions; safer communities; strengthening the charitable and voluntary sector; the environment

Southern England

£279,400 (2021)

CC number: 247941

Trustees: Christian Brodie; Jonathan Wates; Nichola Adams; Luke Wates; Victoria Tanner; Jonathan Heynes.

Correspondent: Rebecca Ray, Grants Officer, Wates House, Station Approach, Leatherhead, Surrey KT22 7SW (tel: 01372 861000; email: director@ watesfoundation.org.uk)

 www.watesfoundation.org.uk

General information

In 1966, three brothers Norman, Sir Ronald and Allan Wates of the Wates building firm (now the Wates

Construction Group) amalgamated their personal charitable trusts into the single entity of The Wates Foundation. The foundation supports issues that reflect the families' broad range of interests. These interests are categorised into seven themes:

- Building social values
- Education and employment
- Community health
- Life transitions
- Environment
- Life transitions
- Safer communities
- Strengthening the charitable and voluntary sector

Beneficiaries included: Northleigh House (£21,000); Birth Trauma Association (£10,000); Different Planet Arts (£7,000); GASP Motor Project (£6,000); Migrants Organise (£5,000); Highreach Holidays (£250).

Financial information

Year end	31/12/2021
Assets	£24,480,000
Income	£357,700
Grant total	£279,400

Further financial information

Grants were broken down as follows:

Community health	£128,000
Education and employment	£76,000
Life transitions	£28,000
Environment	£16,600
Building family values	£16,600
Strengthening the charity sector	£14,300

The foundation changed its year end date to correspond with the Wates Family Enterprise Trust. The financial information is for the nine months ending 31 December 2021.

Exclusions

The foundation does not accept applications for the following:

- Promotion of religion
- Individuals
- Statutory bodies
- Other grant-makers
- Organisations with an income of over £3 million
- Capital projects
- General appeal
- Continuation funding or new bids on behalf of organisations already in receipt of a foundation award

Applications

Unsolicited applications are not accepted. The foundation is a proactive grant-maker and members of the Wates family seek out charities to support.

Sources of information

Accounts; annual report; Charity Commission record; funder's website.

Wellington Management UK Foundation

Improving academic performance and behaviour, reducing absenteeism and developing life skills for economically disadvantaged young people (up to the age of 26)

UK, Germany, Luxembourg and Switzerland

£1 million (2021)

CC number: 1167369

Trustees: James Stoll; Gemma MacDonald; Thomas Horsey; Anna Lunden; Richard Van Lienden; Joanne Carey; Damian Bloom; Nicola Staunton.

Correspondent: The Trustees, c/o Wellington Management International Ltd, 80 Victoria Street, London SW1E 5JL (tel: 020 7126 6000; email: wmukf@wellington.com)

www.wellington.com/en-gb/ community-engagement

General information

The Wellington Management UK Foundation is the UK corporate charity of Wellington Management, one of the world's largest independent investment management firms. Established in 2016, the foundation supports programmes and organisations that improve the education of, and educational opportunities for, economically disadvantaged young people up to 26 years old. The foundation prefers to support organisations in London where the company has a presence. It will also support organisations in Germany, Luxembourg and Switzerland.

According to its website, the foundation seeks to achieve this mission by providing grants to charities and not-for-profit organisations of various sizes that work to 'improve academic performance, improve behaviour, reduce absenteeism and develop life skills for economically disadvantaged youth up to 26 years'. Preference is given to organisations with an annual income of under £2 million.

The foundation's website states that 'Grantee organisations may use [the] funding as they see fit, either for programmatic or operating expenses.' Grants are awarded on annual basis, although multi-year grants will be considered once a relationship has been established. The foundation will consider applications from newer as well as more established organisations. Furthermore, the foundation notes that it prefers to fund organisations that can demonstrate 'the strength of their management and that have a measurable track record of success'.

Beneficiaries included: Action Tutoring and London Music Masters (£51,000 each); Debate Mate, Future Frontiers and London Youth Rowing (£46,000 each); London Thunder Basketball Club and Nova New Opportunities (£20,000 each); Street League and Westminster City School (£10,000 each).

Financial information

Year end	31/12/2021
Assets	£105,000
Income	£1,100,000
Grant total	£1,000,000
Organisations supported	28

Further financial information

During the year, the foundation awarded 28 grants to organisations, of which 25 were based in the UK.

Exclusions

Scholarship programmes are not eligible for funding.

Applications

For current information on the foundation's application process, see its website. Note: in 2021, the foundation did not accept new applications from charities that were not already being funded.

Sources of information

Accounts; annual report; Charity Commission record; funder's website.

Westminster Foundation

General charitable purposes, with a focus on children, young people and families

Westminster (parts of the old Metropolitan Borough of Westminster), Cheshire West and Cheshire, north-west rural Lancashire (near the Forest of Bowland) and North West Sutherland

£ £5.69 million (2021)

CC number: 267618

Trustees: James Hanbury; Mark Preston; Victoria Hornby; The Duke of Westminster.

Correspondent: Oliver Woodford, Grants Manager, The Grosvenor Office, 70 Grosvenor Street, London W1K 3JP (tel: 020 7408 0988; email: westminster. foundation@grosvenor.com)

 www.westminsterfoundation.org.uk

 @WestminsterFdn

General information

The foundation was established in 1974 for general charitable purposes by the fifth Duke of Westminster. In 1987 the Grosvenor Foundation, a separately registered charity, transferred all its assets to the Westminster Foundation. The foundation continues to receive regular donations from Grosvenor Group Ltd and supports a wide range of charities through its grant-making, with a focus on young people in the areas in which the group operates.

The following information is taken from the foundation's website:

What we fund

The Westminster Foundation works with local organisations who create opportunities for young people up to the age of 25, so that they and their families have the resilience, skills and capacity to lead happy and healthy lives. Our priority is to award grants that benefit young people facing deprivation or intergenerational equality.

- Charities registered with the Charity Commission or organisations with exclusively charitable objectives
- Community organisations (e.g. schools, colleges and youth hubs) who understand the local need and have the capacity to support their young people over time
- Charities based in Westminster, Chester, Rural Cheshire, Rural Lancashire or Rural Sutherland
- Initiatives making early positive interventional change
- Both core cost and project specific

Funding

We have three grant giving programmes:

Small Grant Programme
One-off Small Grants are available up to the value of £10,000, for registered charities (or organisations with exclusively charitable objectives) working in Chester, Westminster, and rural communities within Lancashire and Sutherland, where the Grosvenor Estate operates.

Charity Office Space
We offer subsidised charity office accommodation in central London. The offices are provided by the Grosvenor Group for around 20 charities.

Partnership Grant Programme
The Westminster Foundation's primary grant giving programme awards grants on a proactive basis. Proposals are invited by the Trustees where they feel our funding can make the most impact. Partnership Grants are typically awarded for five years at £100,000 per annum.

Beneficiaries included: NHS Charities Together (£5 million); The Prince's Trust (£250,000); The Country Trust (£190,000); Future Men and Young Minds (£100,000 each); Chester Schools Together (£65,000); The Mix (£50,500); Cheshire West Citizens Advice (£20,000).

Financial information

Year end	31/12/2021
Assets	£121,800,000
Income	£13,420,000
Grant total	£5,690,000
Organisations supported	200

Further financial information

Grants paid during the year totalled £5.69 million. According to the Westminster Foundation's annual report, 200 grants were awarded during the year. Grants awarded during 2021 were broken down as follows:

Partnership grants	20	£2 million
Grosvenor property grants	45	£1.42 million
COVID-19 response	16	£647,000
Small grants	43	£424,000
Other grants	38	£104,000
Charity Office portfolio	2	£64,000

Exclusions

The following information has been taken from the foundation's website:

Unfortunately we don't fund:

- Requests for individuals or projects benefiting only one school; including student fees and bursaries
- Holidays or trips including respite programmes
- Projects that are overtly political or religious
- Gifts and prizes for events and auctions
- Organisations that have applied to us unsuccessfully within the previous 12 months
- Capital costs in isolation
- Specific medial conditions and medical research

Applications

Applications for the Small Grant Programme can be made online and there are no deadlines. Charities can also join the waiting list for office space online. Partnership grants are by invitation only.

Sources of information

Accounts; annual report; Charity Commission record; funder's website.

The Willmott Dixon Foundation

The education of children and young people; people with disabilities

UK

£ £20,900 (2020/21)

CC number: 326530

Trustees: Richard Willmott; Colin Enticknap; Wendy McWilliams.

Correspondent: The Trustees, Spirella 2, Icknield Way, Letchworth Garden City, Hertfordshire SG6 4GY (tel: 07974 457508; email: company.secretarial@ willmottdixon.co.uk)

 www.willmottdixon.co.uk/the-willmott-dixon-foundation

General information

Willmott Dixon Group is a privately-owned construction, housing and property development business. The Willmott Dixon Foundation was originally established in 1984 and is chaired by the Group Chief Executive, Rick Willmott.

According to its 2021 annual accounts, the object of the foundation is 'to support projects and causes which promote the training of young people and the welfare of people with special needs'.

Beneficiaries included: Stephen Lawrence Day Foundation (£5,400); Sue Ryder Hospice (£3,800); Josh Charles Bone Cancer Fighting Fund and The Royal Free Charity (£3,500 each); Essex and Herts Air Ambulance (£2,900).

Financial information

Year end	03/04/2021
Assets	£54,300
Income	£56,400
Grant total	£20,900
Organisations supported	4

Further financial information

Only organisations that received grants of over £2,500 were listed as beneficiaries in the charity's accounts. Grants of under £2,500 totalled £1,900.

Note: the financial information covers the period between April 2021 and December 2021. This is due to the foundation changing its reporting year so as to align with the financial year of Willmott Dixon Holdings Ltd.

Applications

Apply in writing to the correspondent.

Sources of information

Accounts; annual report; Charity Commission record; funder's website.

Woodsmith Foundation Ltd

Community services and development; education and training; environment; social welfare; recreation facilities

North York Moors National Park, Scarborough and Redcar and Cleveland

£396,700 (2020/21)

CC number: 1163127

Trustees: Neil Irving; Ian Swales; Jacqueline Flynn; Jonathan Samuel; Dr Elizabeth Walmsley; Sir Martin Narey; William Woods.

Correspondent: The Trustees, Resolution House, Lake View, Scarborough, North Yorkshire YO11 3ZB (email: info@siriusmineralsfoundation.co.uk)

 www.siriusmineralsfoundation.co.uk

General information

The foundation was established in 2013 by Sirius Minerals plc, a fertiliser development company. Today, Sirius Minerals is owned by Anglo American plc and the groups has committed to provide an additional £4 million to the foundation, in advance of future revenues.

The foundation's primary aim is to 'leave a positive legacy from the Woodsmith Mine to the boroughs of Scarborough, Redcar and the North York Moors National Park'. According to its website the foundation's current charitable objectives are to:

- Advance education, including supporting projects and training that benefit people by enhancing their skills
- Promote the general health of the community
- Advance environmental protection and improvement including the enhancing of the local landscape
- Provide and improve facilities in the interests of social welfare and leisure time with the aim to improve residents' well-being
- Help gain skills to those in need, because of financial hardship by being out of work, particularly the long-term unemployed.

Beneficiaries included: A list of beneficiaries was not available.

Financial information

Year end	31/05/2021
Assets	£2,660,000
Income	£1,000,000
Grant total	£396,700

Applications

For up-to-date information on open grant schemes, see the foundation's website.

Sources of information

Accounts; annual report; Charity Commission record; funder's website.

The Xerox (UK) Trust

General charitable purposes including: children and young people; health; people who are disadvantaged

UK

£15,200 (2021)

CC number: 284698

Trustees: Jeffrey McMahon; Cheryl Walsh; Mark Godber; Paul Watson.

Correspondent: Cheryl Walsh, Trust Secretary, Building 4, Uxbridge Business Park, Sanderson Road, Middlesex, Middlesex UB8 1DH (tel: 01895 251133; email: XeroxUKTrust@xerox.com)

General information

Xerox is a multinational company that produces printers, photocopiers, printing presses and printing supplies. This trust supports local or mid-sized organisations working towards the advancement of equality of opportunities; particularly among people who are young, or disadvantaged or who have a disability or terminal illness.

Beneficiaries included: City Escape (£2,200); Bentley Beginnings, Kids Space, and Strength and Learning Through Horses (£2,000 each); The Forest of Avon Trust and Youth on the Move (£1,500 each); EP Youth Ltd and Leeds Weekend Care Association (£1,000 each); Building for the Future (£500).

Financial information

Year end	31/12/2021
Assets	£1,250,000
Income	£38,000
Grant total	£15,200
Organisations supported	10

Applications

Applications can be made in writing to the correspondent. Priority is given to charities with strong links to Xerox (UK) Ltd employees.

Sources of information

Accounts; annual report; Charity Commission record.

Yorkshire Building Society Charitable Foundation

Social welfare; health; disability; homelessness; children; older people

UK, with a preference for areas local to society branches

£407,400 (2021)

CC number: 1069082

Trustees: Erin Fuller; Lloyd Latibeaudiere; Gordon Rogers; Vanessa White.

Correspondent: D. Colley, Secretary, Yorkshire House, Yorkshire Drive, Bradford, West Yorkshire BD5 8LJ (tel: 0345 166 9271; email: corporateresponsibility@ybs.co.uk)

 www.ybs.co.uk/your-society/charitable-foundation/index.html

General information

Established in 1998, the foundation is the charitable arm of Yorkshire Building Society (YBS). The foundation is largely funded by YBS' Small Change Big Difference scheme, whereby members and staff donate the annual pence of interest from their savings or mortgage accounts to the foundation.

Aims

The foundation's main aim is to alleviate poverty, improve health and save lives in the areas where the society's members and staff live and work. It is particularly interested in supporting children, older people, people with disabilities and serious illness and people who are homeless.

Grants

The foundation funds specific projects and/or items that will have a positive impact on the charity's beneficiaries. Although the foundation does not support core costs, the trustees are keen to support full cost recovery for projects.

Examples of project costs funded include:

▸ A proportion of salaries for core staff or project workers
▸ A proportion of rent or utilities
▸ A dedicated laptop for the project
▸ Staff or volunteer training

For capital costs, priority is given to applications where the donation covers the total cost of an item. Examples of previous capital donations include:

▸ Sensory toys for children with special needs
▸ Medical equipment for a hospice
▸ Kitchen equipment for a foodbank, e.g. an industrial freezer

Eligibility

To be eligible charities must:

▸ Be a registered charity
▸ Use the funding to help alleviate poverty, improve health or save lives
▸ Be nominated by a YBS member or colleague
▸ Have beneficiaries in the UK
▸ Have not received a donation in the last two years
▸ Have annual returns submitted to the relevant charity commission

Note: at the time of writing (February 2022) the foundation had relaxed its eligibility criteria in response to the pandemic and was considering applications for running costs. It was also accepting charities that have been unable to submit their most recent accounts. Check the website for updates.

See the foundation's guidelines for full details.

Beneficiaries included: Refugee Action (£30,000); Smart Works – Leeds (£28,000); Canopy Housing and Groundwork – North England and Cumbria (£21,000); Give Bradford – No Child Cold (£10,000); Ace, Age UK and Autism Angels (£2,000 each).

Financial information

Year end	31/12/2021
Assets	£70,200
Income	£406,700
Grant total	£407,400
Organisations supported	215

Further financial information

In 2021, the foundation made 215 donations to charitable organisations. No grants were awarded to individuals. The majority of grants were up to £2,000; however, some larger grants were awarded.

Exclusions

The following will not be considered:

▸ Applications that do not fit the criteria outlined in the guidance notes
▸ Charities serving only a specific sector of the community selected on the basis of political or religious grounds/ advancement
▸ Animal welfare charities
▸ Charities with beneficiaries not in the UK
▸ CICs, community or voluntary organisations that are not registered charities
▸ Individuals
▸ Applications for large capital fundraising appeals, e.g. fundraising for a minibus
▸ Applications for any administration, fundraising or marketing equipment for a charity's own use

Applications

To be eligible for a grant you must be recommended by one of the building society's members or colleagues. If you are a member and would like the foundation to consider supporting a charity, an online application portal can be found on the foundation's web page.

All applications are reviewed on a quarterly basis by the trustees. Deadlines are 31 March, 30 June, 30 September and 31 December annually. You can expect to hear back within three months of submitting an application.

Sources of information

Accounts; annual report; Charity Commission record; funder's website; guidelines for applicants.

The Zochonis Charitable Trust

> A range of charitable purposes, including: social welfare; education; children and young people; homelessness; community work; the armed forces; older people; rescue services

> UK (particularly Greater Manchester) and overseas (particularly Africa)

> £3.42 million (2020/21)

CC number: 274769

Trustees: Christopher Green; Archibald Calder; Paul Milner.

Correspondent: The Trustees, Manchester Business Park, 3500 Aviator Way, Manchester M22 5TG (tel: 0161 435 1005; email: enquiries@ zochonischaritabletrust.com)

General information

Registered in 1978, the trust was established by the late Sir John Zochonis. Sir Zochonis was a former head of PZ Cussons plc, the soap and toiletries manufacturer and had shares in the company. The trust has general charitable objectives but tends to favour local charities with a particular emphasis on education and the welfare of children.

Beneficiaries included: A list of beneficiaries was not available.

Financial information

Year end	05/04/2021
Assets	£171,330,000
Income	£8,760,000
Grant total	£3,420,000
Organisations supported	205

Further financial information

During 2020/21, grants were distributed as follows:

Education	£1.06 million
Health	£769,800
Children and young people	£343,000
Overseas	£333,000
Emergency	£310,000
Homelessness	£235,000
Social provision	£157,000
Community	£57,500
Armed forces/ex-Servicepeople	£52,500
Family	£42,500
Rescue services	£35,000
Older people	£13,800
Religion	£10,000

Applications

Apply in writing to the correspondent. The trust's 2020/21 annual report states that 'grant requests are reviewed by the trustees on an individual basis'.

Sources of information

Accounts; annual report; Charity Commission record.

Zurich Community Trust (UK) Ltd

> Social welfare; community and economic development; helping disadvantaged people

> UK and overseas, with priority given to areas where the company has offices

> £2.33 million (2021)

CC number: 266983

Trustees: Tim Culling; Wayne Myslik; Andrew Jepp; Richard Peden; Stephen Collinson; Timothy Bailey.

Correspondent: Steve Grimmett, Head of ZCT (UK), PO Box 1288, Swindon, Wiltshire SN1 1FL (tel: 07875 886341; email: steve.grimmett@zct.org.uk or zct@ zct.org.uk.)

 www.zct.org.uk

facebook.com/
zurichcommunitytrust

 @ZCTrust

 @_zctrust

General information

The trust was established in 1973. It is the corporate charity of Zurich Insurance and it is one of the longest-established corporate trusts in the UK. Each year the trust awards around £1.75 million in grants and support to causes across the UK.

Partnerships

The trust works with around 100 charities per year. The charities are supported with funding and volunteering from Zurich employees. The trust supports a number of local charities located near the Zurich offices. The trust's website states:

> Although we do fund pilots and specific projects, we understand that what charities need most – and can struggle to secure funding for – is funding in support of core costs. Because of this, we've agreed that a minimum of 50% of our overall Local Grant spend should be allocated to the funding of specific core costs such as salaries.

The trust also works with national partners, as chosen by employees. At the time of writing (November 2022), these include Dementia UK and Place2Be.

Strategic funding

This scheme focuses on the more challenging issues and supports the most vulnerable people in society. The are several funding opportunities available under this scheme and programmes change periodically – see the website for all current grant schemes. The strategic funding programmes are typically long-term. Applications for this programme are by invitation only.

Beneficiaries included: Teach First (£200,000); The GoodGym (£160,000); Mind in Haringey (£115,000); The Soup Kitchen (£56,000); SIFA Fireside (£43,000); 2 Wish Upon A Star (£35,000); The Diana Award (£30,000); The Openwork Foundation (£16,000).

Financial information

Year end	31/12/2021
Assets	£5,010,000
Income	£3,360,000
Grant total	£2,330,000

Applications

Application processes vary between grant schemes and locations. Prospective applicants should see the website for details on how to apply for a given scheme. Application opening/closing dates are also published on the website.

Sources of information

Accounts; annual report; Charity Commission record; funder's website.

Glossary

Charity partners and/or Charity of the Year

Charity of the Year initiatives support a single organisation, typically for a period of a year but sometimes longer. In general, the charity supported is chosen by employees. During the partnership, the charity will benefit from financial contributions from the company and/or employee fundraising or volunteering. Long-term partnerships are on the rise, and we are increasingly seeing more innovative partnerships between companies and charities, which are often cause related.

Community/social investment

Community or social investment is a catch-all term that can describe any type of community support, including cash, in-kind gifts, employee and customer fundraising, volunteering time, commercially led initiatives and management costs. Companies sometimes refer to these various forms of support as 'community contributions'.

Corporate charity

Corporate charities are established by companies as separate, legally constituted entities which are registered and regulated by the Charity Commission. They may be funded by historic gifts of shares, by direct donations from the profits of the company or by customer and employee fundraising.

Corporate social responsibility or charity committee

A corporate social responsibility (CSR) or charity committee is a positive indicator of a company's commitment to its role in society beyond the environmental obligations it is required to meet under law. A committee can act as a vehicle for the continuing evolution of a company's CSR strategy, as well as providing a point of contact for information on a company's CSR practices. Some companies' committees are made up of members of the board of directors, whereas others include employees.

Employee-led support

Employees are often a valuable asset to companies' CSR activities. Staff members lend their fundraising and volunteering efforts to a wide range of local, national and international causes. Fundraising activities can include anything from sponsored runs to employee lotteries, and volunteering can range from individually organised regular commitments to one-off team efforts.

Gifts in kind

Gifts in kind originally referred solely to goods, pieces of furniture or items of equipment (nearly always secondhand). Now, with CSR high on the agenda for many companies, corporates are increasingly offering staff time and skills as gifts in kind.

Market-led giving

Market-led approaches to giving include: selling products with a percentage of the profit donated to charitable causes; sponsoring a team, event or organisation; and funding an initiative that will benefit the company in the future, such as an engineering company funding a STEM initiative at a local university.

In this guide, cause-related marketing initiatives that a company has undertaken during the financial year are detailed in its entry; however, we do not include money raised through such initiatives in the total community contributions figure, because the motivation and priority of such giving is the company's profits, not philanthropy.

Matched funding

Matched funding provides a way for companies to encourage and support employees' charitable fundraising efforts. Typically, companies will match funds raised up to a certain amount per employee per year. Some companies match funds on a pound-for-pound basis, whereas others match up to a certain percentage of funds raised.

Payroll giving

Payroll giving allows employees to make donations from their wages in a tax-efficient way. There are a number of schemes on offer, with the best known perhaps being the Charities Aid Foundation's Give As You Earn (GAYE) scheme (www.cafonline.org/giving-as-a-company/engaging-employees/caf-give-as-you-earn). Most schemes work by taking a monthly donation from the salary of participating employees, although there are some which operate slightly differently. Pennies from Heaven (www.penniesfromheaven.co.uk), for example, works by rounding individual employees' monthly salaries down to the nearest pound.

Pro bono

Pro bono work can provide a way for charities to access invaluable professional skills and knowledge from companies free of charge. Many people think of pro bono work as being the domain of law and accountancy firms; however, companies in this guide from across the corporate sector provide charities with access to various specialisms, sometimes with remarkably innovative outcomes.

Sponsorship

Sponsorship is vastly different from charitable donations: it is a business arrangement that provides a charity with an opportunity to raise funds and the company with the chance to improve its image and promote and sell its products or services. Sponsorship is typically given in the form of money, although it can also take the form of products, services or space.

STEM

Some companies have prioritised the promotion of STEM (science, technology, engineering and maths) subjects as part of their CSR strategy. This could be in the form of special classes or on-site visits for school pupils, or mentoring for university students.

Accreditation schemes and membership bodies

Business in the Community

Business in the Community (BITC) is a business-led membership organisation committed to making community involvement an integral part of successful business practice and to increasing the quality and extent of businesses' activities in the community. BITC works with companies in the UK and overseas to improve the relationship between the commercial and third sectors.

In the 'Company accreditations' list in the next section, we have highlighted those companies which are members of BITC.

Business for Societal Impact

Business for Societal Impact (B4SI) is a group of companies working together to measure corporate community investment (CCI). Its vision is 'A world where every business can measure and manage its social impact, sharing information in an open, transparent, and consistent way.'[1]

The B4SI Framework provides a comprehensive and consistent set of measures for CCI professionals to determine their company's contribution to the community, including cash, time and in-kind donations, as well as management costs. The model also captures the outputs and longer-term impacts of CCI projects on society and the business itself. Currently, the model is used by hundreds of leading businesses, both in the UK and overseas.

Companies which are current members of B4SI are listed in the 'Company accreditations' list in the next section.

Living Wage Foundation

The Living Wage Foundation is a campaigning organisation which aims to persuade UK employers to pay a Living Wage – an independently calculated recommended minimum wage to cover workers' basic needs. To achieve this objective the foundation operates an accreditation scheme for UK companies. To become accredited as a Living Wage Employer, a company must pay all its directly employed staff a Living Wage and have a plan in place to extend that to regularly subcontracted staff as well.

According to the Living Wage Foundation's website, the current Living Wage rates are £11.95 per hour in London and £10.90 per hour in the rest of the UK.[2] There are currently over 11,000 Living Wage Employers across the country.

In the 'Company accreditations' list in the next section, we have marked the companies which are included in a list of Living Wage employers on the Living Wage Foundation's website.

Armed Forces Covenant

The Armed Forces Covenant is a pledge taken by companies, central and local government, charities and community organisations to support armed forces personnel, veterans and their families. The covenant focuses on helping members of the armed forces community have the same access to services and products as any other citizen. According to the covenant's website, support is provided in several areas: education and family wellbeing, housing, employment and training, healthcare, financial assistance and discounted services.[3] To date, over 9,000 organisations have signed the covenant.

The companies in this guide which have signed the covenant are listed in the 'Company accreditations' list in the next section.

Business Disability Forum

Business Disability Forum is a not-for-profit membership organisation that works with businesses and people with disabilities to improve the life experiences of employees and consumers who have disabilities by removing barriers to inclusion. It achieves this by providing training, advice and networking opportunities. The organisation also works closely with the government to inform disability policy and runs campaigns to raise awareness around key issues related to disability in the workplace.

Companies that are members of the Business Disability Forum are listed in the 'Company accreditations' list in the next section.

References

1   'About B4SI' [web page], B4SI, https://b4si.net/about/, accessed 1 February 2023.
2   'Calculation' [web page], Living Wage Foundation, www.livingwage.org.uk/calculation, accessed 1 February 2023.
3   'About' [web page], Armed Forces Covenant, www.armedforcescovenant.gov.uk/about, accessed 1 February 2023.

Company accreditations

	Business for Societal Impact	Business Disability Forum	Living Wage employer	Armed Forces Covenant	Business in the Community
3i Group plc			●		
Abellio Scotrail Ltd			●		
abrdn plc			●	●	
Accenture UK Ltd	●		●	●	
Addleshaw Goddard LLP		●	●		
Admiral Group plc		●		●	●
Adnams plc			●	●	●
Aegon UK plc			●		●
Aggregate Industries UK Ltd				●	
Allen & Overy LLP			●		
Allianz Insurance plc				●	●
Alpkit Ltd			●		
Anglian Water		●		●	●
Anglo American Crop Nutrients Ltd				●	●
Apax Partners LLP			●		
Arup Group Ltd		●	●	●	●
Asda Stores Ltd	●	●		●	●
Associated British Ports				●	
Assura plc			●		
AstraZeneca	●	●	●		●
Autotrader Group plc		●			●
Aviva plc	●	●	●	●	●
Axis Europe plc					●
BAE Systems plc	●		●	●	

COMPANY ACCREDITATIONS

	Business for Societal Impact	Business Disability Forum	Living Wage employer	Armed Forces Covenant	Business in the Community
Baillie Gifford & Co. Ltd		●			
Balfour Beatty plc		●		●	
BAM Construct UK Ltd				●	
Bank of Ireland (UK) plc	●	●			
Barclays plc	●		●	●	●
A. G. Barr plc			●		
Barratt Developments plc		●	●	●	●
Bayer plc	●				
Beazley plc	●		●		
Biffa				●	
Birketts LLP				●	
Birmingham International Airport Ltd		●			
A. F. Blakemore and Son Ltd					●
Boeing United Kingdom Ltd				●	
BP plc			●		●
Brewin Dolphin Holdings				●	●
Brit Ltd		●			
British Airways plc		●		●	●
British American Tobacco plc				●	
British Land Company plc	●				●
Britvic Soft Drinks plc		●			
Bruntwood Group Ltd			●		
BT Group plc	●			●	●
Bupa Ltd	●				●
Burberry Group	●		●		
Cadent Gas Ltd				●	
Calor Gas Ltd			●		●
Capita plc		●	●	●	●
Capital One (Europe) plc			●		
Cargill plc	●				
Central England Co-operative					●
Centrica plc		●			●
Channel 4 Television Corporation		●			
Chelsea FC Holdings Ltd			●		

	Business for Societal Impact	Business Disability Forum	Living Wage employer	Armed Forces Covenant	Business in the Community
Clifford Chance LLP			●	●	
Close Brothers Group plc		●			
Co-operative Group Ltd	●	●			●
Costain Group plc				●	●
Coutts & Co.			●		
Coventry Building Society	●				
CPFC Ltd (Crystal Palace Football Club)			●		
Credit Suisse AG		●	●		
Currys plc		●			
Darlington Building Society			●	●	
Dechra Pharmaceuticals plc			●		
Deloitte LLP			●	●	●
Derwent London plc			●		
Deutsche Bank AG	●	●			
Direct Line Insurance Group plc		●			●
DLA Piper International LLP		●	●		
DWF Group plc			●	●	
Dwr Cymru Welsh Water			●		
Dyson James Group Ltd				●	
E.ON UK plc				●	
EDF Energy Holdings Ltd			●	●	●
Edinburgh Airport Ltd				●	
Everton Football Club Company Ltd			●		
Experian plc	●		●	●	●
Ford Motor Company Ltd					●
Freshfields Bruckhaus Deringer LLP	●		●		●
Fujitsu Services Holdings plc	●	●	●	●	●
Galliford Try Holdings plc				●	
Gamesys Group Ltd					●
Global Media and Entertainment Ltd		●			
The Go-Ahead Group plc		●			
Goldman Sachs International		●	●	●	●
Gowling WLG (UK) LLP		●	●		●
Greggs plc				●	●

COMPANY ACCREDITATIONS

	Business for Societal Impact	Business Disability Forum	Living Wage employer	Armed Forces Covenant	Business in the Community
Alun Griffiths (Contractors) Ltd				●	
GSK plc			●		
Guardian Media Group plc		●			
Hargreaves Lansdown plc			●		
Hastings Group Holdings plc		●		●	
Heathrow Airport Holdings Ltd (formerly BAA Ltd)			●		
Hiscox Ltd			●		
C. Hoare and Co.			●		
Howden Joinery Group plc		●			
HSBC Holdings plc	●		●	●	●
IBM United Kingdom Ltd			●	●	●
Informa plc		●	●		
Intercontinental Hotels Group plc					●
Investec plc	●	●			
ITV plc			●		
William Jackson Foods Ltd				●	
Jaguar Land Rover Automotive plc		●		●	●
Johnson Matthey plc			●		
Jones Lang LaSalle Ltd				●	
Kentucky Fried Chicken (Great Britain) Ltd					●
Kingfisher plc	●				
KPMG LLP	●		●		●
Lancashire Holdings Ltd			●		
Land Securities Group plc		●		●	
Leeds Building Society		●			●
Legal & General Group plc		●	●		●
Leicester City Football Club Ltd			●		
John Lewis Partnership plc		●			
Eli Lilly and Company Ltd		●			
The Liverpool Football Club and Athletic Grounds Ltd			●		
Liverpool Victoria				●	
Lloyd's		●	●	●	
Lloyds Banking Group	●		●	●	●
London City Airport Ltd			●		

	Business for Societal Impact	Business Disability Forum	Living Wage employer	Armed Forces Covenant	Business in the Community
London Luton Airport Ltd			•		
London Stock Exchange Group plc	•		•	•	•
Lush Cosmetics Ltd		•	•		
M&G plc	•	•	•	•	
Manchester United Ltd				•	
Marks and Spencer Group plc					•
Marshall of Cambridge (Holdings) Ltd				•	
Marston's plc		•		•	
Mazars LLP		•	•		
Melton Building Society			•		
Merlin Entertainments Ltd		•			
Microsoft Ltd				•	•
Mills and Reeve LLP		•		•	•
Morgan Stanley & Co. International plc			•	•	•
Wm Morrison Supermarkets plc				•	•
National Express Group plc			•		
National Grid plc	•	•	•		•
Nationwide Building Society				•	
NatWest Group plc	•		•	•	•
NCC Group plc				•	
Newbury Building Society		•			
Newcastle Building Society			•	•	
Next Retail Ltd					•
Nominet UK				•	•
Northumbrian Water Ltd				•	
Norton Rose Fulbright LLP			•		•
Nottingham Building Society			•		
Ocado Group plc				•	
Ovo Energy Ltd		•	•		•
Paragon Banking Group plc					•
Peel L&P Holdings (UK) Ltd			•	•	
Pennon Group plc	•				•
Persimmon plc		•	•	•	
Pets at Home plc		•			

COMPANY ACCREDITATIONS

	Business for Societal Impact	Business Disability Forum	Living Wage employer	Armed Forces Covenant	Business in the Community
Pfizer Ltd	●				●
Premier Foods plc	●	●		●	●
Pret A Manger (Europe) Ltd		●			
PricewaterhouseCoopers LLP					●
Principality Building Society					●
Provident Financial plc		●			
Prudential plc	●				
Quilter plc			●	●	
Rathbone Brothers plc		●			
Reckitt Benckiser Group plc		●			●
Redrow Group plc		●	●		
RELX plc		●	●		
Renishaw plc				●	
Richer Sounds plc			●		
Rolls-Royce plc	●			●	
Rotork plc			●	●	
The Royal London Mutual Insurance Society Ltd			●		●
Royal Mail plc				●	
RSA Insurance Group Ltd	●	●	●		
Saga plc				●	
The Sage Group plc			●	●	●
J Sainsbury plc					●
Samworth Brothers (Holdings) Ltd					●
Santander UK plc			●	●	●
Schroders plc	●	●	●		
ScottishPower UK plc		●		●	
SEGRO plc			●		
Serco Group plc					●
Severn Trent plc		●		●	●
Shaftesbury plc			●		
Shell (UK Ltd)			●	●	●
Shoosmiths LLP		●	●		●
Siemens plc			●	●	
Simmons & Simmons LLP				●	

	Business for Societal Impact	Business Disability Forum	Living Wage employer	Armed Forces Covenant	Business in the Community
Simplyhealth Group Ltd			●		●
Skipton Building Society		●	●		
Sky Ltd	●	●		●	●
Slaughter and May (Trust Ltd)			●		
Smith & Nephew plc		●	●		
Smiths Group plc			●		
Societe Generale International Ltd					●
Sodexo Ltd				●	●
Southern Water Services Ltd					●
SSE plc		●	●	●	
St James's Place plc	●	●	●	●	
St. Modwen Properties plc				●	
Stagecoach Group Ltd				●	
Standard Chartered plc	●	●	●	●	●
TalkTalk Telecom Group Ltd			●	●	
Tata Steel Europe Ltd		●			
Tate & Lyle plc			●		
Taylor Wimpey plc			●		
Tesco plc		●			●
Thales UK Ltd		●		●	●
Thames Water Ltd	●		●		●
the7stars UK Ltd			●		
Timpson Group Ltd			●		
TJX UK					●
Town Centre Securities plc				●	
Toyota Motor Manufacturing (UK) Ltd		●			
Travis Perkins plc		●		●	
Turner and Townsend Ltd				●	
Unilever plc					●
United Utilities Group plc	●				●
Unum Ltd				●	
Virgin Money UK plc		●	●	●	
Viridian International Ltd			●		
Vodafone Group plc		●	●	●	●

COMPANY ACCREDITATIONS

	Business for Societal Impact	Business Disability Forum	Living Wage employer	Armed Forces Covenant	Business in the Community
Wates Group Ltd		●			
Watkin Jones Group plc				●	
Wellington Management International Ltd	●			●	
Wesleyan Assurance Society				●	●
Wessex Water Services Ltd				●	
Wheatley Housing Group Ltd					●
WHSmith plc		●			
Willmott Dixon Holdings Ltd		●	●	●	
WPP Group Ltd		●		●	●
Yorkshire Building Society	●	●			●
Zurich Insurance Group	●		●		

Useful contacts

Business for Societal Impact

Business for Societal Impact (B4SI) is a group of companies that work together to measure corporate community investment.

The Cursitor Building
38 Chancery Lane
Cursitor Street
London
WCA 1EN

Email: b4si@corporate-citizenship.com
Web: www.b4si.net

Business in the Community

Business in the Community (BITC) is a business-led membership organisation, which offers a combination of expert advice and specialist resources to help businesses with community activities.

137 Shepherdess Walk
London
N1 7RQ

Tel: 020 7566 8650
Email: via the online contact form
Web: www.bitc.org.uk

Business in the Community Scotland

Formerly known as Scottish Business in the Community, the organisation changed its name after merging with Business in the Community.

Contact details as above.

British Chambers of Commerce

The British Chambers of Commerce (BCC) is the national representative body of the UK's 53 Accredited Chambers of Commerce, which collectively represent over 75,000 businesses.

65 Petty France
London
SW1H 9EU

Tel: 020 7654 5800
Email: via the online contact form
Web: www.britishchambers.org.uk

Contact details for local Chambers of Commerce can be found on the website.

Charity Chat

Charity Chat is a podcast that covers various issues affecting the sector and provides commentary on fundraising, learning and policy.

Email: via the online contact form
Web: www.charitychat.org.uk

Charity Commission

The Charity Commission is the government body responsible for the regulation of registered charities in England and Wales. It also maintains a Central Register of Charities.

PO Box 211
Bootle
L20 7YX

Tel: 0300 066 9197
Email: via the online contact form
Web: www.gov.uk/government/organisations/charity-commission

Charity Comms

CharityComms is the membership network for communications professionals working for UK charities.

Canopi
7–14 Dover Street
London
SE1 4YR

Web: www.charitycomms.org.uk

Charity Finance Group

Charity Finance Group (CFG) champions best practice in financial management in the voluntary sector, providing information and support including education and training for its members and the wider charity sector.

15–18 White Lion Street
London
N1 9PG

Tel: 0845 345 3192
Email: info@cfg.org.uk
Web: www.cfg.org.uk

Charity IT Association

The Charity IT Association (CITA) provides free IT services and advice to help charities use technology more effectively.

39A Bartholomew Close
London
EC1A 7JN

Tel: 020 8148 6390
Email: contact@cita.org.uk
Web: www.charityithelp.org.uk

Charity Tax Group

Charity Tax Group (CTG) is a membership organisation that makes representations to government on charity taxation.

Church House
Great Smith Street
London
SW1P 3AZ

Tel: 020 7222 1265
Email: via the online contact form
Web: www.charitytaxgroup.org.uk

Charities Trust

Charities Trust is a donation management organisation. It provides a range of services to help charities raise money for good causes.

Suite 20–22
Century Building
Brunswick Business Park
Tower Street
Liverpool
L3 4BJ

Tel: 0151 286 5129
Email: info@charitiestrust.org
Web: www.charitiestrust.org.uk

Chartered Surveyors Voluntary Service

The Chartered Surveyors Voluntary Service (CSVS, Charity Commission no. 1043479) provides professional property advice from Chartered Surveyors for those who would not otherwise be able to afford it. Applicants should contact their local Citizens Advice (www.citizensadvice. org.uk) for a referral.

Web: www.rics.org/csvs

Common Purpose UK

Common Purpose UK is a leadership development organisation. It runs leadership development programmes that support people to work together across geographical and cultural boundaries.

38 Artillery Lane
London
E1 7LS

Tel: 020 7608 8100
Email: info@commonpurpose.org
Web: www.commonpurpose.org.uk

Companies House

Companies House is the UK's registrar of companies. It is responsible for incorporating and dissolving limited companies and maintaining a comprehensive record of company information which is publicly available.

Registrar of Companies (England and Wales)

Crown Way
Cardiff
CF14 3UZ

Registrar of Companies (Northern Ireland)

2nd Floor
The Linenhall
32–38 Linenhall Street
Belfast
BT2 8BG
DX481 N.R. Belfast 1

Registrar of Companies (Scotland)

4th Floor
Edinburgh Quay 2
139 Fountainbridge
Edinburgh
DX ED235 Edinburgh 1

Tel: 0303 1234 500
Email: enquiries@companieshouse. gov.uk
Web: www.companieshouse.gov.uk

Confederation of British Industry

The Confederation of British Industry (CBI) works to promote business interests through lobbying, research and networking. It currently has around 190,000 direct and indirect members across the UK.

Cannon Place
78 Cannon Street
London
EC4N 6HN

Tel: 020 7379 7400
Email: enquiries@cbi.org.uk
Web: www.cbi.org.uk

Co-operative and Community Finance

Co-operative and Community Finance provides business loans to co-operatives and social enterprises in the UK.

1–3 Gloucester Road
Bristol
BS7 8AA

Tel: 0800 464 7262
Email: info@coopfinance.coop
Web: www.coopfinance.coop

Corporate Citizenship

Corporate Citizenship is a global consultancy that helps businesses to fulfil social and environmental responsibilities.

The Cursitor
38 Chancery Lane
London
WC2A 1EN

Email: mail@corporate-citizenship.com
Web: www.corporate-citizenship.com

Directory of Social Change

Tel: 020 4526 5995
Email: cs@dsc.org.uk
Web: www.dsc.org.uk

The Foundation for Social Improvement

The Foundation for Social Improvement (FSI) provides free advice, training and fundraising opportunities for small charities in order to develop a more sustainable small charity sector in the UK.

New Broad Street House
35 Broad Street House
EC2M 1NH

Tel: 020 8142 5147
Email: admin@thefsi.org
Web: www.thefsi.org

In Kind Direct

In Kind Direct distributes donated usable consumer goods on behalf of manufacturers and retailers to UK charities working in the UK and overseas.

11–15 St Mary at Hill
London
EC3R 8EE

Tel: 0300 30 20 200
Email: info@inkinddirect.org
Web: www.inkinddirect.org

Institute of Corporate Responsibility and Sustainability

The Institute of Corporate Responsibility and Sustainability is a professional body dedicated to supporting corporate responsibility practitioners.

21 Holborn Viaduct
London
EC1A 2DY

Email: info@icrs.info
Web: www.icrs.info

Chartered Institute of Fundraising

The Chartered Institute of Fundraising (CIoF) is the professional membership body for UK fundraising and supports fundraisers through training and guidance on best practice.

Canopi
7–14 Great Dover Street
London
SE1 4YR

Tel: 020 7840 1000
Email: info@ciof.org.uk
Web: www.ciof.org.uk

LawWorks

LawWorks is a charity in England and Wales that works to connect volunteer lawyers with people and not-for-profit organisations in need of legal advice.

LawWorks
DX 115
50–52 Chancery Lane
London
WC2A 1HL

Web: www.lawworks.org.uk

National Council for Voluntary Organisations

The National Council for Voluntary Organisations (NCVO) is the umbrella body for the voluntary and community sector in England. It supports the sector by providing training and networking activities. It also represents voluntary organisations to government and conducts research to inform policy development.

Society Building
8 All Saints Street
London
N1 9RL

Tel: 020 7713 6161
Email: ncvo@ncvo.org.uk
Web: www.ncvo.org.uk

National Centre for Universities and Business

The National Centre for Universities and Business supports and promotes collaboration between universities and business in the UK.

DC. 115
The Clarence Centre
6 St George's Circus
London
SE1 6FE

Tel: 020 7383 7667
Email: info@ncub.co.uk
Web: www.ncub.co.uk

National Pro Bono Centre

The National Pro Bono Centre is a hub for pro bono charities across the legal sector. It helps to support a wide range of pro bono projects across England and Wales.

Email: via the online contact form
Web: www.nationalprobonocentre.org.uk

Reach Volunteering

Reach Volunteering supports charities in the UK to recruit volunteers and trustees.

7 Bell Yard
London
WC2A 2JR

Tel: 0203 925 7721
Email: info@reachvolunteering.org.uk
Web: www.reachvolunteering.org.uk

ShareGift

ShareGift works closely with companies, solicitors, stockbrokers and financial advisers to create a pool of charitable funds. It does this by accepting donations of small shareholdings from companies, which it then aggregates and sells.

PO Box 72253
London
SW1P 9LQ

Tel: 020 7930 3737
Email: help@sharegift.org
Web: www.sharegift.org

Trades Union Congress

The Trades Union Congress (TUC) is a national federation of trade unions in England and Wales, representing most trade unions.

Congress House
Great Russell Street
London
WC1B 3LS

Tel: 020 7636 4030
Email: info@tuc.org.uk
Web: www.tuc.org.uk

Volunteering Matters

Volunteering Matters is the UK's leading volunteering charity, engaging more than 20,000 volunteers each year through its programmes.

The Levy Centre
18–24 Lower Clapton Road
London
E5 0PD

Tel: 020 3780 5870
Web: www.volunteeringmatters.org.uk

Charitable causes index

Community enterprise and social entrepreneurship

Community services and development

Crime reduction and public safety

Disability

Disaster relief and humanitarian aid

Employability

Health

Religion

Social welfare

Types of giving index

Payroll giving/GAYE

Take your knowledge further

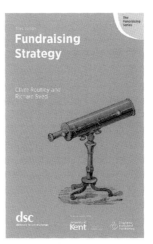

www.dsc.org.uk/fus